FUNDAMENTALS OF

SOIL MECHANICS

FUNDAMENTALS OF

SOIL

MECHANICS

DONALD W. TAYLOR

ASSOCIATE PROFESSOR OF SOIL MECHANICS
MASSACHUSETTS INSTITUTE OF TECHNOLOGY

1948

New York · JOHN WILEY & SONS, Inc.
London · CHAPMAN & HALL, Limited

PRINTED IN THE UNITED STATES OF AMERICA

PREFACE

Soil mechanics is a pioneer science which has grown rapidly during the last two decades. Its introduction into this country —under this name, at least—is generally accredited to Dr. Karl Terzaghi and is considered to have occurred in 1925. With each year since that date soil mechanics has become more widely known, the number of soil mechanics laboratories has increased, more colleges have offered courses in this new subject, and practical applications of this science have become more numerous.

The amount of existing soil mechanics literature has increased rapidly but textbooks and handbooks have been slow to appear, probably because of the extensive scope of the subject. Books of a number of types on this subject are needed, and it is of considerable importance to distinguish between the various types, which include the handbook for the practicing engineer, the manual for the laboratory technician, the textbooks for college courses of undergraduate level and graduate level, and the advanced textbook for the specialist. It is probable that no book can serve more than one or two of these fields to best advantage. This book is written as a textbook for use in graduate courses, but it is presented in such form that by the omission of certain portions it can be used in undergraduate courses. Practicing engineers and specialists in soil engineering may find the book of interest and value but, primarily, it is written for the student. The basic aim of the book is the presentation of fundamentals rather than the furnishing of final answers to practical problems; nevertheless, the book aims to develop the reader's appreciation for the practical significance of the various subjects considered.

I wish to acknowledge and to express appreciation for the privilege of including in this book material that is the work of three of my predecessors on the Soil Mechanics staff of the Massachusetts Institute of Technology. These three engineers, each of whom has played an important part in the growth of soil mechanics, are Dr. Karl Terzaghi, Dr. Glennon Gilboy, and Dr. Arthur Casagrande. Dr. Terzaghi put out a preliminary set of notes for the use of students in 1926 or thereabouts. Dr. Gilboy prepared a set of notes in 1930 that covered approximately one-third of the material of his graduate soil mechanics courses and bore the title *Notes on Soil Mechanics*. I revised and completed these *Notes on Soil Mechanics* in 1938 and 1939. To a degree this book is the outgrowth of these sets of lecture notes.

An attempt is made to include acknowledgment to the originators of material that is presented in this book. However, the development of many of the subjects treated is the result of the efforts of many persons, and in many cases it is not possible to know just how much credit is due to the various participants or even to be certain of the complete list of contributors. For all omissions of credit, where due, regrets are expressed. I wish to acknowledge helpful suggestions and to express my appreciation to Professor Dean Peabody, Jr., and Mr. T. W. Lambe, who read the entire manuscript, to Dr. M. J. Hvorslev, who reviewed Chapter 5, to a number of assistants and students, who have read parts of the manuscript, and especially to Dr. Glennon Gilboy, for his inspiring instruction and supervision during the period when I was his assistant, and to Dr. J. B. Wilbur and Professor C. B. Breed, Head and former Head, respectively, of the Department of Civil and Sanitary Engineering at the Massachusetts Institute of Technology, for suggestions and encouragement.

D. W. T.

Cambridge, Massachusetts
February, 1948

CONTENTS

CONTENTS

NOTATION

The nomenclature used in this book is in close agreement with that recommended in *Soil Mechanics Nomenclature*, Manual of Engineering Practice No. 22, published by the American Society of Civil Engineers in 1941.

The following list contains only the more important of the symbols that appear in the following pages. There are numerous cases in which subscripts are used on a few occasions, or in a single explanation or derivation, to designate special cases and components of various quantities. Also there are numerous isolated uses of symbols that are of minor importance. These items of minor importance or infrequent appearance are explained in the section in which they are used and generally are not included below.

In a few instances a given symbol is used herein to represent two or more entirely different quantities. In general these different quantities do not appear in the same chapter and, when they are used at the same time, special subscripts are introduced so that confusion will not occur.

Numbers that are given in parentheses refer to the section in which the item is described or in which a typical use of the item appears.

A	area
a	distance on earth dam from breakout point of top flow line to toe $(9\cdot11)$; area, usually of small magnitude
a_v	coefficient of compressibility $(10\cdot9)$
B	resultant actuating force $(16\cdot17)$
b	breadth or width, such as breadth of spread footing, base width of dam, width of flow path, width of element of area
C	resultant cohesion $(16\cdot17)$; various constants and coefficients
C_c	compression index $(10\cdot6)$
C_e	expansion index $(10\cdot6)$
C_u	Hazen's uniformity coefficient $(4\cdot9)$
C_ρ	coefficient of settlement $(19\cdot3)$
c	cohesion per unit of area $(15\cdot9)$
c_d	mobilized cohesion $(16\cdot6)$
c_e	effective cohesion $(15\cdot23)$
c_v	coefficient of consolidation $(10\cdot10)$
D	diameter; depth coefficient (Fig. $16\cdot25$)

D_{10}	Hazen's effective size, the 10 per cent size (4·9)
D_d	relative density (3·5)
d	distance; depth; dial reading (10·13)
E	modulus of elasticity
e	void ratio (2·2); efficiency coefficient (20·7)
F	factor of safety (16·6)
G	specific gravity (2·2)
g	acceleration of gravity
H	thickness (10·10); height (16·8, 20·7)
h	hydraulic head (7·4)
h_c	capillary head (8·7)
l	various indices
I_p	plasticity index (4·8)
i	hydraulic gradient (6·2); inclination angle of an earth slope (16·8)
J	resultant seepage force (9·18)
j	seepage force per unit volume (9·18)
K	lateral pressure coefficient (17·7)
k	Darcy's coefficient of permeability (6·3)
k_x, k_y, k_z	components of k (9·6)
k'	effective permeability (9·8)
L	distance; length
L_a	length of arc (16·17)
L_c	length of chord (16·17)
M	moment
M_z	modulus (19·20)
m	distance ratio (11·3)
N	pressure index (11·2); various coefficients (e.g., 19·11)
n	porosity (2·2); distance ratio (11·3, 19·16); parameter (6·2); integer (10·11, 16·18)
n_d	number of potential intervals in a flow net (9·8)
n_f	number of flow paths in a flow net (9·8)
O_P	origin of planes in the Mohr diagram
P	resultant force (16·17, 17·4)
P_P	passive force (17·4)
p	pressure (10·8, 17·4)
p_i	intrinsic pressure (13·6, 15·9)
p_l	pressure on vertical plane (16·9)
p_v	overburden pressure (16·8)
Q	rate of discharge (6·3); resultant applied force (11·2, 17·12); penetration resistance of a pile (20·7)
Q_a	allowable load on a pile (20·8)

q	rate of discharge per running foot (9·3); applied pressure (11·3, 19·3)
q_a	allowable bearing pressure (19·26)
q_b	balanced pressure (19·34)
q_u	ultimate bearing capacity (19·9)
R	radius
r	hydrometer reading (3·10); radius in polar coordinates (9·16)
r'	radius in spherical coordinates (9·16)
S	degree of saturation (2·2); focal distance of parabola (9·10)
s	shearing strength per unit area (13·7, 15·9, 15·23); distance
s_{av}	average shearing strength (16·33)
T	time factor in consolidation theory (10·11)
T_s	surface tension
t	time
t_l	loading period (12·16)
U	consolidation ratio (10·11); resultant neutral force (16·17)
U_z	consolidation at a point (10·9)
u	hydrostatic excess pressure (10·8); velocity (20·7)
u_w	neutral pressure (14·11)
u_z	hydrostatic pressure (12·7)
V	volume
v	velocity
v_s	seepage velocity (6·3)
W	weight
w	water content relative to dry weight (2·2)
w_l	liquid limit (4·8)
w_p	plastic limit (4·8)
x, y, z	Cartesian coordinates
x_t	transformed x distance (9·7)
Z	vertical distance (9·16)
α	angle of stress obliquity (13·2); slope of downstream face of a dam (9·11)
α_m	maximum angle of stress obliquity (13·5)
β	angles
γ	unit weight (2·2)
γ_b	buoyant unit weight (7·2)
γ_s	unit weight of solid matter (2·2)
γ_t	unit weight of soil-water system (2·2, 7·2)
γ_w	unit weight of water (2·2)
δ	angles
ϵ_s	shearing strain (15·12)

ϵ_z	vertical direct strain (19·20)
θ	angle between a plane and the major principal plane in the Mohr diagram (13·4); angle in polar coordinates; angle to vertical (11·2)
μ	coefficient of viscosity; Poisson's ratio
ρ	settlement; penetration of a pile per blow of hammer (20·7)
ρ_a	allowable settlement (19·26)
ρ_u	ultimate settlement (12·14)
σ	direct stress (13·4)
$\sigma_1, \sigma_2, \sigma_3$	principal stresses (13·4)
$\bar{\sigma}$	intergranular direct stress (14·11)
σ_c	consolidation pressure (15·15)
σ_e	effective direct stress (15·23)
σ_f	direct stress on the plane of failure (13•7, 15·4)
σ_t	combined pore-water stress and intergranular direct stress (14·11)
τ	shearing stress (13·4)
ϕ	friction angle (13·7)
ϕ'	friction angle between soil and masonry (17·7)
ϕ_a	apparent friction angle (15·15)
ϕ_d	developed friction angle (16·6)
ϕ_e	effective friction angle (15·23)
ϕ_m	friction angle at the peak point (14·4)
ϕ_u	friction angle at the ultimate point (14·4)
ϕ_w	weighted friction angle (16·29)

Chapter 1

INTRODUCTION

1·1 The Fundamental Role of Soil Problems in Engineering

Every structure, whether it be a building, a bridge, a dam, a type of pavement, or even a ship during its construction, must be founded on soil or ledge. From prehistoric times the choice of a satisfactory foundation has been one of the first problems in any construction project. Since most structures rest on soil, the role of soil as a foundation material and as a construction material has always been one of outstanding importance.

It is interesting to speculate on the history of foundation engineering. In the large cities of early civilizations there were numerous large buildings which must have presented foundation problems much like those encountered in our modern cities. The truly great construction feats represented by the pyramids of Egypt, the temples of Babylon, the Great Wall of China, the aqueducts and roads of the Roman Empire, and other equally great but historically less recognized projects must have had their share of complicated foundation problems. In view of the variable and complicated nature of soil, it probably is safe to say that from prehistoric to modern times few if any types of construction problems have commanded as much special attention and as much originality and genius as those presented by problems associated with the soil.

1·2 The Nature of Soil

A large portion of the difficulties encountered in foundation work is due to the nature of soil. Usually those materials of construction are chosen which best fit the conditions of a given job. A choice of soils is sometimes offered, as, for example, the soil used for an earth dam, but more often the soil must be taken as it occurs at a given site. This situation usually exists in foundation problems, and the only recourse may be to use an-

1

other site if the one desired has unsatisfactory subsurface conditions. If the character of the soil is unsatisfactory, it may be possible, occasionally, to improve it by the injection of some substance; in the great majority of cases, however, the soil must be taken as it is in its natural condition.

It is utterly impossible to use some soils as foundation materials. Peats and organic silts are generally so compressible that they are avoided if possible. Other soils are satisfactory under certain loadings and below certain types of structures; soft clay is an example. The ideal foundation materials are sands, gravels, stiff clays, cemented soils, and rock; it is interesting to note in passing, however, that a rock foundation, which is the best in many ways, may often be unsatisfactory because of the expense of excavating to the desired foundation level. This wide range of soil characteristics holds not only for foundation materials but also for earth as a material of construction for dams and dikes. No other type of material has a greater range of characteristics than soil has.

It is not so much the variable characteristics of soils in general that lead to complex problems as it is the variable nature of the soil at any given construction site. Two specimens of soil taken at points a few feet apart, even if from a soil stratum which would be described as relatively homogeneous, may have properties differing many fold. This variable or erratic character is typical of practically every soil deposit, and often makes difficult the determination of representative soil properties.

In addition to its variable nature, soil is a difficult material to deal with because of the complexity of its physical properties, and because of the large number of properties that must be considered when fairly complete information on its action is desired.

1·3   The Development of Knowledge of Soil Action

The beginning of knowledge of soil action undoubtedly extends into prehistoric time, when the experienced artisan first began to devise methods of avoiding the difficulties inherent in unfavorable types of soils. His procedure was undoubtedly based almost entirely on guesswork or on the limited empirical knowledge furnished by his own and his ancestors' experience. Through ancient times and even within the last few generations practically all improvement was the result of a continuously broadening empirical knowledge. During recent decades rapid advances in knowledge of physics, and more recently in chemistry, could not help improving the scientist's knowledge of fundamentals of soil action. However, until recent years this source of knowledge did not reach the practicing foundation engineer to any important degree, mainly because the nature of soil makes difficult the understanding and application of such concepts.

The scientific approach may be said to be the adoption of the attitude that for the best solution of any problem the fullest possible use must be made of all available knowledge regarding fundamental phenomena. To a limited degree the scientific approach has been used in foundation engineering for some time, the classical earth pressure theories serving as an example. However, only within the last twenty or thirty years has concerted effort been made to develop to any appreciable degree the potentialities of the scientific approach.

1·4 The Development of Practical Applications of Mechanics

The application of the fundamental principles of mechanics to the common materials of construction is far from new. Analysis of steel members to determine stresses and laboratory testing to determine strengths have long been common practice. Rational design methods that are widely used are based on the principle of choosing each member so that its strength shall be greater than its stress by a reasonable margin of safety. Except for simple cases, such studies are statically indeterminate; that is, their solution requires the use of moduli of elasticity and other stress-strain ratios. Such studies of relationships between stress, strain, and strength constitute an important part of applied mechanics. In the so-called elastic materials these relationships are relatively simple, and they can often be determined with a relatively high degree of accuracy. A lower degree of accuracy is obtained when the same types of studies are made on imperfectly elastic materials, such as concrete, but even for such materials the accuracies are considered fairly satisfactory.

Applications of this type in which soil is the material under consideration are much more recent. However, analyses involving the building settlements which are due to compression of underlying soil and those involving possible instability of soil masses because of insufficient shearing strength of the soil are similar, basically, to the analyses of deflections and strengths which are common in the design of the superstructures of buildings.

The reason for the delay until recent times of the introduction of the above-mentioned principles of mechanics to soils is not hard to understand. In steels, a few properties, such as the modulus of elasticity, the yield stress, and Poisson's ratio, are sufficient to describe most of the features of its behavior under any loading. The number of properties needed for an understanding of the action of soil under load is unknown, is large, and sometimes the properties vary with climatic conditions. Moreover, the stress-strain relationships in steel are constant, and they hold up to the elastic limit under any loading or unloading; in soils they are variable, and they depend in a very complicated way on the pressure history of the soil. The variable and complex nature of soil has been mentioned previously; the complicated stress-strain relationships of soils are in large degree the cause of this complex nature.

The mechanics of solids is the basis of the applications mentioned above, but the mechanics of fluids may be discussed similarly. Engineering hydraulics is a well-established field which deals with the flow of water and which has to a considerable degree utilized empirical approaches based on experience and laboratory testing. A trend in recent years toward a more scientific point of view relative to studies of fluid flow is shown by rapid developments in fluid mechanics, which embraces developments in aeromechanics as well as in hydromechanics. In this respect fluid mechanics and soil mechanics are similar subjects, and in the recent rapid advances in soil engineering and hydraulic engineering important parts have been played by soil mechanics and fluid mechanics, respectively. In seepage through soils the flow occurring is usually of the type known as *laminar,* whereas the flow occurring in problems in hydraulic engineering is usually *turbulent,* but there are many considerations which are common to investigations of seepage through soils and problems in engineering hydraulics.

1·5 The Rational Approach to Problems in Soil Engineering

The rational approach may be defined as the approach which has for its aim the best possible understanding of the action or behavior of soils under all conditions encountered in engineering problems.

Three sources may be recognized as contributing to understanding of soil action. The first source is experience, as developed by trial and error during the past and as represented by the conventional and largely empirical procedures of today. The second source is the information on soil action which can be furnished by laboratory tests and investigations. The third source is the scientific approach, or the understanding that results only from a specialized familiarity with all phenomena which have bearing on soil action.

The complementary nature of the three sources cannot be too highly emphasized.

1·6 Soil Mechanics, the Scientific Approach

Soil mechanics is the name given to the scientific approach to understanding of soil action. It may be defined as the science dealing with all phenomena which affect the action of soil in a capacity in any way associated with engineering.

The word mechanics, strictly speaking, does not include chemistry, colloidal physics, and other sciences which have bearing on soil action. However, specialization in the scientific approach surely must embrace all sciences that offer valuable concepts relative to soil action, and thus the name which has been chosen for the scientific approach must be allowed to cover a somewhat broadened meaning. The term soil physics comes closer to expressing the desired meaning, but it has long been used by agricultural scientists and thus has come to be associated with agriculture by engineers.

1·7 Quantitative and Qualitative Applications of Soil Mechanics

In a number of different types of engineering problems quantitative applications of soil mechanics are used. Of two examples that will be mentioned briefly, the first involves seepage. On the cross section of the foundation of a dam it is possible to use a graphical representation of the seepage pattern, known as the flow net; from this net the quantity of underseepage, the magnitude of the uplift force caused by water pressure, and other numerical data may be estimated. The second example refers to compression of soil. Samples from a buried clay stratum may be tested in the laboratory to determine their compressibility, and the test data may be used to predict the settlement which will occur if a building is founded above this stratum.

Since all quantitative analyses on soils do not have the precision sought in some branches of engineering, an estimate of the probable precision becomes an important phase of such analyses. This point, however, is one that should receive more emphasis in other branches of engineering; for example, not many buildings are subjected to loads which can be predicted with sufficient accuracy to allow the precisions often inferred in estimates of stresses in structural members.

Considerations of quantitative applications immediately show the close relationship between laboratory tests and the scientific approach, two of the contributing sources mentioned in Section 1·5. Routine classification tests may be of practical importance but they bear only indirect relationship to soil mechanics. However, testing of soils for mechanical properties, such as permeability and compressibility, is a necessary part of quantitative soil mechanics applications. Laboratory testing programs are, therefore, an important adjunct to soil mechanics, and are commonly considered an important part of soil mechanics itself. Also considered as a part of soil mechanics is the use of some types of tests which cannot be depended upon for numerical accuracy but can be used to advantage for relative comparisons of two or more soils.

Qualitative applications of soil mechanics have an importance which has generally not been given sufficient emphasis. If an embankment is barely safe against danger of a landslide and if it is known that the height of the water table within the embankment is going to be raised, any engineer familiar with fundamentals knows that the seepage forces within the embankment will be increased in magnitude and that a landslide is likely. A decision based on this knowledge is just as much an application of soil mechanics as a decision utilizing hundreds of man-hours of computations and laboratory testing.

Most engineers will probably find that the opportunities for qualitative application are commoner than those for quantitative application. This may be especially true for the construction engineer, who does not specialize in soil or foundation work but who should have some knowledge of soil mechanics, if only to enable him to recognize dangerous situations that may require the opinion of a specialist.

Qualitative applications of soil mechanics greatly resemble many practical applications of geology. Geology treats of the history of the earth as recorded in the materials comprising the earth. Understanding of the origin and past history of a given deposit is often an invaluable aid toward an understanding of its inherent characteristics. The geologist makes use of all scientific concepts, and the aid he can give the engineer is, more often than not, in the form of purely qualitative opinions and recommendations. Qualitative soil mechanics and the geology of soils overlap in many ways, and knowledge of geology is of much value to a specialist in soil mechanics. A comprehension of geological formations, groundwater flow, the processes of cementation and weathering, and the like leads to a better understanding of many characteristics of soils. Moreover, every soil investigation should include adequate investigation of all geological features that have bearing on the problem.

1·8   The Importance of Coordination of Theory and Practice

Theories require assumptions which often are true only to a limited degree. Thus any new theoretical ideas have questionable points which can be removed only by checks under actual conditions.

This statement holds especially true for theories pertaining to soil mechanics because assumptions relative to soil action are always more or less questionable. Such theories may sometimes be checked to a limited degree by laboratory tests on small samples, but often the only final and satisfactory verification requires observations under actual field conditions.

One of the qualifications of a capable and experienced soil engineer is the feel he has developed for soil action or, more scientifically, his intuition regarding soil behavior. The study of soil mechanics is very fruitful in furnishing concepts which are a background for this intuition. Practical experience in construction is also valuable in this respect, and here again it is seen that theory and practical experience complement each other to give results not obtainable by either alone.

1·9 Foundation Engineering and Soil Engineering

Foundation engineering is a widely recognized profession. It is the branch of engineering which is associated with the design, construction, maintenance, and renovation of footings, foundation walls, pile foundations, caissons, and all other structural members which form the foundations of buildings and other engineering structures. It also includes all engineering considerations of the underlying soil and rock in so far as they are associated with the foundation.

Soil engineering differs from foundation engineering in that it does not directly include matters pertaining to the structural members of the foundation. For example, the design of the reinforcing in spread footings usually is not considered soil engineering. However, all problems associated with the soil on which a foundation is based are within the scope of soil engineering. All problems of investigation, design, construction, and maintenance of earth dams, and of all kinds of earth embankments and earth works, as well as all laboratory investigations of soils, whether the investigations are of fundamental nature or are merely routine tests, belong to soil engineering.

Many tasks which have been called foundation engineering should be designated soil engineering, and vice versa. Also many more or less routine investigations which have been classified as soil mechanics or practical applications of soil mechanics should be called soil engineering. The term soil engineering is one which should be given broader use.

1·10 Definition of Soil

The term soil, as used by engineers and as adopted in soil mechanics, covers a much wider range of materials than the same term as used by laymen or as defined by agriculturists and geologists. To the agriculturist, soil is the earth mold within which organic forces are prominent and which is adapted to the support of plant life. To the geologist also, soil is the material in the relatively thin surface zone within which roots occur. According to the broader engineering interpretation, soils are considered to include all earth materials, organic and inorganic, occurring in the zone overlying the rock crust of our planet.

1·11 Discussion of the Dependability of Soil Analysis Data

The limited dependability of results of quantitative soil investigations is a matter which has caused much discussion and which must be honestly faced and carefully considered by all engineers who are engaged in such investigations. It must be realized that few soil analyses give results of high accuracy and that most of them give values which are rough estimates at best. This may be due in part to the use of assumptions that are not strictly true, but limited knowledge of existing conditions is, in many cases, the more important cause. In analyses of seepage quantities, which will be taken as an example, the common procedure is to use for the measure of permeability the results of a limited number of laboratory tests on samples from the site. Frequently there are a few strata somewhere in the underground which are much coarser than the general run of the soil and which are not discovered during the investigations. These coarse strata may be the cause of many times as much seepage as would occur if they were not present, yet the samples may give no indication of their existence. No charge of laxity can be made in such a case, because exhaustive explorations might fail to disclose the existence of the coarse strata. Therefore the effects of such items can only be accounted for in the final stage of the analysis, when the experience and judgment of the engineers in charge are called on to make allowances for factors which the studies are unable to disclose.

The following question has sometimes been advanced: If studies cannot reveal important items of this type and if experience and judgment are the basis of the final decisions anyway, why are the studies made? Two statements may be offered in answer to this question. The first is that many factors which have bearing on a problem may be correctly reflected in the results of a soil investigation, even though certain other factors are not adequately accounted for, and in investigations which cover a number of alternative designs those relative results that pertain to the factors which are correctly reflected may be dependable and may have much value. The second statement is that judgment, which supersedes experience and all other factors in importance and grows largely from experience, is also aided to an important degree by studies of the type under discussion. It goes without saying that theoretical analyses, if used without judgment, are worthless and may even lead to disaster. However, it also must be acknowledged that the engineer whose judgment is relied on for important decisions on many types of problems of a scientific nature must have a good background in theory.

Every analysis discussed in subsequent chapters of this book is subject, to some degree, to qualifications of the type discussed above. Obviously it will not be possible to repeat these qualifications with every procedure described. Therefore, these ideas must be kept in mind and recognized as prerequisites to all such studies of soil mechanics as those discussed herein.

1·12 Scope of This Textbook

The main purpose of this textbook, as its name implies, is the presentation of fundamentals. The ultimate aim is to acquaint the student and the scientifically inclined engineer with those principles of mechanics which will improve his understanding of soil action, both in the qualitative sense and as it applies quantitatively to engineering problems.

In order to make clear the part such information plays in the understanding of soil action, numerous practical applications are given. Such examples are in general chosen as illustrations of fundamental points and not as illustrations of construction procedures.

This text will attempt to show that there is close association between the importance of intuition regarding soil action, the need of a true appreciation that soil mechanics is not an exact science, the realization that for rational decisions in soil engineering a skeptical attitude toward the use of routine procedures must be adopted, and the fact that the main aim in any study of fundamentals is the development of sound judgment.

In connection with the presentation of fundamentals brief descriptions of the more important soil tests will be given. Methods of soil sampling will also be described. In addition, brief discussions of soil classifications and other more or less routine subjects must be included. The principal aim of the textbook, however, is to present fundamental concepts regarding the action of soil as it relates to engineering problems.

Chapter 2

PRELIMINARY CONSIDERATIONS

2·1 Introduction

Before discussion may be started in any branch of soil mechanics notations and definitions must be given. This chapter will be devoted mainly to the presentation of such material.

2·2 Simple Soil Properties

A soil mass is commonly considered to consist of a network or skeleton of solid particles, enclosing voids or interspaces of varying size. The voids may be filled with air, with water, or partly with air and partly with water.

The total volume of a given soil sample is designated by V and consists of two essential parts, the volume of solid matter V_s and

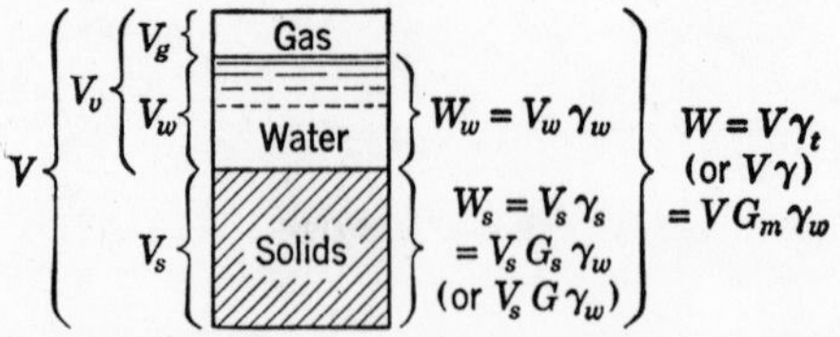

$$V \begin{cases} V_v \begin{cases} V_g \\ V_w \end{cases} \\ V_s \end{cases} \begin{array}{|c|} \hline \text{Gas} \\ \hline \text{Water} \\ \hline \text{Solids} \\ \hline \end{array} \begin{cases} W_w = V_w\,\gamma_w \\ \\ W_s = V_s\,\gamma_s \\ \quad = V_s\,G_s\,\gamma_w \\ (\text{or } V_s\,G\,\gamma_w) \end{cases} \begin{array}{l} W = V\gamma_t \\ (\text{or } V\gamma) \\ = V\,G_m\,\gamma_w \end{array}$$

FIG. 2·1 Diagrammatic representation of soil as a three-phase system, showing weight and volume notations and relationships.

the volume of voids V_v. The volume of voids in turn is subdivided into water volume V_w and gas volume V_g. These volumes are indicated in Fig. 2·1. This figure must be recognized as a diagrammatic representation since it is evident that all void and solid volumes cannot be segregated as shown. However, for studying interrelationships of the terms given in this section such sketches help greatly.

Volume ratios which are used widely in soil mechanics are the porosity, the void ratio, and the degree of saturation.

The *porosity n* of the soil mass is defined as the ratio of volume of the voids to the total volume of the mass.

The *void ratio e* of the mass is defined as the ratio of volume of voids to volume of solid.

The *degree of saturation S* is defined as the ratio of volume of water to volume of voids.

These ratios may be written

$$n = \frac{V_v}{V} \qquad (2 \cdot 1)$$

$$e = \frac{V_v}{V_s} \qquad (2 \cdot 2)$$

$$S = \frac{V_w}{V_v} \qquad (2 \cdot 3)$$

The void ratio is usually expressed as a ratio, whereas porosity and degree of saturation are commonly expressed as percentages.

Porosity as defined above is used in many branches of engineering and is more familiar than the void ratio to engineers in general. However, in soil mechanics it is more convenient in the majority of cases to use the void ratio, principally because, when a given specimen of soil is compressed, the denominator of the void ratio expression remains constant, whereas both numerator and denominator of the porosity expression vary.

The total weight of a soil sample is designated by W, the weight of solids by W_s, and the weight of water by W_w. A ratio of weights which has wide usage is the water content.

The *water content w* of a soil sample is defined in soil mechanics as the ratio of weight of water to weight of solid matter. It is commonly expressed as a percentage and may be written

$$w = \frac{W_w}{W_s} \qquad (2 \cdot 4)$$

The water content defined in equation $2 \cdot 4$ is a ratio, or percentage, of the weight of solids, W_s. This basis is not standard in all branches of science, the water content being defined in geology, for example, as a percentage of total weight. Therefore this definition as given should be carefully noted.

The idealized concept used herein assumes that solid grains and water are two definite and separate phases of a soil. However, the actual situation is much more complex, since water may exist in a number of forms and mineral grains contain combined water. When a sample is heated to evaporate the pore water, certain amounts of combined water may also be driven off, the amount of loss of combined water depending mainly on the temperature used. In order to give a fixed definition of what is to be considered as water, it is commonly stated that all weight lost in evaporation by heating to 105° or 110°C is water; all remaining, solids. In other ways the simple two-phase concept is not strictly true. If salts are dissolved in the water they may change its unit weight appreciably; for example, sea water has a unit weight of about 1.025 grams per cc. If the sample is heated to drive off the water, the salts remain and become part of the solid weight. Therefore the diagram of Fig. 2·1 must be recognized as one based on simplified concepts, but it is widely used and unless otherwise stated will be accepted for all considerations herein.

This idealized concept also implies that the solids are stable. In many soils, such as those which in the past have been transported and worn by streams, this is essentially true, and any loading or other action on the soil will cause no appreciable change, even over long periods of time. On the other hand, it must be realized that many soils are unstable. Soils weathered in place may break down so easily that they really do not have definite grains. Some soils are very susceptible to chemical action, and their properties may change rapidly in certain environments.

Variations in the water content of a given soil change its characteristics to such a marked degree that the importance of this soil property cannot be overemphasized. The notation w for water content was one of the first notations chosen by Terzaghi in his earliest soil mechanics developments, and its use is so firmly entrenched that a change would be difficult. Therefore, some other symbol is preferable for unit weight.

The *unit weight* or weight per unit of volume is a self-explanatory term. It will be designated in this text by the Greek letter γ. The following expressions hold for the mass unit weight or unit weight of the soil mass as a whole, γ_t, the unit weight of solids γ_s, and the unit weight of water γ_w:

$$\gamma_t = \frac{W}{V} = \frac{G + Se}{1 + e} \gamma_w \tag{2.5}$$

$$\gamma_s = \frac{W_s}{V_s} \tag{2.6}$$

$$\gamma_w = \frac{W_w}{V_w} \tag{2.7}$$

The final expression for γ_t in equation 2.5 is derived and explained in Section 7.2. All other terms in the three above equations are represented in Fig. 2.1.

The unit weight of water, γ_w, equals between 1.00 and 0.995 gram per cc under natural conditions, and in most soil mechanics work the value 1 gram per cc is sufficiently accurate. At a temperature of 4°C the value is exactly 1 gram per cc, and is sometimes designated by γ_o. Other subscripts may be used at other definite temperatures when extreme accuracy is justified.

The *specific gravity* is defined in physics textbooks as the ratio between the unit weight of a substance and the unit weight of some reference substance, the reference substance in most instances being pure water at 4°C. Thus, equations which are strictly correct for the mass specific gravity G_m, the specific gravity of solids G_s, and the specific gravity of water G_w are

$$G_m = \frac{\gamma_t}{\gamma_o} \tag{2.8}$$

$$G_s = \frac{\gamma_s}{\gamma_o} \tag{2.9}$$

$$G_w = \frac{\gamma_w}{\gamma_o} \tag{2.10}$$

However, γ_o in the above equations is often replaced by γ_w, since the difference between these two values is seldom appreciable.

The specific gravity of quartz is 2.67, and for the majority of soils its value falls between 2.65 and 2.85. However, a high organic content will lead to lower values, and the presence of some of the less common heavy minerals may lead to larger values.

Values of the specific gravity G_w of pure water are given in tabular form in the next chapter in Table 3·1.

The *density* is described in physics as unit mass or mass per unit of volume, and since mass is equal to weight divided by the gravitational acceleration g, the density may be expressed

$$\rho = \frac{\gamma_m}{g}$$

There is little or no occasion to use numerical values of density in soil mechanics. However, general terms such as "dense" and "very dense" and their opposites "loose" and "very loose" are commonly used to denote relative values within the range of possible void ratios of sand samples.

In the metric system the unit weight in grams per cubic centimeter, the specific gravity, which is a ratio, and the density in grams of mass per cubic centimeter are all numerically equal. Therefore the three terms are sometimes used interchangeably in some fields of engineering. No confusion can occur as long as there is strict adherence to metric units, but when English units are used confusion is likely to result. The following illustration may help to avoid the confusion that can be occasioned by this loose, interchangeable use of terms.

The weight of a sample of dry sand may, in accordance with definitions and notations given above, be expressed as

$$W = G_m \gamma_w V$$

If the volume is 1 cu ft, reasonable values for the other quantities are $W = 100$ lb, $G_m = 1.6$, and $\gamma_w = 62.4$ lb per cu ft. In cgs units, the quantities for the same sample would be $W = 45,300$ grams, $G_m = 1.6$, $\gamma_w = 1$ gram per cc, and $V = 28,300$ cc. Where metric units are used, omission of the γ_w term does not numerically invalidate the formula. However, if this term is removed, the formula, from the viewpoint of units—that is, dimensionally— will be incorrect. Since the first principle of soil mechanics is an understanding of fundamentals, every effort should be made to keep all formulas dimensionally correct.

It has become quite common to designate the mass unit weight by γ rather than by γ_t and the specific gravity of solids by G rather than G_s. Although this dropping of subscripts is not entirely consistent, it is convenient to have the most frequently used notations free of subscript. In the following pages, when these terms appear without subscript, the above-mentioned quantities are to be understood. They are shown in parentheses in Fig. 2·1. Little chance of confusion exists in these cases, and subscripts are available for use whenever any possibility of confusion is present. Similarly, when unit weight is mentioned without further designation, the mass unit weight is understood, and specific gravity without further designation refers to the specific gravity of solids.

2·3 Illustrative Problems

1. Let it be assumed that a soil sample has a mass specific gravity of 1.91, a specific gravity of 2.69, and a water content of 29.0 per cent. The values of the void ratio, the porosity, and the degree of saturation are desired.

When all information given is entirely independent of the size of the sample, the data must be valid for a sample of any size, and the easiest solution is obtained by assuming some convenient value of weight or volume.

Assume
$$V_s = 100 \text{ cc}$$

Since $G = 2.69$,
$$W_s = 269 \text{ grams}$$

Since $w = 29$ per cent,
$$W_w = 269 \times 0.29 = 78 \text{ grams} \quad \text{and} \quad V_w = 78 \text{ cc}$$

Since gas has no weight,
$$W = W_s + W_w = 269 + 78 = 347 \text{ grams}$$

Since $G_m = 1.91$,
$$\gamma_t = 1.91 \text{ grams per cc} \quad \text{and} \quad V = \frac{347}{1.91} = 182 \text{ cc}$$

also
$$V_g = V - V_s - V_w = 182 - 100 - 78 = 4 \text{ cc}$$

These results may be assembled in a form resembling Fig. 2·1:

$$V = 182 \text{ cc} \begin{cases} & 100 \text{ cc } Solids \quad 269 \text{ grams} \\ 82 \begin{cases} 78 & Water \quad 78 \\ 4 & Gas \quad \dots \end{cases} \end{cases} W = 347 \text{ grams}$$

Finally,

$$e = \tfrac{82}{100} = 0.820$$

$$n = \tfrac{82}{182} = 45.0 \text{ per cent}$$

$$S = \tfrac{78}{82} = 95.2 \text{ per cent}$$

2. Determine simple expressions for relationships between (a) water content and void ratio; (b) unit weight and unit weight of solids.

(a)
$$w = \frac{W_w}{W_s} = \frac{\gamma_w V_w}{\gamma_w G V_s} = \frac{\gamma_w S V_v}{\gamma_w G V_s} = \frac{eS}{G}$$

(b)
$$\gamma_t = \frac{W_s + W_w}{V_s + V_v} = \frac{W_s\left(1 + \dfrac{W_w}{W_s}\right)}{V_s\left(1 + \dfrac{V_v}{V_s}\right)} = \gamma_s \frac{1 + w}{1 + e}$$

2·4 Nomenclature

For many years much confusion existed because there was no accepted, standard nomenclature in the field of soil mechanics. This difficulty has been greatly diminished by the publication of a manual entitled *Soil Mechanics Nomenclature* by the American Society of Civil Engineers (6).*

The commonest of the notations which will be used herein are listed in the Notation following the Preface. This list is substantially in agreement with that given in the above-mentioned publication.

2·5 Homogeneity and the Variable Nature of Soils

Soil engineers often state that the more soils they study and the more test pits they examine, the more they are impressed with the degree of variability in typical soil deposits. Recognition of the exceedingly variable nature in almost any soil deposit is important to all engineers working with soils. In any given soil stratum the soil properties generally vary with depth and also vary in horizontal directions.

* Figures in parentheses refer to References at the end of the book.

If the properties of the material are alike at all points in a given mass, the mass is defined as *homogeneous*. It must be recognized that a soil stratum never is truly homogeneous, yet almost all theoretical considerations of soil action must be based on the assumption of homogeneous material. Such analyses must, therefore, refer to a hypothetical material, any property of which is an average of values of the given property throughout the actual soil.

The soil properties at a site may show large local variations, yet there may be no general trends to the variations, and the average properties may be essentially the same in all portions of the site. In other words, there are large variations in properties at points throughout the mass but the average values are essentially constant. Such variations are called *scattering*, and the average values are known as *statistical averages*. In many types of problems in which the statistical average properties are essentially constant the assumption of homogeneity introduces no inaccuracies and offers no difficulties, regardless of the amount of scattering. In such problems the hypothetical material mentioned above may simply be considered to possess statistical averages for properties rather than the true scattering values. On the other hand there are situations in which the properties at critical points, rather than the average properties, control, and in such problems the use of average properties may give misleading results.

An important part of any thorough foundation investigation is the obtaining of a *representative group of samples* of the deposits present or of the critical materials therein. The word representative signifies that the samples should show the range in variation which exists in each soil type and that the number of samples obtained should be sufficient to permit the determination of reasonably dependable values of average soil properties.

2·6 Horizontal Variation

Variation with depth is usually an expected condition in a soil deposit. Of perhaps more importance and more concern to the soil engineer is horizontal variation.

Horizontal variation is a trend toward changes in statistical average conditions in the horizontal direction. It may refer either to variation in soil properties or to variation in strata thicknesses. Variations of the former type are often hard to detect and difficult to determine quantitatively, because the magnitude of variation may be less than the amount of scattering relative to local statistical average values. Included in the category of horizontal variations are local soft spots which the soil engineer must consider, for example, when they exist below individual footings. However, the broader meaning of the term pertains to a definite trend over a considerable distance.

2·7 Aleotropy and Stratification

A relatively homogeneous soil deposit is often referred to as a stratum. Within such a stratum, however, there may be hundreds of small, noticeably different strata, and the word stratification refers to the condition resulting from the existence of these many small strata. If a material has like properties on all orientations of planes, it is called isotropic; if not, it is called anisotropic or aleotropic. Largely because of stratification during their formation, soils are seldom truly isotropic.

Two common types of aleotropy occur in soils. One is alternating strata of materials of different fineness, which is a true stratification. The other is the structural arrangement resulting during deposition or from stress applications, in which variations from a random orientation of particles or particle groups occur. This type of aleotropy occurs in greatest degree in highly compressible soils. It will be considered to be a type of stratification in this text, although this type of aleotropy is not always classified as stratification.

2·8 Units

Two systems of units are in common use, the metric and the English systems. Much could be written on the desirability of adopting the metric system and rejecting the English system but such a discussion will not be attempted here. Since the fundamental aim of soil mechanics is a closer tie between physics and engineering, it is inevitable that both systems will appear and that frequent conversions of units will be necessary. Therefore facility in converting units is important to the soil engineer.

No conversion tables will be given herein, since they are available in the library of any engineer. However, the relationships between stress units are so frequently encountered that they will be mentioned.

1 ton per sq ft = 0.976 kg per sq cm = 0.945 atmosphere

In the above the standard atmosphere, equal to 14.70 lb per sq in., is used. It is seen that these three common units of pressure are equal to each other within about 5 per cent. In instances where accuracies closer than 5 per cent are not needed (as in a large portion of soil mechanics analyses), these three units of pressure may be assumed equal.

PROBLEMS

1. The weight of a watch glass and a sample of saturated clay is 68.959 grams. After drying, the sample weighs 62.011 grams. The watch glass weighs 35.046 grams, and the specific gravity of the soil is 2.80. Determine the void ratio, the water content, and the porosity of the original sample.

2. A moist sand sample has a volume of 464 cc in natural state and a weight of 793 grams. The dry weight is 735 grams, and the specific gravity is 2.68. Determine the void ratio, the porosity, the water content, and the degree of saturation.

3. (a) A dry soil has a void ratio of 0.65, and its grains have a specific gravity of 2.80. Determine the unit weight in pounds per cubic foot.

(b) Sufficient water is added to the sample to give a degree of saturation of 60 per cent. No change in void ratio occurs. Determine the water content and the unit weight.

(c) The sample next is placed below water. Determine the true unit weight (buoyancy not to be considered here) for each of the following assumptions: (1) that the degree of saturation remains at 60 per cent (this condition is not likely to occur); (2) that the degree of saturation becomes 95 per cent (a typical condition); (3) that the sample becomes completely saturated.

(d) Determine the percentage error involved in the value obtained for the true unit weight if the sample actually is 95 per cent saturated but is assumed completely saturated.

4. A saturated clay has a water content of 39.3 per cent and a specific mass gravity of 1.84. Determine the void ratio and the specific gravity.

5. For a certain series of laboratory tests the following data are available:

Volume of container	0.0333 cu ft
Weight of container	3378 grams
Specific gravity of soil	2.86

Five soil specimens at different water contents were placed in turn in the container, a standard method of tamping being used and the container being just filled for each sample; the following data were obtained:

Water content (per cent)	0.201	0.215	0.223	0.233	0.251
Container and wet soil (grams)	5038	5113	5165	5178	5163

Make plots of (a) unit weight versus water content, (b) weight of solids per unit of total volume versus water content, (c) void ratio versus water content. (For further information on this type of test reference may be made to Section 18·2 and Fig. 18·2.)

6. A saturated sample of soil has a volume of 1 cu ft and a weight of 130 lb. The specific gravity of the soil particles is 2.79.

(a) Assume that the pore fluid is pure water and determine the water content and the void ratio.

(b) Assume next that the pore fluid is salt water with a specific gravity of 1.025. Let the weights of solid matter, pure water, and salt content be designated by W_S, W_W, and W_D, respectively. Determine the void ratio and the values of ratios W_W/W_S, $(W_W + W_D)/W_S$, and $W_W/(W_S + W_D)$.

(c) Give suggested names for the three final ratios determined in part (b). Determine the amount of error involved if the assumption of part (a) is used when the assumption of part (b) is the correct one.

Chapter 3

SIMPLE SOIL TESTS AND CLASSIFICATION TESTS

3·1 General

A number of soil tests which are in common use do not require special theoretical considerations. The soil properties they furnish are physical properties rather than mechanical properties. The study of such tests does not belong in any specific chapter of soil mechanics, but the data they furnish are required or are desirable for the majority of soil investigations. Such tests will be presented in this chapter and will include the following.

Simple tests for:	Classification tests for:
Water content	Atterberg limits
Specific gravity	Grain-size distribution
Void ratio	Field or preliminary tests for:
Relative density	Identification of soil types

Although there may be much value in the standardization of laboratory procedures for many types of tests, the aim of this chapter is to outline the fundamental concepts involved. Therefore, very few detailed testing instructions will be given. For standardized procedures the reader is referred to other publications (9, 33).

3·2 Water Content Determination

Determinations of water content are required for all types of soils, in conditions varying from saturation to that in which the moisture is of a hygroscopic nature and in so small a quantity that to the eye the sample appears to be dry. They are also required as a part of many of the more elaborate tests.

The containers and the sizes of samples used may vary widely but in typical cases three measurements are needed. If the weight of the container is designated as W_c, the three measurements are

The original weight of sample and container,
$$W_1 = W_c + W_s + W_w$$
The dried weight of sample and container, $W_2 = W_c + W_s$
The weight of the container, W_c
The water content is expressed in percentage and is given by

$$w = \frac{W_1 - W_2}{W_2 - W_c} \tag{3·1}$$

3·3 Specific Gravity Determination

The specific gravity is relatively unimportant as far as effect on the qualitative behavior of soils is concerned. However, it must be determined for the majority of soils tested, since it is needed for determination of such properties as void ratio and degree of saturation.

On occasion, the presence in many soils of numerous minerals, each having a different specific gravity, may lead to difficulties. For example, in a boulder clay the boulders and other coarse particles may have an average specific gravity which differs appreciably from that of the fines, and many problems occur wherein excessive errors will result if this characteristic is not considered. However, unless otherwise mentioned, the average value for all grains is understood to be referred to when the specific gravity of a soil is mentioned.

The pycnometer or constant volume method has been found to be the most reliable for determinations of specific gravity. Commonly, about 200 grams of dry weight of sample, a 500-cc constant volume or pycnometer bottle, and distilled water are used.

Three weight measurements are necessary. The most important and most difficult of the three is a weight determination of the bottle with soil and water filling it just to the constant volume mark at a known temperature. The greatest care must be used to expel all air from the mixture. The air is expelled by a gentle boiling, which may be obtained either by heating or by evacuating or by both. A dependable reading of the average temperature of the mixture can be obtained only if the temperature is approximately constant throughout. To maintain a con-

stant temperature and to aid in expelling air an almost continuous agitation of the mixture during boiling is desirable.

The other weights required are the dry weight of the soil and
the weight of bottle filled to exactly the same mark with pure
water at the same temperature as in the first measurement. A
calibration of the bottle, giving this weight as a function of
temperature, will eliminate the necessity of a reading for each
test.

The measurements thus are

Weight of pycnometer bottle, soil and water $= W_1$
Weight of pycnometer bottle with pure water $= W_2$
Dry weight of soil $= W_s$

If the soil could be removed from the bottle just after the first
reading and if a volume of water just equal to the soil volume were
removed after the second reading, the weights resulting for the
two processes would be alike. The amount of water which has a
volume equal to the soil volume would weigh $W_s \times G_T/G_s$, wherein
G_T, the specific gravity of water at the temperature of the test,
may be obtained from Table 3·1. Therefore

$$W_1 - W_s = W_2 - W_s \frac{G_T}{G_s}$$

whence

$$G_s = \frac{G_T W_s}{W_s - W_1 + W_2} \tag{3·2}$$

TABLE 3·1 SPECIFIC GRAVITY OF DISTILLED WATER

°C	0	1	2	3	4	5	6	7	8	9
0	0.9999	0.9999	1.0000	1.0000	1.0000	1.0000	1.0000	0.9999	0.9999	0.9998
10	0.99973	0.99963	0.99952	0.99940	0.99927	0.99913	0.99897	0.99880	0.99862	0.99843
20	0.99823	0.99802	0.99780	0.99757	0.99733	0.99707	0.99681	0.99654	0.99626	0.99597
30	0.99568	0.9954	0.9951	0.9947	0.9944	0.9941	0.9937	0.9934	0.9930	0.9926
40	0.9922	0.9919	0.9915	0.9911	0.9907	0.9902	0.9898	0.9894	0.9890	0.9885
50	0.9881	0.9876	0.9872	0.9867	0.9862	0.9857	0.9852	0.9848	0.9842	0.9838
60	0.9832	0.9827	0.9822	0.9817	0.9811	0.9806	0.9800	0.9795	0.9789	0.9784
70	0.9778	0.9772	0.9767	0.9761	0.9755	0.9749	0.9743	0.9737	0.9731	0.9724
80	0.9718	0.9712	0.9706	0.9699	0.9693	0.9686	0.9680	0.9673	0.9667	0.9660
90	0.9653	0.9647	0.9640	0.9633	0.9626	0.9619	0.9612	0.9605	0.9598	0.9591

To get unit weight of water in the English system multiply by 62.424.

As previously mentioned the specific gravity G_s may be designated by G whenever this dropping of subscript leads to no confusion.

3·4   Void Ratio Determinations

Void ratio determinations are very simple in principle, but considerable difficulty is often experienced if accurate determinations are required. Where accuracy is desired a careful study of the precision of the various observations is essential.

Void ratio computations are usually obtained from observations giving the sample volume V, the dry weight of the sample W_s, and the specific gravity of solids G. When the volume of solids is expressed as $W_s/G\gamma_w$ there results

$$e = \frac{V - \dfrac{W_s}{G\gamma_w}}{\dfrac{W_s}{G\gamma_w}} = \frac{G\gamma_w V}{W_s} - 1 \tag{3·3}$$

It may easily be shown also that the void ratio may be expressed as

$$e = \frac{W_w}{W_s}\frac{G}{S} \tag{3·4}$$

By the use of the above equation, it is possible to determine the void ratio of a specimen which is initially saturated or nearly saturated if the weights of water and of soil in the specimen are known. However, the accuracy of such a determination depends largely on the accuracy of the value used for S. This procedure must be used with care, therefore, because many soils which appear to be completely saturated contain appreciable amounts of gas.

3·5   Relative Densities of Granular Soils

The limiting range of void ratios for any given granular soil may be found experimentally, the upper limit by pouring the soil loosely into a container and determining its weight and volume, the lower by tamping and shaking the soil until it has reached a minimum volume, and measuring weight and volume as before.

The location of the void ratio of a given soil sample within the range of these two limiting values offers a convenient measure of the relative compactness, or relative density. The value of the relative density of a given soil under given conditions usually gives a clearer idea of the state of density than the value of the void ratio itself gives.

Consider a sample of sand which has a void ratio e. Let the limiting void ratios of the same sand, determined as outlined above, be e_{max} and e_{min}. Then the *relative density* D_d of the sample is defined by

$$D_d = \frac{e_{max} - e}{e_{max} - e_{min}} \qquad (3\cdot5)$$

A sand in its loosest state has a relative density of zero; in its densest state a value of unity. It should be recognized, however, that different procedures in placing the soil will lead to somewhat different values of the limiting void ratios e_{max} and e_{min}. Thus it is evident that the compacting procedure must be standardized before different observers can obtain like results.

3·6 Atterberg Limit Determinations

A description of the Atterberg Limits and Indices and a discussion of their applicability are given in Section 4·8. Only brief explanations of the tests for determining the limits are given here.[*]

The *liquid limit* w_l is the water content at which a clay is practically liquid but possesses a certain small shearing strength, this arbitrarily chosen strength being presumably the smallest value that it is feasible to measure by a standardized procedure. The apparatus for the determination of this property is shown in Fig. 3·1. A clay is at the liquid limit if 25 blows in this standard apparatus just close a groove of standardized dimensions which is cut in the sample by the grooving tool shown in the figure. Trials at several water contents on thoroughly mixed specimens with water contents determined as explained in Section 3·2 allow the plotting of the curve shown in Fig. 3·2, known as the flow curve. The liquid limit may be read from the curve,

[*] For further details see reference 9.

and a trial just at 25 blows is not needed. The logarithmic scale of blows is used for convenience, since it has been found that it gives a straight line plot.

The *plastic limit* w_p is the smallest water content at which a soil is plastic. It is obtained by rolling out samples at slowly

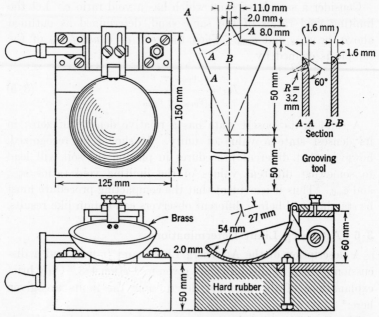

FIG. 3·1 Apparatus for liquid limit determinations. (A. Casagrande.)

decreasing water content until that water content is reached at which a thread ⅛ in. in diameter just begins to crumble. The threads may be rolled on a glass plate with the hand; consistent results can be obtained without special apparatus.

The *shrinkage limit* w_s is the smallest water content that can occur in a clay sample which is completely saturated. Two methods for determining the shrinkage limit will be given, the first for the case in which the specific gravity is not known. In Fig. 3·3 let (*a*) represent a specimen in the plastic state which just fills a container of known volume V_1 and has a weight W_1 which has been measured. This specimen then is

dried gradually. As it reaches the shrinkage limit the specimen
is represented by (*b*), after which it continues to dry with no
further volume change until it reaches the dry state represented
in (*c*). In this state the dry weight W_s is determined and the

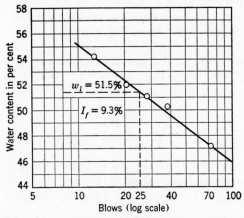

FIG. 3·2 Plot used in liquid limit determinations.

volume V_2 is also obtained. This final volume is best obtained
by displacement of mercury. Into a special dish which is level-
full of mercury the soil sample is so placed as to displace its
volume of mercury. The displaced mercury can then be weighed

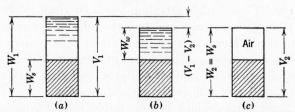

FIG. 3·3 Diagrams used in the derivation of the shrinkage limit expression.

and this weight divided by the unit weight of 13.6 grams per cc
gives the desired volume.

The shrinkage limit equals W_w/W_s as shown in (*b*). The
weight W_w equals W_1 minus W_s minus the weight of water expelled in passing from (*a*) to (*b*); the expelled water has the

volume $V_1 - V_2$ and therefore the weight $\gamma_w(V_1 - V_2)$.   Thus

$$w_s = \frac{(W_1 - W_s) - \gamma_w(V_1 - V_2)}{W_s} \qquad (3\cdot6)$$

This method also gives a determination of the specific gravity which, however, is not so accurate as that obtained by the method described in Section 3·3.   From Fig. 3·3 (a),

$$G\gamma_w = \frac{W_s}{V_s} = \frac{W_s}{V_1 - \dfrac{W_1 - W_s}{\gamma_w}}$$

whence

$$G = \frac{W_s}{V_1\gamma_w - W_1 + W_s} \qquad (3\cdot7)$$

If the specific gravity of the soil is known the shrinkage limit may be determined from values of W_s and V_2.   An expression for W_w is $\gamma_w(V_2 - V_s)$ or $\gamma_w[V_2 - (W_s/G\gamma_w)]$, whence

$$w_s = \frac{\gamma_w V_2}{W_s} - \frac{1}{G} \qquad (3\cdot8)$$

3·7   Determination of Grain-Size Distribution by Sieving

Mechanical analyses or grain-size distribution determinations of coarse materials can easily be made by passing a sample through a set of sieves and weighing the amounts retained on each sieve.   Considerable attention has been given to obtaining a satisfactory screen scale and to correcting for errors inherent in the method.   However, such items are of little concern in this discussion, inasmuch as a high degree of accuracy is unnecessary. The use of a good standard set of sieves, well made and in good condition, will give sufficiently accurate results.

The finest screen which is practicable is a 200-mesh, with openings of 0.074 mm.   If the sample being analyzed contains a large proportion of grains below this diameter, the finer material will have to be studied by other means.   Since soil particles do not pass through the 200-mesh sieve with as much ease as they do through the coarser sieves, an accurate determination of the percentage passing 200-mesh sometimes requires washing the fines through the sieve.

The results of a grain-size analysis are usually expressed by a graph showing the aggregate weight, in per cent of the total weight, of all grains smaller than any given diameter. A logarithmic scale for diameters gives the best representation of size distributions; it will be discussed in greater detail under the subject of size classifications in Section 4·9. In Fig. 3·4,

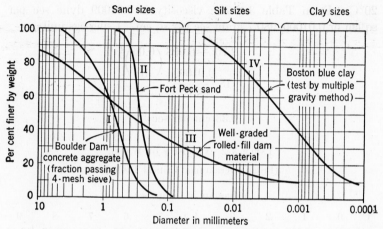

FIG. 3·4 Grain-size distribution curves.

four mechanical analysis curves are shown; curves I and II, for sands, were obtained by sieving.

3·8 Stokes's Law

The most convenient methods for determining the grain-size distribution of soils too fine to be screened are based on the law that grains of different sizes fall through a liquid at different velocities. If a single sphere is allowed to fall through a liquid which is of indefinite extent, its velocity will increase rapidly at first under the acceleration of gravity; however, a constant terminal velocity is practically reached within a few seconds and is maintained indefinitely, as long as conditions are not changed. The terminal velocity is expressed by Stokes's Law:

$$v = \frac{\gamma_s - \gamma_w}{18\mu} D^2 \qquad (3\cdot9)$$

where γ_s and γ_w are the unit weights of sphere and liquid, respectively, μ is the viscosity of the liquid, and D is the diameter of the sphere.

As a numerical example, the time required for settlement in a small test tube like that mentioned in Section 3·13 will be determined. Assume particles with a unit weight of 2.70 grams per cc and a diameter of 0.06 mm falling in water at a temperature of 20°C. From Table 3·2 the viscosity is 0.01009 dyne sec per sq cm or 0.01009/980.7 gram sec per sq cm. Using cgs units,

$$v = \frac{2.70 - 0.998}{18 \dfrac{0.01009}{980.7}} \left(\frac{0.06}{10}\right)^2$$

$$= 0.33 \text{ cm per sec}$$

TABLE 3·2   VISCOSITY OF WATER

(From International Critical Tables)

Values are in millipoises.

°C	0	1	2	3	4	5	6	7	8	9
0	17.94	17.32	16.74	16.19	15.68	15.19	14.73	14.29	13.87	13.48
10	13.10	12.74	12.39	12.06	11.75	11.45	11.16	10.88	10.60	10.34
20	10.09	9.84	9.61	9.38	9.16	8.95	8.75	8.55	8.36	8.18
30	8.00	7.83	7.67	7.51	7.36	7.21	7.06	6.92	6.79	6.66
40	6.54	6.42	6.30	6.18	6.08	5.97	5.87	5.77	5.68	5.58
50	5.49	5.40	5.32	5.24	5.15	5.07	4.99	4.92	4.84	4.77
60	4.70	4.63	4.56	4.50	4.43	4.37	4.31	4.24	4.19	4.13
70	4.07	4.02	3.96	3.91	3.86	3.81	3.76	3.71	3.66	3 62
80	3.57	3.53	3.48	3.44	3.40	3.36	3.32	3.28	3.24	3.20
90	3.17	3.13	3.10	3.06	3.03	2.99	2.96	2.93	2.90	2.87
100	2.84	2.82	2.79	2.76	2.73	2.70	2.67	2.64	2.62	2.59

1 dyne sec per sq cm = 1 poise
1 gram sec per sq cm = 980.7 poises
1 pound sec per sq ft = 478.69 poises
1 poise = 1000 millipoises

The estimated accuracy is 0.1 per cent between 0° and 40°C and 0.5 to 1 per cent at higher temperatures. Values given are for atmospheric pressure. To correct for pressure multiply by $[1 + k(p - 1)10^{-4}]$ where p is the absolute pressure in kilograms per square centimeter and k is a coefficient which is smaller than 2 numerically for all conditions. Therefore variations in viscosity caused by variations in p may be neglected for ordinary pressures.

and the time required to fall through the height of the small test tube (10 cm) is 10/0.330 or 30 sec.

With material of a density approximating that of soil grains, Stokes's Law is applicable for spheres between about 0.2 and 0.0002 mm in diameter falling through water. When the spheres are larger than 0.2 mm, turbulence occurs in the water immediately surrounding the descending sphere, and thus the assumptions on which the derivation of the formula is based are invalidated. When the spheres are smaller than 0.0002 mm Brownian movement occurs and, although Stokes's Law is not necessarily inapplicable, the velocities of settlement are too small to be measurable.

Application of Stokes's Law to the observation, direct or indirect, of the rate of fall of a large number of soil particles suspended in water in a container is inaccurate because:

1. The particles are never truly spherical; in fact the shapes may bear little resemblance to spheres.

2. The body of water is not indefinite in extent, and, since many particles are present, the fall of any particle is influenced by the presence of other particles; similarly, particles near the side walls of the container are affected by the presence of the wall.

3. An average value for specific gravity of grains is used; the value for some particles may differ appreciably from the average value.

The second item is minimized if a fairly large container and a relatively small amount of soil are used. For concentrations of less than 50 grams per liter it has been shown that the influence of the particles on each other is not appreciable. For the general run of soils the third item is not of major importance either.

The first item, however, presents a difficulty that cannot be overcome, and the concept of an equivalent diameter must be introduced; any particle which has the same velocity of fall as a sphere of the same unit weight and of diameter D will be said to have an equivalent diameter D. Thus it must be recognized that the diameter scale for any mechanical analysis plot based on Stokes's Law shows equivalent diameters rather than any actual dimensions of particles.

Values of unit weight and viscosity of water at various temperatures are given in Tables 3·1 and 3·2. A value worth remembering is the rough average of 10^{-5} gram sec per sq cm for viscosity. Also an easily remembered form of Stokes's Law is

$$v = 9000D^2 \qquad (3·10)$$

where v is in centimeters per second, D is in centimeters, and the constant is the value holding for a temperature of 20°C, a specific gravity of 2.67, and settlement in water.

3·9   Methods of Mechanical Analysis by the Sedimentation Principle

A number of methods (see Chapter 2 of reference 86) have been proposed and numerous procedures have been used for determining the grain-size distribution curves of fine-grained materials by the sedimentation principle expressed in Stokes's Law. Only a brief summary of these methods, with short descriptions of the commonest types, can be given herein because of space limitation. A detailed description will be given of the hydrometer method only.

Procedures which make use of Stokes's Law may be arbitrarily grouped according to methods based on:

1. Successive sedimentation.
2. Sedimentation into clear water.
3. Observations of amount of sediment per unit of volume at a given point in the sedimentation tube.
4. Observation of the total amount of soil in suspension above a given elevation.
5. Observations of total sedimented soil.
6. Elutriation.

Successive sedimentation is perhaps the most obvious method of determining the grain-size curve. To determine the per cent that is coarser than any chosen diameter D, the time required for a grain of this diameter to fall through the height of a sedimentation jar is first computed. Then a sample of known dry weight is uniformly dispersed and allowed to settle for the computed time. The resulting sediment will contain all particles larger than diameter D but only a portion of those smaller; for example, it will contain only 25 per cent of the grains of diameter $\frac{1}{2}D$. A repetition will remove still more of the smaller particles from the sediment; after two runs only $\frac{1}{16}$ of the original grains of diameter $\frac{1}{2}D$ will be present. Sufficient repetition will remove practically all grains which are appreciably smaller than diameter D, and the sediment may then be weighed to give a point on the distribution curve. This procedure may be used to separate the sample into fractions if desired, but as a method for determining the distribution it is much too laborious and time-consuming to be of practical value.

Sedimentation into clear water, with the entire sample inserted in the water at a given height at the outset of the test, leads to the simple situation wherein all particles of like grain size reach the base of the sedimentation tube at the same time. At any given elapsed time the minimum diameter in the sediment may be computed by Stokes's Law, and the sediment will contain all particles coarser than this diameter. The weight of the sediment may be approximated by observing the depth of the sediment and assuming that the depth and the weight are proportional. Direct measurements of weight are more accurate, however, and special types of apparatus exist for such determinations. A main disadvantage of this method is that very small samples must be used or the sample, when initially inserted into the sedimentation tube, will be so concentrated that Stokes's Law will not be valid.

The method in which observations are made to determine the concentration in a suspension which originally is uniformly dispersed is used in the hydrometer test, described in Section 3·10. Another application of this method results when side outlets in the sedimentation jar are provided for removal of small samples which are tested for solid content.

The pressure at a point in the suspension at a given depth is equal to a summation of unit weights throughout the height of the suspension above. The pressure is thus a measure of the amount of soil in suspension. Observations of this pressure as a function of elapsed time are sufficient to allow the determination of the grain-size curve. The Wiegner Method (170), which utilizes this principle, has seen considerable use.

Methods based on observations of the total amount of soil which has settled from a suspension are closely related to those discussed in the preceding paragraph, and mechanical analysis curves are similarly obtained.

Elutriation methods are based on the principle that in upward flow of water at a given velocity large particles settle faster than the upward flow, whereas particles smaller than some given diameter are carried upward and may thus be separated out. Various types of elutriation apparatus which have given satisfactory results have been developed, and many testing engineers favor this type of test. However, for simplicity and speed of testing, elutriators can hardly compare with such methods as the hydrometer method. A source of inaccuracy in elutriation is the variation in the upward water velocity over the cross section of the tube.

3·10 The Hydrometer Method

The use of an immersion hydrometer to measure the specific gravity of a liquid is well known. This principle can be extended to the measurement of the varying specific gravity of a soil suspension as the grains settle, thereby determining the grain-size distribution diagram. The hydrometer method (reference 28 and the standardized test in reference 9) is so widely used in this country that a thorough development of the principles of the method will be given.

Step 1   Unit Weights in a Sedimentation Tube

The first step in the presentation of this method is to obtain the expression for unit weight in a suspension at any time and at any depth. The suspension of volume V, containing a total weight W of suspended soil is initially mixed thoroughly. At the instant sedimentation starts every element of volume contains the same concentration of suspended soil; for example, a 1-liter suspension containing 50 grams of soil will have 50 mg of soil in every cubic centimeter. The initial unit weight of the suspension is easily expressed. In each unit of volume of suspension the weight of solids is W/V, and the volume of solids is $W/G\gamma_w V$. Since this unit of volume is composed of solids and water, the volume of water must be $1 - (W/G\gamma_w V)$ and the weight of water $\gamma_w - (W/GV)$. The initial unit weight is thus

$$\gamma_i = \frac{W}{V} + \left(\gamma_w - \frac{W}{GV}\right)$$

or

$$\gamma_i = \gamma_w + \frac{G-1}{G}\frac{W}{V} \tag{3·11}$$

Consider now a point at any depth z below the surface of the suspension and let t designate the time elapsed since the start of sedimentation. The size of particle D, which would just fall from the surface to the depth z in time t, may easily be computed from Stokes's Law, which may be written in the form

$$V = \frac{z}{t} = CD^2$$

whence

$$D = \sqrt{\frac{1}{C}\frac{z}{t}} \tag{3·12}$$

At depth z there are no particles coarser than diameter D, since all such coarse particles will in time t have fallen a distance greater than z. Thus D as expressed by equation 3·12 is called the *limiting diameter*.

In any small element of volume at depth z the weight of all particles of sizes smaller than diameter D is unchanged; since the particles of any given size initially were uniformly dispersed, they have fallen at the same speed, and therefore as many particles of any sizes smaller than D have entered at the top of the element as have left through the bottom of the element. Within the element, therefore, all particles coarser than D have disappeared, and the content of particles smaller than D is unchanged. Let N be the ratio between the weight of particles smaller than D and the weight of all particles in the original soil sample. The weight of solids per unit of volume at depth z and time t becomes NW/V, and the unit weight is

$$\gamma = \gamma_w + \frac{G-1}{G}\frac{NW}{V} \qquad (3\cdot13)$$

whence

$$N = \frac{G}{G-1}\frac{V}{W}(\gamma - \gamma_w) \qquad (3\cdot14)$$

The ratio N of equation $3\cdot14$ represents the fraction of soil finer than the diameter expressed by equation $3\cdot12$. Therefore a determination of unit weight at any known depth and at any elapsed time furnishes a point on the grain-size distribution curve. One procedure for determining such unit weights employs the hydrometer method.

STEP 2   THE ACTION OF THE HYDROMETER

A streamlined hydrometer of the type used for determinations of grain-size distribution curves is shown in Fig. $3\cdot5$ (a). The hydrometer reading r is observed at the surface of the fluid on a scale in the stem of the hydrometer, and when the hydrometer is immersed in a uniform liquid this reading is the specific gravity of the fluid. However, this type of hydrometer usually is calibrated to read unity in pure water at the temperature of calibration, and in other fluids

$$r = \frac{\gamma}{\gamma_c} \quad \text{or} \quad \gamma = r\gamma_c \qquad (3\cdot15)$$

where γ is the unit weight of the fluid and γ_c is the unit weight of water at the temperature of calibration. The reading r is correctly designated as a specific gravity, although the reference material in this case is not water at 4°C, which is commonly used.

When a hydrometer floats in a fluid, the weight of the hydrometer W_H is supported by the buoyancy which is equal to the weight of displaced fluid. If the fluid is of constant unit weight,

$$\gamma \int A \, dz = W_H \qquad (3\cdot16)$$

where A is the area at depth z and the integration includes the entire submerged height of the hydrometer.

After sedimentation has been in progress for a while in a grain-size analysis, the unit weight varies with depth somewhat as shown in Fig. 3·5 (*b*). In this case the buoyancy integral must be written

$$\int \gamma A \, dz = W_H \qquad (3 \cdot 17)$$

If a reading r is obtained in this variable suspension it must be an average specific gravity. The figure shows that the specific gravity is less than r opposite the upper part of the hydrometer, greater than r opposite the lower part, and at some specific depth near the middle of the bulb it must be equal to r. If this specific depth can be located, the hydrometer reading furnishes the unit weight at a known depth.

A. Casagrande (28) demonstrated that, if it is assumed γ varies linearly with depth, the inaccuracies involved in the following demonstration are in general small and never exceed 3 per cent. The expression for linear variation of unit weight may be written

$$\gamma = C_1 + C_2 z \qquad (3 \cdot 18)$$

At the specific depth near the middle of the bulb where γ is equal to $r\gamma_c$ the value of z will be designated by z_r, and

$$r\gamma_c = C_1 + C_2 z_r \qquad (3 \cdot 19)$$

If the value of γ from equation 3·18 is substituted in equation 3·17 and the value of $r\gamma_c$ from equation 3·19 is substituted for γ in equation 3·16, and if the left-hand sides of equations 3·16 and 3·17 are then equated, it is found that

$$z_r = \frac{\int A z \, dz}{\int A \, dz} \qquad (3 \cdot 20)$$

This equation expresses the distance to the center of volume. It signifies that the depth at which the specific gravity is equal to the hydrometer reading r is the depth to the center of immersed volume, commonly called the center of immersion. The hydrometer reading therefore furnishes the unit weight at the depth of the center of immersion.

By calibration of the hydrometer, z_r distances may be obtained for all values of r. As an example, one hydrometer of the type used in grain-size analyses has for its calibration

$$z_r = 9.4 \text{ cm} \quad \text{when } r = 1.030$$
$$z_r = 22.1 \text{ cm} \quad \text{when } r = 1.000 \tag{3·21}$$

and linear variation may be assumed between these limiting values of r.

For each observed value of r the corresponding depth z_r is given by the calibration, the unit weight is given by equation 3·15, and the time is observed; except for corrections which remain to be discussed, these values may be used, respectively, for z, γ, and t in equations 3·12 and 3·14 to furnish the co-ordinates of points on the grain-size distribution curve.

Step 3   Corrections

Hydrometer readings are usually taken at elapsed times of ¼, ½, 1, and 2 minutes with the hydrometer remaining in the suspension for the first two minutes. For these four readings the z_r readings are used as z values in equation 3·12.

Subsequent readings are taken at 5, 10, 20, and 40 minutes, and so on. Just before each of these readings the hydrometer is placed in the suspension, and just after the reading it is removed; thus a correction for immersion, shown by Fig. 3·5 (c), must be introduced. The distance to the center of immersion is shown at the right. However, the particles of limiting diameter D which are at level B have not settled the distance z_r, but have settled the distance $A'B'$ or z_r'; there is a difference because the insertion of the hydrometer increases distance $A'B'$ to distance AB. The difference between these two distances is a constant, approximately equal to one-half the hydrometer volume V_H divided by the area of the jar A_J, and for the five-minute reading and later readings it is the actual distance of settlement, $z_r - (V_H/2A_J)$, which must be used for z in equation 3·12.

The working form of equation 3·12 for the early readings with no immersion correction is, therefore,

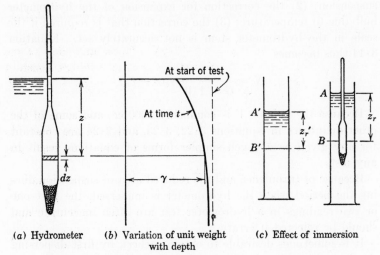

(a) Hydrometer   (b) Variation of unit weight   (c) Effect of immersion
                       with depth

FIG. 3·5   Details pertaining to the hydrometer analysis.

$$D = \sqrt{\frac{18\mu}{\gamma_s - \gamma_w}} \sqrt{\frac{z_r}{t}} \qquad (3\cdot22)$$

and for later readings, for which immersion corrections are required,

$$D = \sqrt{\frac{18\mu}{\gamma_s - \gamma_w}} \sqrt{\frac{z_r - \dfrac{V_H}{2A_J}}{t}} \qquad (3\cdot23)$$

It can be demonstrated that equation $3\cdot23$ applies with reasonable accuracy to the five-minute reading even though the hydrometer is in the suspension for the first two minutes. Calibration curves giving both $z_r - (V_H/2A_J)$ and z_r versus r for any hydrometer are easily prepared and are commonly used.

A number of corrections may be automatically cared for by keeping an extra hydrometer jar containing clear water beside the jar used for the test and obtaining occasional specific gravity readings r_w in the water. The term $\gamma - \gamma_w$ of equation $3\cdot14$ becomes $\gamma_c(r - r_w)$, and three important corrections are common to r and r_w and are eliminated in their difference $(r - r_w)$. These corrections are: (1) the meniscus correction which enters because readings can be made only at the top of the meniscus in an opaque suspension; (2) the correction for expansion of the hydrometer bulb due to temperature; (3) the correction that is required if the scale in the hydrometer stem is not accurately set. Equation 3·14 thus becomes

$$N = \frac{G}{G-1} \frac{V}{W} \gamma_c(r - r_w) \qquad (3·24)$$

Because the volume V is commonly 1000 cc, and some of the other quantities in equations 3·22, 3·23, and 3·24 are constant for any given case, much simpler forms of equations result in any test.

Because of turbulence and the reduced area of suspension during the period when the hydrometer is immersed, the first one or two readings in a hydrometer test are often inaccurate and should be rejected if erratic.

It is sometimes desirable to obtain a check by first dispersing the suspension thoroughly and running the test for 2 minutes without removing the hydrometer, then stopping the test, shaking the suspension once more, and starting again, this time not inserting the hydrometer until the two-minute reading.

In all instances the hydrometer must be inserted and removed slowly and smoothly to cause as little turbulence as possible.

A common range of unit weights for soil hydrometers is 0.995 to 1.030 grams per cc. If the soil to be tested is fine enough so that most of it passes the 200-mesh sieve, the recommended dry weight of sample for tests with these hydrometers is about 45 or 50 grams. If some coarse material is present the weight should be such that the first hydrometer reading will be less than 1.030. For silty soils it is generally more convenient to obtain the dry weight before the test. For many clays the dry weight must be obtained at the conclusion of the test since drying may cause permanent changes in grain sizes.

3·11 The Hydrometer Method under Multiple Gravity

The procedure outlined in the previous section is satisfactory when the grain-size curve is desired only for sizes greater than 1 or 2 microns. In fine clays a large percentage by weight may be finer than these sizes.

An apparatus developed by F. H. Norton (109) for testing

fine clays is an elaboration of the hydrometer method. In this apparatus the jar is suspended at the end of a rotating arm. The centrifugal force caused by rotation introduces an acceleration many times greater than gravity and causes much faster settlement than occurs under gravity alone. Grain-size distribution curves which extend to $\frac{1}{10}$ micron may be obtained in a few hours by the use of this apparatus.

3·12 Prevention of Flocculation

· The conditions under which soil grains tend to adhere and form grain groups or flocs are described in Section 4·7. If flocculation takes place in a soil suspension, Stokes's Law may no longer be used for determining grain sizes. Thus, if there is any tendency toward flocculation, preventive treatment is necessary. When flocculation begins, the individual flocs may sometimes be seen in the suspension, and cloudiness or actual lines of demarcation between clear water and flocculent suspension will follow.

Numerous deflocculating agents, including electrolytes, protective colloids, and organic preparations, have been used. Each seems to work in certain cases but none has yet been found that is satisfactory for all soils, and no satisfactory test to determine which agent is most likely to work has yet been devised.

The material most commonly used as a deflocculating agent is sodium silicate, or water glass, of which 5 cc of 3° Baumé solution per liter of suspension usually give good results. Another material which is often satisfactory is Daxad 23,† of which the approximate equivalent of $\frac{1}{4}$ gram in solid form in 50 grams of soil is required for good results. There are soils in which water glass gives good results and Daxad is unsuccessful, and vice versa. On the infrequent occasions when neither substance gives satisfactory results, there are others which may be tried. Hydrogen peroxide is sometimes effective. Boiling sometimes removes the flocculating tendency. Successive washings of the soil often give the desired result but this procedure is not always practicable with very fine soils. Trials of the efficiency of different deflocculants may sometimes be made to

† A cement deflocculent manufactured by Dewey & Almy Co., Cambridge, Mass.

advantage in test tubes, although actual test conditions give the only conclusive indications.

3·13   Simple Field Tests for Identification Purposes

A considerable amount of experience of the type given by an intimate acquaintance with many soil types is required for high grade results in field identification of soils. However, a familiarity with the following list of relatively simple field tests and with the soil types discussed in Chapter 4 will allow a reasonable facility for rough identifications. Such a familiarity will avoid frequent errors of the more common types and therefore is desirable for every engineer who has any field connection with foundation or soil engineering.

A list of simple tests which are very helpful in the making of rough field identifications and preliminary laboratory identifications of soils has been set up by P. C. Rutledge (123) in a form quite similar to that which follows:

1. Visual examination of the grain size and grain shape of coarse-grained soils, and of the texture and color of fine-grained soils.

2. Determination of strength loss due to structural disturbance, obtained by crushing the soil and working it with the fingers. (The extreme importance of change of structure due to structural disturbance is not adequately emphasized until later chapters.)

3. Determination of the feel of the soil, whether gritty or soapy, by rubbing between the fingers.

4. Determination of the mobility of the pore water, obtained by shaking a piece of soil horizontally in the hand to bring water to its surface if possible and then gently squeezing the specimen. (If shaking easily brings water to the surface, thus producing a shiny or glossy appearance, and the surface dries on squeezing, there is high mobility. If the surface shows no change in appearance during shaking and squeezing, there is a low mobility. For this test the sample must contain sufficient water and, if it is too dry, water must be added; however, there is little difficulty in getting the desired water content.)

5. Determination of grain sizes in fine-grained soils or the

existence of fine particles in coarse soils. (This determination is accomplished by shaking a small sample in a test tube of water and allowing to settle. The time required for particles to fall through a distance of 4 in., which is the length of a small test tube, is about ½ minute for particles of 0.06 mm or 60 microns in diameter and about 50 minutes for particles of 0.006 mm or 6 microns in diameter. A grain-size distribution curve cannot be run in a simple test tube, but a rough idea of sizes can be obtained by noting times as the water clears. Similarly a coarse dirty soil may be recognized because the water is still dirty a minute or so after shaking.)

6. Determination of the strength when dried, obtained by drying a specimen in the sun or on a stove or radiator and testing when dry by pressing or breaking with the fingers.

These tests should be supplemented in the field by other observations which give information of value. The relative density of a sample from a preliminary boring is usually changed from that in the natural state, but in the field it often is possible to observe the natural-state condition. If the samples are from test pits, information regarding their relative density can be obtained from inspection of the walls of the pit, stratification can be observed if it exists, and the extent and variation of the various strata can be studied.

Soil types and their identifications by the above tests are discussed in Section 4·4.

PROBLEMS

1. In a specific gravity test performed at a temperature of 30°C the weight of the pycnometer bottle filled with soil and water is 673.62 grams; at the same temperature the weight of the bottle filled with pure water is 630.80 grams; the weight of the dried soil is 66.14 grams. Determine the specific gravity.

2. A certain soil has a specific gravity of 2.67. A 1000-cc container is just filled with this soil in its loosest possible state, and later the container is filled at the densest state obtainable, the weights of soils for the two samples being 947 and 1302 grams, respectively. The soil in nature is known to have a void ratio of 0.61. Determine the limiting void ratios and the relative density of the soil in natural state.

3. In the Casagrande liquid limit device, specimens of a certain sample of clay at water contents of 46.6, 50.2, 52.0, and 54.2 per cent require 74, 39, 21, and 13 blows, respectively, to close the standard groove. Data from three plastic limit determinations give water contents of 22.6, 22.9, and 22.8 per cent. Determine the liquid limit, the plastic limit, and the plasticity index of this clay.

4. *Screen analysis:* A typical concrete sand; weight of total sample 420.0 grams.

Screen number	8	14	28	35	48	100	200	Pan
Diameter, mm	2.362	1.168	0.589	0.417	0.295	0.147	0.074	...
Weight retained, grams	76.2	84.3	99.1	58.6	42.7	41.4	11.0	4.4

Plot results on semi-logarithmic paper.

5. State the three main reasons why Stokes's Law does not apply rigorously in the hydrometer test and explain what is done to minimize or care for the effects of these factors.

6. A liter suspension containing 49 grams of soil with a specific gravity of 2.72 is prepared for a hydrometer test. It may be assumed that the temperature of the test and the temperature of calibration of the hydrometer are both 4°C. What should be the hydrometer reading if the hydrometer could be immersed and read at the instant sedimentation begins?

7. *Combined mechanical analysis:* Sample from a Vermont rolled-fill dam; specific gravity 2.70.

Screen Analysis Sample weight 159.6 grams			Hydrometer Analysis Sample with no sizes removed, dry weight 99.1 grams					
Screen No.	Diameter, mm	Wt. retained, grams	Time, min	Hydrometer reading		Time, min	Hydrometer reading	
				In suspension	In water		In suspension	In water
10	1.651	9.3	¼	24.0		48	3.1	
20	0.833	11.9	½	20.6		90	2.2	−0.4
35	0.417	18.0	1	17.1		180	1.5	
65	0.208	20.7	2 [1]	13.3	−0.4	332	0.9	−0.4
150	0.104	25.6	5	9.3		1332	0.4	−0.5
200	0.074	10.3	10	6.7				
Pan	.....	63.6	20	4.8				

[1] Hydrometer in suspension for first 2 minutes; in suspension only for readings thereafter.

Temperature of suspension, 21.7°C.
Volume of hydrometer bulb, 28.8 cc.
Temperature of hydrometer calibration, 20°C.
Hydrometer calibration: when $R = 0$, $Z = 22.10$ cm; when $R = 30$, $Z = 9.40$ cm.
Area of hydrometer jar, 28.8 sq cm.
Volume of suspension, 1000 cc.

Plot the grain-size distribution curve on four-cycle semi-logarithmic paper

Chapter 4

CLASSIFICATIONS

4·1 General Discussion

A simple soil classification system, which uses easy methods of identification and gives an approximate but fairly accurate separation into soil groups or soil types, is a great convenience in any routine type of soil engineering project. Preliminary soil surveys for highways are examples of such a project. The classifications according to grain size and according to plastic characteristics, for instance, are widely used.

There is, however, much difference of opinion among soil engineers regarding the importance of classifications and the desirability of a broad endorsement of their use. This matter is largely one of point of view and depends principally on the use to which the classifications are to be put. It has been said that classifications of materials are inherently of such nature that they can be neither correct nor incorrect; that they, like filing systems, are but convenient schemes of grouping. It is inevitable that in any classification there will be borderline cases which may fall into one of two or more groups. Also it is inevitable that, if a large number of soils are grouped by classes according to one classification system, some of these soils will group differently under another classification.

A demand for the development of a dependable classification which will have wide applicability is frequently heard. This demand sometimes even seems to imply that some day all that will be needed for solving soil problems in engineering will be the running of a certain small number of simple tests to determine a few soil constants; after this, when the classification has been perfected, one will need but to look in a handbook under the heading into which the soil falls and read whether or not the soil will be satisfactory for whatever type of problem is under study. Little knowledge of soil action is required to realize the inadequacy of such an idea. Even if it is assumed that such action can be adequately represented by numerical coefficients, the fact remains that a thorough definition of the action of any soil requires a larger number of coefficients than generally realized. A classification can be based on only a few of these coefficients. Thus any classification is worthless, even dangerous, unless the characteristics it is based on are the ones which are important in the problem under consideration. Grain-size classifications, for example, are very convenient, and they may be used to much advantage if it is truly appreciated that they reflect only sizes of grains, a soil characteristic which often is important, may sometimes be the most important individual characteristic, but seldom if ever is the only characteristic which has important effect on soil action in a given problem.

The understanding of soil action is the important issue. Classifications should be avoided in any instance where there is a tendency to use them on an important investigation rather than make adequate studies of the soil characteristics. In the study of fundamentals of soil action, classifications are of minor importance; thus they are briefly discussed herein.

4·2 Standardization of Laboratory Testing Procedures

The dangers inherent in the standardization of certain soil tests are to a certain degree analogous to the dangers in the blind use of classifications. For this reason, standardization will be given brief mention at this point.

Many laboratories which carry out tests on a production basis feel the need of standardized tests to give assurance that their results are on the same basis as those of other laboratories with which they have connections. This point of view must be recognized, and standardization of tests is, to a limited degree, a necessity. However, in all such standardizations, the inherent dangers must be kept constantly in mind by every engineer who makes use of the test results.

Some important soil properties, such as the shearing strength of clays, are functions of a great many variables. Fundamental laboratory research during recent years has greatly improved our understanding of such soil characteristics, but in some respects they still are only partly understood. Any standardization of a test is sure to involve attempts to keep the test as simple as possible. Certain arbitrary testing conditions must be used in place of adequate considerations of variables which may have important effects on the soil property, and thus the action in the simple test may be far from representative of the behavior of the soil in nature. Thus, many leading soil engineers oppose the standardization of certain tests, such as those for shearing strength.

4·3 Types of Classifications Discussed in this Chapter

The types of classification discussed in this chapter are listed below. The section in which each classification is described is noted in parentheses.

Preliminary classification by soil types	(4·4)
Geological classifications	(4·5 and 4·6)
Classification by structure	(4·7)
Atterberg limits	(4·8)
Classification by grain-size distribution	(4·9)
The Casagrande classification of airfield materials	(4·10)

Approximate classification in the field or preliminary classification in the laboratory, on the basis of commonly recognized soil types, is an important part of any preliminary investigation. The simple field tests used for such a classification have been given in Section 3·13. This type of classification is usually called preliminary classification or field classification. Geological classifications by mineralogical content and origin are of general interest only and are covered briefly herein. The qualitative classification by types of structure in sedimentary soils is of considerable value because of the concepts it gives regarding the nature of the soil structure. The tests for the Atterberg limits and the grain-size analysis have already been given in Chapter 3. The Casagrande classification of airport materials serves as an example of soil classification for a given branch of soil engineering.

4·4 Preliminary Classification by Soil Types

An understanding of the fundamentals of soil mechanics and soil behavior requires a familiarity with the common soil types. It does not require a knowledge of locally used nomenclatures, however, and space limitation prevents a detailed enumeration of such information here (for more extensive descriptions see references 102 and 123). Some confusion has always existed relative to classifications by soil types because of various usages of terms and their meanings. However, the meanings given in the following paragraphs are quite generally accepted in the field of foundation engineering.

In the descriptions of basic soil types below, numbers in parentheses refer to the numbers of the simple tests explained in Section 3·13. Combinations or mixtures of these types are common, and a mixture which is designated, for example, as sandy clay, with the word clay last, refers to a mixture in which the clay predominates.

Sand, gravel, and boulders are coarse-grained, cohesionless soils. They are easily identified by test (1). Grain-size ranges are used to distinguish between them, and between sands of different fineness. The term boulder is sometimes limited to sizes greater than 8 in., and gravel to the ¼-in. to 8-in. sizes. Sand sizes are most easily designated by sieve numbers; tests requiring the use of sieves can hardly be called field tests but, by running a few sieve tests in the laboratory, an engineer can train himself to recognize by visual inspection the size corresponding to any given sieve. The greater portion of a coarse sand is retained on a 28-mesh sieve; the greater portion of a medium sand passes a 28-mesh but is retained on a 65-mesh; a fine sand is similarly limited by the 65- and 200-mesh sieves. Sands are designated as compact or dense if a pick is required for their removal; when loose they can be excavated merely by shoveling.

Dirty sand refers to cohesionless sand containing some finer material. It may be identified by shaking in a test tube (5), or by the dust which comes from it if a small handful of the dried material is tossed into the air.

Organic silts are silts which may be mainly inorganic but contain certain amounts of fine, decomposed organic material or organic colloids. The particle sizes are mainly in the range from 0.06 to 0.002 mm. They are highly compressible, relatively impervious, somewhat plastic, and, largely because of the compressibility, are very poor foundation materials. They may usually be identified by their color, which ranges from light gray to dark gray or black, or by the odor resulting from decomposition. When they are molded by the fingers organic silts have a soft feeling by which they may be distinguished from inorganic silts.

Inorganic silt and *rock flour* contain only mineral grains and are free of organic material. Inorganic silts are mostly coarser than 0.002 mm. Rock flour is a similar material but differs in that it may have a considerable percentage of sizes finer than 0.002 mm. These soils may contain bulky grains only, in which case they are relatively imcompressible, or they may contain appreciable amounts of flat or "platy" grains, in which case they may be highly compressible. The more compressible soils tend to have greater plasticity which aids in their recognition. They have high pore-water mobility (4), a gritty feeling (3), little cohesion when dried (6), and, when dried on the hands, they dust off easily. Positive identification is provided by these tests, yet these soils are misclassified more often than any other soil, mainly because they look something like clay. Rock flours not only look like clay in some instances but, on the basis of the grain-size distribution only, they are actually classsified as clay sizes. Such misclassifications may lead to bad construction difficulties because of the quicksand or liquefaction condition * and attending difficult construction conditions to which inorganic silts are readily subject but which do not occur in clays.

Inorganic clay is the correct term for materials generally referred to simply as clay. Clays are composed principally of flat particles finer than 0.002 mm or 2 microns. The colloidal chemist usually quotes ½ micron as a rough upper limit of colloidal sizes; thus many clays are largely of colloidal sizes. Lean clay is the name given to silty clays or clayey silts; fine, colloidal clays of very high plasticity are called fat clays. The degree of cohesion and plasticity and the degree by which the test results differ from those on inorganic silts indicate how fat the clay is. Clays may be identified by the following simple tests: Over a large water content range, clay can be rolled into threads which have noticeable tensile strength. In the wet state

---

* See Section 7·5 for description and further explanation.

it sticks to the hands, fat clays having a distinctly soapy feeling (3). In the dry state it does not brush from the hands easily. The cohesion in the dried state (6) is appreciable in lean clays and pronounced in fat clays. Dried specimens of fat clays can be broken but not crushed or pulverized by hand; when partially dried the material is plastic but very hard to remove from the hands.

Clays are called hard or stiff when they cannot be molded with the fingers and cannot be excavated without the use of a pick; such clays have been compressed to a low water content and are good foundation materials. Clays are called soft when they are easily molded by the fingers and when they can be excavated with a spade; such clays are relatively compressible, have relatively low shearing strength, and cannot withstand large loads.

Varved clays consist of alternate thin layers of silt and fat clay of glacial origin. The light-colored silty varves are deposited during the high water or flood periods of spring and summer, and the darker colored clay varves during the low water or quiet winter periods. Varved clays possess the undesirable qualities of both silt and soft clay. Varved deposits with alternating layers of fine- and coarse-grained silt and even fine- and coarse-grained sand are also found, but the general character of such deposits, as a foundation material, does not differ much from uniform deposits of silt or sand.

Peat is partially carbonized vegetable matter which has low shearing strength, is often permeable, is always extremely compressible, and is the poorest foundation material imaginable. It is easily recognized by its dark color, its fibrous nature, and its odor of decay.

Hardpan is a term often used to describe any hard cemented layer which does not soften when wet. ·The term is sometimes used also as a name for boulder clay or glacial till, which is a very tightly packed deposit of glacial origin ranging from boulders to rock flour.

Loess is a fine-grained, air-borne deposit characterized by a very uniform grain size, a high void ratio, and a slight cementation, which enables it to stand in nearly vertical cuts. In a true loess the cementation is destroyed when the soil is partially or fully saturated, but modified forms of loess exist which retain some cohesion even when submerged.

Shale is a material in the state of transition from clay to slate. Shale itself is sometimes considered a rock but, when it is exposed to the air or has a chance to take on water, it may rapidly decompose.

Topsoil is a name given to weathered surface materials which are capable of supporting plant life.

Fill is a term that applies to all man-made deposits ranging from sand and gravel fills or rock piles to dumps. Fills may contain every imaginable material.

A few of the more common local names for soil types follow.†

Bentonite. An ultra-fine-grained, fat clay formed by the decomposition of volcanic lava; it exhibits the properties of clay to an extreme degree.

Gumbo, adobe. Fat clays containing a little sand; peculiar to certain sections of the country.

Kaolin, China clay. A very pure white clay used in the ceramic industry.

Marl. A crumbly deposit, chiefly clay with sand, containing calcium carbonate and, usually, organic matter.

Caliche. A conglomerate of clay, sand, and gravel cemented by calcium carbonate deposited from groundwater.

4·5 Classification by Mineralogical Composition

The general engineering point of view is that it is often interesting to know the mineralogical composition of a soil although the composition is of primary interest only as it affects the physical properties.

The geologist has a keen interest in the minerals occurring in the rocks he studies, since the structure of the rock depends in large degree on the minerals present. Moreover, the mineralogical content affects to an important degree the properties of soils resulting from the breaking down of rock. For this reason a knowledge of geology is helpful in soil mechanics work, although the study of minerals is not considered to be directly within the scope of fundamental soil mechanics. The reader should consult

† These local names are given by Rutledge in reference 123.

textbooks on principles of geology if a more detailed treatment of classifications by mineralogical composition is desired.

Certain properties of minerals, such as solubility, hardness, and resistance to wear and to crushing, are important. Also important is the base exchange‡ capacity of clay minerals. The mineralogical content often determines the shapes of the individual soil particles. Grains of some minerals such as quartz and feldspar are bulky, whereas those of other materials such as mica and alumina are flat in shape. The presence of only a few flat grains greatly affects the porosity of a soil. Flat grains also have an important effect on the plastic properties, which are discussed in Section 4·8.

The effect of flat grains on the porosity may be illustrated by a relatively simple experiment. For clean dry sands with bulky grains the maximum values of void ratio that can be obtained are about unity. If a small amount of mica is added to such a soil, much larger void ratios may be obtained and void ratios as high as 10 are possible. As a result of these high void ratios, the soil shows a much higher compressibility when subjected to load. In a similar way, plastic clays have flat grains and high compressibility.

The influence of grain shape has been given too little consideration in analyses of soils; it should be given as much thought as grain size in studies of soil behavior.

4·6 Classification by Origin

The origin of a soil may refer either to its constituents or to the agencies responsible for its present status.

By constituents, soils may be classified as:

> I. Inorganic soils
> II. Organic soils
>   1. Plant life
>   2. Animal life

By agencies responsible for their present state, soils may be classified as:

‡ For a discussion of exchangeable bases see reference **67** or reference **173** or textbooks on chemistry.

I. Residual soils
II. Transported soils
  1. Glacial
  2. Aeolian
  3. Sedimentary

Most of the above-mentioned types will be discussed below, some in brief form and others in more or less detail. For more

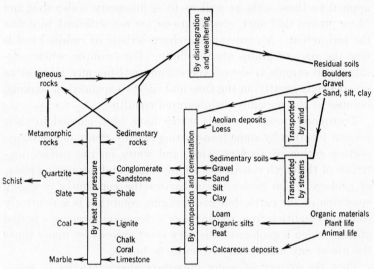

FIG. 4·1   The geological cycle.

complete treatment of many of the points discussed, the student is again referred to textbooks of geology. Many of the items are shown in Fig. 4·1, which presents the geological cycle and shows the parts played by origins and agencies.

Organic soils, which appear in the lower right-hand corner of Fig. 4·1, have been described in Section 4·4. They are such poor soils for foundation purposes that their properties are the subject of much less study than those of more satisfactory soils.

Residual soils are the disintegrated materials above the rock crust, in various stages of cementation, which have not been subjected to the transporting and sorting process of agencies such as water and wind. Such soils are common in many parts of this country but are little known in the glaciated northeastern sections. Their characteristics differ so greatly from those of transported soils that an engineer familiar only with glaciated regions should use great caution in attempting to predict their action. The degree of cementation may vary greatly throughout a residual soil mass, and a gradual transition into rock rather than a definite line of demarcation between soil and rock is to be expected. Classifications by grain sizes (see Section 4·9) may be applied to these soils as well as to sedimentary soils; this fact alone proves that such classifications are not sufficient to define the soil action. An outstanding characteristic of residual soil is that the sizes of grains are indefinite. For example, when a residual soil sample is sieved, the amount passing any given sieve size depends greatly on the time and energy expended in shaking, because of the partially disintegrated condition.

Transported soils are soils which have been carried to their present location by some transporting agent. Study of the transporting action of glaciers, wind, and water on the surface materials of the earth constitutes an important and interesting phase of geology. The geologist emphasizes the constantly changing condition of the earth, but his changing condition is a relatively constant condition from the engineer's viewpoint, because a period of time which a geologist calls very short exceeds by many times the life of any man or any structure he builds.

Thus the history of many important characteristics of soil— such as the smoothness of individual particles, the range of grain sizes, the stratification in a given deposit, and the profiles built up by the placing of various strata on top of each other—can be explained in detail and, although a knowledge of these factors is desirable to the soils engineer, its presentation is not within the scope of this treatise. One phenomenon which the geologist emphasizes and which may well be mentioned here is the remarkable efficiency with which wind and water carry out the sorting process. Scattered all the way from the head waters to the mouth of a river are the particles which once, geologically a long while ago, made up the ledge of the region; in their present state they are sorted to an exceptional degree, and in some cases every particle is worn to a remarkable smoothness. Yet, in spite of this sorting, the variations throughout typical soil deposits are so large that foundation engineers are continuously emphasizing the variable nature of soils.

Glacial deposits occur over large areas of this country. Wind deposits, or aeolian soils, are widespread; the great loess deposits in the midwest portion of this country are an example. However, the commonest types of soil in engineering problems are the water-deposited or sedimentary soils, for which a classification by fundamental types of structure will be given in detail.

4·7 Sedimentary Soil Classification by Structure

The three fundamental types of structure, on the basis of the types of forces in action during the sedimentation process, are

1. Single-grained structure.
2. Honeycomb structure.
3. Flocculent structure.

Combinations of these types are also possible. Features of each type will first be outlined. Combined structure will then be discussed, and a hypothetical explanation of important and well-known characteristics of marine clays will be presented.

Single-grained structure is the simplest type. An accumulation of equal spheres, such as a box full of billiard balls, is the ideal prototype of single-grained structure. This type of structure is observed in materials in which there is little or no tendency for the grains to adhere to one another. Such materials are termed *cohesionless*, and are represented in soils by sands and gravels. This lack of adherence means that in the sedimentation process the only forces which come into play are the weights of the individual particles.

The porosity of a granular mass may vary within rather wide limits according to the manner in which the grains are grouped together. As an illustration, circular disks arranged as in Fig. 4·2 (a) occupy a smaller proportion of the bounding area than when arranged as in (b). Theoretical solution of the analogous problem in three dimensions leads to the result that the porosity of an accumulation of equal spheres ranges from 48 to 26 per cent, or the void ratio ranges from 0.91 to 0.35 (page 11 of reference 104). Granular soils, such as sands, are not accumulations of equal spheres. Nevertheless, the limiting values of porosity are remarkably close to those found for the ideal case. Such soils seldom have porosities above 50 or below 23 per cent, corresponding to void ratios of 1 and 0.3, respectively. The void ratio is commonly used to express the density, but often it is advantageous to use the relative density, as explained in Section 3·5.

Honeycomb structure occurs in soils fine enough to have cohesion. A solid body may be considered a network of molecules held in definite positions by mutual attraction. When two bodies come into contact with each other, the molecules of one body at the point of contact exert an attraction upon those of the other

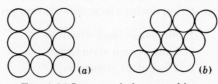

Fig. 4·2 Loose and dense packing.

body. The forces involved are very small, and their effects are negligible when the bodies themselves are of a higher order of size than the molecules. Sand grains, for instance, are so large that the effect of intermolecular attraction at points of contact is quite negligible, and they behave as though there were no force binding them together; hence the term cohesionless.

The finer the grains, however, the more noticeable becomes the effect of intermolecular attraction. Consider a sediment being formed at the bottom of a lake. Let Fig. 4·3 (*a*) represent a portion of the top surface of the sediment. Grain *A* has fallen through the water and has just come into contact with another grain *B* previously deposited. At the instant of contact, intermolecular attraction is set up at the point of contact between *A* and *B*. If the grains are relatively large, as in single-grained structure, this attraction is insignificant, and grain *A* rolls into the position shown in (*b*). Another sediment, shown in Fig. 4·3 (*c*), is composed of grains so small that intermolecular attraction is appreciable in proportion to the weight of a grain. Grain *A* has settled through the water and has just come into contact with grain *B*. The tendency to overturn exists, but is restrained by intermolecular attraction, acting like a patch of glue at the point of contact. Grain A therefore remains in position. In this manner a porous structure, containing large voids, is built up as indicated in (d). Actually the structure is, of course, a three-dimensional framework which cannot be truly shown in a two-dimensional sketch; thus Fig. 4·3 must be recognized as merely a diagrammatic representation.

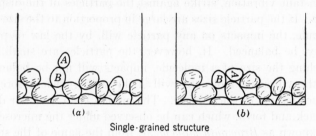

Single-grained structure

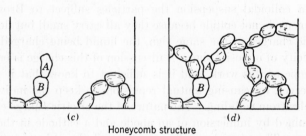

Honeycomb structure

FIG. 4·3 Comparison of formation processes of single-grained and honeycomb structures.

The structure shown in Fig. 4·3 (d), is a honeycomb structure found in fine silts and clays. The intermolecular attraction between grains at the point of contact is known as true cohesional attraction, and the resistance to shear resulting from the attraction is known as *true cohesion*.

Flocculent structure can occur only in very fine-grained soils. Solid particles suspended in a liquid settle at a speed which, as explained in Section 3·8, is proportional to the square of the particle diameter. Thus for fine particles the velocity of settlement is very slow. For particles of colloidal size, this is, smaller than about 0.5×10^{-4} cm in diameter, the velocity of settlement under normal gravity is for all practical purposes inappreciable.

A suspension of such small particles is called a colloidal suspension, the liquid being termed the continuous phase and the particles the disperse phase.

In addition to the force of gravity, however, the molecular impact forces must be given consideration in the study of the action of these small particles. The molecules of a liquid, being in constant vibration, strike against the particles of the disperse phase. If the particle sizes are large in proportion to the size of a molecule, the impacts on any particle will, by the law of probability, be balanced. If, however, the particles are small, approaching the size of a molecule, impacts will not be balanced, and the vibrating molecules will strike with sufficient force to produce motion of the particle. The motion is an irregular darting back and forth, which can be observed under the microscope. It is known as *Brownian movement*, from the name of the scientist who first noted its existence.

In a colloidal suspension the particles subject to Brownian movement do not collide because they all carry small but definite electric charges of the same sign, the liquid being charged with electricity of opposite sign. A discussion of this charge is beyond the scope of this work, and it is sufficient to know that it exists and serves, by causing mutual repulsion, to keep the individual particles from colliding. The nature of the electric charge can be determined by immersion of an anode and a cathode in the suspension. The particles will move toward the pole of opposite sign.

If the mutual repulsion of the particles were removed in some way the small colloidal particles would collide, true cohesional attraction would have a chance to act, and particles would adhere, others inevitably joining and forming, ultimately, an aggregate so large that molecular impacts would balance and Brownian movement would cease. The dimension of the aggregate group of particles would at the same time become so large in comparison to the size of individual particles that settlement would take place.

Aggregate groups of this type are called flocs, and each floc has a honeycomb structure made up of small soil particles. Flocculation occurs when particles adhere, whereas a colloidal suspension is obtained when particles repel and thus remain separated from each other. Flocculation may be caused in a colloidal suspension by the addition of a small quantity of electrolyte. The molecules of the electrolyte ionize and, for example, if the disperse phase is charged negatively, the positive ions are attracted to the negatively charged particles; the charge is thus neutralized.

If a clay in suspension tends to flocculate and prevention of flocculation is desired, some type of deflocculating agent must be added. The main use of deflocculating agents in soil testing has already been explained in Section 3·12.

Flocs are small enough so that when they settle to form a sediment they will be arranged in honeycomb structure. Thus the sediment will have a honeycomb structure of second order, formed by flocs grouped around voids larger than the flocs themselves, each floc being formed by grains grouped around voids larger than the grains themselves. This is called *flocculent structure,* and it is illustrated diagrammatically in Fig. 4·4.

FIG. 4·4 Flocculent structure.

Mixed structure occurs in many marine clays that are very firm and stiff in the undisturbed state, but when worked or remolded by the fingers become very soft. An appreciation of this pronounced change in structure and in strength, which occurs in many soils, is one of the most important concepts of soil action. A hypothesis which offers a possible explanation of this important characteristic in a mixed structure has been advanced by A. Casagrande (29).

When a river flows into a bay of the ocean, there is a decrease in the velocity of flow that causes deposition of the silt particles, the coarsest of the transported soil grains. Simultaneously the salt water, acting as an electrolyte, may cause flocculation and deposition of colloidal matter carried by the stream. Thus, the sedimentary deposit formed consists of a mixture of individual silt particles and flocs. A similar combination may occur in fresh water if the electrolytic conditions are favorable.

As the depth of the deposit increases, material near the bottom is compressed by the weight above. However, the amount of compression is not the same at all points within the mass. The variations that exist in the amounts of compression taking place are shown in Fig. 4·5. Where large spaces exist between silt particles the flocs undergo relatively little compression, whereas flocs located in the smallest gaps between adjacent silt particles are highly compressed. These local highly compressed spots be-

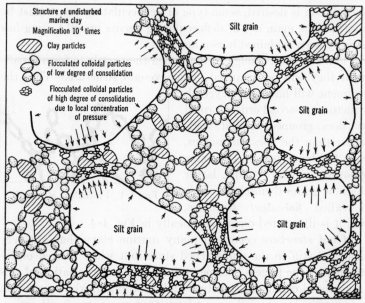

Structure of undisturbed
marine clay
Magnification 10^4 times

Clay particles

Flocculated colloidal particles
of low degree of consolidation

Flocculated colloidal particles
of high degree of consolidation
due to local concentration
of pressure

Silt grain

Silt grain

Silt grain

Silt grain

FIG. 4·5 Structure of undisturbed marine clay. (According to A. Casagrande.)

come what is called *bond clay*, and they may develop strength enough to make the material as a whole very stiff. It is easily seen that a thorough mixing of the clay destroys the localized strength contributed by the bond clay.

The rigidity imparted by the bond clay is strikingly demonstrated by the difference between the results on undisturbed and remolded marine clay samples when tested for compressibility or for shearing strength. A given load increment may compress a remolded sample of typical Boston blue clay two or three times as much as it would the same clay at the same void ratio in undisturbed state, and for some clays the compression in remolded state is of the order of ten times as much as that in undisturbed state. Similarly the shearing strength of specimens at a given water content may be many times greater in natural state than in disturbed state.

Another explanation of the phenomenon of loss of strength by remolding has been given by Terzaghi (page 12 of reference 152). Each particle may be visualized as coated with a film of water in solid state as shown in Fig. 4·6. If preferred, the concept of a layer of adsorbed water molecules may be substituted for the

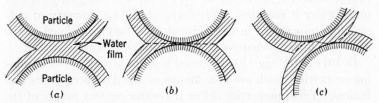

FIG. 4·6 Water film explanation of structural bond. (According to K. Terzaghi.)

concept of the water film. The state of this water is such that its viscosity is exceedingly high. If a soil sample is subjected to direct pressure over a period of centuries, this water with high viscosity is slowly squeezed from between points of nearest contact of adjacent particles, giving the condition shown in (b). The closer contact which results between particles leads to a higher degree of true cohesional attraction. If the direct pressure is removed, the highly viscous water will flow back, but so slowly in some soils that years may elapse before the loss of strength is appreciable. However, remolding moves the particles as shown in (c), and as a result the particles are more widely separated and the strength is lost.

Still another explanation is that over a long period of time, under load, some kind of preferred orientation of molecules is attained in the vicinity of particle-to-particle contacts, giving the strength that is characteristic of the undisturbed state; remolding may be pictured as in some way destroying the preferred orientation. Possibly this explanation is essentially the same as attributing the strength in undisturbed state to some type of cementation.

Whether the bond clay hypothesis or some other explanation is more nearly true is not of great practical importance. The important point is that there is some kind of bond or localized strength at critical points within the sample which is lost by remolding.

4·8 The Atterberg Limits

The physical properties of clays differ greatly at different water contents. A given clay may act almost like a liquid, it may show plastic behavior, or it may be very stiff, depending only on how much water it contains. *Plasticity*, which is a property of outstanding importance in fine-grained soils, may be defined as the ability to undergo changes of shape without rupture.

In 1911 Atterberg (10) proposed a series of tests for determining properties which are now known as the Atterberg limits and indices. These properties define the water content ranges of the plastic state and other states. They are of somewhat empirical nature but are valuable in the investigations of plastic characteristics of any given clay and also in comparisons of clays. In 1932 A. Casagrande (25) presented a digest of Atterberg's work and a thorough account of improved testing procedures. In a more recent paper (23), Casagrande has discussed in considerable detail the relationship between various soil types and their plasticity characteristics. The testing methods for obtaining these properties were described in Section 3·6; the description of the various states and properties follows.

If a sample of a typical marine clay is mixed thoroughly with a sufficiently large amount of water it is in a liquid state. In this condition it flows freely and shows practically no static resistance to distortion; that is, it has no shearing resistance. If the water content is slowly decreased by evaporation, the sample meanwhile being mixed continuously to maintain a uniform condition, it will begin to show a small shearing strength when the water content has decreased sufficiently. The water content at which shearing strength is first noticeable is not a definite value. Therefore, the limit of the liquid state is arbitrarily taken at the water content where the shearing strength has a certain measurable, but small, shearing strength; it is called the *liquid limit* and is designated by w_l.

If the sample is subjected to further decrease in water content it will eventually reach a point at which, when rolled into a thread, it will start to crumble rather than to distort plastically. This water content is called the *plastic limit* and is designated by w_p.

Still further decrease in the water content of the sample will lead finally to the point where the sample can decrease in volume no further. At this point the sample begins to dry at the surface,

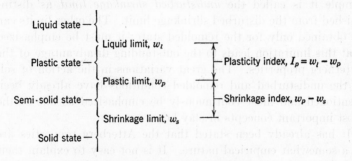

Flow index, I_f; Slope of flow curve (Fig. 3·2)
Toughness index, $I_t = I_p / I_f$

FIG. 4·7 Atterberg limits and indices.

the saturation is no longer complete, and further decrease in water in the voids occurs without change in the void volume. Moreover, the color of the sample begins to change at this point, since the observer inspecting the sample is no longer looking through a water film. This water content is called the *shrinkage limit* and is designated by w_s.

The limits described above are all expressed by their percentage water contents. The range of water content between the liquid and plastic limits, which is an important measure of plastic behavior, is called the *plasticity index* and is designated by I_p. The range of water content between the plastic and shrinkage limits is called the *shrinkage index*.

A summary of states, limits, and indices, the most important of which have been described, together with the notations used for these properties, is shown diagrammatically in Fig. 4·7.

The *flow index* I_f expresses the relationship between the change in water content and the corresponding change in the shearing strength; more specifically it is the slope of the *flow curve* illustrated by Fig. 3·2.

There is a wide variation in the shearing strengths of different clays at their plastic limits; handling shows that some clays have much greater toughness than others. To express this characteristic the *toughness index* I_t is used and is defined as the ratio between the plasticity index and the flow index.

When the shrinkage limit is determined on an undisturbed clay sample it is called the *undisturbed shrinkage limit* as distinguished from the disturbed shrinkage limit. The other limits can be obtained only for the remolded state; it must be emphasized that this limitation leads to the outstanding disadvantage of the Atterberg properties. The great variations in the action of soil in the undisturbed and remolded conditions have already been mentioned and must continuously be emphasized as one of the most important concepts in clay behavior.

It has already been stated that the Atterberg properties are of a somewhat empirical nature. It is not easy to explain their meaning and their value. Many soil engineers ignore these properties, and others determine their values on all clays which they encounter on important projects. Those who determine them regularly are agreed that they are valuable in giving a feel for the character of soils. The plasticity index is a good measure of the degree of plasticity of the soil, and a number of state highway departments have regulations relative to the maximum plasticity index that is to be permitted in certain types of highway fills. A. Casagrande uses the Atterberg limits as an aid in the identification of soils in the airfield soil classification discussed in Section 4·10. In comparing fine rock flours and clays it is found that grain-size distributions are very misleading but that Atterberg properties show up the inherent differences markedly.

Definite applications of Atterberg limits have developed slowly but it is probable that in time these limits will be more widely used and will have many practical applications (for an example of the use of Atterberg limits see the closure discussion in reference 32). Atterberg limit data that are valuable in the identification of soils have been presented by A. Casagrande (23) as given in Fig. 4·8.

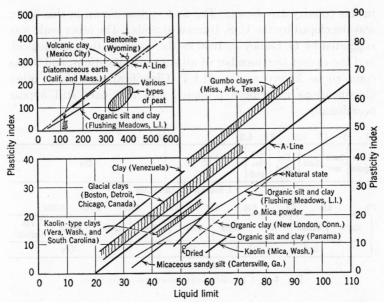

F_{IG}. 4·8 Relation between liquid limit and plasticity index for typical soils. (A. Casagrande.)

4·9 Grain-Size Classifications

One factor upon which soil behavior always depends to some degree is the sizes of the individual grains. The importance of the grain size in this respect is indicated by the classification according to structure (Section 4·7). The most obvious type of soil analysis and the commonest of all soil tests is the grain-size distribution analysis or mechanical analysis, tests for which have already been described in Chapter 3.

In large soil laboratories that make extensive soil investigations and test many soils, large numbers of mechanical analyses are run and, since the complete presentation of the result of each analysis requires an individual curve, the time required for preparing curve sheets sometimes becomes excessive and the data for an entire project become too bulky. Since a high degree of accuracy is not essential in such results, a more condensed form of presentation is often considered desirable. To meet this need, a number of grain-size classifications have been proposed. In Fig. 4·9 two of the classifications that are now in common use

in this countiy are shown. The first system shown in this figure
was developed by the U. S. Bureau of Soils. The other scale was
suggested by G. Gilboy in 1930 as the simplest, the most logical,
and the easiest to remember of all such classifications, and it has
come to be known as the M.I.T. Classification. Many other
classifications have been proposed and new ones still appear
occasionally.

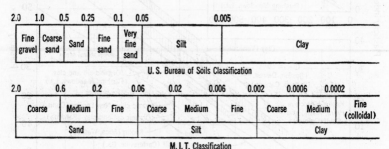

FIG. 4·9 Classifications based on grain size.

The various subdivisions or fractions chosen for the classifications of Fig. 4·9 are purely arbitrary. They could be designated
by the numerical values of their limiting diameters; it would in
many respects be advantageous to use this system rather than
names, which has become the more common practice.

Unfortunately the names which have been given to the various
fractions constitute a second meaning of the terms used. In the
preceding pages, clay has been defined as a soil in which plasticity
is a predominant property. In these classifications, clay sizes are
described as soil particles which come between certain arbitrary,
limiting grain sizes. A fine rock flour, with a large percentage of
bulky grains ranging in diameter from 0.001 to 0.002 mm, would
fall according to size into the class of clays; yet it might not
possess any of the characteristic properties of plastic clay, inasmuch as these properties seem to be due in a large degree to the
presence of flat grains. Many engineers prefer to avoid the use
of the term clay for indicating grain sizes and to depend on diagrams or numerical values of diameters instead. It is suggested
that the term *clay sizes* avoids most of the possible confusion.
Attempts have been made to introduce other systems of names
for the fractions but they never have come into popular use.

There undoubtedly would be some advantages in the establishment of a single standard classification. The advantages, however, are not so great as they have often been claimed to be, and the numerous attempts to establish a standard have met with little success. F. B. Campbell (21) has discussed this subject.

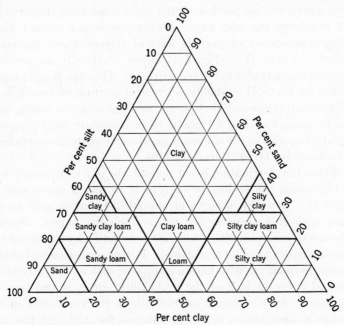

Fig. 4·10 U. S. Bureau of Soils triangular classification chart.

Another type of classification that is based on the grain-size distribution is illustrated in Fig. 4·10. This chart represents the U. S. Bureau of Soils Textural Classification (page 36 of reference 72), which has been rather widely used. The size ranges used for this classification are those of the upper scale of Fig. 4·9, but with sand sizes considered to extend up to 2 mm and with all coarser sizes eliminated. A given soil with given percentages of sand, silt, and clay sizes, respectively, is represented by a given point on a triangular chart of this type. The terminologies and the boundaries of the areas representing the various soil designations on such a chart are arbitrarily chosen; a number of charts of this type have been proposed. A disadvantage of the classification given in Fig. 4·10 is that loam is principally an agricultural term.

A smooth mechanical analysis curve such as curve I of Fig. 4·11 is obtained when there is a normal distribution of grain size throughout the entire range of diameters represented. In a curve with waves, certain portions of the curve must have slopes which are relatively flat and whose distribution is not normal, there being a deficiency of particle sizes at regions where the curve flattens. Curve II of Fig. 4·11 shows practically no particles between diameters of 0.006 and 0.01 mm. Thus the sample represented by curve II probably is either a mixture of two soils of approximately normal distribution, one fine and one coarse, or it has in some way had all grains of intermediate sizes removed. Detailed studies of the shapes of mechanical analysis curves have been made by D. M. Burmister (19).

Where the distribution is not normal, the one satisfactory way of expressing the grain-size analysis is to plot a curve such as curve II. However, a curve of normal distribution may be defined with fair accuracy by two well-chosen points. Several schemes of presenting the grain-size distribution by the use of two characteristics have been proposed. Fitting of mechanical analysis curves to curves with known equations, such as the probability integral curve or half of the probability curve, is one possible approach. Such a fitting method allows the expression of the grain-size distribution by two parameters but, although this procedure is interesting, it has little practical value. Simpler methods based on the same principle merely describe two points on the curve, and several choices have been proposed.

The best known of these methods is that used by Allen Hazen. In his method, the diameter, such that the aggregate weight of all smaller grains is 10 per cent of the total weight of the sample, is called the *effective size*. This diameter is designated by D_{10}, and in curve I of Fig. 4·11 its value is 0.0056 mm. Diameter D_{10} is also known as the 10 per cent size, and it is fairly common practice to designate other percentage sizes by similar notation; for example, for the 60 per cent size, designated by D_{60}, the diameter is such that the aggregate weight of all smaller grains is 60 per cent of the total weight. The ratio of D_{60} to D_{10} is Hazen's *uniformity coefficient,* C_u. In curve I the value of C_u is 0.030 divided by 0.0056, or 5.3. A uniformity coefficient of unity usually means a soil in which the grains are all of practically the same size. A large coefficient corresponds to a large range in sizes. Thus the uniformity coefficient is large when the degree of uniformity is low. Hazen's values have found much wider use

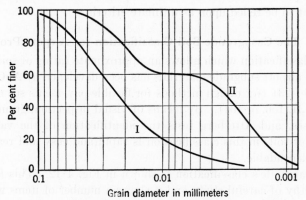

FIG. 4·11 Normal and irregular grain-size curves.

in sanitary engineering than in soil mechanics. However, the term uniform is widely used in soil mechanics to express size uniformity.

The reason for the use of the logarithmic grain-size scale becomes apparent upon consideration of the uniformity. If two samples have the same uniformity but differ in coarseness, the two curves have the same shape on the logarithmic plot, with the curve representing the finer material lying to the right of the other. On a natural scale of grain size, the two curves have little resemblance.

Although grain-size distribution is an important factor, it should be held in mind that the size of grains is but one of the factors on which soil action depends. Important characteristics such as grain shape, mineralogical composition, structure, and relative density cannot be represented by a grain-size analysis. Moreover, certain clay minerals when placed in suspension subdivide into particles that are much smaller than the unit which, in the undisturbed state, would be considered the individual grain.

Misleading conclusions can be obtained when grain-size diagrams alone are studied. However, an experienced soil engineer may obtain valuable indications of the properties of a soil from study of its grain-size distribution in conjunction with other data that often are available, such as Atterberg limits and geological origin.

In general, grain-size distributions should be looked upon as rough guides to further investigation, valuable for that purpose, but not to be relied upon as ultimate criteria.

4·10   The Casagrande Soil Classification for Airport Projects

A classification which allows an approximate rating of soils for use as airport subgrade materials has been developed by A. Casagrande (23) (for design methods for flexible pavements see reference 131, 156, or 164). By means of visual inspection, grain-size analyses, and Atterberg tests the identification of the various types of soils in this classification is rapid and easy and reasonably dependable.

Casagrande's classification is shown in Fig. 4·12. This figure is worthy of careful study and it shows a number of items which will not be discussed in detail. The relationships of the Atterberg tests to the various soils of this classification are shown at the lower left. Correlation of this classification with the California bearing ratio (114 or 164) is shown in the lower right chart. Correlation with the Public Roads classification (page 236 of reference 72) is shown in the final column of the table.

PROBLEMS

1. Prepare an outline covering preliminary classification by soil types. This outline should be as condensed as possible but it should include all important items and identification tests.

2. A sample of soil is shaken up in a test tube and then allowed to stand. As settlement progresses a very clear line of demarcation between suspension and clear water travels from the top to the bottom of the tube in 28 minutes. It is noted that no flocculation occurs. The height of the tube .. is 15 cm. How should the soil be described from these data?

3. A certain soil has 98 per cent by weight finer than 1 mm, 59 per cent finer than 0.1 mm, 24 per cent finer than 0.01 mm, and 11 per cent finer than 0.001 mm. Sketch the size-distribution curve and determine the approximate percentage of the total weight in each of the various size ranges according to the M.I.T. size classification. Determine also Hazen's effective size and uniformity coefficient for this soil.

Chapter 5

SUBSURFACE INVESTIGATIONS

5·1 Introduction

The purpose of subsurface exploration is to determine the extent and the nature of the principal soil strata, to determine the depth to groundwater, and to obtain samples of the various soils for identification. In addition, samples are often wanted for laboratory tests to determine the physical properties of the soils. The thickness and horizontal extent of the various soils encountered, the location of ledge, and other such data are usually shown on a profile of which Fig. 5·1 is an example. Such a representation is sometimes called a stratigraphical profile, but the designation soil profile is more commonly used.

Two classes of explorations which must be definitely distinguished are (a) reconnaissance or preliminary explorations and (b) detailed explorations. In the majority of cases, explorations are made by borings.

5·2 Preliminary Explorations

Preliminary explorations should be conducted at practically every site which is considered for a structure of any importance; cases in which the underground conditions are sufficiently well known to make explorations unnecessary are few indeed. However, the authorization of the relatively small cost of an adequate set of preliminary borings is sometimes given reluctantly. Sometimes borings are slighted because of the time they require. There are few more striking examples of false economy of money and time, because borings when properly taken may pay for themselves, many times over, by allowing a better design and better planning of construction and by warning of difficult conditions that may be encountered. Unless the underground conditions are well known and are of favorable nature, preliminary borings usually should be obtained even before the purchase of

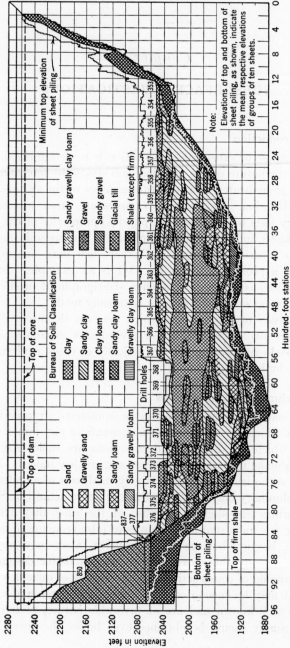

Fig. 5·1 Soil profile along cutoff wall of Fort Peck Dam. (From reference 100, T. A. Middlebrooks.)

the site. They should be made by a reputable firm, and the expense involved may be considered money well spent.

The soil profile which is furnished by a set of preliminary borings is a crude one, and the information obtained relative to the character of the soils encountered is rough. However, preliminary borings give all the information needed for design purposes in the majority of cases. The preliminary borings disclose difficult foundation conditions if they exist at a given site and, if the structure proposed for the site is an important one, more detailed explorations, which use some more elaborate type of sampling, are likely to be required. For the planning of the detailed explorations, the results of the preliminary explorations are needed; thus preliminary explorations are usually a prerequisite to more thorough investigations.

Numerous elaborate sampling devices which have been developed in recent years have as their aim the obtaining of soil samples with an absolute minimum of disturbance of the soil structure. Such samples are called undisturbed samples, and the process of obtaining them is called undisturbed sampling. It is obvious that the word undisturbed must refer to the aim rather than the result, since no sample can be obtained which is entirely free of disturbance. Undisturbed samples often are continuous samples throughout the depth of the critical strata, and they show gradual variations in the soil, thin seams, and so on, whereas preliminary samples give only the limits of the principal strata.

The number and the spacing of the preliminary borings needed at any site vary with many factors and cannot be stated in general terms. Borings should extend to hard bottom or to a depth of one and one-half to two times the smaller dimension of the proposed structure, and they should be deeper if there is any possibility of soils of poor quality at greater depths. What normally is desired from preliminary borings is the profile in approximate form, and a few borings must often be made before the number needed can be known. It is impossible, by borings alone, to disclose all irregularities in the profile; all that can be hoped for is that no major irregularities are missed. Three borings not in a straight line is the smallest number that can give a representation of the horizontal variations. Frequently, it is specified that a boring be made near each corner of a building site, even when the site is small.

When a site which has previously been explored by a thorough boring program is exposed during construction, it usually is found that certain impressions which were obtained from study of the borings were inaccurate. A larger number of borings might have remedied some of the incorrect impressions, but there certainly is an upper limit to the number of borings that can be economically justified. It is undoubtedly true, however, that in many cases more borings pay for themselves by permitting an improved design.

5·3 Methods of Preliminary Investigation

The primary aim of preliminary investigations is the obtaining of an approximate picture of subsoil conditions at nominal cost; therefore, the methods used must be relatively simple.

Sounding rods or probing rods are merely rods which are forced into the ground to sound or probe for hard bottom. They furnish a crude but perhaps the simplest method of preliminary investigation. Their value is limited mainly to cases where it is known that a good layer underlies a poor layer and the information desired is simply the depth to the good layer. No soil samples can be obtained by this method.

Shallow test pits and test trenches constitute perhaps the most obvious method, and one of the most satisfactory methods, of subsurface exploration. They are much used in dam site investigations and are discussed in Section 5·4.

The commonest, and in most cases the best, method of preliminary investigation employs dry-sample borings. This type of boring is described in Section 5·5. Dry samples generally are disturbed in structure but they usually are representative of the original soil to the extent that all sizes of grains are present in correct proportion.

Numerous types of auger boring equipment are used for preliminary investigations; the augers vary from devices resembling a carpenter's tools to those similar to a post hole digger. Rotation of the auger loosens the soil. In many fine-grained cohesive soils and in damp cohesionless soils above the water table, the soil may be raised to ground surface in the auger. When the soil can be raised with the auger, fairly satisfactory boring progress can be made at shallow depths. Auger borings are sometimes made with and sometimes without casing. The samples obtained usually are reasonably representative of the original soil in grain-size distribution. Auger borings are used principally in dam site exploration and in highway work.

Geophysical investigations (reference 70; for an example of seismic explorations, reference 130), based on electrical resistivity or seismographic methods, have been used considerably in recent years for preliminary investigations of dam sites and for mining investigations. When properly correlated with the results of a few borings, they are rapid and economical and they generally give good results. They are of considerable value because they often locate faults, subsurface channels, and other irregularities that are easily missed in ordinary boring programs. They are seldom if ever applicable to building foundation investigations.

For explorations into ledge, some type of core boring (73, 81) must be used. A core boring is taken by rotating a core barrel to which is attached a bit with diamonds or shot or with toothed cutters, which cuts or wears an annular hole into the rock. The central core of rock is the sample. Core boring in rock constitutes an important method of investigation which is beyond the scope of this text. The samples obtained are not of preliminary character. Core borings are sometimes made in soil; such borings are not classified as preliminary borings, however. They are described in Section 5·6.

A summary of fundamental data relative to the various sampling methods, prepared in tabular form by H. A. Mohr (102), is given in Table 5·1.

5·4 Test Pits

Test pits and test trenches are the best means of exploration where conditions are favorable for excavation, since in them the various soils and their relationships can be carefully examined. However, their economical use in preliminary investigations is definitely limited to shallow depths and, in more elaborate investigations below the water table in pervious soils, they usually require the use of pneumatic caissons.* They are widely used for

---

* Described in Section 18·11.

TABLE 5·1 METHODS OF UNDERGROUND EXPLORATION AND SAMPLING

Common Name of Method	Materials in Which Used	Method of Advancing the Hole	Method of Sampling	Value for Foundation Purposes
Wash borings	All soils. Cannot penetrate boulders.	Washing inside a driven casing.	Samples recovered from the wash water.	Almost valueless and dangerous because results are deceptive.
Dry-sample boring	All soils. Cannot penetrate boulders or large obstructions.	Washing inside a driven casing.	Open-end pipe or spoon driven into soil at bottom of hole.	Most reliable of inexpensive methods. Data on compaction of soil obtained by measuring penetration resistance of spoon.
Undisturbed sampling	Samples obtained only from cohesive soils.	Usually washing inside a 6-in. casing. Augers may be used.	Special sampling spoon designed to recover large samples.	Used primarily to obtain samples of compressible soils for laboratory study.
Auger boring	Cohesive soils and cohesionless soils above groundwater elevation.	Augers rotated until filled with soil and then removed to surface.	Samples recovered from material brought up on augers.	Satisfactory for highway exploration at shallow depths.
Well drilling	All soils, boulders, and rock.	Churn drilling with power machine.	Bailed sample of churned material or samples from clay socket.	Clay socket samples are dry samples. Bailed samples are valueless.
Rotary drilling	All soils, boulders, and rock.	Rotating bits operating in a heavy circulating liquid.	Samples recovered from circulating liquid.	Samples are of no value.
Core borings	Boulders, sound rock, and frozen soils.	Rotating coring tools: diamond shot, or steel-tooth cutters.	Cores cut and recovered by tools.	Best method of determining character and condition of rock.
Test pits	All soils. In pervious soils below groundwater level pneumatic caisson or lowering of groundwater is necessary.	Hand digging in sheeted or lagged pit. Power excavation occasionally used.	Samples taken by hand from original position in ground.	Materials can be inspected in natural condition and place.

NOTE: Test rods, sounding rods, jet probings, geophysical methods, and so forth are not included in this table, because no samples are obtained.

This table is taken from "Exploration of Soil Conditions and Sampling Operations" by H. A. Mohr, Soil Mechanics, Series 21, Third Revised Edition, Publication 376 of the Graduate School of Engineering, Harvard University, November 1943.

exploring side hill abutments of dam sites where there is a relatively thin cover of soil above ledge. They are seldom used for exploring building foundations. Although often considered preliminary investigations, high grade samples can be obtained in them and they are not limited to preliminary work.

Care and good technique are required, but samples which are essentially undisturbed may be taken by hand in test pits. If the soil to be sampled contains no coarse particles a thin-walled cylinder with a sharp cutting edge can be worked down carefully into the soil; the procedure is facilitated by excavation below the cutting edge to a slightly larger diameter than that of the final sample. If the specimen has sufficient cohesion to stand under its own weight, it can be removed from the cylinder and coated with paraffin, beeswax, or some other sealing material in preparation for shipment to the laboratory. If the sample is a dense, cohesionless soil, it may be shipped in the tube after the ends have been paraffined and the tube has been capped. Undisturbed samples of loose sand or loose silt can seldom be shipped successfully, because their void ratios are easily decreased by vibration and the sample would soon fill only part of its container. Tests on undisturbed specimens of such soils can be made only at the site. However, such soils generally do not have a structure which is destroyed by disturbance and, if the undisturbed volume of a given specimen is measured in the field and the specimen is shipped in disturbed form, satisfactory values of all the properties which are needed may be determined in the laboratory. Methods for the field measurement of volume are mentioned in Section 18·2. If the soil contains gravel, pebbles, or other large particles, a somewhat irregular block can be formed which is slightly smaller than a square box into which it is to be placed. The box, with top and bottom covers removed, may then be placed over the block and the spaces at the sides filled; paraffin may be used for filling when the sample is completely saturated, and damp sand may be used for partly saturated soil. The top and bottom faces may then be cared for in turn. G. Gilboy (62) developed a method of this type which is shown in Fig. 5·2.

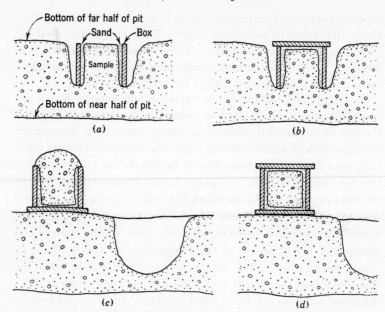

FIG. 5·2 A method of sampling coarse, granular soils in test pits.
(G. Gilboy.)

5·5 Dry-Sample Borings

Samples known as dry samples or, occasionally, drive samples, and which are obtained from borings advanced by the process called "washing," are of nominal cost and, although they may be much disturbed, they are representative of all sizes of the natural sample. The name of this type of boring is not standardized, but the commonest term is dry-sample boring. Dry sampling is the commonest method of preliminary exploration, and it may be used in practically all soils, except soils containing boulders and possibly hardpan.

The boring is made by working through a casing which consists of 2- or 2½-in. extra-heavy steel or wrought iron pipe in 5-ft lengths with strong couplings. A wash pipe, 1 in. in diameter and in 5-ft sections, with a chopping bit and water outlets at its lower end and a cross bar and a water line connection at its upper end, is used for advancing the boring. The wash pipe is churned up and down and twisted, the cross bar being used as a handle to loosen the soil below; water, under pressure, flows out at the bit, aids in the loosening of the soil, and carries it upward. A hand pump and recirculation of the water give best regulation of the amount of water used and allows detection of whether water is taken up by the soil.

A three- or four-legged derrick is used for handling the casing. The casing is driven whenever the open bore hole tends to cave in. In some clays the wash pipe may advance far below the bottom of the casing; in some sands the casing must closely follow the wash pipe. The casing is driven by a weight acting as a drop hammer. During washing, the top of the casing is just above ground level, and a tee attached at its top serves as a water escape to a tub placed below it.

As the process of washing goes on, an experienced operator of the wash pipe can detect, by a combination of the feel of the wash pipe and a careful inspection of the wash water, the occurrence of a change in the type of soil being penetrated. The advance of the wash pipe is then stopped. After the water becomes clear, indicating that all loose soil has been washed out, the flow of water is stopped. Then the wash pipe is withdrawn, each 5-ft section being removed as it is raised.

To obtain a sample, the bit is replaced by a small-diameter sampling spoon which in its simplest form is merely an open pipe. The spoon is lowered and driven into the relatively undisturbed soil at the bottom of the hole to obtain a sample. Therefore, the sample is seldom dry; consequently the name dry sample is disliked by some engineers, but it serves to distinguish this type of sample from the very unsatisfactory samples called wash samples. Wash samples are samples taken directly from the wash water; they are so much mixed and so far from being representative of all sizes, and their results are so misleading, that their use should not be allowed. The dry-sample method is quite successful in obtaining samples of most soil types, but in sands the open pipe must be plugged a short distance above its end to prevent water from the wash pipe from washing it out. After sampling, the spoon is replaced by the bit, and washing again progresses with alternate driving of the casing if necessary. Samples are taken at every change of soil and sometimes at stated intervals if the nature of the soil does not change. Samples are preserved in sample bottles which of course must be properly labeled when the sample is taken. If a boulder is encountered the boring can be continued only if the boulder can be bored or blasted.

An idea of the stiffness of the sample can be obtained by noting the number of blows required to drive the sampler when the sample is taken; the standardized procedure is to record the number of blows required with a 30-in. drop of a 140-lb weight to give 1 ft of penetration.

Instead of an open piece of pipe for a spoon, more elaborate apparatus may be used. A split-spoon sampler is often used in order to facilitate the removal of the sample. The sample barrel is split longitudinally into two parts which are held together by the sampler head and the detachable shoe and cutting edge. In fact, many of the devices used for undisturbed sampling are really nothing but large-sized deluxe dry samplers which in general require larger casing than that used in regular dry sampling.

A log of a dry-sample boring is shown in Fig. 5·3. The water table elevation should always be shown on such a log. Figures at the left are depths; at the right are numbers of blows per foot required to drive the spoon.

5·6   Undisturbed Sampling

When the preliminary borings disclose strata that must be investigated by laboratory tests for such properties as compressibility and shearing strength, borings are needed which give samples that are not detrimentally disturbed in structure.

It was not until about 1930 that the importance of undisturbed structure in samples used for laboratory tests began to be truly appreciated. A. Casagrande (29) published data in 1931 showing the large differences between results of tests on disturbed and those on undisturbed samples. About this time the need of special samplers began to be recognized. Through the efforts of G. Gilboy, A. Casagrande, and S. J. Buchanan (5) the M.I.T. sampler was developed; this is one of the earliest of the so-called undisturbed samplers. Over a period of years many types of special samplers have been proposed, and there has been much discussion of the importance of undisturbed sampling. Special samplers came onto the market and were mentioned frequently

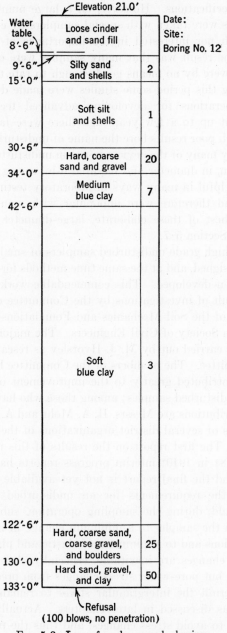

FIG. 5·3 Log of a dry-sample boring.

in boring specifications. However, on a large number of occasions samples were taken with special samplers by crews neither familiar with nor interested in the importance of undisturbed samples. The result was that many samples were called undisturbed that were by no means good enough to rate this designation. During this period some studies were made during actual sampling operations for developing advanced techniques for sampling, but up to a few years ago there were far too many cases in which poor results bore the name of undisturbed samples. Until recently many of the devices in use in undisturbed sampling were 4 to 5 in. in diameter and required 6-in. casing; these large sizes were helpful in many ways in laboratory testing, but were expensive and therefore were unpopular with many engineers. One of the best of these elaborate, large-diameter samplers is described in Section 5·7.

Recently, high grade undisturbed samplers of smaller diameter have been designed, and at the same time methods for their proper use have been developed. This commendable work is, in large part, the result of investigations by the Committee on Sampling and Testing of the Soil Mechanics and Foundations Division of the American Society of Civil Engineers. The major part of the research was carried out by M. J. Hvorslev as research engineer to the Committee. The members of the Committee have cooperated and contributed greatly to the improvement of the art of obtaining undisturbed samples; among those who have made important contributions are Messrs. H. A. Mohr and A. Casagrande and members of several district organizations of the U. S. Engineer Corps. The first report on the results of this research was published (78) in 1940; interim progress reports have not been published, and the final report is not yet available (1947).

To meet the requirements for an undisturbed sample, the sampler should, during the sampling operation, subject the soil below and in the sampler to a minimum change in intergranular stress conditions and to a minimum of elastic and plastic strains. Some stress changes are inevitable, especially changes in pore-water stress, but pore-water stress changes from pressure to tension may permit the intergranular stress to remain essentially unchanged, as discussed in later chapters. Actually, not much can be done to avoid stress changes, and thus the prevention of strains becomes the important requirement. If no water is lost and the sample does not have an appreciable amount of gas in its voids, there can be no volumetric strains; if in addition plastic flow and consequent distortion of the soil layers are avoided, the sample may for ordinary practical purposes be considered undisturbed.

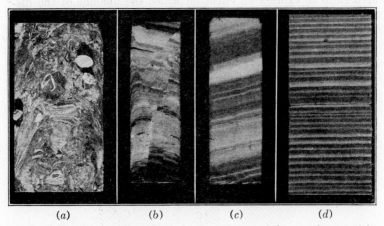

(*a*) (*b*) (*c*) (*d*)

(*a*) Completely mixed soil layers in the upper part of a sample, caused by improper cleaning of the bore hole.

(*b*) Sample with distorted soil layers and shear planes, caused by overdriving of sampler.

(*c*) and (*d*) Relatively undisturbed samples with 100 per cent recovery.

Samples *a* and *d* were obtained by a 4¾-in. Mohr sampler; *b* and *c* by a 2-in. thin-wall sampler; *a, b,* and *c* are soft Boston blue clay; *d* is a varved clay.

Fig. 5·4 Photographs of sliced and partially dried samples. (M. J. Hvorslev.)

A method of studying samples relative to these requirements was proposed by Jürgenson (85) and has been greatly developed by Hvorslev. It consists in slicing a sample longitudinally and then drying it slowly. When the sample is partially dried, the stratification becomes visible to a degree that would hardly be thought possible. Photographs of these sliced specimens prove beyond question many cases of sample disturbance. Figure 5·4 †

† Figures 5·4, 5·6, 5·7, 5·8, and 5·10 are reproduced through the courtesy of the Committee on Sampling and Testing of the Soil Mechanics Division of the American Society of Civil Engineers. These figures were prepared by the U. S. Waterways Experiment Station, Vicksburg, Mississippi. Permission for their use has been granted by the Director of that organization.

shows four specimens with conditions varying from very poor to very good..

It is possible, however, for changes in thickness to occur in the strata during sampling and yet leave the strata free of all signs of distortion. This important consideration has also been carefully studied by Hvorslev, who uses a term designated as area ratio to express an effect on which the amount of the distortion is largely dependent. The area ratio is $(A_m - A_e)/A_e$,

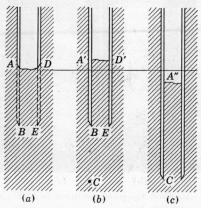

Fɪɢ. 5·5 Sections illustrating recovery ratio during sampling.

where A_m is the maximum cross-sectional area of the sampler shoe, including the sampler wall and the area inside, and A_e is the area at the cutting edge. A related and commoner term is the recovery ratio, which is the ratio between the height of sample obtained and the corresponding distance of penetration of the sampler. Let it be assumed that sampling is started when the cutting edge of the sampler is at elevation A as shown in Fig. 5·5 (a). The sampler is forced into the ground to the elevation of point B as shown in (b). The recovery ratio for this portion of the sample is $A'B/AB$, which is well over unity. The cause of this is the large area ratio; the volume of soil represented in (b) by $A'BED'$ is the soil volume $ABED$ of (a) plus some of the soil which originally was in the position occupied in (b) by the sampler walls. When the sampler is forced farther into the ground the friction between the sample and the sampler wall becomes a more important factor, and when the sampler has penetrated to the elevation of point C in (c) the recovery ratio for the sample as a whole is $A''C/AC$, which is less than unity.

Hvorslev points out that, in well-machined samplers, the recovery ratio may differ 10 per cent either way from unity without noticeably bending the strata in the sample. A compression or elongation of 10 per cent is sufficient, however, to cause an appreciable disturbance to the structure of many types of soil. Moreover, the above discussion indicates that an overall recovery ratio of unity does not mean that the various sections of the sample individually have recovery ratios of unity. If undisturbed samples are to be obtained it is necessary that the entrance of excess soil into the sampler be prevented and that the friction against the side walls be minimized.

The samplers described in Sections 5·7 to 5·10 inclusive are examples of what are probably the four most popular general types of high grade samplers.

5·7 The Mohr Open-Drive Sampler with Flap Valves

The sampler shown in Fig. 5·6 was designed and developed under actual field sampling conditions by H. A. Mohr (102).

This sampler operates through a 6-in. casing, the inside of which is cleaned of soil shavings to the bottom of the casing before sampling. The sampler is lowered to the bottom of the hole and forced a little more than 7 ft into the undisturbed soil; thus the seven 1-ft liners which extend over the major portion of the length of the sampler are filled with soil, and the opening above the top liner contains soil that may be disturbed and mixed with a few shavings which were missed in the cleaning.

The characteristic detail of this device is the group of six doors or flap valves. They fit within the sampler wall while the sampler is pushed into the soil. It is essential that there be fillers between the retracted positions of the valves to give a smooth interior sampler wall, since otherwise disturbance to the sample occurs. Before the sampler is withdrawn, the wire loop is pulled, and a wire is thus made to pass completely through the sample at an elevation which is about 4 in. above the cutting edge. Since the wire initially is behind the flap valves, they are opened slightly when it is pulled, and any later tendency of the soil to fall out causes these flaps to open to the horizontal posi-

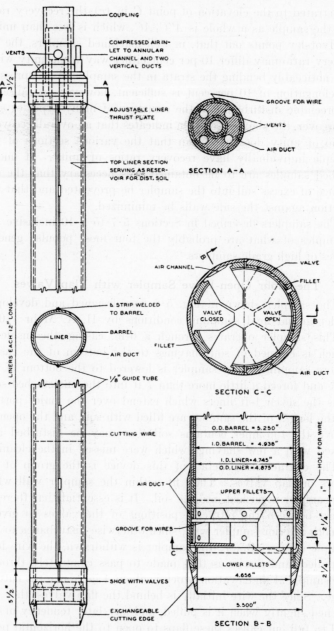

FIG. 5·6   Mohr sampler with flap valves and air ducts.

tion. A compressed air line to the plane of the flaps is sometimes used as a positive means of reducing all suction, and of
thus minimizing the danger of samples failing to come up with
the sampler.

The sampler is removed by a steady pull by block and tackle.
At ground surface it is dissembled, the seven liners are removed,
and the samples are cut by passing a wire saw between adjacent
liners. The ends of the 1-ft samples are coated with paraffin,
capped, and in this form are shipped to the laboratory.

After another length of casing is driven and cleaned, another
string of samples may be taken. Thus sampling may be carried
on continuously.

Among the details which may be noted in the figure are the
removable cutting edge, the slightly larger inside diameter at
the liners than at the cutting edge (to reduce friction as the
sample enters), and the top vents for escape of water from the
sampler when soil is entering.

This sampler has given fairly good results except in cohesionless soils and in soils containing stones or gravel. Its most unfavorable characteristic is its large area ratio, which gives a
variable recovery ratio, as mentioned in the preceding section.
Because of this characteristic, piston-type samplers are now believed to be greatly superior to this type. Thus already this
apparatus is mainly of interest only as an example of a group
of large-diameter samplers that were developed a few years ago
and that were characterized by numerous elaborate details.

5·8 Double-Tube Core Boring Samplers

The use of core borings for soil sampling is practicable if the
sample is protected from erosion by the wash water. This protection can be obtained by the use of a double-core barrel, with
an inner stationary barrel which extends slightly below the outer
rotating barrel. In this type of apparatus the area ratio need
not be considered since no soil is displaced. Instead, the space
for the barrel is cleared by the rotating cutters and by the
washing process.

A double-tube core sampler which was developed by H. L.
Johnson (83) of the U. S. Corps of Engineers, Denison, Texas,
is shown in Fig. 5·7.

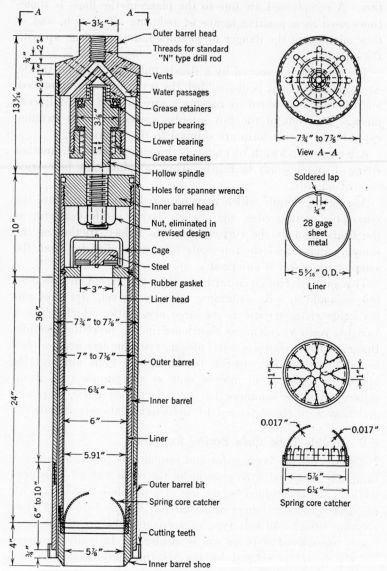

A

A

3½″

2″

¾″

2″ + 1″

2¼″

13³⁄₁₆″

10″

3⅞″

1″

36″

24″

3″

7¾″ to 7⅞″

7″ to 7⅛″

6¾″

6″

5.91″

6″ to 10″

6″ to 10″

4″

¾″

5⅞″

Outer barrel head

Threads for standard "N" type drill rod

Vents

Water passages

Grease retainers

Upper bearing

Lower bearing

Grease retainers

Hollow spindle

Holes for spanner wrench

Inner barrel head

Nut, eliminated in revised design

Cage

Steel

Rubber gasket

Liner head

Outer barrel

Inner barrel

Liner

Outer barrel bit

Spring core catcher

Cutting teeth

Inner barrel shoe

7¾″ to 7⅞″

View *A–A*

Soldered lap

¼″

28 gage sheet metal

5⁵⁄₁₆″ O.D.

Liner

1″

1″

0.017″

0.017″

5⅞″

6¼″

Spring core catcher

FIG. 5·7 Denison double-tube core barrel. (H. L. Johnson.)

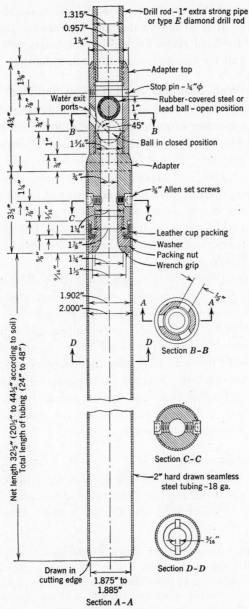

Drill rod – 1″ extra strong pipe or type *E* diamond drill rod

1.315″
0.957″
1¾″

Adapter top

Stop pin – ¼″ϕ

Water exit ports

Rubber-covered steel or lead ball – open position

1⅜″
⅞″

1″
45°

Ball in closed position

¾″
1³⁄₁₆″
¾″
4¾″

Adapter

¾″
1¼″
⅜″ Allen set screws

3½″
⅞″
³⁄₁₆″
1¼″

Leather cup packing
Washer
Packing nut
Wrench grip

1⅛″
⅝″
1¼″
⁹⁄₁₆″
1½″

1.902″
2.000″

Section *B–B*

Section *C–C*

Net length 32½″ (20½″ to 44½″ according to soil)
Total length of tubing (24″ to 48″)

2″ hard drawn seamless steel tubing – 18 ga.

Drawn in cutting edge
1.875″ to 1.885″

Section *A–A*

³⁄₁₆″

Section *D–D*

FIG. 5·8 Two-inch thin-wall sampler with ball check valve. (M. J. Hvorslev.)

Apparatus of this type is reported to give good results in cohesive soils. It is of most value and is probably the best type of sampler for hard clays, for highly compacted soils with some plasticity, and for compact sand at shallow depths.

5·9 Thin-Wall Seamless Steel Tubing Sampler

The recent trend toward samplers of smaller diameter is illustrated by a number of designs using seamless steel tubing of 2 to 3 in. inside diameter, which are designed to obtain samples of various lengths, 2 to 4 ft being common. In soils containing no large particles, and especially in soft soils, these samplers give excellent results, and the small expense of sampling with this relatively simple device makes it very popular. This type is usually considered a preliminary sampler, but the grade of samples obtained is much better than that commonly associated with preliminary work.

A sampler of this type is shown in Fig. 5·8. The use of thin-wall tubing for such samplers was first suggested by H. A. Mohr; it is an essential feature because it leads to a small area ratio. The tubing is used only once, the sample being shipped to the laboratory in it. The check valve shown is needed for some soft soils, but with stiff soils and samplers of small diameters it is not needed. A sharp cutting edge is desirable even though the tubing is thin, and a diameter at the cutting edge which is about 1 per cent smaller than the inside diameter of the tube is a requisite for best results.

5·10 Piston Samplers

The first stationary-piston sampler was built by John Olssen in Sweden about 1923. The retractable-piston sampler was independently developed in the United States. Hvorslev (77) states:

. . . Of the various types of samplers developed to date the piston sampler with a stationary piston has, in the writer's opinion, more advantages and comes closer to fulfilling the requirements of an all purpose sampler than any other type; nevertheless, it is not always possible to obtain a satisfactory sample with a piston sampler nor is this sampler always superior to other types. . . .

The operation of stationary-piston samplers is simple in principle. The essential details are shown diagrammatically in Fig. 5·9. Casing is not always used, but a short length of casing near ground surface is desirable even though it is not carried to the depth of sampling. At the start of a sampling operation the piston rod is clamped to the drill rod and the base of the piston is at the level of the cutting edge of the sampler; this assembly is then lowered into the bore hole and pushed through the disturbed, and then the undisturbed, soil until the cutting edge reaches the elevation of the top of the desired sample. The clamp between the piston rod and the drill rod is removed and the piston rod is clamped to the casing; the drill rod is then forced down a distance equal to the desired length of sample, the base of the piston meanwhile remaining stationary in elevation against the top of the sample. The clamp to the casing is then removed, and the piston rod and drill rod are again clamped and the sampler is raised to ground surface.

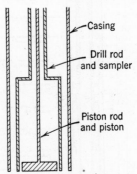

Fig. 5·9 Diagrammatic representation of a stationary-piston sampler.

The stationary-piston type of sampler has a number of outstanding advantages for sampling in many soils. The piston removes shavings of soil which inevitably are missed in the cleaning of the casing preparatory to sampling, and thus removes a common cause of disturbed soil at the top of the sample. The stationary piston prevents the entrance of excess soil and removes all danger of a recovery ratio greater than 100 per cent in the upper portion of the sample. Thus, when an overall recovery ratio of 100 per cent is obtained, the ratio must be 100 per cent in all portions of the sample.

In other types of sampler the water pressure above the sample may be considerably in excess of the static pressure because of limited opportunities for the escape of water while the sample is rapidly entering the sampler. This excess water pressure acts to resist the entrance of the sample into the sampler. It also causes a tighter contact between the sample and the sampler

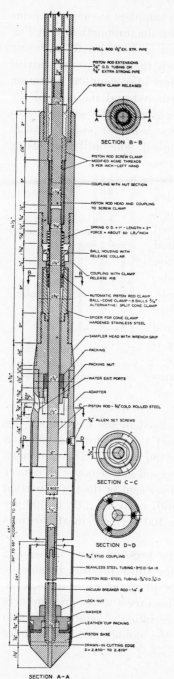

DRILL ROD 1½" EX. STR. PIPE

PISTON ROD EXTENSIONS
¾" O.D. TUBING OR
⅞" EXTRA STRONG PIPE

SCREW CLAMP RELEASED

SECTION B-B

PISTON ROD SCREW CLAMP
MODIFIED ACME THREADS
5 PER INCH-LEFT HAND

COUPLING WITH NUT SECTION

PISTON ROD HEAD AND COUPLING
TO SCREW CLAMP

SPRING O.D. = 1" - LENGTH = 2"
FORCE = ABOUT 50 LB/INCH

BALL HOUSING WITH
RELEASE COLLAR

COUPLING WITH CLAMP
RELEASE RIB

AUTOMATIC PISTON ROD CLAMP
BALL-CONE CLAMP - 8 BALLS ³⁄₁₆"
ALTERNATIVE: SPLIT CONE CLAMP

SPIDER FOR CONE CLAMP
HARDENED STAINLESS STEEL

SAMPLER HEAD WITH WRENCH GRIP

PACKING

PACKING NUT

WATER EXIT PORTS

ADAPTER

PISTON ROD - ¾" COLD ROLLED STEEL

⅜" ALLEN SET SCREWS

SECTION C-C

SECTION D-D

⅜" STUD COUPLING

SEAMLESS STEEL TUBING-3" O.D.-GA.18

PISTON ROD - STEEL TUBING - ¾" O.D ½" I.D

VACUUM BREAKER ROD - ¼" ∅

LOCK NUT

WASHER

LEATHER CUP PACKING

PISTON BASE

DRAWN-IN CUTTING EDGE
D = 2.850" TO 2.870"

SECTION A-A

wall, and thus increases the side friction. The stationary piston completely shields the top of the sample from this water pressure. The side friction tends to increase as the length of sample within the sampler increases, and eventually the recovery ratio must be expected to drop below unity. However, in the stationary-piston sampler the top of the sample must break contact with the piston before the recovery ratio can fall below unity and suction comes into play to aid in retaining this contact. This suction also decreases the magnitude of the side friction.

A stationary-piston sampler 3 in. in diameter, which was designed by Hvorslev and has given good results, is shown in Fig. 5·10. He also has designed similar samplers with diameters up to 4¾ in.

The types of piston samplers that have retractable or free pistons instead of stationary pistons are somewhat simpler in operation and they give good results in stiff soils. However, like open-drive samplers, they are subject to conditions of unfavorable stress on the top of the sample and to the resulting greater side frictions.

In the stationary-piston type of apparatus, the sampler may

Fig. 5·10 Three-inch thin-wall drive sampler with stationary piston. (M. J. Hvorslev.)

be of seamless steel tubing or a barrel with thin metal liners may be used. In the latter type, cutting wires may be introduced near the cutting edge to aid in the prevention of loss of soft samples. The samples are shipped either in the seamless tubes or in the thin liners. Piston samplers which are used both for advance of the bore hole and for sampling must be of heavier construction but they require no casing. For the sampling of difficult soils numerous devices to prevent loss of samples are available. After the sampler is driven, a small, flattened wash pipe can, in some instances, be pushed between the sampler and the casing to just below the sample and be used to break the suction caused by lifting the sampler. An extreme example of a precaution against the loss of the soil is the freezing of the sample just above the cutting edge, a procedure developed by F. A. Fahlquist (50) and used with good success for sampling sands by the Providence District of the U. S. Engineer Corps.

A small area ratio is not so essential in stationary-piston samplers as it is in open-drive samplers, but this ratio should be kept as small as possible in order to reduce driving resistance and to avoid the possibility of disturbance by displaced soil. The feasible length of sampler is believed to range between 5 and 30 diameters, the value for any given case depending greatly on the soil type. Sharp cutting edges are important, and the diameter of the cutting edge should be ½ to 2 per cent smaller than the inside diameter of the sampler. Best results are obtained if the sampler is forced into the ground at a steady, rapid speed of about 1 ft per sec. After the penetration it is well to wait about fifteen minutes for the sample to build up adhesion to the sampler walls. The removal should be slow and without shock.

The piston sampler is not the best type for use on some soils. Highly compacted soils can best be sampled by core boring samplers. Undisturbed samples of dense, coarse, cohesionless soils and of some soils containing pebbles or boulders can be obtained only by freezing and by the use of core borings.

In the majority of soft soils containing no coarse particles it is possible to obtain good results with stationary-piston type samplers. However, the above discussion indicates that proper operation is necesssary and that the work must be done by carefully trained and thoroughly supervised crews. Samples of this type in the larger diameters are expensive, of course, but not much more so than large-diameter samples obtained by other sampling methods. In small sizes, good results are obtainable at costs which are reasonable in relation to the results obtained. At all times it must be realized that undisturbed sampling is an art and that satisfactory results cannot be expected unless unusual care is exercised in every detail of the sampling operations.

PROBLEM

1. Make simplified diagrammatic sketches of the sampling devices described in the final four sections of Chapter 5. All main features should be included for each type of sampler, but notes may be used to cover any detail that is not easily sketched.

Chapter 6

PERMEABILITY

6·1 Effects of Pore Water on Soil Properties

It has already been pointed out that the properties of soils depend to a large degree on the amounts of pore water they contain. In addition the state of stress in the pore water has a pronounced effect on soil action. The part played by the water is thus seen to be an important one.

The facility with which water is able to travel through the pores also has much significance in many types of engineering problems. This property, commonly called the permeability, is one of the most important of soil properties. This chapter is devoted to considerations of permeability and the factors on which it depends.

6·2 General Considerations of Flow of Water

In textbooks on fundamental hydraulics it is shown that flowing water may assume either of two characteristic states of motion. In *laminar flow* each particle travels along a definite path which never intersects the path of any other particle. In *turbulent flow* the paths are irregular and twisting, crossing and recrossing at random.

The fundamental laws that determine the state existing for any given case were determined by Osborne Reynolds. They were derived from his classical experiments, wherein the relationship between the velocity of flow through a pipe and the amount of head lost in friction was a main point of investigation. The basic results of these tests are shown in Fig. 6·1, to natural scale in (*a*) and to logarithmic scale in (*b*). The ordinate in these figures is the hydraulic gradient, which is designated by i and defined as the head loss per unit of distance traveled.

Figure 6·1 shows that at the small velocities in zone I the

gradient is proportional to the velocity, a condition which may be considered the distinguishing characteristic of laminar flow. If the velocity is gradually increased, a point is reached at which eddies begin to form, and a range of uncertain behavior is entered. Further increase in velocity leads eventually to a relationship of velocity to gradient which is the definite curve of zone III. If the velocity is now decreased, the smooth curve persists down to a velocity considerably lower than that at which

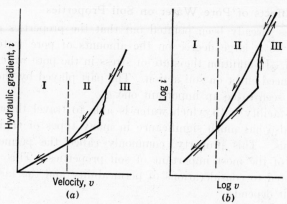

FIG. 6·1 Zones of laminar and turbulent flow.

the eddy formation was previously noted. Further decrease causes a return to laminar flow. The upper limit of zone II, the range of uncertain behavior, is indefinite and of little interest in the present discussion. The lower limit is a definite velocity v_c below which the flow in pipes is always laminar. It is known as the lower critical velocity. Reynolds found that this velocity is inversely proportional to the diameter of the pipe and gave the following general expression, applicable for any fluid and for any system of units:

$$\frac{v_c D \gamma_w}{\mu g} = 2000 \qquad (6\cdot1)$$

where D is the pipe diameter and g is the acceleration of gravity. This expression is known as the Reynolds number for the lower critical velocity. It shows that for water at 10°C or 50°F the product of diameter of pipe in feet and critical velocity in feet per second is 0.030; when the diameter is in centimeters and the velocity is in centimeters per second the product is 28.

At velocities smaller than v_c, and thus in the zone of laminar flow, Fig. 6·1 (*a*) shows that the relationship of velocity to gradient may be written

$$v = C_1 i \qquad (6\cdot2)$$

in which C_1 is a constant of proportionality.   Figure 6·1 (*b*) indicates that in zone III the corresponding relationship is

$$v^n = C_2 i \qquad (6\cdot3)$$

Here C_2 is a constant of proportionality. Reynolds found that the value for n in this expression varies from 1.79 to 2.00. For completely turbulent flow n equals 2, variations from this value being caused by laminar flow persisting adjacent to the wetted surface of the pipe.

Equation 6·1 and the Reynolds numbers cited above show that, for the diameters in common use for pipe lines, the critical velocity is small and therefore the flow is usually turbulent. However, for circular tubes of very small diameter the critical velocity is relatively high, and therefore the flow is usually laminar.

6·3   Darcy's Law for Flow through Soils

The pores of most soils are so small that flow oi water through them is laminar. However, in very coarse soils the flow may sometimes be turbulent; the maximum grain sizes through which flow may always be safely assumed to be laminar are discussed in Section 6·17.

The fundamental physical laws according to which all laminar flow takes place are the dynamical equations of motion, known as the Navier-Stokes equations (for a more extensive discussion see reference 104). An extended discussion of these fundamental laws of flow is not needed and cannot be attempted here. For a few relatively simple shapes of flow channels, these general expressions may be reduced to usable formulas, an example being the flow of a liquid through a round capillary tube, discussed in Section 6·5. The pore channels of a soil mass are so narrow and tortuous, so irregular in cross section, and so complex in their interconnection and subdivision that an analysis of the flow through individual pores is not possible. However, in engineering problems involving seepage through soils it is not the flow through individual pores that is of interest. Instead, the flow desired is the combined flow through all pores of an element of volume which is sufficiently large to give a typical representation of the soil mass as a whole. Studies relative to individual particles or individual pores, which in fine soils are truly of microscopic or submicroscopic size, are sometimes called microscopic studies. In contrast to these are investigations based on average conditions in representative samples, sometimes called macroscopic studies. The macroscopic or statistical average properties are of interest in connection with permeability investigations.

The law for flow through soils is named after Darcy (45) who demonstrated experimentally that the rate of flow is proportional to the gradient. Darcy's Law is written

$$Q = kiA \tag{6.4}$$
or
$$\frac{Q}{A} = v = ki \tag{6.5}$$

The area A in the above equations is the total cross-sectional area of soil mass, across which the discharge Q occurs. In any random cross section through a soil sample this total area A will consist of area within solids A_s and void area A_v. Although originally described as a volumetric ratio, it may now be noted that the void ratio also may be expressed as the area ratio A_v/A_s. Since the velocity v in equation 6.5 is equal to Q divided by the *total* area—not the void area through which the liquid is actually flowing—it should be noted that v must be a superficial velocity. For a condition such as that shown in Fig. 6.2 velocity v must equal the approach velocity v_a or the discharge velocity v_d. Careful distinction between the superficial velocity v and the seepage velocity v_s is important. The discharge may be written

$$Q = Av = A_v v_s \tag{6.6}$$

and since $A_v = nA$ it follows that $v = nv_s$.

In equations 6·4 and 6·5, the term k is Darcy's coefficient of permeability, which herein is called the coefficient of permeability, or simply the permeability. This coefficient, which is the only permeability coefficient in common use in soil mechanics, is best defined as the constant of proportionality between the superficial velocity v and the gradient i. Equation 6·5 shows that k has the dimensional units of a velocity, and it may be called the superficial velocity per unit of gradient. The most commonly used unit for this coefficient in soil testing is 10^{-4} cm per sec, or microns per second.

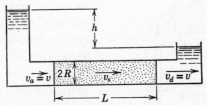

Fig. 6·2 Superficial and seepage velocities in uniform flow.

Since some sciences use permeability coefficients which are different from the Darcy coefficient, it is important that the exact definition be noted in any literature that deals with permeability.

6·4 Permeameters

The various types of apparatus which are used in soil laboratories for determining coefficients of permeability of soils are called permeameters. They are of two basic designs, the constant head type and the variable head type. The principles of each require only brief description. Numerous subdivisions of the two designs are often mentioned, such as upward-flow and downward-flow types, but these are not of major importance, fundamentally.

In an apparatus in which the head remains constant, the quantity of water flowing through a soil sample of known area and length in a given time can be measured. The cross section of such an apparatus is shown in Fig. 6·3. Head water and tail water levels can be kept constant by overflows. The differ-

ence in the elevation of the sample with relation to head and
tail water does not enter the expression, the effective head loss h
depending only on the difference in water levels. The area and
length of the sample, A and L, are measured. The tail water
is caught in a graduate, and the rate of discharge, Q, is measured. From Darcy's Law,

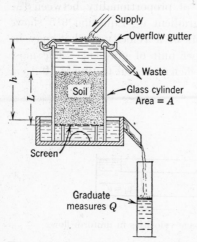

$$k = \frac{QL}{hA}$$

In highly impervious soils the quantity Q is small, and accurate measurements of its value are not easily obtained. Therefore, the constant head permeameter is principally applicable to relatively pervious soils.

FIG. 6·3 Constant-head permeameter.

Instruments operating under variable head furnish more accurate determinations of the permeability of impervious soils. The principle is illustrated in Fig. 6·4. The essential characteristic of the method is that the quantity of percolating water is measured indirectly by observations on the rate of fall of the water level in the standpipe above the specimen. The length L and area A of the sample, and the area a of the standpipe, must be known. In addition, observations must be taken on at least two different levels of the water in the standpipe.

Let h_0 be the measured head at zero time and h_1 the measured head after the lapse of a measured interval of time t_1, as shown in Fig. 6·4. Let h be the head at any intermediate time t. The rate of flow may be expressed as the area of the standpipe multiplied by the velocity of the fall. The velocity of fall is $-dh/dt$, the negative sign signifying that the head h decreases with increasing time. Equating this expression for rate of flow to that furnished by Darcy's Law gives

$$-a\,\frac{dh}{dt} = k\,\frac{h}{L}\,A$$

or

$$-a \int_{h_0}^{h_1} \frac{dh}{h} = k \frac{A}{L} \int_0^{t_1} dt$$

whence

$$k = \frac{aL}{At_1} \log_\epsilon \frac{h_0}{h_1}$$

or

$$k = 2.3 \frac{aL}{At_1} \log_{10} \frac{h_0}{h_1} \qquad (6 \cdot 7)$$

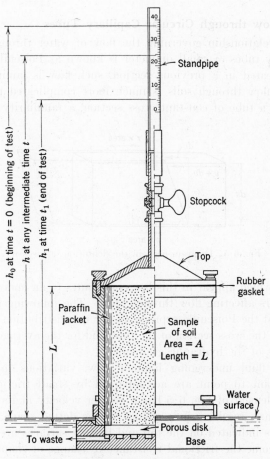

FIG. 6·4 Variable-head permeameter.

All the quantities on the right having been measured, k is readily found.

The permeameter in Fig. 6·4 is an early model designed for testing undisturbed samples. The variable head principle can be altered in many ways to yield accurate results over a wide range of soil types. Different standpipes may be used, with larger standpipe areas for more pervious materials. A much simpler apparatus consisting of a glass tube with a screen at the base and a stopper in the top, through which a smaller tube passes, is generally the most convenient type for testing disturbed samples.

6·5 Flow through Circular Capillary Tubes

The relationship governing the flow of water through round capillary tubes of small diameter is known as Poiseuille's Law. As indicated in a previous section, such flow is laminar. Although flow through soils is much more complicated than flow through a tube of constant cross section, a familiarity with the

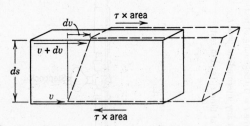

Fig. 6·5   Diagram used in the definition of viscosity.

factors which appear in this law contributes to an understanding of factors affecting flow through soils. The following is a derivation of the Poiseuille expressions for the distribution of velocity over the cross section of the tube and for the average velocity in terms of the hydraulic gradient.

In a fluid undergoing laminar flow, variations in velocity from point to point are accompanied by small friction losses. If the element of Fig. 6·5 has a greater velocity at its top than at its base, resulting in a change to the dotted shape, shearing forces as indicated on the top and bottom surfaces are required to overcome the frictional resistance to change of shape. If the element is of height ds and the difference of velocity between the two faces is dv, then dv/ds, the space rate of change of velocity, is proportional to τ, the shear per unit area on the top and bottom surfaces. The constant of proportionality, designated by μ, is called the coefficient of viscosity or simply the viscosity. Viscosity is thus defined by the expression

$$\tau = \mu \frac{dv}{ds} \qquad (6\cdot 8)$$

At room temperature the viscosity of water is about 10^{-5} gram sec per sq cm; values for other temperatures may be obtained from Table $3\cdot 2$.

The discharge through a tube of radius R and length L, subject to a head loss h, can readily be calculated. Let r be the radius of any concentric cylinder of liquid within the tube. The difference in the heads at the ends of this liquid cylinder is h; the difference in pressures therefore is $\gamma_w h$, and the resultant of the end thrusts on this cylinder is a force of magnitude $\pi r^2 \gamma_w h$, acting toward the right. This force must be balanced by shearing stress on the sides of the tube. According to equation $6\cdot 8$, the shearing stress is $\mu(-dv/dr)$; the maximum velocity is known to be at the center of the tube, and the minus sign merely signifies that the velocity decreases with increase of radius. The total shearing force is this stress multiplied by the area, $2\pi rL$, over which it acts. Its direction, since it resists motion, must be to the left. Treating forces acting to the right as positive, and equating the sum of horizontal forces to zero,

$$\pi r^2 \gamma_w h - 2\pi rL\mu \left(-\frac{dv}{dr} \right) = 0$$

Rearranging,

$$dv = -\frac{\gamma_w h}{2\mu L} r \, dr$$

whence by integration

$$v = -\frac{\gamma_w}{4\mu} \frac{h}{L} r^2 + C$$

It is known that in laminar flow the fluid in contact with the inside surface of the pipe has zero velocity. Thus, when r equals R,

v equals zero, and the equation above shows that C equals $(\gamma_w/4\mu)(h/L)R^2$. Also, h/L equals the hydraulic gradient i, giving

$$v = \frac{\gamma_w i}{4\mu}(R^2 - r^2) \qquad (6 \cdot 9)$$

From equation $6 \cdot 9$ the velocity at any point in the tube can be determined. A parabolic distribution of velocity exists and is shown in Fig. $6 \cdot 6$ (a).

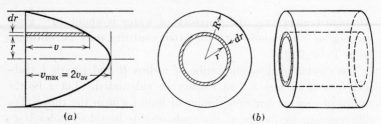

FIG. $6 \cdot 6$ Velocity distribution in a round capillary tube.

The discharge through any annular section such as that shaded in Fig. $6 \cdot 6$ (b) must be the product of velocity v and area $2\pi r\, dr$. Therefore, the total discharge may be written

$$Q = \int_0^R v 2\pi r\, dr$$

Substituting v from equation $6 \cdot 9$ and integrating,

$$Q = \frac{\pi R^4 \gamma_w i}{8\mu}$$

However, a more convenient form of this equation is

$$Q = \frac{\gamma_w R^2}{8\mu}\, ia \qquad (6 \cdot 10)$$

in which a equals πR^2 and is the area of the tube. The average velocity, equal to Q/a, may be expressed

$$v_{\text{av}} = \frac{\gamma_w R^2}{8\mu}\, i \qquad (6 \cdot 11)$$

6·6 Flow through Tubes of Various Cross Sections

If tubes of various shapes and sizes are to be studied, some characteristic dimension must be used to describe the general size of the tube. A dimension employed for this purpose in engineering hydraulics is the hydraulic radius, which is defined as the ratio of area to wetted perimeter; it is designated herein by R_H. The expression wetted perimeter is used in hydraulics because flow often occurs in only a part of the available cross section; for cases considered here, however, the word wetted is not needed, since the tubes treated will be flowing full and the entire perimeter will be wetted. By substitution in equation 6·10, for which case R_H equals $\pi R^2/2\pi R$ or $R/2$, the expression for flow through a *circular tube* becomes

$$Q_{\text{cir}} = \frac{1}{2} \frac{\gamma_w R_H{}^2}{\mu} ia \qquad . (6 \cdot 12)$$

By a derivation similar to that given in Section 6·5, it can be shown that the flow which takes place between two flat, closely spaced, parallel plates is expressed by

$$Q_{\text{pl}} = \frac{1}{3} \frac{\gamma_w R_H{}^2}{\mu} ia \qquad (6 \cdot 13)$$

In this case, $2R_H$ equals the distance between the parallel plates, and the area a equals $2R_H$ times any arbitrarily chosen width of flow area.

From the similarity of equations 6·12 and 6·13 it may be concluded that the flow through any given geometrical shape of cross section is given by

$$Q = C_s \frac{\gamma_w R_H{}^2}{\mu} ia \qquad (6 \cdot 14)$$

where C_s is a shape constant which has a definite value for any specific shape of cross section. The shape constant can be evaluated mathematically for simple shapes only. The value of C_s is independent of size; the dimension R_H expresses the size. The range of C_s for all possible shapes of openings is not known. Extreme differences in shape might be represented by considerably different C_s values, although all such values would probably be of the same order of magnitude. Shapes that are not greatly different may have C_s values that do not vary appreciably.

Let it be assumed that Fig. 6·7 represents the cross section

of a tube of constant but extremely irregular shape. Let the total area of the cross section, including the tube walls (the shaded portions), be designated by A and let the porosity, or ratio of open area to total area, be designated by n. On this basis the area of flow passages is expressed by nA. According to equation 6·14 the flow through this irregular section

FIG. 6·7 Tube of irregular shape.

or any comparable section may be written

$$Q = \left(C_s \frac{\gamma_w}{\mu} R_H{}^2 n \right) iA \qquad (6·15)$$

In the considerations above, the linear dimension R_H should be thought of merely as a distance which is representative of the size of the opening. The method used above for expressing this representative distance is a convenient, simple, and fairly satisfactory one, but it is not the only method that may be used and it is not necessarily the best method. If another method were to be used, the magnitude of the representative dimension would probably be somewhat different for any given shape of opening, and to compensate for this difference there would have to be a somewhat different shape factor. A better method might lead to shape factors which would vary less with shape of opening than do those in the method used.

Although soil passages are infinitely more complex than those of the cross section for which equation 6·15 applies, Fig. 6·7 nevertheless represents a section through which the flow will have many traits in common with flow through soils.

6·7   The Concept of Hydraulic Radius in Soil Pores

The concept of hydraulic radius in soils leads to an expression, originally presented by Kozeny (91), for the effect of the void ratio on the permeability.

The hydraulic radius may be expressed

$$R_H = \frac{A}{P} = \frac{AL}{PL}$$

in which L is the length of the tube. The final form indicates that the ratio of volume to surface area of flow channel may be used as an alternate definition of hydraulic radius. This alternate definition also applies to the average hydraulic gradient in a tube of variable cross section.

When flow takes place through a soil mass the volume of the flow channels is the pore volume, which is expressed by eV_s, wherein e is the void ratio and V_s is the volume of solids. The surface area of flow channels is the total surface area of the soil grains A_s. Thus, an expression for hydraulic radius in soils is

$$R_H = e\,\frac{V_s}{A_s} \qquad\qquad (6\cdot16)$$

The ratio V_s/A_s is a constant for any given specimen of soil. Difficulties may be encountered in some soils if accurate evaluations of this ratio are attempted, because surface areas of irregular grains are not easily determined and a large part of the total surface area may be contributed by a small fraction of very small grains.* However, these difficulties can in no way reduce the significance of the fact that the ratio has a definite, constant value.

Let D_s be the diameter of the spherical grain which has the same ratio of volume to surface area as holds collectively for all grains of a given soil. This ratio of volume to surface area may be expressed for the spherical grain as

---

* Unpublished results of investigations by W. F. Hiltner in the M.I.T. Soil Mechanics Laboratory show that 50 per cent of the surface area of a typical specimen of Boston blue clay occurs in the fraction finer than D_{10}.

$$\frac{V_s}{A_s} = \frac{\frac{1}{6}\pi D_s{}^3}{\pi D_s{}^2} = \frac{1}{6} D_s \qquad (6 \cdot 17)$$

The use of D_s instead of the ratio V_s/A_s serves mainly to emphasize the fact that the ratio has the units of a linear dimension. From equations 6·16 and 6·17,

$$R_H = e \frac{D_s}{6} \qquad (6 \cdot 18)$$

6·8 Effect of Sinuous Paths of Flow through Soils

As a step in the extension of the concepts presented by equation 6·15 and Fig. 6·7 regarding flow through soils, consider the flow through the pores of a homogeneous soil mass across a plane surface which is normal to the general direction of seepage, and compare this flow with that across another similarly chosen plane a short distance away. The pore opening patterns at the two planes will show little resemblance, but all statistical average values relative to pore sizes and shapes will be alike for the two planes. On this basis the soil pores may be considered as a group of tubes of unvarying section.

There is one essential difference between flow through a soil mass and flow through a tube. In the soil the flow is sinuous, winding around soil grains, whereas in the tube it follows straight lines. Because of the winding paths in soil, lateral components of velocity exist in all directions in planes normal to the general direction of flow; however, these lateral components counteract each other over the section as a whole. This condition leads to a difference between the true hydraulic gradient and the gradient used in soils. The true gradient equals the ratio of head loss to length of flow path within which this loss occurs. In soils, the gradient must be considered the ratio of head loss to the straight line distance between initial and final points, this distance being shorter than the true length of the sinuous flow path. However, the ratio between the distance of displacement and the length of the sinuous path is a constant for any given soil structure at a given void ratio, and may therefore be considered merely a shape-factor item that may be included in the constant term which has already been named the shape factor.

Possibly there are other factors regarding shape effect and other constants which would have to be considered to make complete the transition from conditions in straight tubes to those in soil capillaries. However, all such factors may be considered as representable by a composite shape factor.

6·9 Outline of Factors Affecting Permeability

By the use of equation 6·15 and the concepts presented in Sections 6·7 and 6·8 a rational equation for flow through soils may be presented. Substitution of equation 6·18 in 6·15, replacement of the porosity term by $e/(1 + e)$, and introduction of a composite shape factor C to include the factor C_s, the numerical constant, and all other shape effects, gives

$$Q = \left(D_s{}^2 \frac{\gamma_w}{\mu} \frac{e^3}{1 + e} C \right) iA \qquad (6 \cdot 19)$$

From comparison of this equation with Darcy's Law it follows that

$$k = D_s{}^2 \frac{\gamma_w}{\mu} \frac{e^3}{1 + e} C \qquad (6 \cdot 20)$$

From the terms on the right-hand side of equation 6·20, the following outline of the factors which affect permeability may be prepared. The first four factors are indicated by the four terms of the equation in the order given. The final factor is known from experience rather than deduced from theoretical considerations. The figures in parentheses following each item are references to explanatory sections.

1. The permeability of a given soil depends on the second power of a dimension representative of the average grain size; this is represented by the term $D_s{}^2$, designating the square of the diameter of the sphere of equivalent volume-area ratio, which is a constant for any given soil (6·10).

2. It depends on properties of the pore fluid, as shown by the term γ_w/μ (6·11).

3. It depends on the void ratio. The factor C may also depend somewhat on void ratio, and thus may have to be included in void ratio considerations; therefore $Ce^3/(1 + e)$ represents the void ratio effect (6·12 to 6·14).

4. It depends on shapes and arrangements of pores, or on the soil structure, as represented by the composite shape factor C (6·15).

5. It depends on the amount of undissolved gas within the pore water (6·16).

6·10   Effect of Grain Size on Permeability

Poiseuille's Law, as expressed by equation 6·11, shows that the average velocity through a capillary tube is proportional to the square of the diameter of the tube. Therefore, it is reasonable to expect that the seepage velocity through a given soil and the permeability of the soil are proportional to the square of the average pore dimension. Since the item having the greatest effect on sizes of pores in a given soil is the grain size, it may be concluded that the permeability is proportional to the square of the grain size. Thus, simple reasoning leads to the conclusion which was rigorously demonstrated in the derivation of equation 6·20.

Allen Hazen (69) found that the permeability of filter sands could be roughly expressed by

$$k = 100D_{10}{}^2 \qquad (6·21)$$

where cgs units in centimeters and seconds are used for all terms. In this expression D_{10} is the 10 per cent size, which is also known as Hazen's effective size. Hazen's observations were made on sands for which the effective sizes were between 0.1 and 3 mm diameter and for which the uniformity coefficient did not exceed 5. The coefficient, 100, is an average of many values; individual values ranged from 41 to 146, but most of the values were between 81 and 117. Therefore, this formula can be accepted only as an expression of average conditions for the range represented, and it cannot reflect the effects of variables discussed in subsequent sections. Moreover, since it was determined for filter sands, it may not give satisfactory results for soils of other types. Nevertheless, it has considerable value for rough estimates of permeability.

Numerous other relationships of the same type as the above have been determined by various investigators. Since the 10 per cent size is not easily determined in some soils, larger percentage sizes have been used in some investigations. Such studies show that the constant varies considerably with different soil types.

6·11   Effects of Properties of the Pore Fluid

In soil mechanics there will be little occasion to study any pore fluid except water; therefore, when permeability is mentioned herein it is understood that water permeability is referred to.

Equation 6·20 and other equations previously given indicate that the permeability is directly proportional to the unit weight γ_w and inversely proportional to the viscosity μ. Values of γ_w are essentially constant, but values of μ vary considerably with temperature. The effect of fluid properties on the value of the permeability when other factors are constant is thus given by

$$k_1 : k_2 = \mu_2 : \mu_1 \qquad (6·22)$$

It is common practice in soil laboratories to test for permeability at the most convenient temperature and reduce to results for a standard temperature, commonly 20°C, by the use of equation 6·22 and viscosity values from Table 3·2. Since the viscosity of water decreases with increasing temperature it is to be noted that the permeability is higher for higher temperatures.

It is pointed out by Muskat (pages 69–74, 93, 103–109 of reference 104) that a more general coefficient of permeability, k_p, is related to Darcy's coefficient k as follows:

$$k_p = k \, \frac{\mu}{\gamma_w} \qquad (6·23)$$

In any soil the coefficient k_p has the same value for all fluids and all temperatures as long as the void ratio and the structure of the soil skeleton are not changed. It is called the physical permeability, and it should be used in any science in which more than one type of pore fluid commonly occurs. Muskat gives comparisons of k_p as determined from flow of water and from flow of air through the voids of a large number of soils, and shows that sometimes there is good agreement and sometimes the agreement is poor. The cases of disagreement are easily understood when it is recalled that structural arrangement of particles in many fine-grained, saturated soils would surely change during any process that removes the water from the voids.

6·12   Effect of Void Ratio on the Permeability of Sands

From equation 6·20 the relationship of permeability values in a given soil, at a given temperature, under any two conditions of structure and void ratio, may be written

$$k_1 : k_2 = \frac{C_1 e_1{}^3}{1 + e_1} : \frac{C_2 e_2{}^3}{1 + e_2} \qquad (6·24)$$

Equation 6·24 is a rational expression, but it can be used in practice only if knowledge of C values is available. Different types of structure may give different C values, and it is possible that C may change considerably with change of void ratio. Whether C remains constant or varies with the void ratio can be determined only by laboratory testing.

From laboratory investigations on sand samples in which there is no appreciable stratification, it appears that the coefficient C changes very little with change of void ratio. Thus equation 6·24 reduces to the following *approximate* relationship for *sands:*

$$k_1 : k_2 = \frac{e_1{}^3}{1 + e_1} : \frac{e_2{}^3}{1 + e_2} \qquad (6·25)$$

It was stated near the end of Section 6·6 that the use of the concept of hydraulic radius was but one of a number of possible ways of expressing a representative linear dimension. Another approach (page 152 of reference 174) gives in place of equation 6·24 the relationship

$$k_1 : k_2 = C_1' e_1{}^2 : C_2' e_2{}^2 \qquad (6·26)$$

In sands, C' is also found to change only slightly with change of void ratio. The assumption that C' is constant leads to the following as an *approximate* relationship for *sands:*

$$k_1 : k_2 = e_1{}^2 : e_2{}^2 \qquad (6·27)$$

It should be noted that equations 6·25 and 6·27 are approximate, and are valid only for cohesionless soils.

The results of a number of individual tests run at various void ratios on a typical sand by several different observers are shown in Fig. 6·8. The curves indicate the degree to which the variation with void ratio is shown by the two void ratio functions

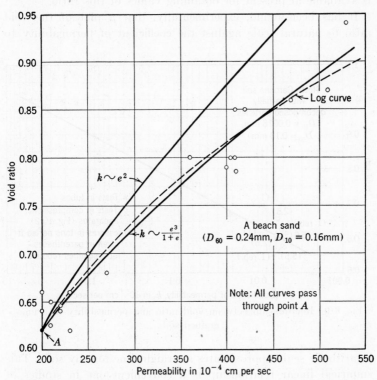

FIG. 6·8 Relationship between void ratio and permeability in sand.

discussed above. In this case equation 6·25 gives the better agreement, but for another type of soil it might not.

6·13 Effect of Void Ratio on the Permeability of Clays

Laboratory testing definitely shows that equations 6·25 and 6·27 are far from correct for clays. A thin surface film of water, which is bound to all particles, and water, which is bound between parallel, plate-shaped soil particles, are the probable explanations. Because of this bound water, seepage occurs only through a part of the pore space. Possibly these equations may be correct under a revised concept wherein the void ratio is replaced by the ratio between the volume of free water and all other volume (page 157 of reference 174). However, no method is available at present for obtaining values of this ratio.

It has been found, experimentally, that a plot of the void ratio to natural scale against the coefficient of permeability to

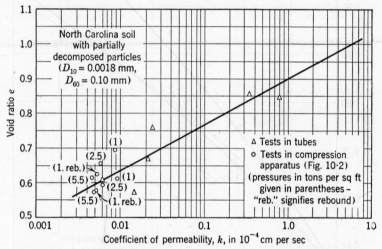

FIG. 6·9 Relationship between void ratio and permeability in a fine-grained soil.

logarithmic scale approximates a straight line for any soil. This empirical linear relationship is a convenient one in studies of the variation of permeability with void ratio in fine-grained soils.

Figure 6·9 shows results of permeability tests in two types of apparatus on a fine-grained soil. Differences in entrapped air content and in structure are the probable reasons for much of the scattering of individual points in this plot. In spite of this scattering, the linear relationship is seen to hold fairly well over the wide range of more than three logarithmic cycles of the permeability scale.

Another example of this type of plot is shown in Fig. 6·10. The samples represented in this figure were from a dike. In Fig. 6·8, which is a natural scale plot and represents a sand, the dashed line is the logarithmic curve which best fits the observed points; this logarithmic curve becomes a straight line on a plot of the semi-logarithmic type. The straight line semi-logarithmic relationship is seen to be valid for the two materials represented in Figs. 6·8 and 6·10.

The above discussion suggests a simple method for determination of the permeability of a soil at any void ratio when values of permeability of the soil are known at two or more void ratios. Two points determine the line on a plot of the type of Figs. 6·9 and 6·10, additional determinations serving as check points. Once the line is drawn, the permeability at any void ratio may be read directly.

6·14 Comparison of the Relative Importance of Two Porosity Effects

Increase in the porosity leads to an increase in the permeability of a soil for two distinct reasons. First, it causes an increase in the percentage of cross-sectional area available for flow; this is demonstrated by the porosity term in equation 6·15. Second, it causes an increase in the dimensions of pores, which increases the average velocity; this is demonstrated by the $R_H{}^2$ term in equation 6·15, R_H being proportional to the void ratio as shown by equation 6·16. The relative contributions of these two factors are not immediately evident and are worthy of investigation.

Reference to the straight line representing the vertical sample in Fig. 6·10 shows that an increase of void ratio from 0.65 to 1.10 causes a change in the coefficient of permeability from 1.8 to 16.7 microns per second, these permeability values being in the ratio of 1 to 9.3. The corresponding porosity change is from 0.39 to 0.52, these values being in the ratio of 1 to 1.33. It is seen that the first factor is of minor importance as compared to the second factor, and the second factor is the cause of an increase which is in the ratio of 1 to 9.3/1.33, or 1 to 7.

6·15 Effect of Structural Arrangement of Particles

It is not hard to visualize the possibility that different methods of placing or compacting may lead to different shapes and arrangements of the voids in a given soil at a given void ratio.

As an example it may be pointed out that soils in situ generally show a certain amount of stratification, because of which the permeability is greater in the horizontal direction than in the vertical direction.

Natural structural arrangement of the type discussed for fine soils in Section 4·7, if once destroyed, probably can never be reconstructed. Thus, for dependable results it may be necessary

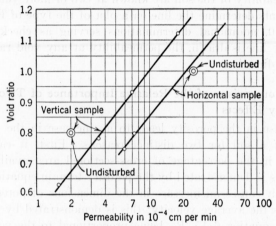

Fig. 6·10   Comparison of direct and indirect permeability determinations. (G. Gilboy.)

that tests on such soils be run on undisturbed samples. If a sample is stratified, the tests should be run with the flow taking place in the direction which it would assume in the sample in nature. If this direction is not known, separate tests with flow both parallel to and normal to the stratification should be conducted.

It is believed that many soils, such as homogeneous cohesionless sands which do not have pronounced stratification, may be essentially free of such effects. To determine whether or not there is a natural structure which has effect on the permeability of a given soil type, a comparison of test results from undisturbed and from disturbed samples may be made.

Figure 6·10 is a comparison of this type obtained by G. Gilboy on two samples from a dike. The specimens were undisturbed, cylindrical samples from test pits, one sampled horizontally and the other vertically. They were tested for permeability in the undisturbed state, with the flow in the direction of sampling, and the natural void ratio was also determined for each sample. The results are plotted as double circles on the semi-logarithmic plot of the figure. Both samples were subsequently broken up and tested for permeability in various states of density. The results are indicated by single circles, through each set of which a straight line has been fitted. The two lines on the plot show that the two samples were inherently somewhat different in permeability; this is not surprising since they were taken some distance apart. If no undisturbed samples had been tested, the indirect method would have given a very close result as far as the permeability of the horizontal sample was concerned. Inasmuch as the path of the water percolating through the dike is more nearly horizontal than vertical, the result is encouraging. The indirect method gave a result about double the actual permeability of the vertical sample. This may be due principally to the fact that the material was deposited and compacted in horizontal layers in the dike. Nevertheless, the result is of the proper order of magnitude, and on the safe side.

These and similar observations lead to the belief that tests on disturbed samples, if carefully and intelligently applied, may often yield results which are reasonably accurate, especially for artificial structures. However, for most dependable results, tests on samples from undisturbed natural deposits of fine-grained soils should, whenever possible, be made directly upon the undisturbed material.

6·16 Effect of Entrapped Air and Foreign Matter in the Voids

In all discussion up to this point it has been assumed that the voids have been completely filled with water. Although the term permeability in its strictest sense possibly refers to such a condition, actual soils in nature usually contain certain small amounts of entrapped gas. Moreover, laboratory specimens frequently contain larger amounts of gas since it is easily acquired unless unusual preventive precautions are taken during sampling and shipping and during preparation for testing.

Entrapped gas, even in very small quantities, has a marked

effect on the coefficient of permeability. Therefore, for correct test data the gas content during the tests should be equal to the gas content that occurs in the natural soil or is likely to occur in the future in the natural soil. It may be very difficult, however, to obtain information on the amount of gas likely to be present in the pore water in nature. Often the best approach available consists of laboratory tests on samples in which the degree of saturation is as high as can feasibly be obtained; the resulting permeability values tend to be too large but are conservative for use in all practical applications in which seepage is undesirable. Space does not permit an extended discussion here of the many factors bearing on this subject. The following is merely an outline of salient points.

Samples which often are spoken of as saturated, and which are in either undisturbed or remolded state, are likely to have small amounts of air or other gases within their voids which are produced by a number of causes. If a dry or damp soil is saturated by capillary rise or by a rise of the free water surface, a certain amount of air is entrapped in the voids. In the deposition of soil through water a natural resistance to perfect wetting is often the cause of air bubbles being retained on the surfaces of the grains. In submerged organic soils chemical action may free certain amounts of organic gases, especially when the pressure in the water is decreased. In the construction of rolled-fill dams the soils are generally placed at the water content at which rolling leads to the maximum density, and in such fills (and similarly in compaction tests) 10 per cent or more of the void volume is usually taken up by entrapped air.

In addition to entrapped gas bubbles, certain amounts of air and other gases always exist in solution in the pore water. At any given temperature and pressure a definite amount of dissolved air is possible, and if this maximum amount is in solution an increase in temperature or a decrease in pressure results in the freeing of air.

It is evident that satisfactory permeability determinations will not be possible unless the freeing of dissolved gas from the water during testing is prevented. Of course, there must be no free air bubbles in the water entering the specimen. In addition, increase in temperature in the water as it passes through the sample is undesirable. Some relief from the latter danger is obtained by warming the water supply slightly, and thereby obtaining a decrease in temperature as the water passes through the soil. However, the positive method of obtaining complete freedom from all effects of gas—a procedure that can be used only on disturbed samples—consists in first evacuating the soil in the dry state and causing saturation with gas-free water, then testing with gas-free water. Gas-free water is best obtained by spraying water into an evacuated container, and, thereafter, protecting the water from contact with the air.† Water in such a state will have an affinity for soluble gas, and if it is used for tests on partially saturated soils any gases present will tend to be dissolved from the voids, but at a rate which is probably too slow to have much remedial effect in short tests.

Even if the amount of entrapped gas does not change appreciably during a test, its volume will change if the pore-water pressure varies. This change points out a disadvantage of the variable-head type of apparatus, in which it may appear that the permeability changes with change of gradient, whereas actually the change is due to varying gas volume resulting from differences in water pressure as the head decreases. A similar type of difficulty occurs in undisturbed samples taken from large distances below the water table. Such soils may undergo swelling, due both to the freeing and to the expansion of gas when the water pressure is lowered, and this volume change introduces not only a different degree of saturation but it also changes all soil properties which vary with the void ratio.

If the volume of the entrapped gas remains constant, decreases in permeability often can still occur during testing because of migration of gas bubbles to critical points of the pore channels. If tap water or even distilled water is used for testing, even though it be deaerated, it may contain enough solid matter of microscopic size to plug up pore passages and cause a decrease of permeability with time. Furthermore there is the possibility that migration of the finest particles of the soil may cause decrease of permeability. Unless distilled water is used, minute amounts of dissolved chemicals may be present in the water and may have considerable effect on the colloidal fraction of the soil.

† An apparatus for accomplishing this is described in reference (11).

These factors are frequently of minor concern, however, as such changes in permeability often occur slowly, and dependable initial observations may often be obtained before appreciable change occurs.

By observation of the precautions mentioned above, fairly consistent values for the coefficient of permeability may usually be obtained, but extreme accuracy or agreement can seldom be expected. However, from the practical viewpoint high accuracies are often unnecessary, since two samples, taken at points a short distance apart in a soil which appears to be fairly uniform, may have permeabilities which differ greatly.

6·17   The Range of Validity of Darcy's Law

At the beginning of this chapter it was pointed out that flow in circular tubes would be laminar if the velocity was less than a critical value, expressed by a Reynolds number of 2000. The range of validity of Darcy's Law has been studied on a similar basis by several investigators whose work is summarized by Muskat (page 56 of reference 104). In soils there is a slow transition from purely laminar flow to a mildly turbulent condition, which precludes an accurate expression for the critical point but which also makes a precise expression unnecessary. A rough but satisfactory criterion of the limit of applicability of Darcy's Law, given by Fancher, Lewis, and Barnes (51) is

$$\frac{v D_a \gamma_w}{\mu g} \lessgtr 1 \qquad (6 \cdot 28)$$

where v is the superficial velocity and D_a is the diameter of the sphere which has a volume equal to the quotient of the volume of solids of a sample and the number of grains in the sample.

The above expression may be used for a simple determination of the grain size of the coarsest uniform soil which should always show laminar flow. Inserting ki for the velocity, using Hazen's rough expression for permeability of sands, given by equation 6·21, and assuming a gradient of unity, gives the following, in cgs units:

$$\frac{(100D^2)iD\gamma_w}{\mu g} = \frac{100 \times 1 \times D^3 \times 1}{10^{-5} \times 980} = 1$$

whence D equals approximately 0.5 mm. It may be noted that the gradient has relatively little effect, eight times as large a gradient giving half as large a diameter.

The Reynolds number of unity in equation 6·28 is admittedly an approximate value which has been conservatively chosen. Its approximate nature is proved by the absence of any account of the void ratio, which surely should have some effect on the relationship.

PROBLEMS

1. A falling head permeability test is to be performed on a soil whose permeability is estimated to be about 0.3×10^{-4} cm per sec. A standpipe of what diameter should be used if the head is to drop from 27.5 cm to 20.0 cm in about 5 min, and if the sample's cross section is 15.0 cm^2 and its length 8.5 cm?

2. A constant head permeability test has been run on a sand sample 25 cm in length and 30 sq cm in area. Under a head of 40 cm the discharge was found to be 200 cc in 116 sec. The specific gravity of the grains was 2.65, the dry weight of the sand was 1320 grams, and the void ratio was 0.506. Determine (*a*) the coefficient of permeability, (*b*) the seepage velocity during the test, and (*c*) the superficial velocity.

3. Determine the order of magnitude of the composite shape factor C of equation 6·19 for perfectly uniform sands that have spherical grains and a void ratio of 0.80, basing this determination on Hazen's approximate expression for permeability. Also make a statement regarding the factors that would be much harder to evaluate in a similar determination for a non-uniform soil.

4. List four variables on which the permeability of a given soil depends. Give for each variable expressions for the variation or, if no expressions can be given, state the precautions that should be taken with respect to the variable so that satisfactory permeability data may be obtained in laboratory tests.

5. A certain cohesionless soil has a permeability of 0.040 cm per sec at a void ratio of 0.38. Make predictions of the permeability of this soil when at a void ratio of 0.46 according to the two functions of void ratio that have been proposed.

6. Permeability tests on a soil sample give the following data:

Run No.	e	Temperature °C	k 10^{-4} cm per sec
1	0.70	25	0.32
2	1.10	40	1.80

Estimate the coefficient of permeability at 20°C for a void ratio of 0.85.

Chapter 7

WEIGHTS, STRESSES AND HEADS, SEEPAGE FORCES

7·1 Introduction

In this chapter a number of concepts will be outlined which are fundamental in nature and important in many branches of soil mechanics. To a certain degree the fundamentals covered are interrelated, much as are all fundamental ideas. However, this chapter, rather than being a treatment of one branch of soil mechanics, is a compilation of a number of fundamentals, all of which will be used frequently in later chapters.

7·2 Unit Weights

The mass of soil represented in Fig. 7·1 has volume V, it is composed of particles of unit weight γ_s or $G\gamma_w$, and it is at void ratio e. The water in the pores has a unit weight γ_w, and the

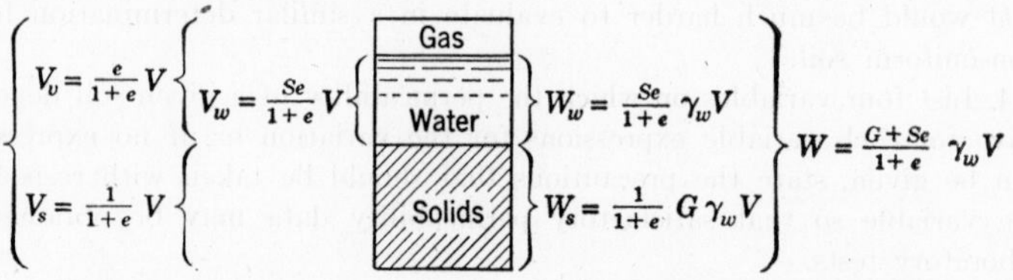

$$V \begin{cases} V_v = \frac{e}{1+e} V \begin{cases} V_w = \frac{Se}{1+e} V \begin{cases} \text{Gas} \\ \text{-----} \\ \text{Water} \\ \text{Solids} \end{cases} W_w = \frac{Se}{1+e} \gamma_w V \\ W_s = \frac{1}{1+e} G \gamma_w V \end{cases} \end{cases} W = \frac{G+Se}{1+e} \gamma_w V \\ V_s = \frac{1}{1+e} V \end{cases}$$

FIG. 7·1 Volume, weight, and unit weight expressions.

degree of saturation of the pores is S. The diagrammatic sketch shows, at the left, the volume of the solids, air, and water, and at the right the corresponding weights are shown. The total weight divided by the total volume, defined as the unit weight, or more specifically as the overall or combined unit weight, may be written

$$\gamma_t = \frac{G + Se}{1 + e} \gamma_w = \frac{1 + w}{1 + e} G\gamma_w \qquad (7\cdot1)$$

In samples of known water content the final expression may be more convenient than the form containing the term S.

If the soil is dry, the values of S and w are zero, and the unit weight may be written

$$\gamma_{\text{dry}} = \frac{G}{1 + e} \gamma_w \qquad (7 \cdot 2)$$

When a soil is submerged, the true unit weight as expressed by equation $7 \cdot 1$ is partly balanced by the buoyant effect of the water, the buoyancy being equal to the weight of water displaced. Thus the effective unit weight is equal to the true unit weight minus the unit weight of water. This effective weight is designated by a number of different terms, including apparent weight and submerged weight. *Submerged weight* is the term that will be used here. The submerged unit weight may be expressed

$$\gamma_{\text{subm}} = \frac{G + Se}{1 + e} \gamma_w - \gamma_w = \frac{G - 1 - e(1 - S)}{1 + e} \gamma_w \qquad (7 \cdot 3)$$

Submerged soils usually are in a state of nearly complete saturation and it is common, and in the great majority of cases it is reasonable, to assume they are completely saturated. The submerged, saturated unit weight is designated by γ_b and expressed

$$\gamma_b = \frac{G - 1}{1 + e} \gamma_w \qquad (7 \cdot 4)$$

It also is sometimes called the *buoyant unit weight* and the effective unit weight for the saturated case.

If a specific gravity of grains of 2.73 and an average value of void ratio of 0.80 are assumed, values of unit weights are as given below. It should be noted, however, that values which differ appreciably from those given will occur when the void ratio or the specific gravity value is unusually high or unusually low.

REPRESENTATIVE VALUES OF UNIT WEIGHTS

$(e = 0.80, G = 2.73)$

Dry soil	1.52 g per cc	or	95 lb per cu ft
Saturated soil	1.96 g per cc	or	122 lb per cu ft
Submerged soil	0.96 g per cc	or	60 lb per cu ft

The difference in meanings between the terms saturated and submerged as used above should be carefully noted; the saturated unit weight is a combined or soil-and-water unit weight, and the submerged unit weight is the effective or buoyant unit weight. Also of importance is the fact that for a given void ratio in a soil containing no air the difference between the saturated and submerged unit weights is exactly the unit weight of water, 62.5 lb per cu ft, or 1 gram per cc.

7·3 Stresses

Stress is defined as force per unit of area. In a loaded soil mass which is below water there will be stresses within the soil skeleton by virtue of forces existing at points of contact of individual particles, and also there generally will be pressure within the pore water. These two types of stress are of such different nature that a clear distinction is of utmost importance.

To develop concepts of stress in soils, the forces acting on a horizontal unit of area at a point at depth z below the surface of a soil stratum will be considered. For simplicity it will be assumed that the free water surface is just at ground level, that the soil is homogeneous, that the surface of the stratum is level, and that in all other respects there are no horizontal variations.

If a random horizontal area of 1 sq ft is pictured at the given depth, this surface passes through grains and through pores. In concepts of stresses, instead of such an area, the surface that must be considered is the one containing the points of grain-to-grain contact, in order that it may include the points of action of the forces which make up intergranular stress. Thus the unit of area should be visualized as a wavy surface which is tangent to but does not cut through soil grains, and which at all points is as close as possible to a flat surface.

Since this wavy surface is within the pore space except for the infinitesimal areas of grain-to-grain contacts, the water pressure acting across it acts over virtually the entire area. Thus the water pressure, which in soil mechanics is commonly called neutral pressure, has a magnitude of $\gamma_w z$ if static water conditions prevail. It should be noted that neutral pressures act on all sides of all particles but they do not cause particles to press against adjacent particles.

The number of intergranular contacts per unit of area may be of very high order of magnitude in fine soils. Since each is essentially a point contact (a finite force acting on an infinitesimal area), the intensity of pressure over the actual bearing points is very large. The individual intergranular forces are very irregular in magnitude and direction; some are small, others relatively large, and they tilt in various directions. However, for the case in question the stress is vertical, and horizontal components balance each other. As in the analysis of individual soil pores in the study of permeability, a picture in terms of individual forces—the microscopic picture—is exceedingly complicated, and the macroscopic or statistical viewpoint must be used. On this basis any force considered is the vector summation of many individual intergranular forces. The area on which this force is considered to act is the plane most closely coinciding with the wavy surface mentioned above. Stresses are expressed by dividing the force by the plane area. The sizes of areas considered must be sufficiently large to give typical representation, since irregularities in magnitudes of forces would prevent an accurate average on an area across which there is only a small number of intergranular forces.

Some question may arise regarding the concept of areas of contact truly being points. In coarse soils there can be little question that contacts are of inappreciable area. In very fine soils the concept of point contacts may not be strictly true, but the definitions of intergranular and water pressures which are given above are essentially correct and are generally accepted.

Intergranular stresses will in general have normal and shearing components. Neutral pressures can have no shearing components. The sum of intergranular and neutral pressure is known as combined pressure or total pressure. Since the term total pressure might be inferred to be a force rather than an intensity, the designation combined pressure will usually be employed herein. Intergranular pressures are frequently spoken of as effective pressures, but the designation intergranular will in general be used herein because of the various meanings which may be associated with the word effective.

Across the horizontal surface of unit area at depth z the combined pressure must be numerically equal to the weight of all matter that rests above. The expression for this combined pressure must be the depth multiplied by the combined unit weight expressed by equation 7·1. For determination of the intergranular pressure, it may be noted that the simplest approach is to deduct the neutral pressure from the combined pressure. The water pressure at depth z is $\gamma_w z$, and therefore the intergranular pressure $\bar{\sigma}$ may be written

$$\bar{\sigma} = \frac{G + e}{1 + e}\,\gamma_w z - \gamma_w z$$

or

$$\bar{\sigma} = \frac{G - 1}{1 + e}\,\gamma_w z \tag{7·5}$$

Since $[(G - 1)/(1 + e)]\gamma_w$ has already been shown to be the expression for the submerged unit weight, the above considerations may be accepted as demonstrating that intergranular pressures in soil masses which are below water depend directly on the submerged unit weight.[*]

7·4 Types of Head

It is shown in all textbooks on hydraulics and fluid mechanics that the total head in the water at any point is equal to the sum of the velocity head, the pressure head, and the elevation head. The velocity head is given by the expression $v^2/2g$, where v is the velocity and g is the acceleration of gravity. Its value is inappreciably small in practically all cases of seepage through soil. For example, a velocity of 1 ft per sec, which is an enormous value as compared to typical seepage velocities, gives a velocity head of only 0.015 ft. Thus velocity heads may be disregarded in practically all seepage problems.

The total head therefore becomes the sum of pressure head and elevation head. The elevation head at any point is the vertical distance above a datum plane which for a given problem may be chosen at any desired elevation; the datum which is usually the most convenient for use in seepage problems is tail water elevation. The pressure head is equal to the water pressure divided by the unit weight of water.

[*] For further considerations of this subject and other subjects treated in this chapter see reference 124.

On a vertical cross section through a saturated soil mass the elevation head in the water at any point is directly represented by its elevation on the section. If it is imagined that a small tube or standpipe is inserted at the point in question, water would rise vertically above the point by a distance equal to the pressure head. Thus the elevation of the water surface in the standpipe represents the total head at the point under consideration. In

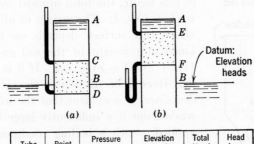

Tube	Point	Pressure Head	Elevation Head	Total Head	Head Loss
(a)	C	AC	BC	AB	AB
	D	BD	–BD	0	
(b)	E	AE	BE	AB	AB
	F	–BF	BF	0	

Fig. 7·2 Illustration of types of head.

typical soil tests, such a standpipe seldom could actually be inserted into the soil mass. However, as a concept the standpipe height is valuable.

The two tubes shown in Fig. 7·2 may be considered to be permeameters. The dimensions of the samples in (a) and (b) are alike, and the elevations of head water and tail water are the same. The pressure and elevation heads are given in the table for points at the top and the bottom of each sample. The standpipes shown at the left of each tube present the graphical illustration of total head described above. The gradients through these samples are alike and, if the soils are alike, the permeabilities and the rates of discharge can differ only because of differences in volumes of air in the pore water. Since the pressures are greater in (a), gas, if present, is more highly compressed and the permeability is somewhat larger.

7·5   Quicksand

As an introduction to the important subject of seepage force, the forces which act on a soil mass will be analyzed under the upward flow condition shown in Fig. 7·3 and the phenomenon known as quicksand will be explained.

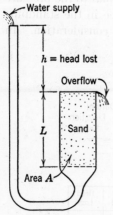

Fig. 7·3 Upward flow with the possibility of quicksand.

Across the bottom surface of the soil mass in this figure, the total upward water force is $(h + L)\gamma_w A$. The weight of all material above this surface depends on the combined unit weight of the soil and equals $[(G + e)/(1 + e)]\gamma_w L A$. If it is assumed that there is no friction on the sides of the container, it is evident that the soil will be washed out if a sufficiently large head h is applied. Such a boiling condition will be just at the point of starting if the upward water force is just equal to the weight of all material above; it may be represented by equating the above expressions:

$$(h + L)\gamma_w A = \frac{G + e}{1 + e}\gamma_w L A \qquad (7·6)$$

whence

$$\frac{h}{L} = \frac{G - 1}{1 + e} \qquad (7·7)$$

Equation 7·7 states that an upward gradient of magnitude $(G - 1)/(1 + e)$ will be just sufficient to start the phenomenon of boiling in granular soils. This gradient is called the critical gradient, and in general its value is approximately equal to unity.

This phenomenon is quicksand. A saturated sand becomes quick—quick meaning alive—if upward flow at a gradient of approximately unity occurs at its surface. Quicksand, contrary to a popular belief, is not a type of sand but is a flow condition occurring within a sand. An upward gradient which exceeds unity will cause a quick condition in a mass of pebbles as quickly as it will in a fine sand. The reason why quicksand is of much commoner occurrence in fine sands is explained by Darcy's Law; to maintain a gradient of unity, the velocity at which water must be supplied at the point of inflow varies as the permeability; therefore a quicksand cannot occur in a coarse soil unless a large quantity of water can be supplied.

The examples of quick conditions which can be cited are numerous, and a few typical cases will be mentioned. In an excavation which must be carried into sand below the water table, pumping will usually be resorted to, in order to allow working in the dry, and seepage of water into the excavation will occur. If upward gradients of unity result, quicksand is imminent. Quicksand may occur naturally in instances where the water below a saturated sand deposit is under greater than the usual static water pressure. Such a condition results if pervious underground strata are continuous to distant high ground and are subject to the higher water heads existing at the distant high points. Artesian wells make use of this condition, and high pressures of this type causing upward flow are sometimes referred to as artesian pressures, and the condition is called an artesian condition. A most interesting illustration of sand boils occurs behind embankments, such as the levees of the Mississippi River, in times of flood. Such boils cause much concern and endanger the leeves. A common way to fight them is to form enclosing rings of sandbags, sometimes to appreciable heights; these allow a ponding of water which causes a backpressure and decreases the gradient.

A widespread myth exists regarding the danger of animals and men being sucked down into quicksand. Before the truth of this myth is investigated, it should be recalled that a man is just able to float in fresh water which has a weight of 62.5 lb per cu ft, whereas in salt water, which weighs about 64 lb per cu ft, floating is relatively easy. Quicksand has a unit weight of $[(G + e)/(1 + e)]\gamma_w$, which is in general well over 100 lb per cu ft, and it is impossible for a man to avoid floating in it. Admittedly a man or an animal, caught in quicksand, might in his panic exhaust himself, collapse on his face, and drown, but considerations of the laws of physics disprove the existence of any forces which would tend to suck him down.

Quicksand presents many difficulties in construction operations as, for example, in a caisson where an area has been unwatered and upward flow is taking place. Moreover, when the upward gradient is smaller than unity the same type of force is present in a magnitude proportional to the gradient, and although a quick condition does not occur similar construction difficulties may be present to a smaller degree. Thus the fundamental study of this phenomenon must not be limited to the spectacular example of quicksand, but must search into the more general phenomenon of which quicksand is but an illustration.

7·6   Seepage Forces

Seepage forces are the cause of quicksand and they also have an important effect in many engineering problems in which there is no quick condition. For example, they are present in clays, which are subject to seepage, but in clays the internal strength known as cohesion prevents the occurrence of boiling. They are also present when the upward gradient is not of sufficient magnitude to cause a quick condition. Further analysis into the upward flow considered in the preceding section will be used to obtain a definition of seepage force and an expression of its magnitude.

The head h in Fig. 7·3 is used up in forcing water through pore passages of length L. This head is dissipated in viscous friction and, as always when energy is dissipated in friction, a force or drag is exerted in the direction of motion. In this case the drag is exerted on the soil grains which form the walls of the pore passages. The analysis in Section 7·5 treated the entire soil-water mass and the entire force pushing upward from below. In contrast, the framework of individual soil particles only will now be analyzed. The effective weight of the submerged mass is the submerged weight $[(G-1)/(1+e)]\gamma_w LA$. The head dissipated is h and, therefore, an upward force $h\gamma_w A$ is dissipated, or transferred by viscous friction into an upward frictional drag on the particles. When a quick condition is incipient in a sandy soil, these forces are equal and

$$h\gamma_w A = \frac{G-1}{1+e}\gamma_w LA \qquad (7\cdot8)$$

which again leads to equation 7·7. The only difference between equations 7·6 and 7·8 is that both sides of equation 7·6 include a force $\gamma_w LA$ which, for the left-hand side, is the weight of pore water plus the reaction to the buoyancy and, for the right-hand side, is the corresponding supporting force furnished by water pressure.

This upward force of seepage, whether or not it is sufficient to cause a quick condition and whether it is acting in sandy or clayey material, may be written $h\gamma_w A$, as in the left-hand side of equation 7·8. In uniform flow it is distributed uniformly throughout the volume of the soil LA, and the force per unit of volume is therefore $h\gamma_w A/LA$, which equals $i\gamma_w$. This important relationship may be worded: *The seepage force in an isotropic soil acts in the direction of flow and has a magnitude of $i\gamma_w$ per unit of volume.*

A seepage force is just as definite a force as a weight is. In fact, seepage forces and gravitational forces are of such similar nature that the first step in force analyses in which seepage occurs is often to determine their vector sum, which is called the resultant body force.

This combination of gravitational and seepage forces may be accomplished in either of two ways, the derivations of this and the preceding section serving as illustrations of the two approaches. A combination of the *total weight* and the *boundary neutral force* is the first approach, and is the one used in the preceding section. A combination of the *submerged weight* and the *seepage force* is the second approach, and is the one used in this section. When the combination gives a zero force, a quick condition exists. In all instances the *two approaches give identical results.* The fact that seepage force does not appear in the first approach does not in any way mean that effects of seepage are not cared for.

The above analysis demonstrates the identity of the two approaches of caring for seepage forces when flow is vertically upward in isotropic soils. A rigorous demonstration of the analogous relationship for flow in any direction through stratified soils is withheld until Section 9·17, since concepts that are developed later are needed for the general demonstration.

7·7 Protective Filters

Since an understanding of the functioning of protective filters requires an understanding of seepage forces, a brief explanation of this very practical subject serves as an illustration of concepts given in the previous sections.

If upward flow is occurring through a sandy soil and if the upward gradient at the surface is larger than unity, a quick condition must be expected.   Figure 7·3 shows, however, that if a quick condition is imminent it can be prevented if a loading is brought into play from above to hold the sand in place.

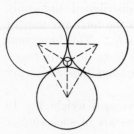

Such a loading may be accomplished by placing a filter of coarser material above the sand.   In addition to supplying weight there are two other important requirements which the filter material must meet: first, the filter material must be fine enough to prevent the passage through its pores of particles from the material below; second, it must be coarse enough so that the head dissipated by flow of water through it, and therefore the seepage forces developed within it, will be relatively small.

Fig. 7·4 Illustration of a filter requirement.

As a rough approximation of the maximum size of particles that may be used for the filter material without danger of penetration of fines through its pores, an analysis based on perfect spheres of uniform size may be considered.   If three equal spheres touch as shown in Fig. 7·4, they have diameters 6.5 times as large as the diameter of a small sphere which would just pass through the center opening.   Since the opening shown between the large particles in Fig. 7·4 is the smallest that can occur, an attempt to rationalize would be likely to lead to the conclusion that for loose packing the size of the filter material would have to be limited to somewhat less than 6.5 times the size of the foundation material.   However, it has been demonstrated by G. E. Bertram in laboratory investigations (11) that the grain size of a uniform filter material may be as much as 10 times that of a uniform foundation material before there is appreciable washing through.   This limiting size ratio appears to depend only in minor degree on the porosity of the filter material and the sharpness of the grains.

A criterion which was advanced by Terzaghi, and which, after investigations of its validity, has been recommended by the U. S. Waterways Experiment Station (160, 159) may be written

$$\frac{D_{15} \text{ (of filter)}}{D_{85} \text{ (of foundation)}} < (4 \text{ to } 5) < \frac{D_{15} \text{ (of filter)}}{D_{15} \text{ (of foundation)}} \qquad (7 \cdot 9)$$

The first two terms state the first requirement; to prevent the foundation material from passing through the pores of the filter the 15 per cent size of the filter material must not exceed 4 or 5 times the 85 per cent size of the foundation material. The second and third terms cover the second requirement; to keep seepage forces within the filter to permissibly small magnitude the ratio of 15 per cent sizes of filter and foundation materials must exceed 4 or 5.

Since the velocity of flow through foundation and filter usually is essentially the same, Darcy's Law indicates that the gradient is inversely proportional to the permeability. Since the permeability is approximately proportional to $(D_{15})^2$, the seepage forces per unit of volume in a filter meeting the second requirement above will be of the order of $\frac{1}{16}$ to $\frac{1}{25}$ of those in the foundation.

In practice, protective filters are often constructed in layers, each layer coarser than that below. Because of this they often are called *reversed filters*. Between any two adjacent layers the requirements cited above must be satisfied. Filters are also of much practical value in preventing the erosion of fine foundation materials when there is no danger of a quick condition. Filter protection is an item of outstanding importance in the design of earth dams.

PROBLEMS

1. Determine the largest and smallest values that will occur for the dry unit weight and the combined and the buoyant unit weight of completely saturated granular soils, assuming that void ratios of such a soil may have values ranging from 0.4 to 1.0 and that the specific gravity will range between 2.60 and 2.80.

2. Peat deposits often have void ratios as high as 10, and the specific gravity of the solid phase often is less than 2. On the basis of the figures quoted, determine the buoyant unit weight of such a material.

3. Determine the approximate depth at which the intergranular pressure on the horizontal plane is equal to 1 ton per sq ft in (*a*) a typical deposit of dry soil, and (*b*) a typical deposit of submerged soil.

4. For each of the cases, (*a*), (*b*), and (*c*) in the accompanying diagram, determine the pressure head, the elevation head and the total head at the entering end, the exit end, and point *A* of the sample.

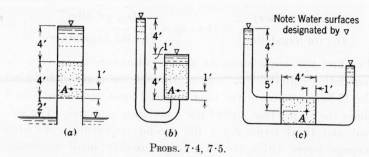

PROBS. 7·4, 7·5.

5. For each of the cases, (*a*), (*b*), and (*c*), shown in the diagram, determine the superficial velocity, the seepage velocity, and the seepage force per unit of volume for each of the following cases: (1) a permeability of 0.1 cm per sec and a porosity of 50 per cent; (2) a permeability of 0.001 cm per sec and a porosity of 40 per cent.

6. The foundation soil at the toe of a masonry dam has a porosity of 41 per cent and a specific gravity of grains of 2.68. To assure safety against piping, the specifications state that the upward gradient must not exceed 25 per cent of the gradient at which a quick condition occurs. What is the maximum permissible upward gradient?

7. In a container filled with each of the following materials, at a porosity of 43 per cent determine the upward gradient required to cause a quick condition: (*a*) lead shot with a specific gravity of 11.4; (*b*) fiber beads with a specific gravity of 1.50; (*c*) sand with a specific gravity of 2.70.

8. The filter protection that is to be placed between the foundation and a rock drain that is located near the toe of an earth dam consists of 3 layers. Grain sizes of the material are as follows:

	D_{15}, mm	D_{85}, mm
Foundation, finest specimens	0.024	0.1
Foundation, coarsest specimens	0.12	0.9
Filter layer *A*	0.3	1
Filter layer *B*	2	3.5
Filter layer *C*	5	10
Rock drain	15	40

Analyze this filter relative to the U.S.W.E.S. filter requirements, and give comments on the probable seriousness of any instances of failure to meet the requirements.

Chapter 8

CAPILLARITY

8·1 The Fundamental Concept of Surface Tension

The concept that the surfaces of liquids are in a state of tension is a familiar one, and it is widely utilized. Actually it is known that no skin or thin foreign surface really is in existence at the surface, and that the interaction of surface molecules causes a condition analogous to a surface subjected to tension. The surface tension concept is therefore an analogy, but it explains the surface behavior in such satisfactory manner that the actual molecular phenomena need not be gone into. The magnitudes of these apparent tensions have been quantitatively investigated with sufficient accuracy to allow certain important surface effects in soil mechanics to be analyzed on a rational basis.

8·2 The Basic Relationship between Curvature and Pressure Difference

If a curved surface of thin flexible material of any kind is under tension, equilibrium requires that there must be different pressures in the media just within and just outside of the surface. This requirement must hold for balloons, for sails, and for flexible pipe, as well as for liquid surfaces, and the basic relationship between the radius of curvature, the pressure difference, and the tension may easily be obtained.

Let Fig. 8·1 represent a cross section of any curved surface, on the two sides of which different pressures act. First, let it be assumed that this figure represents a typical cross section of the surface of a circular cylinder of radius R_1, and consider only the portion of the surface which extends a unit of distance normal to the section.

On any small area of the surface, designated by ΔL_a, the forces are $p\Delta L_a$ on the outside and $(p + p_e)\Delta L_a$ on the inside, their

137

combination giving $p_e \Delta L_a$ acting outward. When such forces are summed over the entire arc, it is seen that components parallel to the chord will balance each other, whereas components normal to the chord will equal $p_e \Delta L_c$ and will sum to give a resultant force of $p_e 2R_1 \sin \theta$. For equilibrium, this force must be balanced by the downward components of the tensions T_s; thus

$$2T_s \sin \theta = p_e 2R_1 \sin \theta$$

and for this surface of *single curvature* of radius R_1

$$p_e = \frac{T_s}{R_1} \tag{8·1}$$

Since p_e is a pressure and R_1 is a distance, T_s is a force per unit of length.

Consider next the case of a curved surface which in addition has curvature normal to the section of Fig. 8·1. Equation 8·1

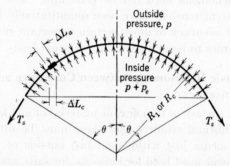

Fig. 8·1 Cross section used in the derivation of relationships between pressure difference, surface curvature, and surface tension.

may still be accepted as expressing the relationship between curvature and end forces for a portion of the surface extending a small distance in the third direction normal to the section. However, a cross section in this third direction would show end forces capable of carrying an additional pressure excess which may be expressed by a similar equation. The total pressure excess for this case of *double curvature* may be obtained by adding the two components, and

$$p_e = T_s \left(\frac{1}{R_1} + \frac{1}{R_2} \right) \tag{8·2}$$

where R_1 and R_2 are radii of curvature in coordinate directions.

When the radius of curvature, designated by R_c, is the same in all directions, the case is called uniform curvature and the above equation becomes

$$p_e = \frac{2T_s}{R_c} \tag{8·3}$$

8·3   Rise of Water in Capillary Tubes

A good illustration of the fundamental relationship demonstrated in the preceding section is given by water in small capillary tubes.

The phenomenon known as capillarity results from a combination of the surface tension of a liquid and the tendency of some liquids to wet surfaces with which they come into contact; this wetting causes a curvature of the liquid surface, as shown in Fig. 8·2. The surface of a liquid meets that of the solid at a definite angle, known as the contact angle. Pure water meets clean glass at a contact angle of zero and a meniscus such as shown in the figure results. The water rises by capillarity to the height h_c. Within a tube of small diameter, when the contact angle is zero, the curvature of the meniscus is equal to the radius of the tube, and the amount of capillary rise may be determined by the following use of the fundamental relationship of the previous section.

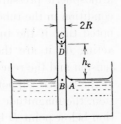

Fig. 8·2   Capillary rise.

At points A and C there is atmospheric pressure. Furthermore, since point B is at the same level as A its pressure is atmospheric. Since point D is higher than point B by the head h_c, the pressure at D must be less than atmospheric by the amount $h_c\gamma_w$. Since the surface curvature is R and the pressure difference is $h_c\gamma_w$, it follows from equation 8·3 that

$$h_c = \frac{2T_s}{\gamma_w R} \tag{8·4}$$

The surface tension is different in different liquids, and in any one liquid it decreases with increasing temperature. A rough value for water at ordinary temperatures is 75 dynes per cm. The capillary rise in a tube of 1-mm diameter would be

$$\frac{2 \times \frac{75}{980}}{1 \times \frac{1}{2} \times 0.1} = 3 \text{ cm}$$

and a tube of 0.1-mm diameter would have a rise of 30 cm.

The above relationship may be obtained very simply by another method. If the water column BC is imagined to be isolated from the surrounding tube, it may be noted that the weight of the water column, equal to $\gamma_w h_c \pi R^2$ must be carried by the surface tension acting over the circumference of the tube, equal to $2\pi R T_s$. Equating these two expressions again leads to equation 8·4.

In the liquid the stress just below the meniscus, referred to atmospheric pressure as a basis, is a tension of $\gamma_w h_c$. The stress condition in the tube is also of interest. From Fig. 8·2 it may be noted that if the tube is assumed weightless the vertical forces acting on it are the downward weight applied by the surface tension and the reaction at the point where the tube is supported. If the tube is supported at its base, its walls are under compression, the magnitude of the total compressive force at any elevation below point D being $\gamma_w h_c \pi R^2$.

It is also evident that the height h_c represents a definite amount of potential energy. When the end of a capillary tube is placed in water a certain definite amount of work is done to lift water against gravity through a height h_c. The energy utilized in the performance of this work is the surface energy of the meniscus.

8·4 Considerations in Capillary Tubes of Variable Radius

If a capillary tube of constant radius is placed in water, there will be rise of water within it to a height h_c. If the tube is completely filled, by being lowered under water, and then raised, the meniscus will again come to rest at a height h_c above free water surface, as long as pure water and a clean tube are used. However, if the tube is of irregular cross section, the amount of rise cannot be expressed so simply.

In Fig. 8·3, tube (a) is of constant radius R_1, and the amount of capillary rise h_{c1} is definite. In tube (b), rise can take place only to the top of the tube and thus the pressure difference at the meniscus can only be about two thirds of that for tube (a). Equation 8·3 must hold, however, and thus the meniscus must

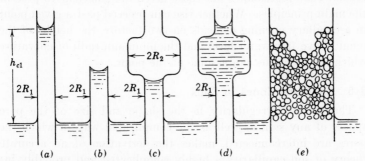

FIG. 8·3 Capillary rise in tubes of constant and variable cross section.

assume a radius larger than the radius of the tube, whereas the surface tension, instead of acting parallel to the tube's surface, will act at an angle giving a vertical component just sufficient to support the capillary column.

If the tube is not of constant cross section, capillary rises such as are shown in (c) and (d) are possible. The column cannot rise past the center of the bulb, where the radius is R_2, unless the height at this point is less than the capillary rise corresponding to radius R_2. In (c) the rise, therefore, is barely above the base of the bulb. However, if the bulb is filled by being lowered below water surface, then raised while filled, and if the water is allowed to run out until the equilibrium condition is reached, a rise of height h_{c1} results as shown in (d). It may be noted that the capillary column held in place by surface tension is the same in (a) and (d); in (d) the water between this column and the bulb is supported by the bulb.

At (e) the large tube extending to height h_c is filled with soil particles, and all passageways between particles are small. At the surface all such passageways are much smaller than $2R_1$ except for one gap at the center where a large opening exists. As shown by the figure, capillary rise for this case would fill all but the one large opening. The pressure difference, at any point on any meniscus, is equal to or slightly less than $\gamma_w h_{c1}$ for this case, and the curvature must be in agreement with equation 8·2.

Additional examples might be given of the rise in tubes of irregular sizes and shapes but those given are sufficient to present the main principles. Whether rise can proceed past a given point in a capillary opening depends on two factors, the height of the point above free water level and the minimum radii of curvature which the meniscus can assume at the point.

8·5 Capillary Zones in Soils

The marked irregularity in the shape and size of the pore spaces of any soil, as well as the complicated way in which the pores are interconnected, makes the derivation of an accurate theory of soil capillarity a highly complicated and probably insolvable problem. However, useful qualitative deductions may be drawn from the elementary cases outlined in the previous section.

If a soil in the state of a dry powder is brought into contact with water, the water will at once tend to be drawn into the voids by capillary action. The velocity at which the sample is wetted by capillary flow is dependent on varying pore dimensions, yet to the observer this velocity often is quite steady. However, the interconnected pore openings vary greatly in size, and the velocity at which water first reaches any individual point within any individual pore depends greatly on the pore area at the point. The larger pores do not fill so readily as the smaller pores, and water may completely surround and trap air within a large pore.

Thus, even at small heights above free water surface the degree of saturation caused by capillary rise is considerably below 100 per cent, and with increasing height this quantity tends to become increasingly smaller. Finally, there is a limiting height above which no water can be drawn by capillarity. For an appreciable height above the free water surface, however, the degree of saturation attained is relatively large, whereas the zone immediately above free water surface is commonly, but questionably, spoken of as essentially saturated.

The height of the zone containing capillary water is still more indefinite in a mass that has formerly been saturated and, after a lowering of the water table, partially drained. In such a case water is retained in many pores that would not be filled by capillary rise, much as in Fig. 8·3 (*d*) water is retained in the bulb but in (*c*) the bulb does not fill. Thus, high percentages of saturation are common in fine sands and silts at heights above free water that are considerably greater than could be similarly saturated by capillary rise.

Furthermore, capillary water in a form known as *contact moisture* will be present in considerable amounts in fine soils. At points where grains touch or nearly touch, rain water or other surface water percolating down through the soil has a chance to collect as shown in Fig. 8·4. A

Fig. 8·4 Contact capillary water.

small amount of water surrounding a contact point forms a meniscus, and surface tension may hold this water in place indefinitely. If near ground surface, evaporation may eventually remove this water, but evaporation occurs to a very limited degree at appreciable depths below the surface. The magnitude of the tension in contact water does not depend on the elevation relative to the free water surface.

Much has been said about the capillary fringe which exists above the water table in soils. However, a much truer picture of capillary water is given by a three-zone conception suggested by Terzaghi. These three zones are the zones of capillary saturation, partial capillary saturation, and contact moisture. In the so-called zone of capillary saturation, the degree of saturation is well below 100 per cent. The height of this zone depends on the water table history; the zone extends to a greater height if the mass has previously been saturated. The zone of partial capillary saturation extends, with a decreasing degree of saturation, from the top of the zone of capillary saturation to a height above free water surface that varies inversely as some representative pore size. The height of the zone and the degree of saturation at any point in it are also greater if the water table has previously been at a higher elevation. The water in this zone is connected, whereas the air voids may be or they may not be connected. The zone of contact moisture extends upward from the top of the zone of partial saturation, generally to, or nearly to, ground surface. The water in this zone consists of relatively small unconnected masses, but fairly large values of water content are possible, especially in fine soils.

8·6 Capillary Pressures in Soil

All water within the capillary zones in soil is under tension; in other words its pressure is less than atmospheric pressure. At all points where menisci touch soil grains capillary forces act, causing a grain-to-grain pressure within the soil, much as the capillary tube was in compression in Fig. 8·2. Intergranular pressure of this type is called capillary pressure. Wherever capillary water exists, the occurrence of capillary pressures within the soil is inevitable.

The force across any unit of area within a soil mass, as explained in Section 7·3, is made up of intergranular pressure and water pressure. The combined pressure may be expressed

$$\sigma_t = \bar{\sigma} + u_w \tag{8·5}$$

where σ_t is the combined pressure, $\bar{\sigma}$ is the normal component of the intergranular pressure $\bar{p}$, and u_w is the water pressure. At all points where the stress in the water is negative, the intergranular pressure must be of greater magnitude than the combined pressure; the amount by which it is greater is numerically equal to the tension in the water. The capillary pressure is caused by the pull of menisci on soil grains; thus it is an intergranular pressure, but it depends directly in magnitude on the tension in the pore water adjacent to the menisci. Capillary pressures lead to greater strength, since the strength characteristics of the soil depend directly on the intergranular pressure.

Capillary pressures, and the shearing strengths they cause in find sands, may be of appreciable magnitude. The good driving conditions on the automobile race course at Daytona Beach, Florida, are reported to result from such pressures. In clays the magnitudes of capillary pressures which can occur are very large.

In order to obtain concepts of possible magnitudes of capillary pressures in clays, let it be assumed for this discussion that water is capable of carrying an unlimited amount of tension. Clays of high colloidal content have a large fraction of grains finer than 0.5 micron, and the general dimensions of openings between adjacent grains are likely to be somewhat smaller than the particle sizes. Therefore, pore spaces with dimensions of the order of 0.2 micron, allowing radii of curvature of the order of 0.1 micron, are entirely reasonable in such soils. Assuming uniform curvature, a radius of curvature of 0.1 micron corresponds, according to equation 8·3, to a capillary pressure of

$$\frac{2T_s}{R_c} = \frac{2 \times \frac{75}{980}}{10^{-5}} = 15,000 \text{ grams per sq cm}$$

In the small clay sample discussed in connection with the descriptions of the Atterberg limits in Chapter 4, no externally applied pressure is acting while the sample is pictured as gradually drying out; thus the combined pressure, σ_t of equation 8·5, is zero. The cause of the compression and the increasing stiffness as the sample gradually dries is the increasing capillary pressure. Therefore, it may be noted that the capillary pressure for the clay considered in the above example is equal to 15 kg per sq cm when the shrinkage limit is reached.

Since σ_t equals zero, the pore water must, according to equation 8·5, be under a tension of 15 kg per sq cm. It is known that in order to compress this same clay to the void ratio occurring at the shrinkage limit by a direct application of pressure in a laboratory loading device, the pressure required would be of the order of magnitude of 15 kg per sq cm. When the compression is caused by capillary pressures, whether 15 kg per sq cm of tension in the water is possible may well be questioned. Ordinary water can carry only 1 kg per sq cm of tension, but in fine capillaries it is known that somewhat larger tensions are possible; and in capillaries with dimensions of less than a micron the properties of water may easily differ from those in ordinary water. Since the action under capillary pressure is essentially the same as it would be with the water able to carry unlimited tension, it makes little difference to the engineer whether the water is truly under this tension or an analogous action occurs instead, a portion of the tension being contributed perhaps by forces of some kind in the zone of adsorbed molecules adjacent to grain-to-grain contacts. Thus, the possibility is recognized that the concept of water carrying very high tensions may be an analogy, just as the concept of surface tension is an analogy.

When a clay sample is taken from a bore hole by undisturbed sampling methods the stress in the pore water is changed from pressure to tension. Assume, for example, that before sampling a specimen has an intergranular pressure of 1.5 kg per sq cm, a neutral pressure of 1.0 kg per sq cm, and a combined pressure of 2.5 kg per sq cm. After the sample has been removed there no longer is overburden pressure on it, and therefore the soil tends to expand; this tendency develops capillary menisci at the surface of the sample, and expansion is prevented by the ensuing capillary pressure. After the sample is removed its combined pressure has become zero, but the intergranular pressure, if it is assumed that no appreciable disturbance has occurred, remains nearly as large as 1.5 kg per sq cm because the void ratio is essentially unchanged. Thus the neutral stress must be a tension of nearly 1.5 kg per sq cm.

8·7 Rate of Horizontal Capillary Saturation; The Capillarity-Permeability Test

Assume that a soil sample has been brought to a state of dry powder, has been thoroughly mixed, and then has been packed into a glass tube having a screen over one end and a vented stopper in the other, as shown in Fig. 8·5. If the tube is now immersed in a shallow depth of water in a horizontal position, the water proceeds into the interior of the soil by capillary action. The distance of saturation may be expressed as a function of time.

The capillary energy utilized in drawing the water through the soil is dependent on the surface energy of the menisci in the voids. If the sample has been placed in the tube with proper care, the void distribution will, by the law of probability, be uniform throughout. It is known from laboratory investigations that, while saturation of this type proceeds, the menisci are developed essentially to the maximum curvature possible for the void sizes existing within the sample. Corresponding to this curvature is the capillary head h_c, which under the conditions existing in this test is a constant for a given soil at a given void ratio. If the pressure is atmospheric in the air voids just ahead of the menisci, then the pressure on the other side of the menisci in the water at all times is $-\gamma_w h_c$.

Let the area of the tube be A, and the porosity of the sample n. If the line of saturation has proceeded a distance x, the head used in forcing the water through the sample is expended in dis-

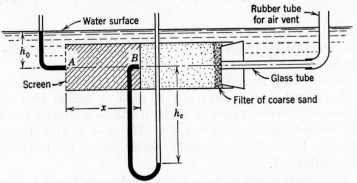

Fig. 8·5 Diagrammatic view of apparatus used for the capillarity-permeability test, showing the standpipe concept.

tance x. The magnitude of head expended may be determined by the use of concepts explained in Section 7·4.

At point A the elevation head is $-h_0$, the pressure head is $+h_0$, and the total head is zero. At point B the elevation head is $-h_0$, the pressure head is $-h_c$, and the total head is $-(h_0 + h_c)$. Therefore the head lost in passing from A to B is $h_0 + h_c$. If standpipes could be inserted at points A and B water would stand at the elevations shown in the tubes in the figure, and these elevations would differ by $h_0 + h_c$.

The head h_0 is the average depth of submergence. If a fine-grained sample is placed a small distance below water surface, h_0 may be negligible. When h_0 is relatively large, it may be made to be the true average depth for all points of the sample by slowly revolving the tube about its axis as saturation progresses; otherwise h_0 varies at different points and the head loss is greater at the bottom than it is at the top of the sample.

The conditions prevailing for any value of x are given by Darcy's Law, which, if complete saturation * is assumed, may be written

$$nv_s = ki$$

or

$$n \frac{dx}{dt} = k \frac{h_c + h_0}{x} \qquad (8 \cdot 6)$$

whence

$$\frac{x_2{}^2 - x_1{}^2}{t_2 - t_1} = \frac{2k}{n} (h_c + h_0) \qquad (8 \cdot 7)$$

Equation $8 \cdot 7$ shows that a parabolic relationship exists between the saturated length and the time. It may be noted that t need not be zero when x is zero, although it frequently may be.

As saturation progresses in an actual test of this type, observation of values of x and t may be made at regular intervals. A plot of x^2 versus t may be made; it will be a straight line if the parabolic relationship is valid. The slope of this straight line may be measured to furnish a value for the left-hand side of equation $8 \cdot 7$.

This equation still contains the two unknowns k and h_c after the left-hand side is evaluated. However, a second equation containing the same two unknowns may be obtained as follows. The first stage of the test may be concluded when the sample is about one-half saturated. The sample may then be subjected to a much larger value of h_0 and a second stage conducted. This large h_0 value is best imposed by clamping a head water tube to the left end of the sample tube. The results of the two stages allow a solution for k and h_c.

This two-stage test is known as the capillarity-permeability test. It may have value as a control test in earth dam construction. Its main disadvantage is that the soil must be placed dry, and in dry state the greatest density obtainable is generally much less than that required in an actual dam.

* If saturation is not complete the left-hand side of the equation should read Snv_s. Complete saturation is assumed here although recent investigations indicate that this assumption usually involves a considerable sacrifice of accuracy.

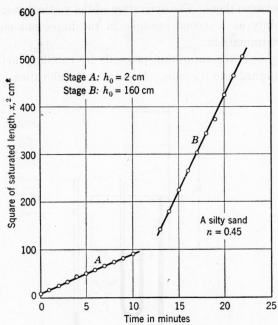

FIG. 8·6   Plot of capillarity-permeability test.

The plot of the data of a typical capillarity-permeability test is shown in Fig. 8·6. Equation 8·7 for each of the branches of this test gives

$$\frac{91 - 9}{10 \times 60} = \frac{2k}{0.45}(h_c + 2)$$

and

$$\frac{480 - 157}{(21.5 - 13.5)60} = \frac{2k}{0.45}(h_c + 160)$$

whence

$$h_c = 38 \text{ cm}$$

and

$$k = 7.6 \times 10^{-4} \text{ cm per sec}$$

8·8   Rate of Vertical Capillary Saturation

The test described in Section 8·7 is generally preferred to a vertical capillarity test in practical testing, although there is little

choice between them. The derivation of the vertical case is given
here mainly as a second example in the important subject of
head determinations.

In Fig. 8·7, the saturation proceeds by capillary action vertically upward into the tube. At point A the elevation and pres-

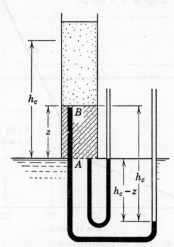

Fig. 8·7   The standpipe concept
in vertical, capillary flow.

sure heads are both zero; at B the elevation head is z, and the
pressure head is $-h_c$. Thus the gradient is $(h_c - z)/z$. The
differential equation for speed of saturation, of the same form
as equation 8·6, is

$$n \frac{dz}{dt} = k \frac{h_c - z}{z} \qquad (8 \cdot 8)$$

If the value of z is zero when t is zero, and if it is assumed that h_c
and k are constants, the solution of equation 8·8 is

$$t = \frac{nh_c}{k} \left[-\ln\left(1 - \frac{z}{h_c}\right) - \frac{z}{h_c} \right] \qquad (8 \cdot 9)$$

The values of the rise z in this type of test must now be considered in relation to the heights of the various zones of the
capillary fringe, discussed in Section 8·5. As soon as z becomes

larger than the height of the bottom of the zone of partial capillary saturation the increasing air content leads to variations in both h_c and k. The permeability decreases and eventually becomes so small that tests run to determine the height of the zone of partial capillary saturation require periods of time extending into months or years. The height to the top of the zone of partial saturation bears little relationship to the constant capillary head h_c, since the former depends on dimensions of the smaller pores and the latter acts only when there is a maximum degree of saturation and depends on dimensions of the larger pores.

From laboratory tests it has been found that as long as z is less than about 20 per cent of h_c saturation is relatively high and h_c and k are essentially constant.

8·9 General Relationships

Expressions which have been derived for permeability, capillary rise, and speed of capillary saturation furnish a number of approximate relationships between the grain size and the various soil properties which have been discussed.

For a given soil, let D_1 be some given per cent size, the 10 per cent size, for example. Let it be assumed that a second, coarser soil has a grain-size distribution curve of similar shape and slope and that its corresponding per cent size is D_2. In the following considerations it is assumed that the properties of the two soils, including density, structure, temperature, and degree of saturation, are similar. For various corresponding properties of the two soils, subscripts 1 and 2 are used.

It has already been explained in Section 6·10 that the following approximate relationship exists between permeabilities:

$$k_1:k_2 = D_1{}^2:D_2{}^2 \qquad (8·10)$$

The capillary heads and the heights of the various zones of the capillary fringe, according to equation 8·4, are approximately in the relationship:

$$h_{c1}:h_{c2} = D_2:D_1 \qquad (8·11)$$

If all other heads are small compared to the capillary head, then in capillary tests of either of the types outlined in Sections 8·7 and 8·8 the speeds at which saturations progress at any given saturated length are, according to equations 8·6 and 8·8, in the approximate relationship:

$$v_1 : v_2 = k_1 h_{c1} : k_2 h_{c2} = D_1 : D_2 \qquad (8 \cdot 12)$$

The times required for tests on a given length of sample are shown by equation 8·7 to be in the following approximate relationship:

$$t_1 : t_2 = k_2 h_{c2} : k_1 h_{c1} = D_2 : D_1 \qquad (8 \cdot 13)$$

The same relationship holds for vertical tests, and to demonstrate that this is true equation 8·9 may be expanded into series form.

In vertical capillarity tests carried on until the heights reached are some given percentage of the capillary head, the times required, according to equation 8·9, are in the approximate relationship:

$$t_1 : t_2 = \frac{h_{c1}}{k_1} : \frac{h_{c2}}{k_2} = D_2{}^3 : D_1{}^3 \qquad (8 \cdot 14)$$

8·10 The Approximate Relationship between the Permeability and the Capillary Head

By a comparison of flow and capillarity relationships for capillary tubes and soil capillaries, an approximate relationship between the permeability and the capillary head of a soil may be obtained.

If a round capillary tube, open at one end and vented to the atmosphere at the other, is placed just below water in a horizontal position, the water will be drawn through the tube by capillarity in a manner analogous to that indicated for the soil sample of Fig. 8·5. A brief consideration of the mechanics of the action will show that a straight line relationship between x^2 and t as derived for the soil must also hold for the tube.

The velocity of flow through a circular tube is given by equation 6·11. For a capillary tube the gradient is h_r/x, where h_r is the capillary head and x is as defined for the horizontal capillary test for soil. The relationship between capillary head and radius, given by equation 8·4, may be used to eliminate the radius. The following expression for the velocity of flow through a capillary tube under its capillary head h_r will result:

$$v = \frac{T_s{}^2}{2\gamma_w \mu h_r x} \qquad (8 \cdot 15)$$

For any given soil, the velocity of horizontal capillary travel, from equation 8·6 with h_0 assumed negligible, is

$$\frac{dx}{dt} = \frac{kh_c}{nx} \qquad (8·16)$$

There must be some size of capillary tube which would show the same speed of capillary progress as shown by a given soil, and this size of tube may be determined by equating the right-hand sides of equations 8·15 and 8·16. Because of the irregular nature of soil capillaries, the capillary heads for this tube and this soil cannot be expected to be alike. Laboratory investigations, in which tests similar in principle to the capillarity-permeability test described in Section 8·7 are employed, usually show, however, that for a given soil type h_r is roughly a constant multiple of h_c. Therefore, in the expression

$$h_r = Bh_c \qquad (8·17)$$

the coefficient B may be expected to be approximately constant for a given soil type.

Equating the right-hand sides of equations 8·15 and 8·16 and eliminating h_r by the use of equation 8·17 gives

$$k = \frac{T_s{}^2}{2\mu\gamma_w} \frac{n}{Bh_c{}^2} \qquad (8·18)$$

The first term in this expression for permeability consists of water properties only, and at 20°C in pure water this term has a value of 290 cc per sec. The coefficient B varies considerably for different types of soils, and it varies somewhat in a given soil at different porosities, but in general its value falls between 20 and 300. Values of B/n appear to have a slightly smaller relative range than B, varying from about 50 to 600. In the test of Fig. 8·7, the values of B and B/n are 118 and 262, respectively.

On the basis of these numerical values, equation 8·18 furnishes the following expression:

$$\frac{0.7}{\sqrt{k}} < h_c < \frac{2.4}{\sqrt{k}} \qquad (8·19)$$

where the units are in centimeters and seconds.

As an example, a soil having a permeability of 4 microns per sec has a capillary head which is probably between 35 and 120 cm.

After a number of capillarity-permeability tests of the type described in Section 8·7 have been run on samples of a given soil type, the range of the numerical values corresponding to those in expression 8·19 may be determined, and it usually will be relatively small as compared to the range here quoted.

If the range in numerical values is found to be small for a given soil type, an average numerical value may be used to give an equation which may be used in place of expression 8·19; this equation may then be used, if desired, in place of one of the two stages of the horizontal capillarity test explained in Section 8·7.

PROBLEMS

1. On the basis of the assumptions that double curvature exists and that the effective size of pore openings with reference to capillary behavior is a constant C times the grain size for any uniform soil at any given void ratio, determine capillary head ranges, expressed as multiples of some function of C, for the various M.I.T. grain-size classes.

2. *Capillarity-permeability test.* Given the following data for a soil sample subjected to a capillarity-permeability test and a falling head permeability test in the same container. Determine the coefficient of permeability by each method and for assumptions of both 100 per cent and 85 per cent saturation; also determine the capillary head.

Sample Data		Falling Head Test Data	
Length of sample	21.0 cm	Area of standpipe	0.1175 cm²
Diameter of sample	4.20 cm	Initial head	42.85 cm
Specific gravity	2.68	Final head	27.5 cm
Dry weight of sample	305.7 grams	Time required for	
Temperature	20 °C	drop (average of	
Degree of saturation	85% (approx)	3 runs)	2 min, 22 sec

Horizontal Capillarity Test Data

First Stage Depth of submergence, $h_0 = 3.5$ cm			Second Stage $h_0 = 109.0$ cm		
Wetted distance, cm	Time		Wetted distance, cm	Time	
	Min	Sec		Min	Sec
0	0	0	11	10	11
1	0	9	12	11	03
2	0	26	13	12	04
3	1	23	14	13	11
4	2	03	15	14	26
5	3	17	16	15	28
6	4	22	17	16	48
7	5	38	18	18	25
8	7	02	19	20	02
9	8	49	20	21	38
10	9	54	21	23	38

3. Compare the theoretical rates of horizontal and vertical capillary travel by plotting for each the curve of time versus capillary travel for a sample having a permeability of 2.3×10^{-4} cm per sec, a porosity of 0.43, and a capillary head of 145 cm. Consider the center line of the horizontal sample and the bottom of the vertical sample to be negligible distances below the surface of the water in which they are submerged. Make the plot for a period of one day.

Chapter 9

SEEPAGE

9·1 Flow Nets

The use of the graphical representation of flow through soil which is known as the flow net is of great assistance in numerous types of engineering problems. From the flow net, information may be obtained on such important items as the amount of seepage or leakage below a dam, the uplift pressure caused by the water on the base of a concrete dam, and the possibility of danger of a quick or liquefaction condition at points where seepage water comes to the ground surface.

The path which a particle of water follows in its course of seepage through a saturated soil mass is called a *flow line*. Examples of flow lines are the smooth, solid, curved lines passing below the sheet pile wall shown in cross section in Fig. 9·1. These lines may be determined in a number of ways; on models of such sections constructed between glass plates, for example, flow lines may readily be found by injecting small amounts of dye and observing the paths followed.

Each flow line starts at some point on line AB where it has a pressure head h_t, and after gradually dissipating this head in viscous friction, terminates at the line CD where the head is zero. Along each flow line there must be a point where the water has dissipated any given specific portion of its potential. A line connecting all such points of equal head is called an equipotential line. The dashed line running from point R to the impervious wall is the equipotential line along which the head equals $\frac{2}{3}h_t$.

It is evident that unlimited numbers of flow lines and equipotential lines exist. Flow nets consist of a collection or nest of flow lines intersecting a nest of equipotential lines. Of the unlimited number of each type of lines to choose from, the ones

156

chosen are those giving the general picture in most convenient form, as explained later.

Since the gradient in passing from one equipotential to another equals the potential drop divided by the distance traversed, it is evident that the gradients are maximum along paths normal to equipotentials. In isotropic soil, flow must follow paths of greatest gradient, much as bodies rolling or sliding down hill tend to pick the steepest path. Therefore flow lines must cross equipotentials at right angles. This is seen to be the case at all crossings in Fig. 9·1.

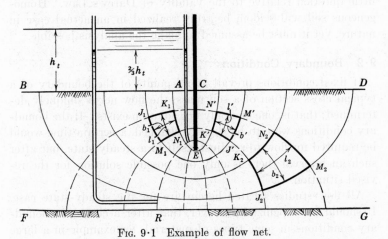

Fig. 9·1 Example of flow net.

A section of the type illustrated by this figure usually represents a typical cross section of a long wall. All flow lines in such a case are parallel to the plane of the figure, and the condition is known as two-dimensional flow. All cases considered in this chapter are two-dimensional. In general, flow of water through earth masses is three-dimensional, but this condition is too complicated for practical analysis and the fundamentals of flow can best be shown by using the simple two-dimensional case. It should be evident, however, that in no actual embankment will seepage be truly restricted to two-dimensional flow, and a point which must not be overlooked is the probable existence, at abutments for example, of more adverse conditions of seepage than those which occur in the idealized assumed section.

There are two types of two-dimensional flow. In the typical cross-section type, as illustrated by Fig. 9·1, the section shown is the same as all sections parallel to it. This is the type to which the major portion of the considerations of this chapter apply. In the second type, which is illustrated by flow into a well, all vertical sections through the center line of the well are alike, and a typical radial section is used. This type is called the radial flow net.

Two assumptions made in seepage analyses are that Darcy's Law is valid and that the soil is homogeneous. There can be little question relative to the validity of Darcy's Law. Homogeneous soil will seldom be truly realized in an actual case in nature, yet it must be assumed to make the analysis possible.

9·2 Boundary Conditions

If fixed conditions prevail at all points of the boundary of a typical cross section of a soil mass, the flow net is uniquely determined; that is, one and only one solution exists. If the boundary conditions were to be slightly changed, a certain time would be required for flow to readjust itself to a steady state, but after such an interval there is only one possible solution for the revised situation.

All flow studies treated herein are for the steady-state case. It should be recognized, however, that after a change in boundary conditions in some types of material, for example in a large mass of highly impervious and very compressible soil, a long interval of time may elapse before a steady state is attained.

The expression of the boundary conditions consists of statements of head or flow conditions at all boundary points. Such conditions for the case illustrated in Fig. 9·1 are completely defined by the four following statements.

1. Line AB, including its prolongation to the left as far as the section extends, is an equipotential line along which the head equals h_t.

2. From point A, which touches the piling at the surface of the soil, a line following the impervious surface of the pile down one side to E and thence up on the other side to C is a flow line.

3. Line CD, including its prolongation to the right, is an equipotential line along which the head equals zero.

4. The line FG, including its extensions to both right and left, is a flow line.

The expressions of boundary conditions are frequently, though not always, four in number. However, cases are often encountered in which some boundaries are neither equipotential nor flow lines. In addition, the flow boundaries are not always so clearly defined as in Fig. 9·1. For example, in Fig. 9·8 the bottom flow line is the impervious ledge surface ED but the top flow line seeks its own path according to certain fundamental laws. The head is the same at all points on the upstream slope since greater elevation heads near B are balanced by greater pressure heads near E; thus BE is the equipotential line along which the head equals h_t. Explanation of the complicated upper and downstream boundaries for this case are given later.

The head at any point in the soil mass is designated by h, and in general it will consist of a combination of pressure head and elevation head. The tail water elevation, illustrated by line CD of Fig. 9·1, is commonly adopted as the datum for elevation heads. The concept that the head at a given point is shown by the height to which water would rise in a standpipe inserted at the point was developed in Section 7·4; it will be very valuable in flow net studies. If standpipes were to be inserted at a number of different points on a given equipotential line, they all would show water rising to the same elevation. This is illustrated by the two standpipes shown in Fig. 9·1.

9·3 "Square" Figures

Figure 9·1 shows that the figures formed by adjacent pairs of flow and equipotential lines, figure $J_1K_1M_1N_1$ for example, resemble squares. All four corners of each such figure form right angles and the mean distances between opposite faces are alike. Although this does not constitute a square according to the strict meaning of the word, it may be noted that if such a figure is subdivided into four figures and then is further subdivided, there is an approach toward true squares. Thus the use of a very large number of closely spaced lines would truly give squares, and in flow net analysis the term square figures has come into common use for figures of the sizes commonly used.

The significance behind the use of square figures is very important, and it will now be demonstrated.

For use in cases of two-dimensional flow, Darcy's Law may be written

$$\frac{Q}{y} = ki\frac{A}{y}$$

where y is the dimension of the soil mass in the direction normal to the section. Designating Q/y by q and A/y by b, and defining q as the discharge per running foot (that is, per foot normal to the section) and b as the trace of the area gives the form

$$q = kib \qquad (9 \cdot 1)$$

This equation may be used to express the discharge through any figure of a flow net. To investigate relationships which must result if all figures are squares, a comparison of expressions for any two figures is used. The figures $J_1K_1M_1N_1$ and $J_2K_2M_2N_2$ are arbitrarily chosen as any two figures of the net, and $J'K'M'N'$, which is bounded by the same flow lines as the first figure and by the same equipotential lines as the second figure, is used as an auxiliary figure. Darcy's Law for the discharge through any figure may be written

$$\Delta q = kib = k\frac{\Delta h}{l}b = k\,\Delta h\,\frac{b}{l}$$

where Δh represents the head loss in crossing the figure, and dimensions b and l are illustrated in Fig. $9\cdot 1$. The expressions in this form for each of the three figures under consideration are

$$\Delta q_1 = k\,\Delta h_1\,\frac{b_1}{l_1}$$

$$\Delta q' = k\,\Delta h'\,\frac{b'}{l'} \qquad (9 \cdot 2)$$

$$\Delta q_2 = k\,\Delta h_2\,\frac{b_2}{l_2}$$

The value of k is the same for all figures and, since the three figures which are being analyzed are squares, the ratios b_1/l_1, b'/l' and

b_2/l_2 are all equal to unity. Since the auxiliary square has the same flow line boundaries as the first square, $\Delta q'$ equals Δq_1. Since it has the same equipotential boundaries as the second square, $\Delta h'$ equals Δh_2. The insertion of these equalities into equations 9·2 furnishes the following relationships:

$$\Delta q_1 = \Delta q_2 \quad \text{and} \quad \Delta h_1 = \Delta h_2 \qquad (9\cdot3)$$

Thus it is seen that when all figures are squares there must be the same quantity of flow through each figure and the same head drop in crossing each figure. It follows that flows between adjacent pairs of flow lines are alike throughout and potential differences between successive equipotential lines are alike throughout.

Conversely it may easily be seen by inspection of equations 9·2 that, in order to have the same flow through each flow path and the same drops between successive equipotentials, all figures must have the same b/l ratio, but it is not necessary that the value of the ratio be unity. In flow net analyses, however, square figures are far more convenient than rectangular figures, and therefore they are almost always used.

The relative sizes of squares at various points of flow net offer complete information on relative gradients at the various points. Since the gradient in each figure is represented by $\Delta h/l$, and since Δh values are alike for all figures, the gradients vary inversely as l. Thus the gradient is large where squares are small, and vice versa.

9·4 Graphical Determination of Flow Nets

For cross sections with boundary conditions that are completely defined, the commonest procedure for obtaining flow nets is a graphical, trial-sketching method, sometimes called the Forchheimer Solution (58).

The graphical method is in general the quickest, the most practical, as well as the most commonly used of all methods available for the determination of flow nets. It requires little equipment and it gives the investigator valuable understanding or feel for the flow pattern and the way in which the pattern would change were the boundaries to be revised slightly. Other methods are frequently considered valuable primarily because they may be used as checks on the graphical method.

To become proficient in flow net sketching both practice and a natural aptitude for this type of method are required. However, reasonably good nets are obtainable after a relatively small amount of practice. The only requirements are adherence to the boundary conditions and the use of square figures.

A. Casagrande (26) * presented the first thorough treatment of the seepage problem in English literature. Casagrande's paper, which is a valuable reference on the subject, includes the following items in a list of suggestions for the beginner in flow net sketching:

Use every opportunity to study the appearance of well-constructed flow nets; when the picture is sufficiently absorbed in your mind, try to draw the same flow net without looking at the available solution; repeat this until you are able to sketch this flow net in a satisfactory manner.

Four or five flow channels are usually sufficient for the first attempts; the use of too many flow channels may distract the attention from the essential features.

Always watch the appearance of the entire flow net. Do not try to adjust details before the entire flow net is approximately correct.

The beginner usually makes the mistake of drawing too sharp transitions between straight and curved sections of flow lines or equipotential lines. Keep in mind that all transitions are smooth; of elliptical or parabolic shape. The size of the squares in each channel will change gradually.

These suggestions are very helpful, but they cannot be classified as complete instructions. A somewhat different type of procedure and one with more explicit instructions has been set up by the author and is outlined below. It is called the *procedure by explicit trials*. This procedure has been found to be of considerable value to the beginner in flow net sketching, and it also has value in developing an intuition for flow net characteristics. It should be followed meticulously until the principles on which it is based are well understood. Later the results it gives can be anticipated without carrying the trials to completion, and much

* For other early publications on this subject see references 58 and 44

time can be saved by considering the net as a whole and in other ways adhering to the suggestions given above. The explicit trial procedure should not be considered valuable only to the beginner, since it has other important uses. Whenever results by random trials or adjustments are not satisfactory or are not being obtained as fast as desired, the explicit trial system is likely to be found helpful. When an especially accurate net is desired, the final sketch can be checked to advantage by the use of the explicit trial method. In very complex nets on non-homogeneous sections random trials may lead to much confusion which explicit trials may relieve.

As the first step in the explicit trial method, one trial flow line or one trial equipotential line is sketched in adjacent to a boundary flow line or boundary equipotential. This sketched line is definitely a trial line, and by the novice its location must largely be chosen by guess. The experienced sketcher will of course be able to make a better first estimate of the proper position for such a line. Once this first trial line has been drawn, no further guesses enter until it is known whether or not the trial line is correct.

The heavy line in Fig. 9·2 (a) is a trial line. It is seen to be in agreement with the boundary conditions, since it meets the head water and tail water equipotential lines at right angles. Once this first line has been chosen, the procedure to be followed consists of a gradual expansion by sketching, adhering rigorously to square figures, working from square to square, and paying little or no attention to the bottom flow line. The net drawn is thus accurate beyond question, if the trial line is correct. Finally, either a sketched flow line will cross the bottom flow line, an inconsistency proving an incorrect start, or else the net will be seen to come into agreement with the bottom flow line, proving the net to be correctly drawn throughout. It is very unlikely that a correct net will be obtained in the first trial. In each instance where proof of an incorrect start is obtained, however, there also will be indications pointing out in what way it was incorrect; these indications will permit the choice of a second trial that probably will be more nearly correct.

The gradual expansion process in Fig. 9·2 (*a*) is carried out as follows. Starting at the left, the flow path between the trial flow line and the top boundary flow line is divided into squares. Only by chance will the number of squares in this path be an integer. However, to avoid working with a fraction of a square, it usually is desirable to revise the trial line until a case with an integral number of squares is obtained. For example, if there are 9.3 squares in the path, a revision to 10 squares may be obtained by changing the trial line by amounts sufficient to revise the width of the path throughout in the ratio 9.3 to 10. The path above the heavy line in Fig. 9·2 (*a*) contains just 10 squares.

The first square in the path is of irregular form and is called a singular square. The basic requirement for this square, as for all squares, is that continuous subdivision give an approach to true squares. The two lines which subdivide this square into four smaller squares should have approximately equal lengths, a characteristic that aids in sketching singular squares. It may also be noted that in Fig. 9·2 this singular square is nearly symmetrical, another condition that aids somewhat in sketching such squares. Another form of singular square is illustrated by the first figure in the bottom flow path of Fig. 9·1, and for this type, also, subdivision aids in sketching the square correctly.

After the squares are in satisfactory form in the top flow path, rough downward extensions of the equipotential lines forming the sides of these squares may be drawn. These extensions point out approximate widths of squares such as *C* and *D*; if the other dimension of the squares are set equal to these widths and irregularities are smoothed out, the flow line forming their bases may be sketched. All this sketching should be done lightly since, once this last-mentioned flow line is drawn, the equipotential lines which were extended roughly should be erased and resketched, care being used to obtain right-angle intersections. The equality of dimensions in each square should then be rechecked, and further expansion downward should not be attempted until all is consistent in the squares of this path. Then the downward expansion to give the squares of the next path is a repetition of that already followed in the last path completed. Successive expansion of this type leads, in Fig. 9·2 (*a*), to the sketched flow line which forms the bottom of squares E and F. It is seen that this line is inconsistent with the actual bottom flow line. It is too low at square E and too high at square F for agreement with

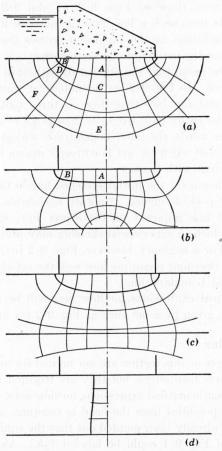

FIG. 9·2 Example of the flow net sketching procedure by explicit trials.

the bottom boundary condition. Therefore square E and squares above it are too large, or square F and squares above it are too small. This must mean that in the top flow path the size of square A was too large relative to that of square B, and another trial must be made to remedy this condition. In Fig. 9·2 (b) it is seen that the relative sizes of squares A and B have been revised in the correct direction, but the expansion in this figure shows that square B is too large as compared to A. This indicates that a correct initial trial line must have a shape intermediate between those of Figs. 9·2 (a) and 9·2 (b). Figure 9·2 (c) starts from such a line, and the agreement with bottom boundary conditions as the expansion crosses the bottom flow line shows that the net is quite close to correct.

It should be noted that the number of paths will be an integer only by chance. In Fig. 9·2 (c) the number of paths is approximately 3.3, and the fact that there is three tenths of a path throughout the entire path length is final proof of a satisfactory net. In other words, the lower boundary is seldom a line of the sketched net, but when the net is correctly drawn this boundary line is consistent with the net.

The line chosen for the initial sketched line in this example is not the only possible choice. Another reasonable choice is the equipotential line adjacent to the center line, shown in Fig. 9·2 (d). In fact an experienced sketcher may prefer to start on this basis. For a beginner, however, Figs. 9·2 (a), (b), and (c) offer simpler decisions regarding how well the net obtained agrees with the final boundary line.

Mathematical expressions for flow nets will be presented before the data given by a net such as Fig. 9·2 (c) are considered.

9·5   The Flux

The concepts of this section are not needed for an understanding of flow nets themselves, but they are required for an understanding of mathematical expressions for flow nets.

Along equipotential lines the head is constant, and as an example it has already been pointed out that the equipotential line through R of Fig. 9·1 could be labeled $\frac{2}{3}h_t$. Along each flow line the function that is constant will be called the flux. Between the head and the flux exists what is known as a conjugate relationship. To explain this relationship, some discussion is needed.

For use in this discussion, let q be defined as the flow that takes place above any given flow line and let q_t designate the total flow. The ratio of flow to permeability above any given flow line is q/k. At the top flow line of any given flow net, q/k

is zero. At the bottom flow line q/k equals q_t/k. The value of q/k at all points of any given flow line is a constant which depends only on the cross section, and is independent of soil properties. Herein this variable, q/k, is called the flux.

From equations 9·2, when square figures are used, it is seen that for each square the following relationship must hold:

$$\Delta \frac{q}{k} = \Delta h \qquad (9\cdot4)$$

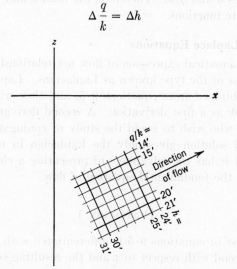

Fig. 9·3 Example of values of conjugate functions throughout a flow square.

With reference to Fig. 9·3, which represents a typical square of a flow net, equation 9·4 may be said to signify that $\Delta q/k$, which is the q/k change measured across the square in the direction normal to the flow, is equal to Δh, the head change measured across the square along the flow direction. Arbitrarily chosen numerical values are shown on the figure for purposes of illustration, and it is seen that both sides of equation 9·4 here have a value of 5 ft.

From Fig. 9·3 the following expressions may be written

$$\frac{\partial h}{\partial x} = \frac{\partial \frac{q}{k}}{\partial z} \quad \text{and} \quad \frac{\partial h}{\partial z} = -\frac{\partial \frac{q}{k}}{\partial x} \qquad (9\cdot5)$$

These expressions state that the difference in heads at two points which are a small distance apart in one coordinate direction must equal the difference in q/k values at two points which are the same small distance apart in the other coordinate direction.

Mathematical textbooks define conjugate functions as functions that obey the relationships expressed by equations 9·5 between the variables h and q/k. Therefore, the head h and the flux q/k are conjugate functions.

9·6   The Laplace Equations

The mathematical expression of flow net relationships is given by equations of the type known as Laplacians. Laplacians may easily be obtained from equations 9·5, and they will be so obtained below as a first derivation. A second derivation is given for readers who wish to avoid the study of conjugate functions. The second solution gives only the Laplacian in terms of the head h, but it has the advantage of presenting a clearer understanding of the fundamental equation of flow.

DERIVATION 1

If the first of equations 9·5 is differentiated with respect to x and the second with respect to z and the resulting equations are added, there results

$$\frac{\partial^2 h}{\partial x^2} + \frac{\partial^2 h}{\partial z^2} = 0 \qquad (9·6)$$

Similarly, if the first of equations 9·5 is differentiated with respect to z and the second with respect to x and the resulting equations are subtracted, there results

$$\frac{\partial^2 \frac{q}{k}}{\partial x^2} + \frac{\partial^2 \frac{q}{k}}{\partial z^2} = 0 \qquad (9·7)$$

Equations 9·6 and 9·7 are the Laplacians of the conjugate variables h and q/k. A statement of their meaning will be given after the second derivation.

DERIVATION 2

In order to obtain a solution which is as general as possible, let it be assumed that the soil mass under consideration is stratified. The permeability in such a mass is greater in directions parallel to the strata that in the direction normal to the strata. The coordinate system which will be used has the x axis in the direction of maximum permeability, k_x, and the z axis in the direction of minimum permeability, k_z. In the y direction the permeability, k_y, may fall anywhere between k_x and k_z, but normally it will equal k_x since generally both the y and x axes are parallel to the strata.

At any point in the mass let h be the total head. Let it be assumed that the point is at the center of a small element of dimensions dx, dy, and dz.

The component of gradient in the x direction through the point at the center of the element is i_x, and it may be expressed $-\partial h/\partial x$, the minus sign showing that h must decrease as x increases if flow is to be in the positive direction. The x component of gradient across the face of the element nearest the x origin will differ from the above expression unless the gradient is constant. The change of gradient in unit distance along the x direction may be written $\partial i_x/\partial x$, and the gradient at this face must equal the gradient at the center, $-\partial h/\partial x$, plus the product of the distance between the points, $-\frac{1}{2}\,dx$, and the change of gradient per unit of distance, $\partial i_x/\partial x$. Thus the x component of gradient across the face nearest the x origin is

$$-\frac{\partial h}{\partial x} + \frac{\partial}{\partial x}\left(-\frac{\partial h}{\partial x}\right)\left(-\frac{dx}{2}\right) \quad \text{or} \quad -\frac{\partial h}{\partial x} + \frac{\partial^2 h}{\partial x^2}\frac{dx}{2}$$

and according to Darcy's Law the flow across the face is

$$k_x\left(-\frac{\partial h}{\partial x} + \frac{\partial^2 h}{\partial x^2}\frac{dx}{2}\right)dy\,dz \qquad (9\cdot8)$$

Similarly the expression for flow in the x direction across the face farthest from the x origin may be shown to be

$$k_x\left(-\frac{\partial h}{\partial x} - \frac{\partial^2 h}{\partial x^2}\frac{dx}{2}\right)dy\,dz \qquad (9\cdot9)$$

Expression 9·8 is a flow into the element; expression 9·9 is a flow from the element. The net rate of increase of water within the element, as caused by the x component of seepage, may be written as expression 9·8 minus expression 9·9, giving

$$k_x \frac{\partial^2 h}{\partial x^2} dx \, dy \, dz \qquad (9\cdot10)$$

Similar expressions for combined rates of increase of water within the element, caused by components of flow in the y and z directions, may be set up. The sum of the rates for the three coordinate directions gives the rate of change of volume.

$$\left(k_x \frac{\partial^2 h}{\partial x^2} + k_y \frac{\partial^2 h}{\partial y^2} + k_z \frac{\partial^2 h}{\partial z^2} \right) dx \, dy \, dz \qquad (9\cdot11)$$

In flow net studies, steady flow exists, and thus there are no volume changes. For the two-dimensional case there is no flow in the y direction; thus the y term becomes zero. Under these conditions expression 9·11 reduces to

$$k_x \frac{\partial^2 h}{\partial x^2} + k_z \frac{\partial^2 h}{\partial z^2} = 0 \qquad (9\cdot12)$$

For an isotropic material with no difference in permeability in different directions, the k values are equal and they cancel, showing that the flow net is independent of the magnitude of the permeability, and equation 9·12 reduces to

$$\frac{\partial^2 h}{\partial x^2} + \frac{\partial^2 h}{\partial z^2} = 0 \qquad (9\cdot13)$$

This is the same Laplacian as given by equation 9·6. A clear visualization of its meaning is not difficult. The equation presents the fundamental relationship for steady flow based on Darcy's Law in isotropic soils, and states simply that the sum of the components of space rates of gradient change must be zero. In other words, gradient changes in the x direction must be balanced by gradient changes of opposite sign in the z direction if the volume is to remain constant.

9·7   The Scale Transformation to Account for Stratification

In all sedimentary deposits, as well as in most earth embankments, there is a pronounced tendency for the permeability to be greater in the horizontal than in the vertical direction. It is believed that the horizontal coefficient of permeability may often be as much as five or ten times as large as the vertical value. The study of flow nets would be of very little value indeed if no allowance could be made for this important practical item. Fortunately, stratification can be taken into account without difficulty.

Equation 9·12 of the previous section is *not* a Laplacian. Since this equation applies for a soil mass in which stratification exists, and since flow nets which consist of square figures must be thought of as valid only where Laplacians apply, it is seen that the flow net principles which have been outlined cannot be applied directly on a cross section where there is stratification. However, the demonstration which follows shows that the use of a simple scale transformation leads to a distorted plot on which the flow net principles apply.

Equation 9·12 may be written

$$\frac{\partial^2 h}{\left(\dfrac{k_z}{k_x}\right)\partial x^2} + \frac{\partial^2 h}{\partial z^2} = 0 \tag{9·14}$$

If x_t is defined as a new coordinate variable, measured in the same direction as x and equal to x multiplied by a constant, as expressed by

$$x_t = \sqrt{\frac{k_z}{k_x}}\, x \tag{9·15}$$

then it can be demonstrated that, if the variable x_t is used in place of variable x in equation 9·14, the following expression results:

$$\frac{\partial^2 h}{\partial x_t^2} + \frac{\partial^2 h}{\partial z^2} = 0 \tag{9·16}$$

This equation is a Laplacian in the coordinate variables x_t and z. Thus, if a cross section through stratified soil is drawn to distorted scale, the true z scale and the transformed or foreshortened x_t scale being used for coordinates, the flow net may be sketched on it.

The above derivation points out a rule that must be clearly understood and must never be violated. *When the soil of a given cross section possesses stratification, the section must be transformed before a flow net is sketched.*

Several investigators of the subject of seepage have developed formulas or have tabulated data obtained from flow nets.† Flow net data from such sources are valid only for transformed sections, and it is the transformed dimensions of the section under consideration that apply when such data are used.

It should be noted that, in the above treatment, the x direction is defined as the direction of maximum permeability. In the majority of cases this direction will be horizontal, but when the maximum permeability is in a diagonal direction the x axis and the transformed or x_t axis must be taken in this diagonal direction.

An alternative method of carrying out the transformation is to retain natural dimensions in the x direction and transform by using an expanded scale in the z direction. The resulting section, however, is geometrically similar to that obtained by the use of the natural z scale and the foreshortened x_t scale.

9·8 Determination of Quantity of Seepage

The quantity of seepage may easily be determined once the flow net is available. The expression for discharge through any square is shown by equations 9·2 and 9·4 to be

$$\Delta q = k \, \Delta h$$

The number of flow paths and the number of equipotential drops along each path may be counted on any flow net; these numbers will be designated, respectively, by n_f and n_d. In Fig. 9·1 it is seen that n_f equals about 4.5 and n_d equals 9; in Fig. 9·2 (c) n_f equals 3.3 and n_d equals 8. Since all paths have like flow and all drops are equal, expressions for the total seepage and for the total head dissipated within the flow net are

$$q_t = n_f \, \Delta q \quad \text{and} \quad h_t = n_d \, \Delta h$$

† See, for example, Fig. 18·8.

The substitution of these two expressions into that above leads to

$$q_t = \frac{n_f}{n_d} k h_t \tag{9·17}$$

The fundamental form of equation 9·17 should be carefully noted. The seepage for any given cross section equals the product of three quantities—a constant which depends only on the geometry of the cross section, the effective permeability of the soil, and the head dissipated in passing through the section. If English units are used, the discharge is commonly in cubic feet per second per running foot, the constant is dimensionless, the permeability is in feet per second, and the head is in feet.

If the section is transformed by changing vertical dimensions, or if the direction of maximum permeability is not horizontal, the transformation changes the dimension h_t. However, the quantity h_t in equation 9·17 is, fundamentally, an amount of dissipated head, and it is the true value of this head that must be used in applications of the formula.

When equation 9·17 is used for a transformed section, the value that applies for permeability may be explained by a simple demonstration. In most flow nets a square can be found in which the flow is essentially parallel to the x_t axis; for example, a square near the center line in Fig. 9·2 may be considered. Such a square is shown in Fig. 9·4, to transformed scale in (a) and to natural

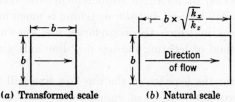

(a) **Transformed scale**   (b) **Natural scale**

Fig. 9·4 Diagram used for the derivation of the expression for effective permeability.

scale in (b). In (a) the permeability has the effective value, designated by k', and the flow through the square, according to equation 9·2, is $k' \dfrac{\Delta h}{b} b$. In (b) the permeability value in the horizontal direction must apply because the sketch is to natural scale and the flow is horizontal. Thus, a second expression for flow through the figure is $k_x \dfrac{\Delta h}{b\sqrt{k_x/k_z}} b$. Equating the two expressions for flow through the figure gives

$$k' = \sqrt{k_x k_z} \qquad (9\cdot18)$$

As an example, let it be assumed that a dam of impervious material of 50-ft base width rests on the surface of a granular stratum of 10-ft depth, below which there is impervious ledge; that the horizontal and vertical permeabilities are respectively 90×10^{-4} and 10×10^{-4} cm per sec; and that the head is 15 ft. To transformed scale the base width becomes $\sqrt{\frac{10}{90}} \times \frac{50}{10}$ or $1\frac{2}{3}$ times the depth of soil, and therefore the net of Fig. $9\cdot2$ (c) applies. The seepage in foot and second units may be expressed as follows:

$$q_t = \frac{n_f}{n_d} k' h_t$$

$$= \frac{3.3}{8} \times \frac{10^{-4}\sqrt{90 \times 10}}{30.5} \times 15$$

$$= 6.1 \times 10^{-4} \text{ cu ft per sec per ft}$$

9·9 Cross Sections with Top Flow Lines at Atmospheric Pressure

If the boundary conditions are not completely defined, as in the cross section of an earth embankment, the trial sketching method may still be used, but the sketching is much more difficult than for cases in which the boundaries are known. For this reason a method of locating the top flow line aids greatly in the solution.

Solutions for the location of the top flow line will be obtained herein for two simple cases of embankment cross sections. Although the typical earth dam will not have a simple homogeneous section, these simple cases furnish good illustrations of the conditions any top flow line must follow. Furthermore, the location of the top flow line for a simple case can often be used for the first trial in the sketching of a more complicated embankment section. For one of the cases considered several procedures for obtaining the top flow line are presented, not because more than one procedure is required, but to show the various fundamental methods of approach that are available.

Three conditions that the top flow line must obey are illustrated

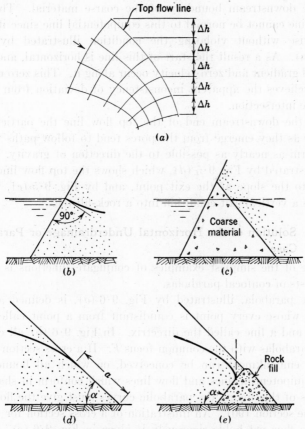

Fɪɢ. 9·5 Characteristics of top flow lines.

in Fig. 9·5. Since this line is at atmospheric pressure the only type of head that can exist along it is elevation head. Therefore, there must be constant drops in elevation between the points at which successive equipotentials meet the top flow line, as shown in Fig. 9·5 (a).

At its starting point, the top flow line must be normal to the upstream slope, which is an equipotential line. This is shown in

Fig. 9·5 (*b*). An exception occurs, however, in the case shown in Fig. 9·5 (*c*). In this cross section the coarse material at the upstream face is so pervious that it does not offer appreciable resistance to flow. Therefore, the upstream equipotential line is the downstream boundary of the coarse material. The top flow line cannot be normal to this equipotential line since it cannot rise without violating the condition illustrated by Fig. 9·5 (*a*). As a result the start of this line is horizontal, and zero initial gradient and zero velocity occur along it. This zero condition relieves the apparent inconsistency of deviation from a 90-degree intersection.

At the downstream end of the top flow line the particles of water as they emerge from the pores tend to follow paths which conform as nearly as possible to the direction of gravity. This is illustrated by Fig. 9·5 (*d*), which shows the top flow line tangent to the slope at the exit point, and by Fig. 9·5 (*e*), which shows a vertical exit condition into a rock-fill toe.

9·10 Solution of the Horizontal Underdrainage or Parabolic Case

One of the simplest examples of conjugate functions is given by nests of confocal parabolas.

The parabola, illustrated by Fig. 9·6 (*a*), is defined as the curve whose every point is equidistant from a point called the focus and a line called the directrix. In Fig. 9·6 (*b*) all curves are parabolas with the common focus *F*. If a cross section of an earth embankment can be conceived, on which all boundaries are equipotential lines and flow lines which conform in shape to curves of this figure, the parabolic curves must give the flow net for the section (90). An illustration of a cross section for which such a flow net holds rigorously is given in Fig. 9·6 (*c*). Here *BC* and *DF* are flow lines, and *BD* and *FC* are equipotential lines. The only boundary of this flow net which is an unusual one for a homogeneous dam with underdrainage is the upstream equipotential line. Figure 9·6 (*d*) shows the commonest case of upstream equipotential boundary; the flow net for this section will not consist of true parabolas, although there will be close resemblance to them in the downstream portions of the net.

Analysis has shown that the top flow line of Fig. 9·6 (*d*) is close to parabolic except for a short distance of reversed curvature near point B. This parabola produced backwards reaches

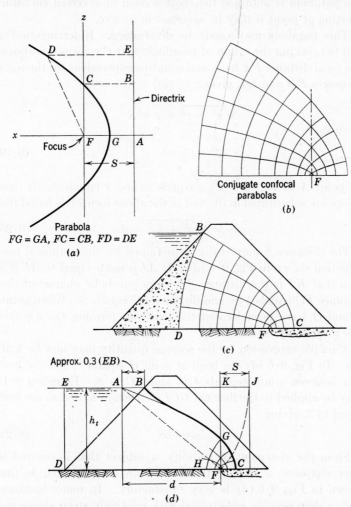

Parabola
$FG = GA$, $FC = CB$, $FD = DE$
(a)

Conjugate confocal parabolas
(b)

Directrix

Focus

Approx. 0.3 (EB)

FIG. 9·6   The flow net consisting of confocal parabolas.

head water elevation at point A. A. Casagrande suggests the use of the approximate relationship that the distance BA equals 0.3 times the distance BE for dams with reasonably flat upstream slopes. Thus the top flow line may be obtained by construction of the parabola that has its focus at point F and that passes through point A, which is called a corrected entrance point. Once the parabola is obtained the short section of reversed curvature starting at point B may be sketched in by eye.

This parabola may easily be determined. Referring to Fig. 9·6 (*a*), taking the origin of coordinates at the focus, expressing the focal distance FA by S, and equating expressions for the equal distances FD and DE gives

$$\sqrt{x^2 + z^2} = x + S$$

whence

$$x = \frac{z^2 - S^2}{2S} \qquad (9\cdot19)$$

At point A in Fig. 9·6 (*d*), z equals h_t and x equals d. If these values are substituted in the first of the above forms it is found that

$$S = \sqrt{d^2 + h_t{}^2} - d \qquad (9\cdot20)$$

The distance S may easily be obtained by the graphical construction shown in Fig. 9·6 (*d*). If AJ is made equal to AF it is seen that KJ is the distance S. From parabolic characteristics, distance FC equals ½S, and distance FG equals S. When points C and G have been located the parabola forming the top flow line may easily be sketched.

A simple expression for the seepage quantity may now be written. In Fig. 9·6 (*d*) the head at point G equals S, and the head loss between equipotentials GH and FC is S. Equation 9·17 may be applied to the flow net $GCFH$, wherein n_f and n_d are each equal to 3, giving

$$q_t = kS \qquad (9\cdot21)$$

From the viewpoint of stability, a subject that is covered in later chapters, a dam of the underdrainage type such as that shown in Fig. 9·6 (*d*) is very satisfactory. In many instances such a dam may be constructed with relatively steep slopes and still be more stable than a dam with much flatter slopes but with a less satisfactory system of drainage. However, the seepage through a dam with underdrainage is larger than that through dams in which the top flow lines break out on diagonal discharge faces, as illustrated by Figs. 9·5 (*d*) and (*e*).

9·11 Top Flow Lines in Dams with Sloping Discharge Faces Determined by Correction to Parabolic Case

The slope of the discharge face will be designated herein by the angle α, measured clockwise from the horizontal. Thus the underdrainage case is defined by an α of 180 degrees. Flow nets

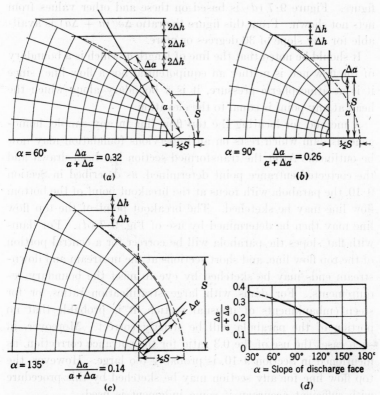

FIG. 9·7 Flow nets for downstream portions of dams with various discharge slopes, showing comparison with the parabolic case. (A. Casagrande.)

that have been sketched by A. Casagrande for the downstream portions of dams with α values of 60, 90, and 135 degrees, respectively, are given in Fig. 9·7. On each of these sketches the intersection of the bottom flow line with the discharge face has been used as a focus to give the parabolas shown by dotted lines. It may be noted that in each sketch the top flow line is in close agreement with the parabola, except for a short final portion of its path.

Distances measured along the discharge face, from the parabola to the actual breakout point, are shown on these flow nets with the designation Δa, and distances below the breakout point are designated by a. Values of $\Delta a/(a + \Delta a)$ are noted on each figure. Figure 9·7 (*d*) is based on these and other values from nets not shown. From this figure the ratio $\Delta a/(a + \Delta a)$ is available for any slope of 30 degrees or more.

It should be noted that the line of length a, which is a boundary of the flow net, is neither an equipotential nor a flow line; since it is at atmospheric pressure, it is a boundary along which the head at any point is equal to the elevation.

A method for locating the top flow line in any simple, homogeneous dam which rests on an impervious foundation may now be outlined. After the transformed section has been drawn and the corrected entrance point determined, as described in Section 9·10, the parabola with focus at the breakout point of the bottom flow line may be sketched. The breakout point of the top flow line may then be determined by use of Fig. 9·7 (*d*). For dams with flat slopes the parabola will be correct for a central portion of the top flow line, and short sections at the upstream and downstream ends may be sketched by eye to meet the boundary requirements. For dams with large stratification ratios, or for steep embankments of unusual section, it is probable that no portion of the parabola will be strictly correct. Moreover, in such cases the use of the 0.3 ratio for the entrance correction, as mentioned in Section 9·10, is probably too large. However, the top flow line for any section may be sketched by this procedure with sufficient accuracy if some judgment is used.

The flow nets of Fig. 9·7 indicate that a central section of the flow net resembles closely the flow net of parabolas, shown in Fig. 9·6 (*b*). For this reason the seepage through all dams with flat slopes may be determined with good accuracy from the simple equation holding for the truly parabolic net. According to equations 9·20 and 9·21 this seepage expression is

$$q_t = k(\sqrt{d^2 + h_t{}^2} - d) \qquad (9·22)$$

9·12   The L. Casagrande Solution for a Triangular Dam

For triangular dams on impervious foundations with discharge faces at 90 degrees or less to the horizontal, a method developed by L. Casagrande gives a simple and reasonably accurate solution for the seepage quantity and for the location of the top flow line.

In Fig. 9·8 the top flow line will actually start at B, but introduction of the entrance correction that is explained in Section

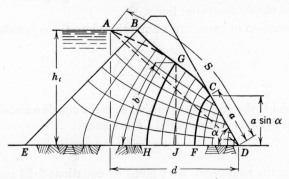

Fig. 9·8   The L. Casagrande method for the determination of the top flow line.

9·10 gives point A as an assumed or corrected initial point. The top flow line ends at point C, the location of which is desired and is defined by the distance a.

Let z be the vertical coordinate, measured from the tail water or foundation level. Instead of the horizontal coordinate x in the solution for the top flow line, in this case it will be simpler to use s, the slope distance, for the second variable; this variable is defined by the differential relationship $ds^2 = dx^2 + dz^2$.

The general equation for flow across any equipotential such as GH, expressed in the form of equation 9·1, is

$$q = k\, i_{av}(GH)$$

The first of two assumptions introduced in this method is that distance GH is equal to its projection on the vertical, that is, to the z coordinate of point G. The inaccuracy thus introduced is appreciable, but will be small for dams with flat slopes. In Fig.

9·8, where the slopes are relatively steep, the inaccuracy is considerably less than 10 per cent.

The second assumption concerns the expression used for gradient. Along the top flow line the only head is the elevation head, designated by z, and at points such as G the gradient is $-dz/ds$. Adjacent to line GH the sizes of squares are essentially alike and, since the gradient is inversely proportional to the size of square, the gradient must be approximately constant. It is assumed that the gradient at the top flow line is the average gradient for all points of the equipotential line.

Introduction of these two assumptions into the equation above gives

$$q = k \left(-\frac{dz}{ds} \right) z \qquad (9 \cdot 23)$$

At point C the gradient equals $\sin \alpha$, and z equals $a \sin \alpha$. Thus equation 9·23 for equipotential CF becomes

$$q = ka \sin^2 \alpha \qquad (9 \cdot 24)$$

Equating the expressions for q given by equations 9·23 and 9·24, rearranging and indicating the integration required for the solution, gives

$$-\int_{h_t}^{a \sin \alpha} z \, dz = a \sin^2 \alpha \int_0^{S-a} ds$$

The limits are indicated in Fig. 9·8. At point A, the corrected initial point of the top flow line, z is equal to h_t. The value of s, which may now be defined as the distance along the flow line, is at this point equal to zero. The distance along the top flow line to point C and thence to point D is for convenience designated by S. At point C, the location of which is desired, s equals $S - a$ and z equals $a \sin \alpha$. The solution of the above equation is

$$a = S - \sqrt{S^2 - (h_t \csc \alpha)^2} \qquad (9 \cdot 25)$$

The dimension S differs only slightly from the straight line distance AD. In Fig. 9·8 this difference is about 4 per cent, and it is less in dams with flatter slopes. Thus an approximate expression for this distance is

$$S = \sqrt{d^2 + h_t{}^2} \qquad (9 \cdot 26)$$

and substitution of equation 9·26 into 9·25 gives

$$a = \sqrt{d^2 + h_t^2} - \sqrt{d^2 - h_t^2 \cot^2 \alpha} \qquad (9\cdot27)$$

A graphical solution for the distance a, based on equation 9·27, was developed by L. Casagrande and is given in Fig. 9·9. A solution for the distance $a \sin \alpha$ which avoids the approximation of equation 9·26 has been obtained by Gilboy (16). This solution gives an equation that is too involved for practical use, and the method is represented by the chart shown in Fig. 9·10.

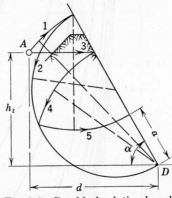

FIG. 9·9 Graphical solution based on the L. Casagrande method.

Once the distance a has been obtained the seepage may be computed by the use of equation 9·24. After point C is located the top flow line and the net may be obtained by sketching, with an accuracy that usually is sufficient.

The following procedure is a graphical method of carrying out the solution developed above. The combination of equations 9·23 and 9·24 may be written

$$\Delta s = z \left(\frac{\Delta z}{a \sin^2 \alpha} \right) \qquad (9\cdot28)$$

Fig. 9·11 shows the downstream portion of the dam represented in Fig. 9·8. Any point C on the downstream slope may be taken as the terminal point of the top flow line, and CD may be defined as distance a to some unknown scale. The distance $a \sin^2 \alpha$ is shown in the figure.

Let it be assumed that the top flow line is divided into sections, each section having a constant head drop Δz. Any constant may be used for the head drop, a convenient choice being a given fraction of $a \sin^2 \alpha$. Equation 9·28 shows that if

$$\Delta z = Ca \sin^2 \alpha$$

then

$$\Delta s = Cz \qquad (9\cdot29)$$

For the example which will be presented C will be assumed equal to unity.

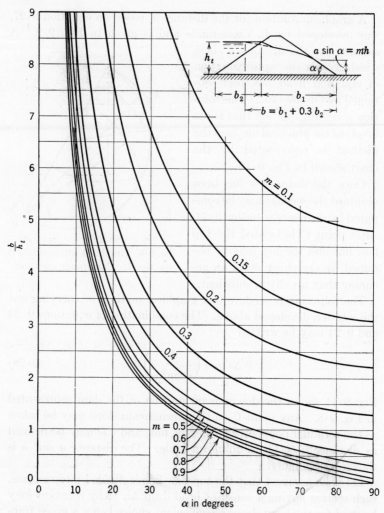

FIG. 9·10 Chart for solutions by the L. Casagrande method. (G. Gilboy.)

For locating the final section of the top flow line the head drop Δz_1 is laid off equal to $a \sin^2 \alpha$ in Fig. 9·11. The average ordinate z_1 is labeled. By setting Δs_1 equal to z_1 as shown, point L

on the top flow line is obtained. By a repetition of this process, point M is located.

A larger number of points and a better determination of the location of the top flow line may be obtained by use of a smaller value of C; for example, a value of $\frac{1}{4}$ will give four times as many points.

For the given section the slope of line AD appears in Fig. 9·8. From point D in Fig. 9·11 this slope may be laid off, its inter-

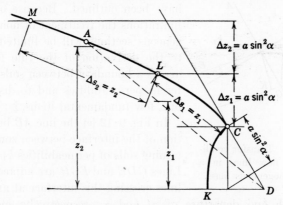

FIG. 9·11 Graphical construction of the top flow line, based on the L. Casagrande differential equation.

section with the smooth sketched flow line MLC being point A, the corrected initial point. After point A has been located, the scale of the figure may easily be determined, and the rest of the section may then be drawn.

It now may be pointed out that by trial sketching it is possible to obtain the flow net for a section such as Fig. 9·8 without recourse to methods like those presented for locating points on top flow lines. The procedure consists simply in starting at a point such as C in Fig. 9·11, with an unknown scale. The equipotential CK may be sketched by eye with reasonable accuracy. By gradually working backwards, using the trial sketching procedure, the net may be developed. The top flow line is obtained as a part of this process. Actually such a procedure differs from that in Fig. 9·11 only in that it involves the use of the intuition for

Darcy's Law which is furnished by a familiarity with the trial sketching method, whereas the procedure illustrated in Fig. 9·11 uses equation 9·29 which is an expression for this law.

9·13 Non-Homogeneous Sections

When a number of soils of different permeabilities occur in a cross section which is being analyzed for seepage, the details of the solution may become very complicated, but the fundamental

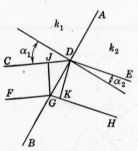

principles differ little from those which have been outlined. Because of space limitations the treatment of non-homogeneous sections will be limited herein to the derivation of the rule for flow across a boundary between soils of different permeabilities and to discussion of a few fundamental items. ‡

FIG. 9·12 Transfer condition for flow lines in a non-homogeneous mass.

In Fig. 9·12 let the line AB be a portion of the interface between zones containing soils of permeabilities k_1 and k_2. Lines CDE and FGH are adjacent flow lines crossing this interface at angles of approach and departure of α_1 and α_2, respectively, measured from the normal to the interface. Sufficient magnification of scale has been used to cause all lines to appear straight in the figure. The Lines GJ and DK are equipotential lines, and Δh designates the equal drops in potential in distances JD and GK. Expressions for the flow occurring between these two flow lines, within the two soils, may be written

$$q = kib = k_1 \frac{\Delta h}{JD} JG = k_2 \frac{\Delta h}{GK} DK$$

and, since $JD/JG = \tan \alpha_1$ and $GK/DK = \tan \alpha_2$,

$$\frac{k_1}{k_2} = \frac{\tan \alpha_1}{\tan \alpha_2} \qquad (9 \cdot 30)$$

‡ Flow nets for a number of non-homogeneous sections of earth dams are shown in reference 162.

Flow net sketching by the trial method may be very time-consuming on non-homogeneous sections but, except for the following of the rule given by equation 9·30, no new principles are involved. Starting with a trial line, taken as discussed in Section 9·4, the expansion by squares may be carried across any interface between zones of different permeability; then all the net on the far side of the interface should be erased and equation 9·30 should be used for a new start of each flow line in the second zone. The final check, as in the simpler case, is obtained when the final boundary is reached.

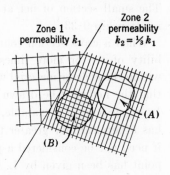

FIG. 9·13 Square figure relationships for the non-homogeneous case.

For the sketching in the second zone, a different b/l ratio, a different Δh, or a different Δq from that used in the first zone is necessary. The relationships for the various choices that are possible may be derived from

$$\Delta q = k \, \Delta h \, \frac{b}{l}$$

If it is desired that Δh and Δq values be the same for figures of both zones, the relationship required between figure shapes is

$$\left(\frac{b}{l}\right)_2 : \left(\frac{b}{l}\right)_1 = k_1 : k_2 \qquad (9 \cdot 31)$$

An illustration is given in Fig. 9·13. In zone 1, the net is composed of squares. The main net in zone 2 has Δh and Δq values which are the same as in zone 1, the shapes of figures being as expressed by relationship 9·31.

If it is desired that all figures be squares with like flow quantities, the relationship required between head drops is

$$\Delta h_2 : \Delta h_1 = k_1 : k_2 \qquad (9 \cdot 32)$$

The small section of net at A illustrates the case expressed by relationship 9·32.

If it is desired that all figures be squares with like head drops in both zones, the relationship required between flow quantities is

$$\Delta q_2 : \Delta q_1 = k_2 : k_1 \qquad (9 \cdot 33)$$

The small section of net at B illustrates the case expressed by relationship $9 \cdot 33$.

When a cross section contains two zones, one with a permeability of ten or more times that of the other, the head losses within the coarser material will often be of such minor magnitude that the net need be drawn only for the zone of finer material. In Fig. $9 \cdot 5$ (c), for example, if the zone labeled "coarse material" has a permeability greater than 10 times that in the other zone it need not be considered a part of the net. An example of this point has been given by L. Casagrande (34) for the non-homogeneous dam shown in Fig. $9 \cdot 14$. This figure shows that, when the second zone has a permeability 5 times that of the first, the

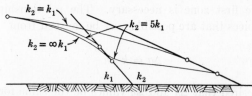

Fig. $9 \cdot 14$ Effect of the relative permeability of the downstream section on the location of the top flow line. (L. Casagrande.)

top flow line in the first zone is not greatly different from what it is when the second zone has infinite permeability and thus offers no resistance to flow.

If there is stratification in a non-homogeneous dam and the same stratification ratio holds in all zones, the transformation may be carried out as for homogeneous sections. If there are different stratification ratios in different zones, no general procedure applies rigorously for transforming the section as a whole. This will not often be a limitation in practical analyses, however, since stratification ratios in nature are seldom known accurately.

9·14   Methods for Obtaining Flow Nets

Methods available for determining flow nets are the following:

1. Mathematical solutions.
2. Capillary flow analogy.
3. Electrical analogy.
4. Earth dams models.
5. Graphical solution by trial sketching.

The last method has already been covered in detail. A short discussion of each of the others will be given in this section.

In a few relatively simple cases the boundary conditions may be expressed by equations, and solutions may be obtained by mathematical procedure. Although this approach is occasionally helpful in the checking of other methods, it is largely of academic interest. A paper by W. Weaver (166) which relates to this method illustrates the complexity of the mathematics for a few cases which are relatively simple of solution by other methods.

Capillary flow between two closely spaced parallel plates follows a law analogous to two-dimensional flow through soils, as shown by equation 6·13. Therefore, models utilizing capillary flow between plates, subject to boundary conditions which are analogous to those of a given seepage problem, may be used to determine the flow net. For the analogy to be valid, it is essential that the distance between the two plates be constant at all points. This method in many ways is similar to the earth dam model discussed below. It has been used mostly as a check on other methods of solution.

More extensive use has been made of the electrical analogy method than of the above method. In the flow of electricity the current is proportional to the voltage drop; therefore there is an analogy to flow through soils wherein seepage is proportional to head dissipated, the conductivity in the analogy corresponding to the permeability of the soil. In the section shown in Fig. 9·1 it may be noted that an analogous electrical setup is easily constructed as follows: Metal bars are placed along lines *BA* and *CD*, and different electrical potentials are imposed on these bars. Along lines *AEC* and *FG* insulating boundaries, which prevent current from crossing these lines, are placed. Of course it is necessary that the insulation effectively separate points A and C. In the space corresponding to the cross section of the soil mass some medium which is a conductor is placed; examples of conductors used for this purpose are a small depth of salt solution and a sheet of metal foil. All conditions thus are analogous to the earth section of Fig. 9·1, and equipotentials may be obtained by readings on a Wheatstone bridge. It is of interest to note that direct determinations of flow lines may be obtained by interchanging the locations of the metal bars and insulators. Since the potential and the flux are conjugate functions, the equipotentials obtained by the use of the interchanged boundaries are flow lines for the original boundaries. The electrical analogy method offers numerous advantages over other methods. It has the disadvantage that top flow lines such as the one in Fig. 9·6 (*d*) must be located by trial.

Earth dam models have been used quite widely for the determination of flow lines. Such models are most commonly constructed between two parallel glass plates. A flume that is used for such models is illustrated in Fig. 9·15. By the injection of spots of dye at various initial points flow lines may be traced. Occasionally the actual soil from the dam under study is used in the model. However, it has been shown that for given boundary conditions the net is not dependent on the permeability. Thus the use of soil from the site offers no real advantages, and often has the disadvantage of excessive capillarity effects.

The main advantage in the use of earth models and capillary analogy models, as compared to electrical analogy models, is that direct determinations of locations of top flow lines are obtainable. Capillarity effects may make accurate determinations of top flow lines difficult, however, and if there is a large capillary rise it may badly distort the flow net. Soils that would be too coarse for use in dams are often used in models because heights of capillarity zones in models are then smaller and are thus more representative of capillary zones in nature. Satisfactory minimization of heights of capillary zones in models has sometimes been obtained by the use of wetting agents, which lower the surface tension of the water and thus decrease the heights of capillary rise. As far as the quantity of seepage is concerned the

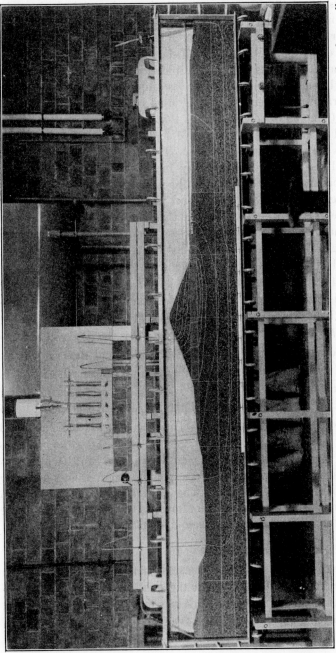

Fig. 9·15 Model flume for seepage studies of earth dams. Before photographing, flow lines were drawn on the glass wall of the flume. (Cincinnati Testing Laboratory, Ohio River Division, Corps of Engineers, U. S. Army.)

effects of capillarity may generally be neglected in both model and prototype, since the seepage through the capillary zone is of minor importance in most cases.

In earth dam models the soil should be placed in as uniform a condition as possible. If stratification occurs in the prototype and the model is constructed of isotropic soil, it is evident that the transformed section must be used in the model. Tests indicate (page 39 of reference 134) that model dams constructed of a soil of uniform grain size have a permeability which is essentially the same in all directions. However, if the soil used in the model has greater permeability in the horizontal than in the vertical direction, the slopes in the model must be modified.

The method for caring for such a situation may best be explained by an example. Assume that a triangular dam in nature will have slopes of 3 horizontally to 1 vertically and a horizontal permeability 10 times as large as the vertical permeability. A model of this dam is to be constructed of soil which, because of stratification during placing, will have a horizontal permeability that is twice as large as the vertical permeability. The determination of the slopes to be used in the model is required.

If H is the height of the actual dam, $6H$ is the base width. The transformation factor of the soil of the actual dam is $\sqrt{k_z/k_x}$ or $\sqrt{0.1}$, and the base width of the transformed section is $6H\sqrt{0.1}$ or $1.90H$. The base width of an isotropic model of height H' would be $1.90H'$ but the soil used in the model has a transformation factor of $\sqrt{0.5}$. Thus the base width of the model must be $1.90H' \div \sqrt{0.5}$, or $2.68H'$, and the slopes in the model must be 1.34 horizontally to 1 vertically. In this model, as in all stratified sections, flow lines and equipotential lines generally will not cross at right angles. The flow line pattern obtained from the model should therefore be redrawn to transformed scale before any attempt is made to sketch equipotential lines.

9·15 Radial Flow Nets

The second type of two-dimensional flow mentioned in Section 9·1 occurs when the flow net is the same for all radial cross sections through a given axis. This axis may be the center line of a well, a caisson, or any other type of opening that acts as a boundary of cylindrical shape to the saturated soil mass. In this type of section the direction of flow at every point is toward some point on the axis of symmetry. The flow net for such a section is called a radial flow net.

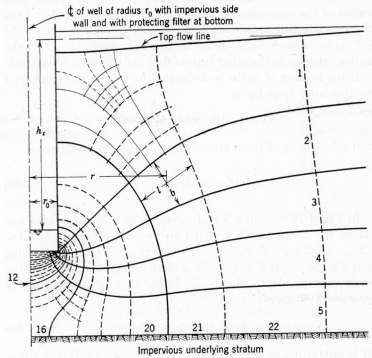

Fɪɢ. 9·16 Example of radial flow net.

An example of radial flow is given by Fig. 9·16, in which a well with an impervious wall that extends part way through a pervious stratum is represented. Dimension notations are shown on a typical rectangle of the flow net. The width of flow path, b, multiplied by the distance normal to the section, $2\pi r$, gives the area $2\pi rb$. The flow through any figure of the flow net may be expressed

$$\Delta Q = k \frac{\Delta h}{l} 2\pi rb$$

or

$$\Delta Q = 2\pi k \ \Delta h \left(\frac{rb}{l}\right) \qquad (9\cdot34)$$

If both ΔQ and Δh of equation $9\cdot34$ are to have values that are the same for every figure of the radial flow net, it is seen that values of the expression rb/l must be alike for all figures. Thus the characteristic requirement of the radial flow net is that the b/l ratio for each figure must be inversely proportional to the radius, whereas in the other type of flow net this ratio is constant.

If the number of paths is designated by n_f and the number of equipotential drops by n_d,

$$Q = n_f \ \Delta Q \quad \text{and} \quad h_t = n_d \ \Delta h$$

and substitution of these expressions into equation $9\cdot34$ gives

$$Q = 2\pi k h_t \ \frac{n_f}{n_d} \left(\frac{rb}{l}\right) \qquad (9\cdot35)$$

In Fig. $9\cdot16$ n_f equals 5 and n_d equals 22. In the labeled rectangle the dimensions r, b, and l are respectively equal to $5.1r_0$, $1.8r_0$, and $2.3r_0$. Thus, for this rectangle, rb/l is equal to $4.0r_0$, and if a computation were to be made for any other rectangle, the same value would be obtained. Substitution of these values in equation $9\cdot36$ gives

$$Q = 2\pi k h_t \tfrac{5}{2}\tfrac{}{2}(4.0r_0) = 5.7 k h_t r_0 \qquad (9\cdot36)$$

It is interesting to note that solutions obtained by Harza (page 1364 of reference 68) by the use of electrical analogy apparatus gave qualities of flow that were between 4.8 and 5.6 times $k h_t r_0$ for cross sections of the type of Fig. $9\cdot16$. These investigations showed that the radial extent of the cross section, the depth below the well, and the depth of the soil have little effect on the results, since practically all head is lost near the entrance to the well.

9·16 Simple Cases of Radial Flow

For two simple cases of radial flow equations for the head in terms of the radius are easily obtained.

CASE A

The simplest case of radial flow is illustrated in Fig. 9·17 (*a*). A perfectly round island has at its center a well which penetrates through a pervious, homogeneous, horizontal stratum of constant thickness, Z. As long as the water surface in the well is above the pervious stratum, the seepage through this stratum is everywhere radial and horizontal.

For this condition of radial, horizontal flow the gradient at all points is dh/dr. The dimension b of equation 9·34 is the constant stratum thickness Z. The flow across any vertical cylindrical surface at radius r may be written

$$Q = k \frac{dh}{dr} 2\pi r Z$$

whence

$$h = \frac{Q}{2\pi kZ} \log_e \frac{r}{r_0} \quad (9\cdot37)$$

In this equation h is the head loss between radius r and the radius of the well, r_0.

It may be noted that this is a one-dimensional case, since the only space variable is the radius. The seepage pattern

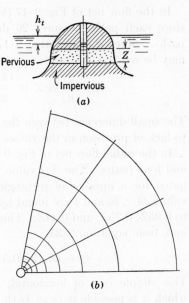

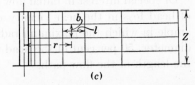

Fig. 9·17 The case of radial, horizontal flow.

is the same for all horizontal planes through the pervious stratum, and therefore a flow net of the type consisting entirely of squares may be drawn. This type of net is shown in Fig. 9·17 (*b*). Moreover, the seepage pattern is the same on all radial vertical planes through the center line of the well, and a flow net of the radial type may also be drawn. This net is shown in Fig. 9·17 (*c*).

The two types of flow nets in this figure are drawn with the maximum radius equal to 40 times the well radius. With r equal to $40r_0$, according to equation 9·37, the flow is

$$Q = 1.71kh_tZ$$

In the flow net of Fig. 9·17 (b) there are eight head drops, and since each path measures 26 degrees there are 360/26 or 13.8 paths. Since q of equation 9·17 is equal to Q/Z, the discharge may be written

$$Q = \frac{n_f}{n_d} kh_tZ = \frac{13.8}{8} kh_tZ = 1.73kh_tZ$$

The small difference between the above expressions is due entirely to lack of precision in the values obtained for n_f and n_d.

In the radial flow net of Fig. 9·17 (c) there are eight head drops and four paths. The rb/l value would be found constant if evaluated for a number of rectangles; for the labeled rectangle the values of r, b, and l are found by scaling to be equal respectively to $0.95Z$, $0.25Z$, and $0.44Z$. Thus the rb/l value is equal to $0.54Z$ and, from equation 9·35,

$$Q = kh_t\tfrac{4}{8}2\pi(0.54Z) = 1.70kh_tZ$$

This simple case of horizontal, radial flow is the only one for which it is possible to draw both types of flow net.

Of special interest in radial flow is the relatively large proportion of head loss in the near vicinity of the well. For the above example in which the maximum radius is equal to 40 times the well diameter, 50 per cent of the head is lost in the final 14 per cent of the length of the flow path.

Case B

When the flow everywhere is directed toward a single point, the expression for flow is best written in spherical coordinates, the spherical radius designated by r', rather than the polar coordinates used above, being employed. In such a case the area across which flow occurs at any given radius is the spherical surface of area $4\pi(r')^2$, and the discharge may be written

$$Q = k\frac{dh}{dr'}4\pi(r')^2$$

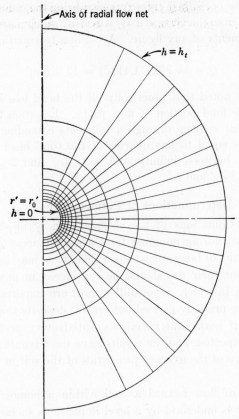

FIG. 9·18 Radial flow net for spherically radial flow.

If the head is h at radius r' and is zero at radius r_0' the solution of the differential equation is

$$h = \frac{Q}{4\pi k r_0'}\left(1 - \frac{r_0'}{r'}\right) \qquad (9\cdot38)$$

When the maximum radius r' is equal to 10 times the minimum radius r_0', the discharge according to equation 9·38 is

$$Q = 13.9 k h_t r_0'$$

The radial flow net for this case is given in Fig. 9·18. In this figure there are ten head drops and twenty flow paths. The constant value of rb/l (r in this expression being the radius measured horizontally from the vertical axis) is $1.11r_0'$, which may be checked by measurements of any figure. According to equation 9·35 the discharge is

$$Q = kh_t \tfrac{20}{10} 2\pi (1.11r_0') = 13.9kh_t r_0'$$

It may be noted that practically all the head loss in this case occurs in the final portion of flow paths. Equation 9·38 shows that for radial seepage through a soil mass extending to infinite radius, losses equal to one quarter of the total head loss occur, respectively, between infinity and $4r_0'$, $4r_0'$ and $2r_0'$, $2r_0'$ and $1\tfrac{1}{3}r_0'$, and $1\tfrac{1}{3}r_0'$ and r_0'.

9·17 Field Determinations of Permeability

Field determinations of the coefficient of permeability from data obtained during pumping tests are often more dependable than the results of laboratory tests. Field tests may be relatively expensive, but their use should be considered in any extensive investigation in which permeability data are important. When field tests are properly carried out on soil deposits that are relatively free of horizontal variations, satisfactory accuracy may usually be expected, and the results have the advantage of being representative of the average properties of the soil in its natural state.

The case of flow toward a well within a homogeneous soil stratum that is underlaid by a level impervious surface is represented by Fig. 9·19. An approximate formula for the permeability is easily obtained for this case. This derivation is attributed to Theim and Forchheimer. When the flow toward the well is approximately horizontal at two radii such as those shown in the figure, the gradient may be expressed as dz/dr without appreciable error, giving

$$Q = k \frac{dz}{dr} 2\pi rz$$

or

$$\int_{r_1}^{r_2} \frac{dr}{r} = \frac{2\pi k}{Q} \int_{z_1}^{z_2} z \, dz$$

whence

$$k = \frac{Q \log_e \dfrac{r_1}{r_2}}{\pi (z_1^2 - z_2^2)} \qquad (9 \cdot 39)$$

If observations are available for Q, and for z and r values at two points on the top flow line, a solution for k is obtainable. However, for good determinations a number of details must be given attention. Because of rapid head drops near the well and because of the possibility that the soil may be disturbed adjacent to the well, the r values chosen must be considerably larger than the radius of the well. Under natural conditions a considerable

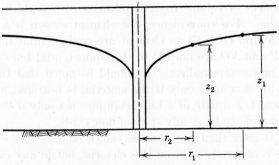

FIG. 9·19 Section used in the derivation of an expression for field determinations of permeability.

variation often exists between conditions on various radial planes; a definite, level, impervious, underlying stratum does not often occur; and there may be many variations from the assumed homogeneous condition. Thus, for a proper representation of conditions, depths to the water table and to the impervious boundary should be obtained along a number of radial lines to permit the determination of the average conditions for the various lines. Pumping must be continued for an appreciable period in soils of low permeability in order to be sure that a steady state of flow has been reached. If the Q values are observed before there is a steady state of flow, the results may indicate a permeability value which is much too large, even though the observations are taken when the rate of inflow is changing very slowly.

A number of other field methods which are of practical interest are available for estimating permeabilities. Foremost among these (167) are groundwater velocity methods, based on determinations of velocity by the tracing of dye or salt injections, and methods using flow relationships during drawdown.

9·18   Demonstration of the Basic Seepage Force Relationship

In Section 7·6 the subject of seepage force was introduced. The basic seepage force relationship will now be developed. The following analysis holds for flow in any direction, for either isotropic or stratified soil, and for either steady or variable flow.

In Fig. 9·20 let the figure *MNOP* represent the cross section of an element of volume from a soil mass within which seepage is occurring. For convenience, the element chosen is a square. Sides *MN* and *OP* of this element are equipotential lines, and sides *MP* and *NO* are normal to the equipotential lines and are lines of maximum gradient. It should be noted that lines *MP* and *NO* are flow lines only if the material is isotropic, and that the element is a square of a Laplacian flow net only if the material is isotropic and a steady state of flow exists.

There is more than one possible choice relative to the system of forces considered to act on this element, but in any event the forces which are considered and are in equilibrium are three in number. For a first choice, the material in the element may be considered to be a two-phase mass of soil and water. In this case the forces in equilibrium are the total weight of the soil-water mass, the resultant force contributed by all water pressures on the boundaries of the mass, and the resultant force caused by all intergranular pressures across the boundaries. For a second choice, the mass to be analyzed may be considered to be the soil skeleton only. In this case, the forces are the total weight of all soil grains, the force representing the resultant effect of water on the surfaces of all individual soil particles, and the resultant force caused by all intergranular pressures across the boundaries of the mass. A third choice, differing slightly from the second, is explained later.

In each case, the boundary intergranular force is one of the three forces to be considered, and it is sometimes called the *restraining force;* it must be equal in magnitude to, and must act in the opposite direction to, the vector sum of the other two forces. The sum of the other two forces is called herein the *resultant body force,* and it is the force caused by the combined action of water and gravity. The various choices of forces,

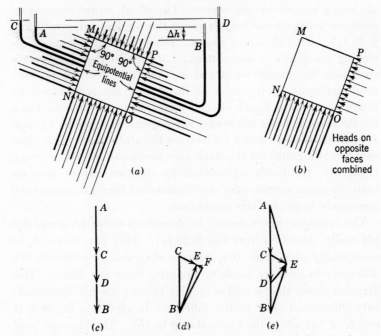

FIG. 9·20 Diagrams of boundary neutral pressures and force polygons showing weights, buoyancy, and seepage force and their relationships.

therefore, merely represent different viewpoints relative to the weights and the water effects which make up the body force.

In order to give a complete discussion of all forces, all possible weights and water forces will be analyzed in detail. Gravitational forces, or weights, will be considered first. The weight of the soil-water mass, equal to $[(G + e)/(1 + e)]\gamma_w A$, is represented in Fig. 9·20 (c) by vector AB. The true weight of the grains is $[G/(1 + e)]\gamma_w A$, the submerged weight of the grains is $[(G - 1)/(1 + e)]\gamma_w A$, and the weight of water is $[e/(1 + e)]\gamma_w A$; these forces are represented in the figure by vectors AD, AC, and DB, respectively. It may be noted that the vector

difference, *CB*, between the total weight *AB* and the submerged
weight *AC*, is the weight of a water mass of the same volume as
the element. Force *BC* is the *buoyancy,* and the *total weight
AB plus the buoyancy BC equals the submerged weight AC.*

The second step in the analysis of forces is the consideration
of forces caused by the water. Graphical representations of
pressure heads on the boundaries of the mass are shown in Fig.
9·20 (*a*). Two cases are shown. For a case with seepage occurring the heads on equipotentials *MN* and *OP* are shown respectively by standpipes *A* and *B*. For this case the pressure
head diagrams on the sides of the square are represented by
heavy vectors, the length of each vector being the pressure head.
On the same figure a static case is represented, standpipes *C* and
D showing the free water surface for the static case. The pressure head diagrams for the static case are shown by light vectors.
Obviously, the heads represented by the two sets of pressure
head diagrams cannot exist simultaneously; they are superposed
here solely to aid in their comparison.

The resultant forces caused by boundary water pressures are
not easily visualized from Fig. 9·20 (*a*). They can, however, be
quite easily seen from (*b*), wherein diagrams representing the
difference in pressure heads on opposite faces are shown. This
diagram shows that actual standpipe heights are not important;
only differences such as the difference in elevation between *A*
and *B* of (*a*) affect the heads shown in (*b*). The pressure head
shown on side *NO* in (*b*) is seen to be constant and to be the
same for both the seepage case and the static case. Because of
head dissipated in seepage, however, the pressure head shown
on side *PO* is less for the seepage case than for the static case.

During the dissipation of pressure head in viscous friction,
which occurs while the seeping water makes its way through fine
soil capillaries, the pressure in the water is being transferred by
viscous drag to the soil skeleton. Since the difference in the
light and heavy diagrams of pressure heads in (*b*) represents
pressure lost in viscous friction, it follows that an equal and
opposite pressure has been transferred, by drag on particle surfaces, to the intergranular structure. This force that is transferred to the soil structure is the seepage force. Seepage forces

always act normal to equipotential lines, but only in isotropic soils is this direction the same as that of flow lines.

Force polygons of water forces may now be drawn, and they are shown in (*d*). The resultant of forces in the water across surfaces *MP* and *NO* of (*a*) is represented in (*d*) by vector *BF* for both the seepage case and the static case. Across surfaces *MN* and *PO*, the resultant of forces in the water is *FE* for the case with seepage and *FC* for the static case. For the case with seepage vector *CE* represents the seepage force. The resultant of all water pressures for the static case is the buoyancy, represented by vector *BC*. The resultant of all water pressures with seepage occurring is represented by vector *BE*. The diagram shows that the *resultant* of *boundary water pressures BE*, during seepage, is equal to the vector sum of the *static-state buoyancy BC* and the *seepage force CE*.

The relationships of all forces caused by gravity and by water are shown in (*e*). In this diagram *AE* is the resultant body force; *EA* must, therefore, be the resultant of all boundary intergranular pressures.

As has been mentioned, the body force *AE* may be obtained by more than one combination of weight and water forces. The possible combinations are the vector sums, respectively, of *AB* and *BE*, *AD* and *DE*, and *AC* and *CE*. The first of these is a combination of the total weight and the resultant boundary neutral force; it is the one most often used in practical problems. The second possibility is a combination of the true weight of the grains and the resultant effect of water on grain surfaces; it is of interest mainly because it points out that the resultant effect of the water on the grains is composed of buoyancy to the grains *DC* plus the seepage force *CE*. The third choice is a combination of the submerged weight and the seepage force; it is perhaps the one which furnishes the clearest understanding of seepage effects.

The considerations for a small element may easily be extended to a large mass by the summation of forces for all the elements of volume which make up the mass. One additional factor must be considered, however. At the top of any capillary zone, the surface tension of the water exerts capillary pressure on the soil, as explained in Section 8·6. When the forces on masses topped by capillary zones are being considered, the force due to the capillary pressure must be included whenever either the second or the third of the possible combinations outlined in the previous paragraph are used.

In subsequent chapters it will be shown that information regarding magnitudes of body forces is required for analyses of the stability of earth embankments and foundations. In fact, this important type of analysis often consists simply of studies to determine whether or not the boundary intergranular stresses which can be counted on are of sufficient magnitude to resist the existing body forces.

The magnitude of the seepage force per unit of length in the third dimension, acting on the element of Fig. 9·20 (a), may be expressed

$$J = \gamma_w \, \Delta h \, b$$

where b represents the dimensions OP and MP. This force divided by b^2, the area of the element, gives the seepage force per unit of volume:

$$j = \gamma_w i_m \tag{9·40}$$

where i_m represents $\Delta h/b$, which is the maximum gradient. This maximum gradient is the gradient along lines normal to equipotentials. It should be noted that its value in stratified soil may be considerably larger than the gradient along flow paths. Attention should also be given to the fact that seepage forces are always normal to equipotential lines.

PROBLEMS

1. Describe the transformation used for flow net studies of stratified soils. Assuming that a complete understanding has been obtained relative to the procedures for determining the flow net, the seepage quantity, the uplift diagram and values of gradients at all points for an isotropic soil, explain all points needed to extend the understanding to stratified soil.

2. The accompanying figure shows the cross section of a dam above a foundation which has vertical and horizontal permeabilities of 1 and 6 microns per sec respectively.

(a) Redraw the section to true scale and draw the flow net on this section.

(b) Determine the seepage in cubic feet per day per 100 ft of dam.

(c) Sketch the diagram of uplift pressure on the base of the dam.

(*d*) Determine the pressure head, the elevation head, and the total head at the point directly below the cutoff wall and at the level of the underlying ledge.

(*e*) Determine the gradients at the toe and at a point 80 ft downstream of the toe.

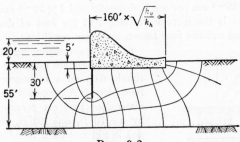

PROB. 9·2.

3. A deposit of cohesionless soil with a permeability of 10^{-3} ft per sec has a depth of 40 ft with impervious ledge below. A sheet pile wall is driven into this deposit to a depth of 30 ft. The wall extends above the surface of the soil, and a 10-ft depth of water acts on one side. Sketch the flow net and determine the seepage quantity.

4 to 7 inclusive. Sketch the flow net for the section shown in the appropriate figure, assuming that the figure shows the transformed section.

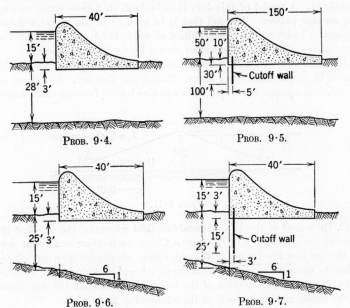

PROB. 9·4.

PROB. 9·5.

PROB. 9·6.

PROB. 9·7.

8. A concrete dam has lines of sheet piling at both heel and toe which extend halfway down to an impervious stratum. The head on the dam is 30 ft. From a flow net made up of "square" figures on the transformed scale it is found that there are five seepage paths and sixteen equipotential drops. The average value for the coefficient of permeability may be taken as 5×10^{-4} cm per sec horizontally and 1×10^{-4} cm per sec vertically. What is the seepage in cubic feet per foot of dam? Make a sketch pointing out the four known boundary conditions.

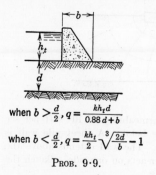

when $b > \dfrac{d}{2}$, $q = \dfrac{k h_t d}{0.88\, d + b}$

when $b < \dfrac{d}{2}$, $q = \dfrac{k h_t}{2} \sqrt[3]{\dfrac{2d}{b} - 1}$

PROB. 9·9.

9. In the accompanying figure approximate formulas are given for flow below a simple dam on a homogeneous isotropic foundation. A proposed dam will have dimensions that are represented roughly by $h = 30$ ft, $b = 100$ ft, and $d = 90$ ft, and it will rest on a foundation in which the coefficients of permeability in the horizontal and vertical directions are 50×10^{-4} and 5×10^{-4} cm per sec, respectively. Obtain an estimate of the seepage below the dam.

10. A proposed dam is to have slopes of 1 on 3 (1 vertical on 3 horizontal), and it is to be composed of soil with horizontal and vertical permeabilities of 14 and 2×10^{-4} cm per sec, respectively. A model of this dam is to be built in a glass flume to study the seepage pattern. The soil that is to be used in the model will have horizontal and vertical permeabilities of 400×10^{-4} and 300×10^{-4} cm per sec, respectively. What slopes should be used for the model?

11. Determine by the Kozeny method the top flow line through the dam shown in the accompanying figure. Sketch the flow net. Determine the quantity of seepage from the sketch and also by the formula and compare.

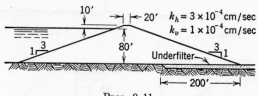

PROB. 9·11.

12. By means of the L. Casagrande method determine the top flow line through the dam shown in the figure. Check the location of the exit point of the top flow line by use of Gilboy's chart. Sketch the flow net. Determine the quantity of seepage from the sketch and by formula and compare.

13. Determine the location of the top flow line through the dam shown in the figure, making use only of the relationship $\Delta s = C z$.

14. By the method based on correction of the Kozeny parabola determine the location of the point of exit of the top flow line through the dam shown in the figure. Determine the quantity of seepage by the formulas of both the Kozeny and the L. Casagrande methods.

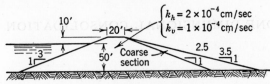

PROBS. 9·12, 9·13, 9·14.

15. An island with a 400-ft radius has conditions resembling Fig. 9·16 (a) except that within a radius of 200 ft of the central point on the island the permeability of the underlying sand stratum is 50×10^{-4} cm per sec, whereas the permeability outside of the 200-ft radius averages 2×10^{-4} cm per sec. The pervious stratum is of 20-ft thickness, and a well of 4-ft diameter has been driven through this stratum. It is to be assumed that some type of protection has been used to prevent inflow of sand into the well. The head used up in seepage through the sand is 40 ft.

(a) Sketch the flow net on the horizontal plane through the sand stratum and determine the seepage quantity.

(b) Check the results of part (a) by the use of two simultaneous equations of the same type as equation 9·37.

(c) Compare the inflow with that which would occur if the permeabilities of the two portions of the sand stratum were to be interchanged.

16. At a certain point on a typical cross section through a mass of saturated, homogeneous, isotropic soil, seeping water follows a path inclined downward at 15 degrees to the horizontal. The hydraulic gradient is 0.20, and the pore water at the point is at a pressure of 1500 lb per sq ft. The void ratio of the soil is 0.80, and the specific gravity of the grains is 2.70. Determine the magnitudes of the resultant boundary water force, the seepage force, the true weight, and the buoyant weight of a flow net square with 1-ft dimensions, centered on the given point, and show all forces to scale on a force diagram.

Chapter 10

ONE-DIMENSIONAL CONSOLIDATION

10·1   Stress-Strain-Time Relationships

The application of stresses to any material causes strains. In some materials a certain amount of time is required for the occurrence of the strains. In such materials, the stresses, the strains, and the time bear certain definite relationships to each other; these relationships are mechanical properties of the material, and are called stress-strain-time relationships. The first examples of relationships of this type in this book are presented in this chapter.

The simplest relationships of this type are those which hold for elastic materials, in which stress and strain are proportional and independent of time. When the loadings are known it is possible, by the use of methods based on the theory of elasticity, to compute stresses, strains, and displacements at all points in certain simple types of elastic members such as beams and columns. It is also possible to compute stresses caused by surface loads within an elastic mass of infinite dimensions, as explained in the next chapter.

If it were possible to develop a more general theory, of the same type as the theory of elasticity but valid for materials with more complicated stress-strain relationships, it would find many important applications. However, solutions based on the theory of elasticity are far from easy for all but the simplest of cases, and any general theory which covers even minor variations from simple, elastic conditions becomes unbelievably complex. Whereas elastic theory considerations require the use of only two stress-strain constants, the modulus of elasticity and Poisson's ratio being the two most commonly used, a general theory involves a large, unknown number of complex stress-strain and stress-strain-time relationships. Thus the obtaining of a general stress-strain theory for plastic materials, and especially for cases where time effects enter, must be acknowledged as an impossible goal. This is especially true for soils; all soils show a limited amount of elastic action, but plastic soils have stress-strain relationships and time effects that are probably as complex as those of any other material.

There are certain simple cases of practical interest that involve stresses, strains, and time effects in non-elastic materials and that can be solved. One-dimensional compression of soils, which is treated in this chapter, is an important example.

There are also certain types of soil problems in which the loading causes stresses and strains that are approximately proportional. In problems of this type, expressions from elastic theory are often used for determining stresses; the procedure is explained in Chapter 11.

Soil engineering problems in which data on stress-strain and stress-strain-time relationships are needed are of two basic types. The first type includes all cases wherein there is no possibility of the stresses being sufficiently large to overtax the strength of the soil in shear, but wherein the strains lead to what may be serious magnitudes of displacements or settlements within the soil mass. Common examples of this type of problem are considered in Chapters 10 to 12 inclusive and in Chapter 19. The second type includes cases in which there is danger of the shearing stresses exceeding the shearing strength of the soil. Problems of this type are called *stability problems*, and examples are presented in Chapters 13 to 19 inclusive.

10·2 Compressibility of Soils

It has been pointed out in Chapter 2 that a soil may be considered to be a skeleton of solid grains enclosing voids which may be filled with gas, with liquid, or with a combination of gas and liquid. If a sample of soil is placed under stress in such a way that its volume is decreased, there are three possible factors to which this decrease might conceivably be attributed:

1. A compression of the solid matter.
2. A compression of water and air within the voids.
3. An escape of water and air from the voids.

Under the loads usually encountered in soil masses, the solid matter and the pore water, being relatively incompressible, do not undergo appreciable volume change. For this reason, it is sufficiently accurate to consider the decrease in volume of a mass, if it is completely saturated, as due entirely to an escape of water from the voids.

In a partially saturated soil mass the situation is much more complex, since a small amount of compressible gas within the pores may allow appreciable compression of the sample as a whole, even though there is no escape of pore water. However, sedimentary clay deposits usually are almost completely saturated, and in analyses of submerged clay strata in their natural states complete saturation is usually assumed. When saturated clays are discussed herein, a condition of complete saturation is assumed unless otherwise stated.

These considerations indicate that the compressibility of a soil is not governed to any appreciable degree by the compressibility of the mineral grains of which it is composed. It is rather a function of the extent to which the grains can deform and shift their positions. More specifically, the compressibility of a soil mass depends on the rigidity of the soil skeleton. The rigidity, in turn, is dependent on the structural arrangement of particles and, in fine-grained soils, on the degree to which adjacent particles are bonded together.

A honeycombed structure, or in general any structure with high porosity, is more compressible than a dense structure. A soil composed predominantly of flat grains is more compressible than one containing mostly spherical grains. A soil in remolded state may be much more compressible than the same soil in natural state.

When the pressure on a given soil is increased, a decrease in volume must always occur. If the pressure is later decreased to its previous value some expansion will take place, but the volume rebound will not be by any means so great as the preceding compression. In other words, soils show some elastic tendency but they are elastic to, at most, a small degree.

An actual separation of strains into elastic and non-elastic portions is not possible. However, a few general statements relative to such a subdivision may be made. That portion of the compression which is due to change in relative positions of the soil grains is to a large degree non-elastic. A pressure applied to a soil mass may cause a given grain to slip down along another, but it is scarcely conceivable that removal of the pressure would cause this grain to rise again. On the other hand, the portion of the compression which is due to deformation of the individual grains is predominantly elastic. Under the usual pressures, the grains are seldom stressed beyond the elastic limit, and are capable of regaining substantially their original shapes when the pressure is removed. There is another important type of strain rebound which occurs in fine-grained soils. Between parallel, small, flat soil particles small amounts of water are held by microscopic forces, the amounts of water depending on the pressure on the soil skeleton. When the pressure is increased some of this water is squeezed out. When the pressure is decreased these forces cause water to be drawn in. This drawing of water into small apertures is the phenomenon known as swelling, and the degree to which a soil swells is in many instances of much practical importance. Considerable time may be required either for the squeezing of water from between plates or for swelling.

10·3 One-Dimensional Compression and Consolidation

The discussion in the previous section refers to compressions in general.* It is not possible to analyze the general case, but an analysis of the case in which compressions take place in one direction only is relatively simple.

One-dimensional compression is the condition treated in the theoretical analysis given in the following pages. This simple type of compression holds, except for minor variations caused by side friction, in the laboratory test described in this chapter. The weights of buildings cause compressions in the underground which at shallow depths are definitely three-dimensional, but which, in deeply buried strata, are essentially one-dimensional. If a constant depth of fill is placed over a very large area of ground surface, below which there is no horizontal variation in the soil, compressions below the central portions of the area

---

* For theoretical considerations of three-dimensional compression and consolidation see reference 14.

approach a truly one-dimensional case. Thus concepts from the one-dimensional analysis will have important practical applications.

As the compressions occur there must be escape of pore water. This escape takes place according to Darcy's Law. If the soil under compression has a low coefficient of permeability a long time may be required for the compression to take place.

The gradual process which involves, simultaneously, a slow escape of water and a gradual compression, and which will be shown later to involve also a gradual pressure adjustment, is called consolidation. This definition is a general one, valid for the three-dimensional as well as the one-dimensional case. There has been controversy regarding the proper definition of consolidation as the term is understood in soil mechanics. It is suggested that the definition given herein, according to which consolidation is a gradual process involving drainage, compression, and stress transfer, is preferable to the definition used by some soil engineers, according to which consolidation is merely compression under static loading. Unfortunately there is also wide disagreement in the meanings given this term by soil engineers and geologists; in geology consolidation refers to the degree to which a material is compacted or solidified.

10·4   Compressibility and Consolidation Apparatus and Tests

For the determination of the compressibility characteristics and the speed at which compressions occur in soils under one-dimensional compression an apparatus of the type shown in Fig. 10·1 is used. This apparatus † is called a consolidometer. In addition to the unit shown, a means of loading is required, and a photograph of a complete assembly is shown in Fig. 10·2.

In this apparatus the soil sample is placed within a ring 4¼ in. in inside diameter and 1¼ in. long or high. When undisturbed clay samples are to be tested, specimens are carefully cut to size, a 4¼-in. diameter cutting edge being used. The ring,

---

† The first apparatus of this type was built by K. Terzaghi and was called an oedometer. The first design for large-diameter samples was prepared by A. Casagrande in 1932 or 1933. An apparatus essentially the same as that shown in Fig. 10·1 was designed by G. Gilboy in 1933 and its description was first published in reference 62.

which is detachable from the rest of the apparatus, is next eased over the sample, and the sample may then be cut to height. For satisfactory results, samples must be in as near the undisturbed, natural condition as possible, and a very careful technique in cutting to size and placing is essential.

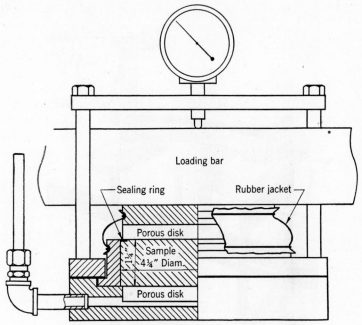

Fig. 10·1   Consolidometer of 4¼-inch diameter.

Other important details of the consolidometer are shown in the figure. Disks of porous refractory material provide free drainage at the top and the bottom of the sample. A thin sealing ring, either L-shaped or flat, has been found necessary with some soft clays to prevent material from squeezing past the upper disk. A choice of two methods is available for the prevention of evaporation at the top surface. A cylinder of thin sheet rubber may be bound into the depressions in the ring and the top bearing plate, or a cylindrical wall of thin metal may be placed around and projecting above the ring, with standing water in it to above the level of the top of the ring. A standpipe and pressure line can be attached to the bottom drainage connection to allow the use of the consolidometer as an upward flow permeameter and permit direct determinations of the permeability of the sample. The amount of compression which the sample undergoes is indicated

Fig. 10·2 Consolidation machine.

on the extensometer dial. Loads are applied to the cover above the upper porous stone.

The following testing procedure is, with minor variations, applicable to any type of soil.

Loads are applied in steps, each load doubling the previous value, the loading intensities commonly used being ¼, ½, 1, 2, 4, 8, and 16 tons per sq ft or kg per sq cm. Each load is allowed to stand until compression has practically ceased. In sands the increment duration need be only a few minutes. In clays compression continues for a long period of time, and the use of one-day durations is quite common.

For each increment a curve of compression versus time is obtained. At the end of each increment the void ratio of the sample is determined. The final data consist, therefore, of a time curve for each increment and the compression data for the test as a whole. The compression data, or final stress-strain relationships, are presented in the form of a curve of pressure versus void ratio, with a point on the curve for the final condition of each pressure increment.

Accurate determinations of void ratio are essential and may be computed from the following data: the cross-sectional area A of the container; the unit weight of solids γ_s; the weight of solid matter W_s, obtained by drying and weighing the sample at the conclusion of the test; the sample thickness Z, determined directly at least once during the test and obtained at other times by the application of thickness changes, as given by extensometer dial readings, to the direct determination. The direct thickness determination may be obtained from known constant thicknesses of apparatus parts and a careful measurement, by extensometer gage, of the distance from the top of the ring to the top of the upper cover. The void ratio is given by the expression

$$e = \frac{V}{V_s} - 1$$

where

$$V = ZA \quad \text{and} \quad V_s = \frac{W_s}{\gamma_s}$$

10·5 Compression of Sands

The pressure-versus-void-ratio curve for a typical sand under one-dimensional compression, on which the load is first raised in steps to 3.3 kg per sq cm, then released in steps to zero, and later built again to 6 kg per sq cm, is shown in Fig. 10·3. The shape of the various branches of this figure are worthy of careful study.

A typical curve showing the time versus the compression caused by an increment of load on this sand is shown in Fig. 10·4. This figure shows that in sands the major part of the compression takes place almost instantaneously. In this example all but about 5 per cent of the compression has occurred after the load has been acting for 1 minute.

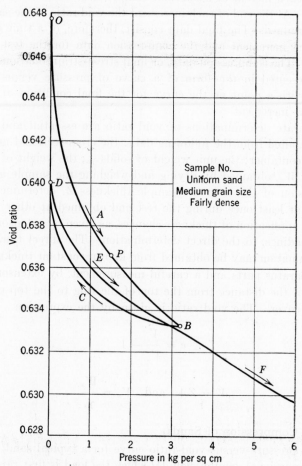

Sample No.___
Uniform sand
Medium grain size
Fairly dense

Fig. 10·3 Compression diagram for sand.

The time lag during compression in sands is largely of frictional nature. In coarse, clean samples it is about the same whether the sand is saturated or dry. After an increment of load has been applied there is not a uniform and smooth rearrangement of grains from initial to final positions, but a successive, irregular, localized building up and breaking down of stresses in grain groups. A continuous rearrangement of particle positions occurs, and any two particles that are pressed tightly together

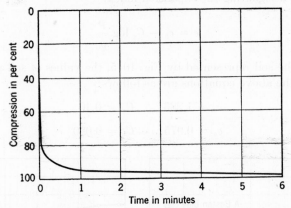

Fig. 10·4 Time curve for a typical load increment on sand.

and rolling on each other at one instant may in the next instant undergo a sudden jump in position relative to each other. The time lag in reaching the final state is called the frictional lag.

10·6 Compression and Consolidation of Clays

A typical pressure-versus-void-ratio curve for a clay is shown in Fig. 10·5, in (a) to natural pressure scale and in (b) to logarithmic pressure scale. A time curve for a typical pressure increment on this soil is given in Fig. 10·6.

As shown by Fig. 10·5, the compression curve at pressures above a certain value, in this case above about 4 kg per sq cm, is approximately a straight line on the logarithmic plot; in this straight line range it may be represented by the empirical equation

$$e = e_c - C_c \log_{10} \frac{p}{p_0} \qquad (10·1)$$

where e_c is the void ratio at pressure p_0. The value arbitrarily chosen for p_0 usually is 1 ton per sq ft or 1 kg per sq cm, although the straight line often has to be projected backward to reach this pressure. The slope of the curve on the semi-logarithmic plot is negative; the numerical value of this slope is designated by C_c and is called the compression index.

The expansion or rebound curve may be similarly expressed, with C_e designating the expansion index:

$$e = e_e - C_e \log \frac{p}{p_0} \tag{10·2}$$

For the soil represented by Fig. 10·5, the values of soil properties in the above equations are as follows:

$$e_c = 1.285; \qquad C_c = 0.40$$
$$e_e = 0.975; \qquad C_e = 0.080$$

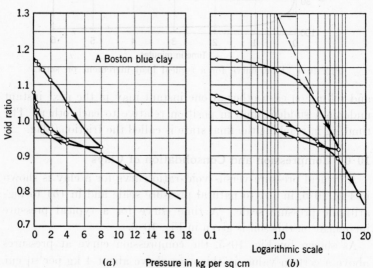

(a)   Pressure in kg per sq cm   (b)

FIG. 10·5   Compression diagrams for clay.

In Fig. 10·5 (b) it can be noted that the curvature of the initial line at pressures smaller than 4 kg per sq cm resembles the curvature of the recompression branch at pressures smaller than about 10 kg per sq cm. This resemblance indicates that the specimen was probably subjected to a pressure of about 3 or 4 kg per sq cm at some time before its removal from the ground. Therefore, the curved portion of the initial line is a recompression curve, and the conclusion may be drawn that convex curvature on this type of semi-logarithmic plot always indicates recompression.

10·7 Time Lags during the Compression of Clay

It is a well-known characteristic of clays that considerable time is required for the occurrence of the compression caused by a given increment of load. This action is shown by Fig. 10·6. Foundation engineers also know well that buildings founded above thick clay strata undergo settlements that continue for

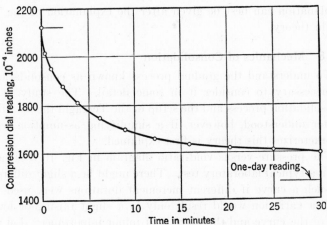

FIG. 10·6 Time curve for a typical load increment on clay.

long periods of time at steadily decreasing rates and that may still be occurring at an appreciable rate after many years.

Two phenomena contribute to this large time lag. The first has already been explained; it is due to time required for the escape of the pore water. It is called the hydrodynamic lag. It is well understood and it is due basically to the viscosity which retards the flow of the pore water. The second factor is a complex one which herein will be called the plastic lag. It is only partially understood, and it is due to plastic action in adsorbed water near grain-to-grain contacts or points of nearest approach to contact. The frictional lag in sands may be thought of as a simple form of plastic lag.

A theory of consolidation advanced by Terzaghi about two

decades ago will be explained in detail in the following pages. It presents a good understanding of hydrodynamic lag and rates of settlement. The Terzaghi theory does not recognize the existence of plastic lag; thus this theory can be only a limited representation of the true action of clay undergoing compression. Moreover, the use of the Terzaghi theory for predicting settlements must be looked upon as a procedure which may not always give satisfactory results.

The plastic lag is still not well enough understood to warrant more than a brief, qualitative, hypothetical explanation. This explanation can best be given after the explanation of the Terzaghi theory.

10·8 Mechanics of Consolidation

To understand the gradual process known as consolidation it is necessary to consider it in some detail. The study of the consolidation process and the setup of the Terzaghi theory will be better understood, however, if a simplifying assumption which characterizes this theory is first explained.

The pressure-versus-void-ratio diagram in Fig. 10·5 is taken from a typical laboratory test. There might be a slight difference in such a curve if different increment durations were used, but such a variation would result only in a slight raising or lowering of the curve and therefore is of minor importance. Let Fig. 10·7 represent the portion of a curve of pressure versus void ratio for a pressure increment from p_1 to p_2. It is assumed in the theory that this curve is a straight line in any increment, an assumption which may be accepted as reasonably correct. It is also assumed that this relationship between pressure and void ratio holds under all conditions, with no variation because of time effects or any other factor. If there were no plasticity and no plastic lag in clay, this assumption would probably be acceptable. However, clays are highly plastic and, once this assumption is made, it must be realized that a phenomenon of major importance is ignored and results may thereby be considerably affected. On the basis of this simplified relationship that is assumed to exist between pressure and void ratio, the process of consolidation may now be explained.

Just before the application of an increment of pressure a sample may be assumed throughout its depth to be under conditions represented by point A of Fig. 10·7. The intergranular pressure throughout is p_1 and the void ratio e_1. An instant after the increment is applied the total pressure acting on the sample is p_2, but the void ratio is still e_1. The pressure p_2 cannot be effective within the soil until the void ratio becomes e_2. Consequently the pressure in the soil (that is, the intergranular pressure) must still be p_1.

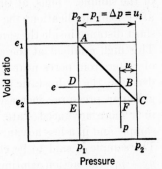

This concept is fundamental and must be clearly understood in order to obtain a true idea of the nature of consolidation. The increase in stress represented by the difference $p_2 - p_1$ tends to produce a strain represented by $e_1 - e_2$. On account of hydrodynamic lag, however, the strain cannot take place at once. Hence the conclusion is inevitable that the increased stress cannot act at once.

FIG. 10·7 Pressure-versus-void-ratio relationship for a typical pressure increment, according to the Terzaghi theory.

On the other hand, the pressure acting on the sample has actually been increased to p_2. If the conclusion is valid that the pressure in the soil immediately after the increase is still p_1, the question how the added pressure is carried arises. There is only one possibility: the added pressure is carried by the water in the voids of the soil. It is assumed, as noted earlier, that strains produced in the water by the applied stresses are so small in comparison to those in the soil as to be negligible. Therefore, at the instant of time under consideration, the pressure in the soil skeleton is still p_1; a pressure of $p_2 - p_1$ has just been thrown into the water, making the total pressure in the sample p_2, which is equal to the total applied pressure.

The stress existing in the water filling the voids of a soil, when produced by transient conditions similar to those outlined above, is designated as hydrostatic excess pressure. This pressure is represented by u. The initial value of u is the maximum value; it is equal to $p_2 - p_1$ and is designated by u_i.

The conditions which will prevail in the next succeeding instant of time depend on circumstances. If the entire sample were to be hermetically sealed, so that no water could escape, it seems evident that the conditions mentioned above would be maintained indefinitely. However, the condition fulfilled in the consolidation device by the presence of porous disks is the prompt elimination of hydrostatic excess pressure at the top and the bottom surfaces of the sample. Thus, at the surface of the sample at the instant after load application, the water pressure is zero, whereas at a short distance inside the sample the water pressure still is $p_2 - p_1$. This high gradient at the surface is the cause of rapid drainage of water from pores near the surface. Gradually the void ratios decrease, the hydrostatic excess pressures decrease, and the intergranular pressures increase, this gradual process always being in a more advanced state near the top and the bottom of the sample and in a less advanced state near the center of the sample. The sample is said to be *consolidating* under the stress increase $p_2 - p_1$; the action continues until at all points the void ratio has become e_2. The hydrostatic excess pressure has then become zero; theoretically, no more water is forced out; the pressure in the soil skeleton is p_2; and the sample is said to be *consolidated* under the stress p_2.

The phrases "under the stress increase $p_2 - p_1$" and "under the stress p_2" should be carefully noted. As stated earlier in the chapter, consolidation is a relative term, referring to the degree to which the gradual process has advanced, not to the solidity of the material. For example, a clay stratum in nature under light load may be completely consolidated under its load, yet be in a relatively soft condition. Another stratum may be heavily loaded and quite stiff, yet not completely consolidated under its applied load.

The process of consolidation may be better understood by reference to a mechanical analogy. In Fig. 10·8, (a) to (e), are shown the various lengths assumed by a spring under various loads. In the lower row of sketches the same spring is assumed to be immersed in a watertight cylinder filled with water. In (g) a frictionless but tightly fitting piston has been placed in the cylinder and loaded with a total load of 20 lb. The piston is provided with a stopcock, which is assumed to be closed so that no water can escape. Under the 20-lb load, the spring would tend to assume the length shown at (*e*), but it cannot do so unless the piston descends, and the piston cannot descend because the water cannot escape. The compressibility of the spring is assumed to be so great that the strains produced in the water and in the walls of the cylinder are negligible in comparison. Consequently the spring cannot take any of the superimposed

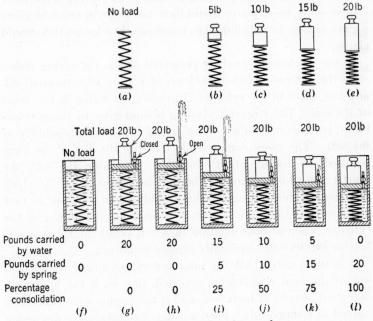

FIG. 10·8 The piston and spring analogy.

load, and the water must carry it all. If the term consolidation may be applied to the spring, it may be said to be unconsolidated under the applied load.

Now suppose the stopcock is opened. Sketch (*h*) represents conditions immediately afterward. The water spurts out on account of the pressure to which it is subjected. In the first instant, the pressure conditions are unchanged, as noted below the figure.

As the water escapes, the piston sinks lower and lower, compressing the spring. At (*i*), the length of the spring is the same as at (*b*). The spring consequently must be carrying 5 lb, the

water 15 lb, and consolidation is 25 per cent complete. At (j)
the length is the same as at (c), at (k) the same as at (d), and
at (l) the same as at (e). The resulting pressure conditions are
as indicated. The length of time required for the spring to pass
from one state of consolidation to the next depends, obviously,
on the rapidity with which the water escapes, that is, on the size
of the stopcock opening. In addition, if the spring were more
compressible, more water would have to escape in order to allow
a given change in consolidation; consequently a longer time would
elapse.

In the mechanical analogy presented above, the spring represents the compressible soil skeleton of a mass of saturated soil,
and the water in the cylinder represents the water in the voids
of the soil. The stopcock opening is analogous to the permeability, the compressibility of the spring to the compressibility of
the soil. The more compressible the soil, the longer the time
required for consolidation; the more permeable the soil, the
shorter the time required. The one important detail in which
this analogy fails to agree with consolidation in a soil is that
pressure conditions are the same throughout the height of the
cylinder, whereas consolidation in a soil begins at the top and
bottom surfaces and gradually progresses inward.

It is to be noted that the same general argument would hold
true if the load effects were reversed, that is, if the load were
decreased instead of increased, and if the sample were expanding
instead of compressing. For the sake of clearness the discussion
will be continued on the basis of compression, but it should be
kept in mind that a similar argument could be applied to the
expansion characteristics.

10·9   The Consolidation Ratio and the Coefficient of Compressibility

As a measure of the degree to which consolidation has pro-
gressed at any point within a consolidating sample, the ratio between the void ratio change attained and the final void ratio
change is used. This is the ratio between the ordinate change
along AB and AC in Fig. 10·7. The ratio is designated by U_z
and it is expressed

$$U_z = \frac{e_1 - e}{e_1 - e_2} \qquad (10\cdot 3)$$

The consolidation ratio is frequently called simply the consolidation; often it is expressed in per cent and called the per cent consolidation. Since compressions are directly proportional to void ratio changes, the consolidation of any element of height of a sample is equal to the ratio between the compression attained in this element and the ultimate amount of compression.

From Fig. 10·7, it is seen that at any point

$$p_2 = p_1 + u_i = p + u \qquad (10\cdot 4)$$

The slope of the straight line curve of pressure versus void ratio is negative, the expression for its numerical value being

$$a_v = \frac{e_1 - e_2}{p_2 - p_1} = -\frac{de}{dp} \qquad (10\cdot 5)$$

The property a_v is a strain-stress ratio of the soil called the coefficient of compressibility. It is numerically equal to the slope of the curve on the natural scale plot of pressure versus void ratio. All soil characteristics appearing in the theory are given the subscript v.

It may be seen in Fig. 10·7 and may be shown by use of equations 10·4 and 10·5 that equation 10·3 may be extended as follows:

$$U_z = \frac{e_1 - e}{e_1 - e_2} = \frac{p - p_1}{p_2 - p_1} = 1 - \frac{u}{u_i} \qquad (10\cdot 6)$$

It is evident that U_z equals zero at the instant when the applied stress is increased to p_2 and that it increases gradually to 100 per cent as the void ratio decreases from e_1 to e_2. The intergranular pressure meanwhile increases from p_1 to p_2, and the hydrostatic excess pressure dissipates from u_i to zero. The expression in terms of e in equation 10·6 may be accepted as the fundamental one, the other forms holding only under the Terzaghi assumption of linear relationships.

10·10   The Terzaghi Consolidation Theory

The theoretical study of consolidation has for its purpose the setting up of an equation from which the pressure and void ratio values may be known at any point and at any time in a stratum of consolidating soil of any thickness. From such an equation the change in overall thickness of the strata after any interval of time may readily be determined by integration.

The analysis given below was developed by Terzaghi (Section 20 of reference 143). It leads to functions that may be recognized as analogous to those expressing the flow of heat. The assumptions which are used in this theory are

1. Homogeneous soil.
2. Complete saturation.
3. Negligible compressibility of soil grains and water.
4. Action of infinitesimal masses no different from that of larger, representative masses.
5. One-dimensional compression.
6. One-dimensional flow.
7. The validity of Darcy's Law.
8. Constant values for certain soil properties which actually vary somewhat with pressure.
9. The greatly idealized pressure-versus-void-ratio relationship of Fig. 10·7.

The first three assumptions have been discussed in previous sections, and they represent assumed conditions that do not vary in any important degree from actual conditions. The fourth assumption is of academic interest only and has little bearing from the practical viewpoint; it is included because the differential equations which must be used treat infinitesimal distances, and an infinitesimal mass consisting of part of a grain cannot show the same action as a representative group of grains. The fifth and sixth assumptions are closely realized in the laboratory test; their degree of validity must, however, be reviewed later in applications to cases in nature. The seventh assumption may be accepted with little question. Assumption eight introduces some errors, as may easily be demonstrated by more detailed analyses, but it is believed that in most instances these are of minor importance.

It is assumption nine that leads to the limited validity of the theory. The only justification for its use is that a more correct relationship would make the analysis unduly complex.

The fundamental expression for flow in saturated earth masses has been derived in Section 9·6. Expression 9·11 represents the time rate of change of volume and reads:

$$\left(k_x \frac{\partial^2 h}{\partial x^2} + k_y \frac{\partial^2 h}{\partial y^2} + k_z \frac{\partial^2 h}{\partial z^2} \right) dx\, dy\, dz$$

This expression is dependent only on assumptions one to four inclusive and seven. For one-dimensional flow, which is assumption six, the absence of gradient in the x and y directions eliminates the first two terms of the parentheses. The permeability k_z may, from this point on, be designated simply by k, giving

$$k \frac{\partial^2 h}{\partial z^2} dx\, dy\, dz \qquad (10\cdot7)$$

The volume of the element is $dx\, dy\, dz$, the pore volume is $dx\, dy\, dz\, \dfrac{e}{1+e}$, and, since all changes in volume must be changes in pore volume, a second expression for the time rate of change of volume may be written

$$\frac{\partial}{\partial t} \left(dx\, dy\, dz\, \frac{e}{1+e} \right)$$

Since $\dfrac{dx\, dy\, dz}{1+e}$ is the constant volume of solids, the above expression may be written $\dfrac{dx\, dy\, dz}{1+e} \dfrac{\partial e}{\partial t}$. Equating this expression to expression 10·7 and canceling $dx\, dy\, dz$ gives

$$k \frac{\partial^2 h}{\partial z^2} = \frac{1}{1+e} \frac{\partial e}{\partial t}$$

Only heads due to hydrostatic excess pressures will tend to cause flow in the case under consideration. Thus h in the above equation may be replaced by u/γ_w, giving

$$\frac{k}{\gamma_w} \frac{\partial^2 u}{\partial z^2} = \frac{1}{1+e} \frac{\partial e}{\partial t} \qquad (10\cdot8)$$

The hydrostatic excess pressure u is not necessarily the only pressure in the water. In addition static water pressures of unrestricted magnitudes may exist, but they play no part in consolidation because they do not tend to cause flow.

The steps of the derivation up to this point contain no assumptions which can be seriously questioned. If a more accurate treatment than the following is desired it must result from the use of a more correct relationship between pressure and void ratio than that used for assumption nine.

Equation 10·4 shows that dp equals $-du$. Substitution of this expression into equation 10·5 gives the following expression of assumption nine:

$$de = a_v \, du \qquad (10·9)$$

The substitution of this relationship in equation 10·8 gives

$$\left[\frac{k(1 + e)}{a_v \gamma_w}\right] \frac{\partial^2 u}{\partial z^2} = \frac{\partial u}{\partial t}$$

The group of terms in the bracket may be written

$$\frac{k(1 + e)}{a_v \gamma_w} = c_v \qquad (10·10)$$

The soil property designated by c_v is called the coefficient of consolidation.‡ Its insertion in the equation above gives

$$c_v \frac{\partial^2 u}{\partial z^2} = \frac{\partial u}{\partial t} \qquad (10·11)$$

In the consolidation theory the z coordinate distance is measured downward from the surface of the clay sample. The thickness of the sample is designated by $2H$, the distance H thus being the length of the longest drainage path.

The boundary conditions for this case of one-dimensional consolidation may be expressed as follows:

1. There is complete drainage at the top of the sample.
2. There is complete drainage at the bottom of the sample.

‡ Readers of consolidation literature should observe that this expression for coefficient of consolidation conflicts with an older expression defining the coefficient as equal to $k/[a_v \gamma_w(1 + e)]$. See note to this effect in reference 6.

3. The initial hydrostatic excess pressure u_i is equal to the pressure increment $p_2 - p_1$. (The case of main interest is that wherein u_i is a constant, but solutions are possible when u_i varies with depth.)

The mathematical expressions for these three boundary conditions are

1.   When $z = 0$, $u = 0$

2.   When $z = 2H$, $u = 0$ (10·12)

3.   When $t = 0$, $u = u_i$

The next step is to obtain the solution of equation 10·11 for boundary conditions 10·12.

10·11   The Mathematical Solution for the Consolidation Expression

An understanding of the hypothesis of this theory is important to any engineer who uses the theory to predict settlements. Whether or not the mathematics of the solution is of interest will depend on his point of view, and this part of the derivation may be omitted if desired. In Section 10·12 the final solution is discussed. The solution of equation 10·11 for boundary conditions 10·12 follows.

Assume that u is a product of some function of z and some function of t; that is,

$$u = F(z) \cdot \Phi(t) \qquad (10 \cdot 13)$$

Equation 10·11 may then be written §

$$c_v \Phi(t) F''(z) = F(z) \Phi'(t)$$

or

$$\frac{F''(z)}{F(z)} = \frac{\Phi'(t)}{c_v \Phi(t)} \qquad (10 \cdot 14)$$

Since the left member of this equation does not contain the variable t, its value cannot be altered by a change in t; therefore, if the equality is to be preserved, a change in t must not affect the

§ $\Phi'(t)$ represents $\dfrac{\partial}{\partial t} \Phi(t)$; $F''(z)$ represents $\dfrac{\partial^2}{\partial z^2} F(z)$; and so on.

value of the right member. A similar argument holds true if z is considered variable. Hence each term must be equal to a constant. For convenience, call this constant $-A^2$. On this basis the left member of equation $10 \cdot 14$ gives

$$F''(z) = -A^2 F(z)$$

It is immediately evident to the mathematician, and may be quickly verified by trial, that the expression which satisfies this relationship is

$$F(z) = C_1 \cos Az + C_2 \sin Az$$

in which C_1 and C_2 are arbitrary constants.

The right member of equation $10 \cdot 14$ gives

$$\Phi'(t) = -A^2 c_v \Phi(t)$$

The expression which satisfies this relationship is

$$\Phi(t) = C_3 \epsilon^{-A^2 c_v t}$$

in which ϵ is the Napierian base and C_3 is an arbitrary constant. Thus equation $10 \cdot 13$ becomes

$$u = (C_4 \cos Az + C_5 \sin Az)\epsilon^{-A^2 c_v t} \qquad (10 \cdot 15)$$

The remaining requirement is the satisfying of boundary conditions $10 \cdot 12$. The first condition is satisfied if $C_4 = 0$. This leaves

$$u = C_5 (\sin Az)\epsilon^{-A^2 c_v t} \qquad (10 \cdot 16)$$

The second condition will be satisfied if $2AH = n\pi$, wherein n is any integer. Then

$$u = C_5 \sin \frac{n\pi z}{2H} \, \epsilon^{-n^2 \pi^2 c_v t / 4H^2} \qquad (10 \cdot 17)$$

The term C_5 is merely an arbitrary constant, and n can assume any integral value whatever. Therefore a series of the form

$$u = B_1 \sin \frac{\pi z}{2H} \epsilon^{-\pi^2 c_v t / 4H^2} + B_2 \sin \frac{2\pi z}{2H} \epsilon^{-4\pi^2 c_v t / 4H^2} + \cdots$$

$$+ B_n \sin \frac{n\pi z}{2H} \epsilon^{-n^2 \pi^2 c_v t / 4H^2} + \cdots$$

in which B_1, B_2, $\cdots B_n$, $\cdots$ are constants, will still be a solution. This series may be written in abbreviated form:

$$u = \sum_{n=1}^{n=\infty} B_n \sin \frac{n\pi z}{2H} \, \epsilon^{-n^2\pi^2 c_v t/4H^2} \tag{10·18}$$

The third boundary condition will be fulfilled if the constants B_n in equation 10·18 are determined so that

$$u_i = \sum_{n=1}^{n=\infty} B_n \sin \frac{n\pi z}{2H} \tag{10·19}$$

This is a common type of Fourier expansion, and the constants may be readily determined by the use of the following relationships, which appear in practically all lists of definite integrals.

$$\int_0^\pi \sin mx \sin nx \, dx = 0$$

and

$$\int_0^\pi \sin^2 nx \, dx = \frac{\pi}{2}$$

where m and n are unequal integers. With change of variable from x to $\pi z/2H$, these expressions become

$$\int_0^{2H} \sin \frac{m\pi z}{2H} \sin \frac{n\pi z}{2H} \, dz = 0 \tag{10·20}$$

and

$$\int_0^{2H} \sin^2 \frac{n\pi z}{2H} \, dz = H \tag{10·21}$$

If both sides of equation 10·19 are multiplied by $\sin (n\pi z/2H) \, dz$ and integrated between 0 and $2H$, all terms in the series except the nth term will assume the form of equation 10·20 and vanish; the nth term will be in the form of equation 10·21 and will have a definite value. Thus

$$\int_0^{2H} u_i \sin \frac{n\pi z}{2H} \, dz = B_n \int_0^{2H} \sin^2 \frac{n\pi z}{2H} \, dz = B_n H$$

whence

$$B_n = \frac{1}{H} \int_0^{2H} u_i \sin \frac{n\pi z}{2H} \, dz \qquad (10\cdot22)$$

When this value is placed in equation 10·18 the solution becomes

$$u = \sum_{n=1}^{n=\infty} \left(\frac{1}{H} \int_0^{2H} u_i \sin \frac{n\pi z}{2H} \, dz \right) \left(\sin \frac{n\pi z}{2H} \right) \epsilon^{-n^2\pi^2 c_v t/4H^2} \qquad (10\cdot23)$$

This equation is perfectly general for the conditions assumed, and it enables the hydrostatic excess u to be computed for a soil mass under any initial system of stress u_i, at any depth z, and at any time t.

Equation 10·23 may be written in more general form, since time t appears as a multiple of c_v/H^2, which is a constant for any given case. Let

$$T = \frac{c_v t}{H^2} \qquad (10\cdot24)$$

An analysis of the units of the quantities involved shows that T is a dimensionless number, and it is called the time factor. The insertion of equation 10·24 in equation 10·23 gives the following form, which holds for any homogeneous stratum:

$$u = \sum_{n=1}^{n=\infty} \left(\frac{1}{H} \int_0^{2H} u_i \sin \frac{n\pi z}{2H} \, dz \right) \left(\sin \frac{n\pi z}{2H} \right) \epsilon^{-\frac{1}{4}n^2\pi^2 T} \qquad (10\cdot25)$$

In particular, if u_i is a constant u_0, the equation becomes

$$u = \sum_{n=1}^{n=\infty} \frac{2u_0}{n\pi} (1 - \cos n\pi) \left(\sin \frac{n\pi z}{2H} \right) \epsilon^{-\frac{1}{4}n^2\pi^2 T}$$

When n is even, $1 - \cos n\pi$ vanishes; when n is odd, this factor becomes 2. Therefore it is convenient to let $n = 2m + 1$, in which m is an integer. The substitution of

$$M = \tfrac{1}{2}\pi(2m + 1) \qquad (10\cdot26)$$

is of considerable aid in the simplification of the writing of equations which follow, since M appears frequently. After these substitutions are made the equation for constant initial hydrostatic excess becomes

$$u = \sum_{m=0}^{m=\infty} \frac{2u_0}{M}\left(\sin\frac{Mz}{H}\right)\epsilon^{-M^2T} \tag{10.27}$$

In terms of the consolidation ratio, defined by equation 10·6, the expression becomes

$$U_z = 1 - \sum_{m=0}^{m=\infty} \frac{2}{M}\left(\sin\frac{Mz}{H}\right)\epsilon^{-M^2T} \tag{10.28}$$

This equation is represented by Fig. 10·9, as is explained in the following section.

The average degree of consolidation over the depth of the stratum at any time during the consolidation process can now be determined. The average initial hydrostatic excess may be expressed

$$\frac{1}{2H}\int_0^{2H} u_i \, dz$$

Similarly, the average hydrostatic excess at any intermediate time t is

$$\frac{1}{2H}\int_0^{2H} u \, dz$$

The average consolidation ratio U is the average value of U_z over the depth of the stratum. It is equal to the average value of $1 - u/u_i$, and it may be expressed

$$U = 1 - \frac{\displaystyle\int_0^{2H} u \, dz}{\displaystyle\int_0^{2H} u_i \, dz} \tag{10.29}$$

Substitution of the value of u given by equation 10·25 and integration gives

$$U = 1 - \sum_{m=0}^{m=\infty} \frac{2\displaystyle\int_0^{2H} u_i \sin\frac{Mz}{H}\,dz}{M\displaystyle\int_0^{2H} u_i \, dz}\,\epsilon^{-M^2T} \tag{10.30}$$

In the special case of constant initial hydrostatic excess u_0, the equation becomes

$$U = 1 - \sum_{m=0}^{m=\infty} \frac{2}{M^2} \epsilon^{-M^2 T} \qquad (10\cdot31)$$

Equation $10\cdot31 \parallel$ is represented by curve I of Fig. $10\cdot10$.

10·12 Discussion of Theoretical Consolidation Relationships

One-dimensional consolidation, subject to the condition of constant initial hydrostatic excess pressure, is the type of consolidation that is of major interest herein. It applies in the laboratory consolidation test and is commonly assumed, although it generally is not strictly applicable, in cases of consolidation in nature. Equations $10\cdot28$ and $10\cdot31$ are the final results of its mathematical solution.

Equation $10\cdot28$ contains only abstract numbers. Values of U_z may be obtained by assigning values of z/H and T to allow the determination of the family of curves shown in Fig. $10\cdot9$. Once this chart is available, the formula is no longer needed, and tedious computations to obtain values from it are no longer required.

In an especially instructive manner Fig. $10\cdot9$ presents the entire picture of the theoretical process of consolidation. It is seen that consolidation proceeds most rapidly at the drained faces and least rapidly at the center of the layer. Consider, for example, the curve for a T value of 0.1. This curve represents conditions after the lapse of a certain definite time, measured from the beginning of the consolidation process. The actual corresponding number of minutes or years in a natural layer is a constant multiple of T, the constant depending on the values of c_v and H as shown by equation $10\cdot24$. At this time and at a depth equal to one-tenth the height of the layer, consolidation is 65 per cent complete, whereas at the center of the layer only 5 per cent consolidation has taken place. As time goes on, the

---

$\parallel$ It has been found that equation $10\cdot31$ may be represented with high precision by the following empirical expressions:

When $U < 60$ per cent, $T = \dfrac{\pi}{4} U^2$

When $U > 60$ per cent, $T = 0.9332 \log_{10} (1 - U) - 0.0851$

percentage consolidation at every point increases. Finally, after the lapse of a theoretically infinite time, consolidation is 100 per cent complete at all depths, the hydrostatic excess pressure is zero, and all applied pressure is carried by the soil grains.

Equation 10·31 expresses the relationship between time and the average state of consolidation over the height of the stratum.

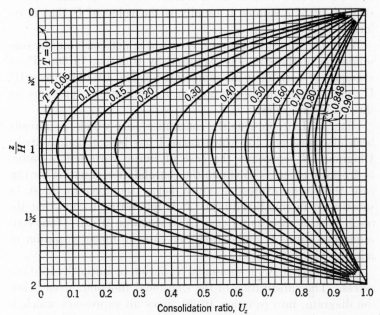

FIG. 10·9 Consolidation as a function of depth and time factor.

The plot of this equation is curve I of Fig. 10·10. If the T value of 0.1 is again used for illustration, it is seen from Fig. 10·10 that the average consolidation is 35 per cent; therefore in Fig. 10·9 the average abscissa of the curve for this time factor is 35 per cent, and the area to the left of the curve is 35 per cent of the total area of the chart. Furthermore, 35 per cent of the drainage and 35 per cent of the compressions that take place according to theory during the consolidation process have occurred when the time factor is 0.1.

In the application of consolidation theory to the prediction of settlements, which is the subject of Chapter 12, only the average consolidation need be considered. In this type of analysis curve I of Fig. 10·10 is the relationship that is commonly used, and Fig. 10·9 is of value mainly in the explanation of the consolidation process. Therefore, values of U_z, representing consolidations at various points, are used much less than values of U, representing the average consolidation or the consolidation of the stratum as a whole, and when mention is made of the consolidation of a stratum or of a sample it usually is the value of U that is referred to.

When the initial hydrostatic excess u_i is not constant the consolidation of the strata is expressed by equation 10·30. Three examples of variable u_i are represented in Fig. 10·10 by cases IB, II, and III. In the upper portion of the figure u_i diagrams for these cases are shown.

Diagram IA represents the constant u_i case which has already been discussed and for which curve I has been found to apply. Diagram IB represents the case of linear variation of initial hydrostatic excess. To obtain the consolidation equation for this case the linear expression given below the diagram must be substituted in equation 10·30. It is interesting to find that the result for this case, as for case IA, is equation 10·31. Thus consolidation curve I applies for any case of linear variation of initial hydrostatic excess.

Diagram II shows a sinusoidal variation of initial hydrostatic excess. The substitution of the sinusoidal function, given below the diagram, into equation 10·30, gives an expression which is represented by consolidation curve II.

Actual cases may be closely approximated by combinations of cases I and II. For example, diagram III represents a typical case and its u_i relationship may be expressed as a linear relationship minus a sinusoidal relationship. It is not difficult to demonstrate that the solution for case III is obtained by weighting U values from consolidation curves I and II in proportion to the areas of the respective u_i diagrams. For example, if u_3 is numerically equal to $0.25u_1$ in diagram III, the area to the left of the diagonal straight line is 119 per cent of the area to the left of the u_i curve, and the area of the sinusoidal deduction is 19 per cent of the area to the left of the u_i curve. For any time factor, the value of U for case III is equal to 1.19 times the U

value on curve I at the given time factor minus 0.19 times the U value on curve II at this time factor. Consolidation curve III is obtained in this manner and is shown on the figure by a dashed line.

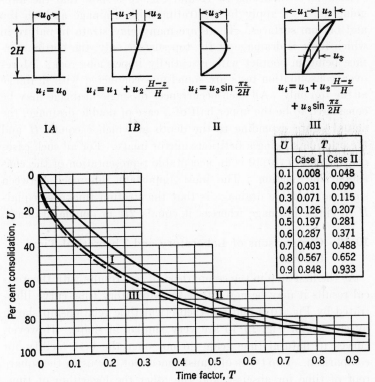

FIG. 10·10 Consolidation curves according to the Terzaghi theory.

Consolidation curve III is not greatly different from curve I. This similarity of curves, the extremely approximate nature of the main assumption in the Terzaghi theory, and the questionable assumption of one-dimensional drainage are all factors that lead to the generally accepted conclusion that curve I is an adequate representation of typical cases in nature. By the same reasoning case I may be accepted as reasonably representative of cases wherein the initial gradient is larger near the center of the layer than it is near the drainage surface; such cases are unusual in that a portion of the stratum undergoes initial expansion, which cannot be expressed in terms of the coefficient of compressibility, but this condition need not be considered in detail because it dissipates quickly.

Boundary conditions 10·12 and Fig. 10·9 show that the foregoing analyses apply for a stratum with drainage at both top and bottom surfaces. There are many clay strata in nature in which there is drainage at the top surface only, the bottom surface being in contact with essentially impervious rock. Moreover, consolidation tests are sometimes conducted with drainage at the top only. All such occurrences of single drainage may be considered to be the upper half of a case of double drainage, the actual strata extending to the depth at which z equals H and the other half being a fictitious mirror image. For all such cases curve I of Fig. 10·10 is an acceptable representation of the consolidation function. The most important difference between single and double drainage is that the stratum thickness equals H in single drainage whereas it equals $2H$ in double drainage.

10·13 Comparisons of Laboratory and Theoretical Time Curves

As the first step in the comparison of test results with theoretical results it may be noted that the laboratory time curve illustrated by Fig. 10·6 and the theoretical time relationship shown by curve I of Fig. 10·10 are very similar in shape. However, curves to natural time scale do not offer the best facility for comparison. Two types of transformed plot, one using the square root of time for abscissa and the other the logarithm of time, are found to show certain characteristics of the relationships to much better advantage. In Fig. 10·11, the square root of time plot is used; the laboratory time curve for a typical increment is shown in (*a*) and the theoretical curve in (*b*). In Fig. 10·12 the logarithm of time plot is presented. The resemblances between the laboratory and the theoretical curves in each of these figures are immediately evident.

Methods of determining the coefficient of consolidation from laboratory data by the use of characteristics of the curves as they appear in Figs. 10·11 and 10·12 are called fitting methods.

(*a*) *The Square Root of Time Fitting Method.* It is seen from Fig. 10·11 (*b*) that the theoretical curve on the square root plot is a straight line up to about 60 per cent consolidation. It may be determined from values tabulated on Fig. 10·10 that the

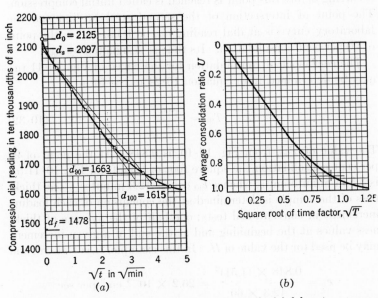

FIG. 10·11 The square root of time fitting method: (*a*) laboratory curve; (*b*) theoretical curve.

abscissa of the curve of Fig. 10·11 (*b*) at 90 per cent consolidation is 1.15 times the abscissa of an extension of the straight line. This characteristic of the theoretical curve is utilized to determine a point of 90 per cent consolidation on the laboratory time curve. This method, devised by the author, is known as the square root fitting method.

On the laboratory plot a straight line may usually be drawn which is in close agreement with the observed points of the early portion of the compression. Such a line is shown in Fig. 10·11 (*a*). A second line, coinciding with the first line at zero time and having all abscissas 1.15 times as large as corresponding values on the first curve, may next be drawn. The common point on these straight lines at zero time generally is a little below the zero of the compression scale, owing at least in part to the immediate compression of small amounts of gas in the pores. This point, which is at dial reading d_s or 2097 in Fig. 10·11 (a), is called the corrected zero point; the compression occurring before this point is reached is called initial compression. The point of intersection of the second straight line and the laboratory curve is at dial reading d_{90} or 1663, and is the point of 90 per cent consolidation. Its time is designated by t_{90}.

The coefficient of consolidation for the curve of Fig. 10·11 (a) may be determined from equation 10·24 in the form

$$T_{90} = \frac{c_v t_{90}}{H^2} \qquad (10·32)$$

The value of T_{90}, from Fig. 10·10, is 0.848. At the point of 90 per cent consolidation the square root of time from Fig. 10·11 (a) is 3.5 in minute units, whence t_{90} equals 12.3 minutes. The thickness of the sample is determined at the conclusion of each loading increment in conventional tests; one half of the average of thickness values at the beginning and at the end of a given increment may be used for the value of H. In this example, H is 1.51 cm, and

$$c_v = \frac{0.848 \times (1.51)^2}{12.3 \times 60} = 26.2 \times 10^{-4} \text{ cm}^2 \text{ per sec}$$

The total compression is equal to the difference between the initial dial reading d_0, in this case 2125, and the one-day dial reading d_f of 1478; therefore, the total compression is 647×10^{-4} in. The primary compression, which is the compression corresponding to the theory and which is represented by the total ordinate range in Figs. 10·11 (b) and 10·12 (b), is obviously only a part of the total compression. The ratio between primary and total compression is called the primary compression ratio; it is designated by r and it may be expressed as follows:

$$r = \frac{\frac{10}{9}(d_s - d_{90})}{d_0 - d_f} \qquad (10·33)$$

For the example in Fig. 10·11 (a)

$$r = \frac{10}{9} \frac{2097 - 1663}{2125 - 1478} = 0.745$$

From the above discussion it is seen that the total compression in a loading increment of a laboratory test has three parts. In Fig. 10·11 (a) the initial compression extends from d_0 to d_s, the primary compression extends from d_s to d_{100}, and the third part, called secondary compression, extends from d_{100} to d_f. In the example the parts are 4.3, 74.5, and 21.2 per cent, respectively, of the total.

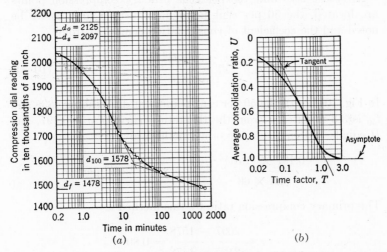

Fig. 10·12 The logarithm of time fitting method: (a) laboratory curve; (b) theoretical curve.

The secondary compression occurs at a speed which is dependent only on the plastic characteristics of the clay, since in this zone the speed of compression is so slow that escape of water is no longer a controlling factor. Secondary compression and related plastic phenomena are discussed further in Section 10·15.

(b) *The Logarithm of Time Fitting Method.* The intersection of the tangent and the asymptote to the theoretical consolidation curve shown in Fig. 10·12 (b) is at the ordinate of 100 per cent consolidation. The use of the intersection of the two corresponding tangents to the laboratory curve of Fig. 10·12 (a) was suggested by A. Casagrande to determine the point of 100 per cent primary compression.

Since the early portion of the curve is known to approximate a parabola, the corrected zero point may be located as follows: The difference in ordinates between two points with times in the ratio of 4 to 1 on the early part of the curve may be marked off; then a distance equal to this difference may be stepped off above the upper point to obtain the corrected zero point. This corrected point may be checked by retrials, different points on the curve being used.

After the zero and 100 per cent primary compression points are located, the 50 per cent point and its time may easily be noted and the coefficient of consolidation computed from

$$c_v = \frac{T_{50} H^2}{t_{50}} \qquad (10 \cdot 34)$$

In Fig. $10 \cdot 12 \, (a)$, the 50 per cent point is at dial reading 1838 and t_{50} is 3.3 minutes. From the theoretical curve T_{50} is 0.197, and H equals 1.51 cm, as in the other method, giving

$$c_v = \frac{0.197 \times (1.51)^2}{3.3 \times 60} = 22.7 \times 10^{-4} \text{ cm}^2 \text{ per sec}$$

The primary compression ratio by this method is

$$r = \frac{2097 - 1578}{2125 - 1478} = 0.80$$

The two fitting methods in general show fairly good agreement. The differences of 13 and 7 per cent in c_v and r values respectively in this example are larger than usual. In some cases the square root plot does not show a straight line portion, but the logarithmic plot gives satisfactory determinations. On the other hand, good results may be obtained by the square root method on some soils exhibiting so much secondary compression that the logarithmic plot does not show the characteristic shape used to locate the 100 per cent point.

$10 \cdot 14$ Form of Presentation of Test Data

For each loading increment, the values of the coefficient of consolidation and the primary compression ratio are computed, using one of the fitting methods outlined in the previous section. The test results may be assembled to advantage on a single plot. On the upper section of this plot the curve of void ratio versus log pressure is given. Below, also plotted against log pressure, values of coefficient of consolidation and primary compression ratio are presented. As these properties are for the load increment rather than for a specific pressure, some arbitrary decision must be made regarding the pressure at which values are to be plotted; the arithmetic mean pressure is commonly used. Void ratio values are of course plotted against the final pressure p_2, but other properties—determined, for example, for the load increment from 1 to 2 kg per sq cm—are plotted at the mean pressure, in this instance 1.5 kg per sq cm. Examples of test data for four soils are given in Fig. 10·13. For the determination of data in this figure the square root fitting method was used.

10·15 Plastic Time Lag and Plastic Structural Resistance to Compression

The plastic time lag, as stated in Section 10·7, is a phenomenon which is not considered in the Terzaghi theory. The noticeable variation of the latter part of the laboratory curve of Fig. 10·12 (a) from the theoretical curves of (b) is evidence of the plastic lag which occurs after the conclusion of primary compression. This lag, however, occurs also during the primary compression.

An extensive laboratory investigation into plastic phenomena during consolidation has been conducted in which direct measurements of pore pressures in consolidating samples were made (138). A presentation of the details of this study does not fall within the scope of this textbook. However, a brief explanation of plastic phenomena is needed to give a satisfactory understanding of the difference between the actual behavior during consolidation and that for the simplified case covered by the Terzaghi theory.

In Fig. 10·14 let it be assumed that line AB represents the pressure-versus-void-ratio relationship as determined from increments of one-day duration in a conventional laboratory test on a given soil. As seen in Fig. 10·13, this relationship on the semi-logarithmic plot usually is an essentially straight line for pressures above the precompression range. It is indicated by Fig. 10·12 (a) that if increments of longer duration were to be used a

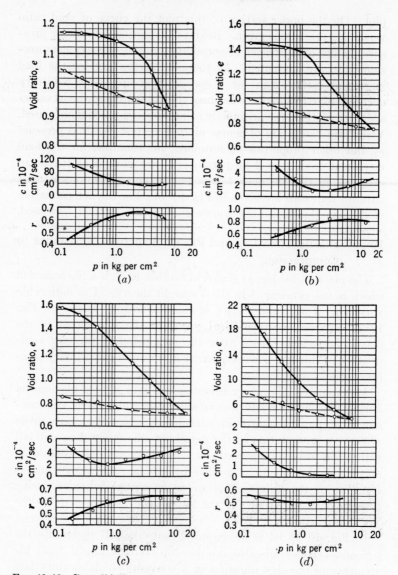

FIG. 10·13 Consolidation characteristics of four undisturbed soils: (a) a Boston blue clay; (b) a Chicago clay; (c) a Newfoundland silt; (d) a Newfoundland peat.

slightly lower final void ratio would result at any given pressure, giving a line slightly lower than *AB* but essentially parallel to it. If sufficient time were allowed, presumably the sample would eventually cease compressing, although possibly the time required might be many decades or centuries. It may be assumed that line *CD* is an approximate representation of the pressure-void-ratio relationship for some rela-

tively long duration, say for ten-year increment durations. Probably very little further compression would occur if further time were allowed, and thus this curve nearly coincides with the ultimate or static con-dition and is labeled as such.

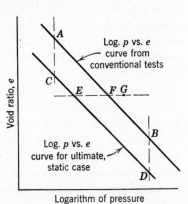

Fig. 10·14 Diagram illustrating plastic resistance.

If the void ratio of a speci-men of this soil is that of point *E*, the intergranular pressure is not a fixed value as assumed by Terzaghi but it depends on the speed at which compression is occurring. If the specimen is in the early stages of consolidation, the sample is compressing at a relatively high speed and the in-tergranular pressure is given by a point such as *G*. If the speci-men is a laboratory sample which is just at the end of an incre-ment of one-day duration, the speed of compression is much smaller and the pressure is represented by point *F*. If the speci-men has been at the void ratio for many years, its speed of com-pression is practically zero, and its intergranular pressure is approximately that of point *E*.

Intergranular pressure may, on this basis, be considered to con-sist of two parts, the static case pressure represented by points on line *CD*, and the pressure which is required to overcome plastic resistance to compression. This second part of the inter-granular pressure is called plastic resistance, and its magnitude in the three instances given in the previous paragraph are re-spectively, *EG*, *EF*, and zero. The magnitude of the plastic resistance is dependent mainly on speed of compression. However, other variables may have some effect on its value; at very slow speeds of compression it is possible that some type of cementation or bonding action may occur, and compression may introduce some structural change which may affect this resistance.

In Fig. 10·12 (a) the 100 per cent primary point may now be defined as the point at which the speed of compression has become so slow that the escape of water necessary for subsequent compression can occur freely; in other words, no appreciable gradient is required for subsequent drainage and therefore hydrostatic excess pressures no longer are of appreciable magnitude. There is ample experimental evidence that the hydrostatic pressure practically reaches a zero value just about at the 100 per cent primary compression point. During secondary compression the speed of compression continuously decreases, plastic resistance to compression becomes continuously smaller, and there is a steady approach toward the static case line of Fig. 10·14.

During the primary compression, the speeds of compression are large; thus the plastic resistance is relatively large and, correspondingly, the hydrostatic excess pressure must be smaller than the values indicated by the Terzaghi theory. Equation 10·4 should be revised to read

$$p_2 = p_s + p_p + u$$

in which p_s depends only on the void ratio and is the value from the static curve of Fig. 10·14, and p_p is the plastic resistance, which depends mainly on the speed of compression. Since values of hydrostatic excess pressure during consolidation are smaller than values according to the Terzaghi theory, it follows that gradients are smaller and that drainage is slower than the theory indicates. This additional amount of time required for the occurrence of the primary compression is the plastic time lag.

The degree to which these considerations cause the action during consolidation to differ from that given by the Terzaghi theory ¶ depends mainly on the degree to which the plastic re-

¶ More recent discussion of factors of this type is given by Terzaghi in reference 150.

sistance supplants the hydrostatic excess pressures assumed in the theory. Laboratory investigations show that when the standardized procedure outlined in this chapter is used, the plastic resistance supplants only a minor part of the hydrostatic excess pressure. Therefore test data such as those in Fig. 10·13 have satisfactory accuracy even though they are based on a theory which neglects plastic lag. It must be realized, however, that test data based on the Terzaghi theory may not be acceptable unless the load increment ratio and the sample thickness are approximately the standardized values listed in Section 10·4. It has been demonstrated (138) that the use of smaller load increment ratios must be avoided. Recent research by W. Enkeboll (48) indicates, however, that satisfactory data can be obtained on specimens with diameter and thickness of 2¾ and ¾ in., respectively.

As further demonstration of this point, direct determinations of permeability, obtained by use of the consolidometer as an upward flow, variable head permeameter as mentioned in Section 10·4, may be compared with values of permeability determined indirectly by computations based on equation 10·10. Such comparisons give reasonable results in tests on standard-sized samples with standard load increments, but are inconsistent at smaller pressure increments.

PROBLEMS

1. Define the term consolidation as used in soil mechanics and also give a brief definition of this term as used in geology.

2. Define the following terms: (*a*) hydrostatic pressure; (*b*) hydrostatic excess pressure; (*c*) neutral pressure; (*d*) intergranular pressure; (*e*) combined pressure; (*f*) capillary pressure. Give the interrelationship between (*a*), (*b*), and (*c*); between (*c*), (*d*), and (*e*); and between (*f*) and (*c*).

3. Determine the amount of error introduced at the point of 50 per cent consolidation by the assumption of linear variation between void ratio and pressure, if the true variation is represented by a straight line on the plot of void ratio versus the logarithm of pressure, for the following loading conditions: (*a*) $\Delta p = p_1$; (*b*) $\Delta p = 0.3p_1$.

4. For a constant initial hydrostatic excess, and for a time factor of 0.2, obtain the curve of consolidation versus depth by evaluation of the series expression. Obtain points for depths of 0, ⅓H, ⅔H, and H, and use a sufficient number of terms to give consolidation values to the nearest 0.001.

5. By evaluation of the series expression, determine values of average consolidation to the nearest 0.001 for the following time factors: 0.1, 0.25, 1.0. Also determine average consolidation values by use of the empirical expression given in the footnote on page 234.

6. The compression curve for a certain clay is a straight line on the semilogarithmic plot, and it passes through the points $e = 1.21$, $p = 0.5$ kg per cm², and $e = 0.68$, $p = 8$ kg per cm². Determine an equation for this relationship.

7. *Consolidation Test.*

Sample: a Chicago clay.
Specific gravity, 2.70.
Dry weight of sample, 329.99 grams.
Area of sample container, 93.31 sq cm.
Direct measurements of sample thickness:

1.254 in. when under ⅛ kg per cm² (dial reading 2843)
1.238 in. when under ½ kg per cm² (dial reading 2694)
1.215 in. when under 1 kg per cm² (dial reading 2458)

DIAL READINGS IN THOUSANDTH INCHES

Elapsed Time, minutes	Loading Increment, kg per cm²						
	⅛ to ¼	¼ to ½	½ to 1	1 to 2	2 to 4	4 to 8	8 to 16
0	2843	2796	2694	2458	1500	3100	3102
¼	2834	2780	2664	2421	1451	3047	3040
1	2829	2768	2647	2379	1408	2999	2985
2¼	2824	2761	2629	2337	1354	2946	2931
4	2820	2751	2610	2288	1304	2896	2873
6¼	2817	2742	2592	2239	1248	2841	2822
9	2813	2735	2576	2190	1197	2791	2768
12¼	2811	2729	2562	2142	1143	2743	2728
16	2809	2724	2553	2098	1093	2701	2690
20¼	2808	2720	2546	2044	1043	2660	2658
25	2807	2717	2540	2013	999	2630	2636
30¼	2806	2715	2533	1969	956	2602	....
36	2805	2713	2529	1937	922	2575	2602
42¼	2804	2710	....	1905	892	....	....
60	2803	2709	2517	1837	830	2525	2568
100	2802	2706	2508	1740	765	2496	2537
200	2801	2702	2493	1640	722	2471	2518
400	2799	2699	2478	1585	693	2446	2499
1440	2796	2694	2458	1500	642	2399	2468
(reset to)	....	....	....	....	3100	3102	....

Obtain the compression curve and curves of coefficient of consolidation and primary compression ratio for this soil from the data given; use the square root fitting method.

8. Obtain the results called for in Prob. 7 by use of the logarithmic fitting method.

9. From the data of Prob. 7 obtain the compression curve, and for the two arbitrarily chosen incrementts, ¼ to ½ and 4 to 8 kg per cm², obtain coefficients of consolidation and primary compression ratios by the two fitting methods and compare the results by the two methods.

Chapter 11

USE OF ELASTIC THEORY FOR ESTIMATING STRESSES IN SOILS

11·1 General

The theory of elasticity * with its expressions of interrelationships of stresses and strains, is familiar to students of mechanics. It has been of great practical value to the civil engineer in the analysis of stresses and strains in statically indeterminate structures of steel. In recent years, it has come into common use for estimating stresses caused within soil masses by externally applied loads. This chapter presents methods based on elastic theory for estimating stresses in soils.

An engineer who employs these methods should first be familiar with the hypothesis of elastic theory. These fundamentals are presented in the early chapters of textbooks (for example see reference 153) on mechanics, and therefore will not be covered herein. One point must be mentioned, however, since mechanics textbooks may not give it sufficient emphasis to provide the proper viewpoint relative to applications to soils. According to elastic theory, constant ratios exist between stresses and strains. For the theory to be applicable, the real requirement is not that the material necessarily be elastic, but that there must be constant ratios between stresses and the corresponding strains. Therefore, in non-elastic soil masses the so-called elastic theory may be applied to any cases in which stresses and strains may reasonably be assumed to adhere to constant ratios. Some types of loading on soils cause strains which are approximately proportional to the stresses; under other loading conditions, such as those in which failure in shear is imminent, the strains are anything but proportional to the stresses. If there is variation from proportionality between stresses and strains the degree of the variation plays an important part in the determination of the

---

* For a treatise see, for example, reference 98.

amount of question that must be attached to results from equations based on elastic theory.

Before an engineer can claim proficiency in soil analyses utilizing such methods, he should have a fair degree of understanding of the limited degrees to which they are valid in various types of soil problems. The degrees of dependability which may be attached to the results of such methods, and a number of complex and controversial phases of the subject, are discussed in Section 11·7.

11·2 The Boussinesq Equations

The equations expressing the stress components caused by a perpendicular, point, surface force, at points within an elastic, isotropic, homogeneous mass which extends infinitely in all directions from a level surface, are attributed to Boussinesq (16). The components and the coordinates which are used in these expressions are illustrated in Fig. 11·1. The equations † are shown below.

$$\sigma_z = \frac{Q}{2\pi} \frac{3z^3}{(r^2 + z^2)^{5/2}} = \frac{Q}{2\pi z^2} \left(3 \cos^5 \theta\right)$$

$$\sigma_r = \frac{Q}{2\pi} \left(\frac{3r^2 z}{(r^2 + z^2)^{5/2}} - \frac{1 - 2\mu}{r^2 + z^2 + z\sqrt{r^2 + z^2}} \right) \qquad (11·1)$$

$$= \frac{Q}{2\pi z^2} \left(3 \sin^2 \theta \cos^3 \theta - \frac{(1 - 2\mu) \cos^2 \theta}{1 + \cos \theta} \right)$$

$$\sigma_t = -\frac{Q}{2\pi} \left(1 - 2\mu\right) \left(\frac{z}{(r^2 + z^2)^{3/2}} - \frac{1}{r^2 + z^2 + z\sqrt{r^2 + z^2}} \right)$$

$$= -\frac{Q}{2\pi z^2} \left(1 - 2\mu\right) \left(\cos^3 \theta - \frac{\cos^2 \theta}{1 + \cos \theta} \right)$$

$$\tau_{rz} = \frac{Q}{2\pi} \frac{3rz^2}{(r^2 + z^2)^{5/2}} = \frac{Q}{2\pi z^2} \left(3 \sin \theta \cos^4 \theta\right)$$

The coefficient designated by μ in these equations is known as Poisson's ratio. It has values in elastic materials that are al-

† For the derivation of these expressions see pages 328–339 of reference 153.

ways between zero and 0.5. The value for steel is about 0.3, and the value for a material showing no volume changes during loading is 0.5.

The relationships existing between the stresses on the various planes through any point of a stressed mass are derived in Section 13·4. For detailed study of elastic theory a knowledge of these relationships is required. However, the elastic applications discussed in Chapters 11 and 12 are limited mainly to the use of vertical stresses, and these applications do not require knowledge of other stresses.

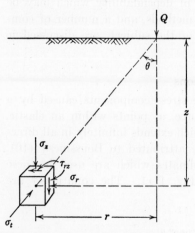

Fig. 11·1 Stresses in cylindrical coordinates caused by a surface, vertical, point load.

Six stresses are needed in general to define the stress system at a point but, because of radial symmetry, the vertical component and the horizontal component of shearing stress on radial planes in Fig. 11·1 are each equal to zero.

Therefore the four stresses expressed in equations 11·1 are sufficient. Because of radial symmetry only two coordinates appear in the equations. Of the two forms given in equations 11·1 the first contains the variables r and z, the second θ and z. The relationship between the two systems is given by

$$\theta = \tan^{-1}\frac{r}{z}$$

The first equation of this group is used in the following chapter on settlement analysis, and it is the only one which will be used herein to any important degree. It often is written

$$\sigma_z = \frac{Q}{z^2}\frac{\dfrac{3}{2\pi}}{\left[1+\left(\dfrac{r}{z}\right)^2\right]^{5/2}} \qquad (11\cdot2)$$

and in this form it may be noted that the two space variables are the depth z and the ratio r/z. Reference to the second form of equations 11·1 shows that all stresses are (a) directly proportional to the load; (b) inversely proportional to the depth

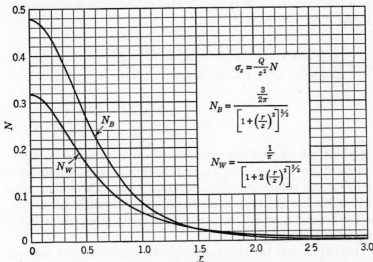

$$\sigma_z = \frac{Q}{z^2} N$$

$$N_B = \frac{\frac{3}{2\pi}}{\left[1 + \left(\frac{r}{z}\right)^2\right]^{5/2}}$$

$$N_W = \frac{\frac{1}{\pi}}{\left[1 + 2\left(\frac{r}{z}\right)^2\right]^{3/2}}$$

Fig. 11·2 Chart for determining vertical stresses caused by surface point loads in elastic materials.

squared, which is an example of the familiar inverse-square law that also holds for light intensity; (c) proportional to some function of the angle θ or of the ratio r/z. Therefore, any of the stresses given in equations 11·1 may be written in the form

$$\sigma = \frac{Q}{z^2} N \tag{11·3}$$

in which N for any given stress is a function only of θ or of r/z. Equation 11·2 may be written

$$\sigma_z = \frac{Q}{z^2} N_B \tag{11·4}$$

in which N_B denotes the Boussinesq index for the vertical stress. In Fig. 11·2 the curve of N_B as a function of r/z is given. This curve will be found convenient for use in pressure analyses.

11·3 Stress Caused by a Loaded Surface Area

For the case wherein the loading consists of a uniform intensity over a rectangular area of the surface of the mass of infinite extent, Newmark (108) has derived an expression for the stresses at a point below a corner of this area by integration of equation 11·2. The expression is

$$\sigma_z = \frac{q}{4\pi} \left[\frac{2mn\sqrt{m^2 + n^2 + 1}}{m^2 + n^2 + 1 + m^2 n^2} \frac{m^2 + n^2 + 2}{m^2 + n^2 + 1} \right.$$

$$\left. + \sin^{-1} \frac{2mn\sqrt{m^2 + n^2 + 1}}{m^2 + n^2 + 1 + m^2 n^2} \right] \quad (11·5)$$

in which q is the uniform intensity of surface loading on a rectangle of dimensions mz by nz, and the stress σ_z occurs at distance z below the corner of this rectangular area. The second term within the bracket is an angle in radians; this angle is less than $\pi/2$ when $m^2 + n^2 + 1$ is larger than $m^2 n^2$; otherwise it is between $\pi/2$ and π.

It is of interest to note that the above expression does not contain the dimension z, proof that for any magnitude of z the underground stress depends only on the ratios m and n and the surface intensity.

A chart which represents equation 11·5 for unit loading intensity and for ranges of m and n from 0.1 to 10 is given in Fig. 11·3.‡ If m and n are less than about 0.3, the loading may be assumed to be a point load, and equation 11·2, which is for point loads may be used with satisfactory accuracy, as is demonstrated in the following section. From the chart it is seen that if either m or n is greater than about 3 the stress caused is not appreciably different from the stress which would result if this m or n value were infinitely large. Since equation 11·5 is symmetrical in m and n, the m and n values are interchangeable in Fig. 11·3, and ordinates and abscissas may be either m or n.

When the stress is desired at a point that is not below the corner of the loaded area, it may be determined by considering the loaded area to be a combination of four rectangles, each with

‡ Other convenient charts and tables are given in references 49 and 107.

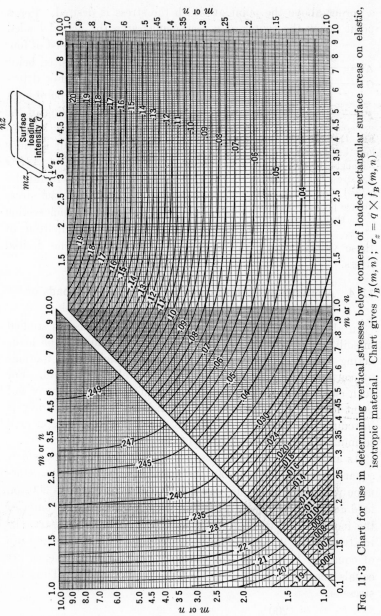

FIG. 11·3 Chart for use in determining vertical stresses below corners of loaded rectangular surface areas on elastic, isotropic material. Chart gives $f_B(m, n)$; $\sigma_z = q \times f_B(m, n)$.

a corner above the point at which the stress is desired. For a point below the center of a rectangular area the actual loaded area must be considered to consist of four

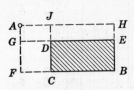

FIG. 11·4 Sketch showing the combination of rectangles used to obtain the stress below point A caused by a uniform surface pressure over the shaded area.

equal quadrants, the point desired being below their common corner. For determination of the stress below a point such as A in Fig. 11·4, due to loading of the rectangle $BCDE$, the area may be considered to be composed of four sections as follows: $AHBF - AHEG + AJDG - AJCF$. Each of these four rectangles has a corner at point A, and the stress below point A due to loading each section may be computed; a combination of these values, with signs as indicated above, gives the desired stress.

11·4 Application of the Point Load Formula to Loads on Small Areas

In all instances in which the transmission of stress is studied in soils, applied loads will not be point loads, but will be loads acting over finite areas. In cases of individual spread footings of conventional sizes the loaded area is relatively small. For such cases it is of considerable interest to know whether or not point load formulas can be used and, if so, what inaccuracy is introduced as compared to results using the more complicated formula which applies for loaded areas.

As an example, let it be assumed that a footing which is 8 ft square carries a load of 200 tons and that it is desired to determine whether or not it is reasonable to assume that this 200-ton load acts as a point load when the stress just below the center of the footing at a depth of 20 ft is being figured. The stress directly below a 200-ton point load may be computed by the use of equation 11·4. For this example r equals zero, whence r/z equals zero and, from Fig. 11·4, N_B equals 0.478. Thus the stress is

$$\frac{200}{(20)^2} \times 0.478 = 0.239 \text{ ton per sq ft}$$

Actually the load is distributed over the 8 by 8 ft area, the average stress q is 3.12 tons per sq ft, and the stress caused at a depth of 20 ft below the center of the area may be obtained by the use of equation 11·5 or Fig. 11·3. Thus the footing area is made up of four areas, each of which is 4 ft square, and for each of the four areas both m and n are equal to 4/20 or 0.2. Thus the stress is

$$4 \times 3.12 \times 0.0179 = 0.224 \text{ ton per sq ft}$$

Thus 0.224 ton per sq ft is the correct value for the stress, and it is seen that for this case, in which the breadth-depth ratio is 8/20 or 0.4, the assumption of point loading gives a value which is about 7 per cent too large. The allowable percentage error will vary considerably in different cases; perhaps 7 per cent is larger than should be allowed in general but in many cases it would be permissible.

This example furnishes the values in the first and last lines of Table 11·1 on page 258. For the same total load on various other areas, the stresses at the 20-ft depth are also shown in this table.

A rule quite commonly accepted is that the area of loading must have dimensions which are less than one third of the depth if the loads are to be treated as point loads. From Table 11·1 it would appear that the errors resulting when this rule is used will not exceed about 5 per cent.

The previous example does not quite meet the requirement of this rule. However, the requirement would be met if the 8 by 8 ft area were divided into four equal squares and if the load of 200 tons were treated as 4 point loads of 50 tons each acting at the centers of each of these squares. Under these conditions the breadth-depth ratio of each square is one fifth, which is well within the prescribed limitation. The radial distance from the center of each square to the center of the entire area is $2\sqrt{2}$ ft, the r/z value for each section is 0.141, and N_B equals 0.454. On this basis the stress at the 20-ft depth is

$$4 \times \frac{50}{(20)^2} \times 0.454 = 0.227 \text{ ton per sq ft}$$

and the use of the point load expression has given an error of about only 1 per cent.

TABLE 11·1   EFFECT OF SIZE OF LOADED AREA ON INDUCED STRESS

200-Ton Load on Area of (feet)	Vertical Stress at 20-Ft Depth, tons per sq ft	Excess over Value for Point Load, per cent	b/z Ratio
8 × 8	0.224	7	0.4
6 × 6	0.230	4	0.3
4 × 4	0.235	2	0.2
2 × 2	0.238	1	0.1
Point	0.239	..	0

A subdivision similar to that used in the above example allows the computation of stresses below any loaded area by the use of point load formulas.

11·5   The Westergaard Equations

Typical clay strata usually have partings or thin lenses of coarser material within them. The material in such lenses greatly accentuates the non-isotropic condition that is so common in sedimentary soils, and it is the cause of a greatly increased resistance to lateral strain.

An elastic solution that is based on conditions which are analogous, to a degree, to the extreme condition of this type has recently been obtained by Westergaard (168). In this derivation an elastic material is assumed to be laterally reinforced by numerous, closely spaced, horizontal sheets of negligible thickness but of infinite rigidity, which prevent the mass as a whole from undergoing lateral strain. This material may, therefore, be viewed as representative of an extreme case of non-isotropic condition. Westergaard's expression for the vertical stress caused by a point load is

$$\sigma_z = \frac{Q}{z^2} \frac{\frac{1}{2\pi}\sqrt{\frac{1-2\mu}{2-2\mu}}}{\left[\frac{1+2\mu}{2-2\mu} + \left(\frac{r}{z}\right)^2\right]^{3/2}} \tag{11·6}$$

At points directly below the load, the stresses have maximum values when Poisson's ratio μ has its minimum value of zero. This value seems as reasonable as any for use in connection with soil anaylses, since in most analyses it gives larger stresses than would be obtained by the use of any other value for Poisson's ratio. It gives

$$\sigma_z = \frac{Q}{z^2} \frac{\dfrac{1}{\pi}}{\left[1 + 2\left(\dfrac{r}{z}\right)^2\right]^{3/2}} = \frac{Q}{z^2} N_W \qquad (11 \cdot 7)$$

This expression is in the form of equation $11 \cdot 2$, and it resembles equation $11 \cdot 3$, which represents the isotropic case. In Fig. $11 \cdot 2$, a plot of N_W as a function of r/z is given.

For stresses below a uniformly loaded area, an integration of equation $11 \cdot 6$ furnishes the expression

$$\sigma_z = \frac{q}{2\pi} \cot^{-1} \sqrt{\left(\frac{1 - 2\mu}{2 - 2\mu}\right)\left(\frac{1}{m^2} + \frac{1}{n^2}\right) + \left(\frac{1 - 2\mu}{2 - 2\mu}\right)^2 \frac{1}{m^2 n^2}} \qquad (11 \cdot 8)$$

When μ is set equal to zero the expression becomes

$$\sigma_z = \frac{q}{2\pi} \cot^{-1} \sqrt{\frac{1}{2m^2} + \frac{1}{2n^2} + \frac{1}{4m^2 n^2}} \qquad (11 \cdot 9)$$

In equations $11 \cdot 8$ and $11 \cdot 9$ the notations are the same as those used in equation $11 \cdot 5$, which is the corresponding formula for the Boussinesq case. A chart that may be used to obtain σ_z values according to equation $11 \cdot 9$ is presented in Fig. $11 \cdot 5$.

11·6 Comparison of the Boussinesq and Westergaard Expressions

For cases of point loads with r/z less than about 0.8 and for cases of loaded areas with m and n values less than about unity, it is of interest to note that the Westergaard formulas, assuming μ equal to zero, give values of vertical stresses which are approximately equal to two thirds of the values given by the Boussinesq formulas.

No definite proof can be given that either of these solutions is more accurate than the other for the general run of applica-

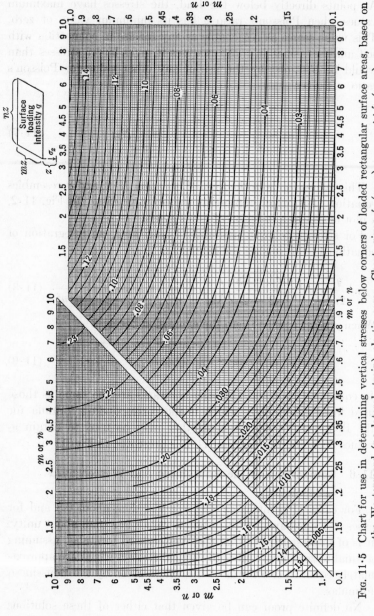

FIG. 11-5 Chart for use in determining vertical stresses below corners of loaded rectangular surface areas, based on the Westergaard (no lateral strain) elastic case. Chart gives $f_W(m, n)$; $\sigma_z = q \times f_W(m, n)$.

tions to soils. However, the stratified condition upon which the Westergaard solution is based is certainly nearer to the conditions existing in sedimentary soils than the isotropic condition assumed by Boussinesq. It has also been found that estimates of settlements obtained by use of the Boussinesq equations for determination of stresses, which is a procedure that has been in use for some time, are in the great majority of cases larger than observed settlements. This may be somewhat of an indication that the Boussinesq equations give stress values which are too large, although it also could be the result of other assumptions that are used in settlement estimates. At any rate the Westergaard equations now tend to be accepted as somewhat preferable to the Boussinesq equations for use in settlement predictions.

11·7 Factors Governing the Degree of Validity of Elastic Theory when Used for Determining Stresses in Soils

In many instances our limited knowledge of the subject makes it difficult to make definite statements regarding the accuracies obtainable when formulas based on the theory of elasticity are used for stress determinations in soil masses. However, the subject is of sufficient importance to justify a brief general discussion of a few of the most significant factors which have bearing on such accuracies.

The equations from elastic theory which have been presented in this chapter are rigorously correct only for materials in which stresses and strains are proportional. Moreover, each formula is valid only for the specific conditions upon which it is based. When these equations are used for estimating stresses in soils, the inaccuracies that occur because soils are not elastic are of unknown magnitude and are not well understood. Inaccuracies due to deviations from the conditions upon which specific formulas are based can be discussed more thoroughly.

The conditions existing in any problem are seldom exactly comparable to the conditions upon which available formulas are based. Point loads applied below ground surface cause somewhat smaller stresses than are caused at the same distance below the elevation of load application by surface loads, yet formulas that are valid only for surface loading are often applied to shallow footings. When the soil is underlain by a weaker soil or by a stronger soil or by ledge, the stresses near the discontinunity differ considerably in some instances from those in a homogeneous clay stratum of infinite depth. Formulas § which cover effects of discontinuities are sometimes used, but such formulas often require extensive computations and they represent only extreme cases such as a perfectly rigid or a perfectly flexible discontinuity; thus their use merely reduces and does not eliminate the inaccuracies that would occur if simpler formulas were used. These and similar variations from assumed conditions may result in appreciable inaccuracy of results. However, such items probably are of less importance and are likely to introduce less error than is caused by the distinctly limited applicability of elastic theory to soils.

As stated in Section 11·1, the basic assumption in the theory of elasticity is proportionality between stress and strain. The main question in this discussion, therefore, is the degree to which this proportionality holds in soils under the loadings which are to be applied. In many cases soil specimens can be subjected to the stresses that will be applied to the soil mass at a proposed project, and strains can be observed and plotted against the stresses. In such cases an indication of the applicability of elastic theory is furnished if straight line plots are obtained; moreover, the theory may be applicable in such a case even though a subsequent increase or decrease in the load would show the proportionality no longer holding and thus demonstrate that the material is not truly elastic. Two examples of common stress-strain curves will be discussed in some detail to explain this point more clearly.

Consider first the typical curve for one-dimensional compression shown by Fig. 10·5 (a). If any point on the curve is taken as an origin and a small pressure increase is considered, it is reasonable to assume the curve to be a straight line; in fact this assumption was used in the consolidation theory. Thus the intergranular pressure increases are approximately proportional to the void ratio changes and, since the void ratio changes for small increments are approximately proportional to the vertical strains, it may be concluded that within this increment the

§ Examples appear in references 13, 85, and 111.

vertical intergranular stress increase is proportional to the vertical strain. Qualifications may immediately be noted, however. The figure shows that if the stress is decreased the proportionality no longer holds. In addition, all effects of plastic lag, or any other factor involving the time element, bring in complications which represent limitations to the validity of the assumed simple proportionality, but which are too complex to allow even an attempt at an explanation in this brief discussion. It may be mentioned, however, that the slow, continuous occurrence of strain during secondary compression is entirely contrary to elastic behavior.

The curve of Fig. 10·5 (a) also illustrates another point. Since the curve becomes flatter at high pressures, the stress-strain ratio becomes larger with increasing pressure. This is an example of a fundamental trend, which applies to all materials, according to which stress-strain relationships are not constants but are proportional to the internal, or intrinsic, pressure.‖ With increasing depths below ground surface, all stress-strain ratios in soils tend to increase, whereas no elastic theory solutions are available which are based on such a variation in the material under consideration.¶ It is probable that in many cases this variation is not so large but that the overall action is about the same as in the hypothetical case in which the stress-strain relationships are constant and equal to the actual average value. However, in cases such as that of a sand stratum near ground surface, the assumption of a proportionality between stress and strain which does not change with depth is far from correct.

The second example of stress-strain curves which will be given refers to the action of soils in shear. A discussion of stress-strain relationships in shear at this point must be of limited scope because shear is not discussed until later chapters. However, a

‖ In an interesting example of this trend, Terzaghi lists a number of metals on page 109 of reference 143 and gives internal pressures and stress-strain moduli in one-dimensional compression, equal to $E(1 - \mu) \div (1 - \mu - 2\mu^2)$, in which E is Young's modulus; the moduli of the various metals are greatly different but they are approximately proportional to the internal pressures.

¶ For a solution of the complicated case of two layers with different moduli see reference 20.

few basic ideas pertaining to elastic theory applicability can be presented.

Assume that a gradually increasing axial pressure p is applied to a cylindrical specimen of soil, causing it to undergo shearing strain which increases until failure in shear is reached. If the specimen is of clay the pressure can be applied directly. However, assume that the specimen is a cylinder of sand of length L and volume V, which is enclosed in a thin rubber covering and is originally subjected to a pressure p_0 which acts over its entire surface * as shown in Fig. 11·6 (*a*). As the additional axial pressure p is increased, with p_0 remaining constant, axial compression occurs, and a curve such as that shown in Fig. 11·6 (*b*) results. Moreover, volume changes occur, and the volume strain during loading is known from much research by means of such tests to be about as shown in Fig. 11·6 (*c*). At point B the sample may be said to reach failure in shear. It is seen that the stress-strain relationships shown by the curves in (*b*) and (*c*) might be considered to be roughly constant ratios until points A and A' are reached. As failure is approached, however, the assumption of a constant relationship is far from valid. Furthermore, research on such specimens shows that the constant relationship holds only if the axial pressure never decreases. It may be concluded that applications of elastic theory to soil cannot be justified unless the stress changes that are to occur in the given case are to be increases only and unless the shearing stresses are to be small relative to the shearing stresses that would cause failure.

Another questionable factor may enter during shear, even when the shearing stresses are small. When saturated soil masses are subjected to load, there often is no opportunity for drainage and volume changes to occur. As a result the intergranular pressures tend to decrease.† If this stress decrease is of appreciable magnitude it may have considerable effect on the applicability of elastic theory.

The meaning of the elastic property known as Poisson's ratio becomes obscure as soon as it is used in connection with non-elastic materials. A property which may be used in its place,

---

* See Section 14·3 for further explanation of this type of test.

† Discussed in more detail in Section 14·11.

to avoid confusion and controversy, is the volumetric stress-strain ratio.‡ The direct stresses and the volumetric strain, which appear in this expression, are quantities which can be clearly visualized.

The general shape of stress distribution curves on horizontal planes below ground surface is illustrated by Fig. 11·2. It is known that the distribution curve below a point load is of this general shape in any material. The N_B curve is for an elastic

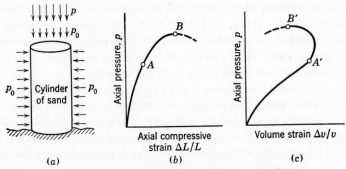

FIG. 11·6 Stress-strain relationships in shear.

isotropic material, the N_W curve for a material having a large resistance to lateral strain. The N_B curve shows the larger concentration of stress below the applied load and the smaller stresses at large radii. In sand deposits there is a greater concentration of stress below the applied load and smaller stresses at large radii than in the N_B curve; in other words, the typical distribution curve in sands is related to the N_B curve approximately as the N_B curve is related to the N_W curve. The shape of the distribution curve in sand may be attributed to the fact that the pressures on vertical planes in natural sand deposits tend to be much smaller than those on horizontal planes,§ giving

‡ The volumetric stress-strain ratio in any type of material is equal to $\dfrac{\frac{1}{3}(\Delta\sigma_x + \Delta\sigma_y + \Delta\sigma_z)}{\Delta V/V}$, in which the stresses denoted by $\Delta\sigma$ are direct stresses; they are discussed in detail in Chapter 13. In elastic materials the volumetric stress-strain ratio is equal to $\dfrac{E}{3(1 - 2\mu)}$.

§ This subject is discussed in Chapter 17.

a non-isotropic condition which is of the opposite type from that upon which the Westergaard derivation of Section 11·5 is based. Therefore, the formulas from elastic theory, based either on the Boussinesq or the Westergaard conditions, are not applicable for estimating stresses induced into sand deposits by surface loadings. Modifications of the formulas of elastic theory for use in sands by the use of a concentration factor (41) have been proposed, but the validity of these modified formulas is questionable unless they are used as strictly empirical expressions.

When stresses are transmitted through a sand layer into an underlying clay layer, all effects of the existence of the sand at small depths are commonly neglected in estimates of stresses within the clay. The amount of inaccuracy resulting from this non-homogeneous condition is hard to evaluate.

In engineering estimates it always is desirable to know something of the probable accuracy of the final results, and estimates often include investigations and give statements regarding probable accuracies. The fact that this cannot be done, because of lack of knowledge of probable accuracies, is one of the most unsatisfactory points about estimates of pressures in soils which are based on formulas from elastic theory.

There is a great need for field measurements to check estimated stresses in soils, although field measurements of soil pressures are not easily obtained and are themselves subject to inaccuracies that are not easy to evaluate. However, a number of stress investigations involving field measurements of stresses, some of these quite elaborate, are being undertaken nowadays.‖ The main hope for better understanding of the items discussed above resides in such undertakings and, although their value may rest largely in a long range improvement in understanding of fundamentals rather than in immediate value for the job in question, they should be encouraged in every way by all soil engineers.

‖ For example, see stress and strain data in references **110** and **157** and descriptions of cells for measuring pressures within soil masses in reference **163**.

PROBLEMS

1. The center of a rectangular area at ground surface has Cartesian coordinates $(0,0)$ and the corners have coordinates $(\pm 6, \pm 15)$, all dimensions being in feet. The area carries a uniform pressure of 1.5 tons per sq ft. Estimate the stresses at a depth of 20 ft below ground surface at each of the following locations: $(0,0)$, $(0,15)$, $(6,0)$, $(6,15)$, and $(10,25)$; obtain values by both Boussinesq and Westergaard methods and also determine the ratio of the stresses as given by the two methods.

2. Compute data and draw a curve of σ_z/Q versus depth for points directly below a point load Q. On the same plot draw curves of σ_z/Q versus depth for points directly below the center of square footings with breadths of 5 ft and 15 ft respectively, each carrying a uniformly distributed load Q. On the basis of this plot, make a statement relative to the range within which loaded areas may be considered to act as point loads.

3. Determine the necessary data and plot the curve of vertical pressure versus radius at a depth of 20 ft below a 30-ton point load, basing the computations on the Boussinesq formula. Using for original data the coordinates of points that are taken from this curve only, obtain the corresponding curve that holds at a depth of 25 ft.

4. For comparison with the Westergaard point load curve of Fig. 11·2, obtain curves with the same coordinates, these curves to represent stress indices $\sigma_z z^2/Q$ at depth z and radius r, measured from the center of a square area carrying a uniformly distributed load Q. Four curves are to be obtained. Curves are desired for conditions along a line coinciding with the diagonal and along a line through the central point and parallel to the side of the square; curves are also wanted for squares with breadths of both $0.2z$ and $0.4z$. Points are to be obtained at r/z values of 0, 0.2, 0.4, 0.6, and 0.8. On each curve the point that falls below the perimeter of the square is to be marked, and the curve based on point loads should also be shown.

Chapter 12

SETTLEMENT ANALYSIS

12·1 General

A building that is founded above a buried stratum of compressible soil undergoes settlements because of the compressions that take place in the buried stratum. The type of analysis that is used to predict the magnitudes of these settlements and the times required for their occurrence is called either a *settlement analysis* or a *consolidation analysis*. If it is assumed that there is one-dimensional compression and one-dimensional drainage in the buried stratum, use may be made of the method of settlement analysis that is explained in this chapter and is based on concepts developed in Chapter 10.

This method of analysis is one of the important contributions of soil mechanics to practical foundation engineering. It is typical of soil analyses in general in that it illustrates the many simplifying or idealizing assumptions which must be made and the relatively low degree of accuracy in final results that must often be expected. The engineer working on such analyses must continually bear in mind the many assumptions he has to make and their probable degree of dependability, in order that he may appreciate the degree of approximation that should be attached to final results.

12·2 Outline of Procedure

The settlement analysis may be divided into three parts. The first part consists of the obtaining of the soil profile and representative soil samples and the determination of average soil properties. The second part consists of the analysis of pressures in the subsurface stratum. The final part of the analysis makes use of concepts from the theory of consolidation and data from the first and second parts to furnish the final settlement predictions.

12·3 The Soil Profile and Soil Properties

To obtain the profile, it is required that a sufficient number of borings be taken to indicate the limits of the various underground strata and to furnish the location of the water table and water-bearing strata. A plot of the borings will invariably show some irregularities in the various strata. In favorable cases all borings may be sufficiently alike to allow the choosing of an idealized profile which differs only slightly from any individual boring and which is a close representation of average strata characteristics. More often there will be considerable variation among the various borings, but also in this case a simplified, representative profile must be chosen, and the choice usually requires a good deal of judgment and some guessing. If the irregularities are entirely a haphazard scattering, the idealized profile chosen will be free of horizontal variation.

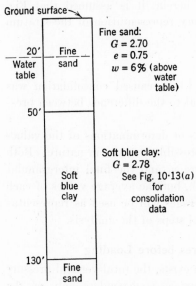

Fig. 12·1 Subsurface conditions assumed in the illustrative problem.

If definite trends in horizontal variation are recognizable in the boring data, a simplified section with a simplified representation of the horizontal variations is usually needed. Adequate boring data and good judgment in the interpretations are prime requisites which deserve much more consideration than is often given to them, but further discussion of the matter is beyond the scope of this text.

A relatively simple profile is shown in Fig. 12·1, its critical features being a clay stratum with no horizontal variation and with sand above and below it. This profile will be used for purposes of illustration in this chapter, since a simple case will best serve the purposes of developing the principles of the analysis.

It will be assumed that Fig. 10·13 (a) is the plot of test data for a sample taken about at the mid-depth of this stratum. Normally, samples from a number of depths are obtained and tested, and there may be quite large variations in the consolidation test data from the various samples. In such a case the common practice is to average the results from the various depths. For the simple example presented herein, it is assumed that Fig. 10·13 (a) furnishes a satisfactory representation of the stratum as a whole.

12·4 The Pressure Analysis

In Chapter 10 the loading which caused consolidation was designated by Δp, and was equal to the difference between pressures p_2 and p_1.

The pressure analysis consists of determinations of the values of these pressures for the compressible stratum in nature. Both the initial intergranular pressure p_1 and the final intergranular pressure p_2 will vary with depth, but the average values of each may be obtained and these averages will be used as representative p_1 and p_2 values in the final steps of the analysis.

12·5 Computation of Pressures before Loading

When no horizontal variation exists, the total vertical pressure at any depth below ground surface is dependent only on the weight of the overlying material.

For the profile of Fig. 12·1 computations are shown in the upper lines of Table 12·1 for total pressures, water pressures, and neutral pressures at elevations -20 and -50. Since these figures follow directly from the expressions for unit weight given in Section 7·2, they need no special comment.

The unit weight of the clay must be known before pressures within the clay can be computed. If values of natural unit weight or natural void ratio are obtained for the samples as received, these values should be used to compute the pressures. Otherwise some type of trial method based on the use of the pressure versus void ratio curve must be used. The use of this curve gives values of unit weight which are somewhat too large, since the remolding caused by sampling and testing causes a

TABLE 12·1 TABULATION OF COMPUTATIONS FOR PRELOADING PRESSURES

(Pressures in tons per square foot)

Elevation	Total Overburden Pressure	Water Pressure	Intergranular Pressure
At −20	$20 \times 1.06 \times \dfrac{2.70}{1.75} \times \dfrac{62.5}{2000} = 1.020$	0	1.020
−20 to −50	$30 \times \dfrac{2.70 + 0.75}{1.75} \times \dfrac{62.5}{2000} = 1.845$	$30 \times \dfrac{62.5}{2000} = 0.935$	$30 \times \dfrac{1.70}{1.75} \times \dfrac{62.5}{2000} = 0.910$
At −50	$\overline{2.865}$	$\overline{0.935}$	$\overline{1.930}$
−50 to −90	$40 \times \dfrac{117.5}{2000} = 2.350$	$40 \times \dfrac{62.5}{2000} = 1.250$	$40 \times \dfrac{55}{2000} = 1.100$
At −90	$\overline{5.215}$	$\overline{2.185}$	$\overline{3.030}$
−90 to −130	$40 \times \dfrac{117.5}{2000} = 2.350$	$40 \times \dfrac{62.5}{2000} = 1.250$	$40 \times \dfrac{55}{2000} = 1.100$
At −130	$\overline{7.565}$	$\overline{3.435}$	$\overline{4.130}$

slightly smaller value of void ratio at any given pressure in the test than the value occurring at the same pressure in nature. This inaccuracy, however, is of small magnitude.

In the trial process, extreme accuracy is neither warranted nor needed and the following procedure is a satisfactory one. The saturated clay is, for a first trial, assumed to have some reasonable value of submerged or buoyant unit weight, say 60 lb per cu ft. At the top of the clay stratum the intergranular pressure is 1.930 tons per sq ft or 3860 lb per sq ft, as shown in Table 12·1, and at the mid-depth of the stratum the intergranular pressure is

$$3860 + 40 \times 60 = 6260 \text{ lb per sq ft} = 3.06 \text{ kg per sq cm}$$

At this pressure the curve of pressure versus void ratio of Fig. 10·13 (*a*) shows a void ratio of 1.03. The value of submerged unit weight, instead of being 60 lb per cu ft as assumed above, may now be shown to be nearer to

$$\frac{G-1}{1+e}\gamma_w = \frac{1.78}{2.03} \times 62.5 = 55 \text{ lb per cu ft}$$

A retrial in which 55 lb per cu ft is used proves to be consistent. Thus 55 lb per cu ft submerged and 55 + 62.5 or 117.5 lb per cu ft total are the average unit weights of the clay between elevations −50 and −130. No appreciable inaccuracy results from the assumption that these average values hold throughout the depth. In the lower lines of Table 12·1 the computations for pressures in the clay stratum are shown.

12·6   Intergranular Pressure Conditions before Loading

To obtain intergranular pressures, the neutral pressure values may in all instances be subtracted from total pressure values, as shown by the data in Table 12·1. However, the values of neutral pressures which hold just before loading in a consolidation analysis are in some cases different from those of the simple static case. Four possible preloading pressure conditions are of practical interest:

(*a*) The simple static case.
(*b*) The residual hydrostatic excess case.

(c) The artesian case.

(d) The precompressed case.

Combinations of these cases also occur. In the following sections, separate explanations of each of these four basic conditions are presented.

12·7 The Static Case

The simplest preloading neutral pressure condition and the one commonly expected is that containing only hydrostatic pressure, the neutral pressure at any depth thus being equal to the unit weight of water multiplied by the depth below the free water surface.

This simple hydrostatic pressure is shown in Fig. 12·2 by distances measured to the left of the vertical reference line, that is, by horizontal distances between the lines through points A and O. Similarly, horizontal distances between the lines through A and B are total pressures. In (a) the static pressure is the only pressure in the water, and the shaded area represents intergranular pressures.

It may be noted that the neutral pressure determinations could be avoided in this case and the intergranular pressure determined directly by the use of submerged unit weights for all zones in which the soil is below the water table. The procedure used, however, furnishes a graphical picture of neutral pressures which leads up to the more complicated cases. The hydrostatic pressures which have been plotted to the left of the vertical reference line play no direct part in consolidation.

12·8 The Case of Residual Hydrostatic Excess Pressure

A condition of partial consolidation under the preloading overburden exists if part of the overburden has been recently placed, as for example in made land or delta deposits.

To illustrate this case, let it be assumed that the soil between elevations -20 and 0 is fill, placed about a decade ago. The intergranular pressures which existed within the clay before the placing of this fill are represented by distances between lines through points O and B_0 in Fig. 12·2 (b). The pressure caused by the fill that was added is thus represented by the distance

B_0B. As discussed in Chapter 10, the load represented by horizontal distances such as B_0B must, just after the placing of the fill, have been carried by the water as hydrostatic excess pressure. During the intervening years the process of consolidation has been going on. Accompanied by settlement, the hydrostatic excess has completely dissipated at the drained surfaces of the clay stratum but has only partially dissipated within the clay.

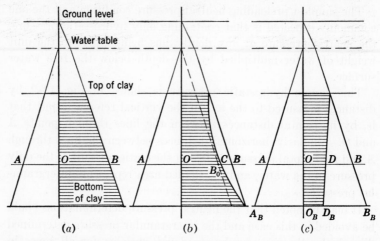

Fig. 12·2 Initial intergranular pressures for various cases of neutral pressure: (*a*) simple hydrostatic case; (*b*) case of partial consolidation; (*c*) artesian case.

The remaining hydrostatic excess pressure, which is represented in Fig. 12·2 (*b*) by distances between the lines through C and B, is called residual hydrostatic excess pressure.

In this case total pressures, represented by AB, and static neutral pressures, represented by AO, are the same as in the preceding case. The total neutral pressure, however, is greater in case (*b*) than in case (*a*) since it includes the hydrostatic excess pressure CB. The intergranular pressure, shown by the shaded area, is correspondingly smaller. If allowed a sufficient time for consolidation it is evident that case (*b*) would merge into case (*a*). Any structure built above the stratum illustrated by Fig. 12·2 (*b*) must eventually undergo not only the settlement caused by its own weight but also the settlement inherent in the residual hydrostatic excess pressure.

12·9   The Artesian Case

The water pressure at the top of the clay layer normally depends only on the elevation of the free water surface above the clay, but the water pressure at the bottom of the clay stratum may depend on very different conditions. A sand stratum below such a clay deposit may be of great horizontal extent and may extend or may merge into pervious strata that extend to distant high ground. The sand below the clay may, therefore, be subject to high pressures of an artesian nature. Such a condition is sufficiently common to make dangerous the use, without investigation, of the assumptions relative to pressures at the bottom of the clay which were used in cases (a) and (b).

The neutral pressure at the bottom of the clay cannot exceed the total pressure, since such a condition would cause an uplifting of the entire mass of clay and overlying deposits. However, a condition such as that indicated in Fig. 12·2 (c) may occur. In this instance the pressure in the water at the base of the clay stratum consists of the static pressure $A_B O_B$ plus the relatively large pressure $D_B B_B$. Because of pressure $D_B B_B$, water is seeping steadily upward through the clay, although this seepage occurs at such a low velocity in a typical clay that there is very little volume of flow. The neutral pressures resulting within the clay from the pressure $D_B B_B$, as it dissipates in flow upward, are shown in Fig. 12·2 (c) by horizontal distances between lines through D and B and are termed artesian pressures. At any depth it may be seen that the intergranular pressure in case (c) is less than that in case (a) by an amount equal to the artesian pressure. If the artesian pressure below the clay remains constant it merely is the cause of smaller intergranular pressures and has no tendency to cause consolidation. However, any changes of conditions which lead to decreases in the artesian pressure, such as the driving of artesian wells into the sand below the clay, may be the cause of large amounts of consolidation.

It can be demonstrated without difficulty that the basic consolidation relationships are not changed by the presence of artesian pressure. The total head in the water at any point is equal to the sum of the pressure head and the elevation head. On the basis that the datum of elevation heads is the free water surface and that the distance from this datum to the top of the clay stratum is z_0, the elevation head is $-z - z_0$. The water pressure equals the hydrostatic excess pressure u plus the water pressure after the completion of consolidation u_u. The value of u_u is the static pressure $\gamma_w(z + z_0)$ plus the artesian pressure $u_a(z/2H)$, in which u_a is the artesian pressure at the bottom of the clay stratum. The artesian head varies linearly from zero at the top to the value holding at the bottom of the stratum, for the same reasons that the head is dissipated uniformly over the length of the sample in a permeability test. Thus

$$h = (-z - z_0) + \frac{u}{\gamma_w} + \frac{1}{\gamma_w}\left(\gamma_w z + \gamma_w z_0 + u_a \frac{z}{2H}\right)$$

$$= \frac{1}{\gamma_w}\left(u + u_a \frac{z}{2H}\right)$$

$$\frac{\partial h}{\partial z} = \frac{1}{\gamma_w}\left(\frac{\partial u}{\partial z} + \frac{u_a}{2H}\right)$$

$$\frac{\partial^2 h}{\partial z^2} = \frac{1}{\gamma_w}\frac{\partial^2 u}{\partial z^2} \tag{12.1}$$

These expressions show that, when there is artesian pressure, a constant gradient $u_a/2H$ and a steady upward flow are superposed on the gradients and the flows that are characteristic of the consolidation process, but that the existence of artesian pressure does not invalidate basic differential equation 10.8 of the consolidation theory.

12.10 The Precompressed Case

Many clay strata have been subjected in past ages to loads greater than those existing at present. If the loading has not changed for many decades a small expansion will have taken place, and the simple, static neutral pressure may now exist in the pore water. Thus this case results from unusual past pressures and it is not necessarily a special neutral pressure condition.

Precompression may have been caused in a number of ways: by the load of glaciers of past ages, by overburden which has since been removed by erosion, by the loads of buildings that have been demolished, or by capillary pressures which have acted on the surface of the clay at some time in the past when it has been above the water table and subject to evaporation. The last of these items, often spoken of as surface drying, probably occurs more frequently than usually realized. Often the type of previous loading cannot be determined, but it is the existence and the amount of precompression more than the cause that are of major interest.

The construction of a building above a precompressed clay stratum causes recompression rather than compression, and in analyses of recompression the coefficient of compressibility that applies is the relatively flat slope in the recompression range of the pressure-versus-void-ratio curve. Therefore, settlements during recompression are small in comparison to those occurring under the same pressure increase in virgin compression. When large degrees of precompression exist the settlements during recompression under ordinary load increments are sometimes too small to be of practical interest. However, fairly large amounts of swelling occur upon release of load in some clays, and fairly large amounts of upward displacement have been observed in excavations for foundations above such deposits. In such clays the settlements caused by reloadings are often of appreciable magnitude.

12·11 Determinations of Preloading Pressure Conditions

A geological investigation of a site may yield information on the age of the various strata, the time which has elapsed since there has been deposition of soil at the site, the erosion which has occurred at the site in past ages, the water table and artesian conditions and other matters which may aid in determining which of the cases outlined in the previous sections holds in any given case. If fill has been placed on a site during recent years, information on amounts of fill and dates of placing may be available from records in municipal engineering offices or from old maps.

Such sources of information, however, are largely qualitative and often not sufficient for consolidation analysis. The following is a method, based on test data, for determination of the maximum intergranular pressure to which a given undisturbed sample has been subjected in its history. This method was developed by A. Casagrande (27).

In Fig. 12·3 (*a*) the curve of the logarithm of pressure versus void ratio for a typical undisturbed sample is shown. The shapes of the compression, rebound, and recompression branches have been discussed in Chapter 10. It has also been called to attention that the curvature of the original branch, which resembles

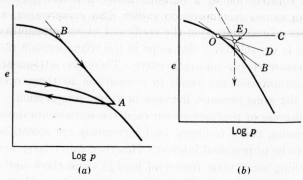

Fig. 12·3 Determination of the maximum past pressure.

a recompression curve, indicates a previous compression in nature to a pressure approximately equal to that at point *B*. The method that will be given is based on the assumption that the unknown location of point *B* relative to the adjacent curve is the same as the location of point *A* relative to the adjacent recompression curve. The following construction, if applied to the recompression curve, has been found to give point *A*, and therefore it is used on the upper curve as an empirical method for locating point *B*.

Point *O* of Fig. 12·3 (*b*) is the point of maximum curvature; it may be located quite accurately by eye. Through this point three lines are drawn, first the horizontal line *OC*, then the tangent *OB*, and finally the bisector *OD* of the angle formed by the first and second lines. The straight line portion of the curve is produced backward and its intersection with line *OD* gives point *E*, the desired point.

For each sample which has been tested in the laboratory, the maximum previous intergranular pressure may be determined by this method. These values may then be plotted, at appropriate depths, on pressure diagrams of the type used in Fig. 12·2, to give a curve of *maximum past pressure*.

The past pressure curve may then be compared with the intergranular pressure curve for the simple hydrostatic case, illustrated by the line through *B* in Fig. 12·2 (*a*). If the lines coincide, a simple static case is indicated. If there is agreement at the top and at the bottom of the clay stratum but the past pressure curve falls to the left at the center of the stratum, residual hydrostatic excess is indicated. If there is agreement at the top but the past pressure curve falls to the left at the bottom, one of the following conditions is indicated: the stratum may have drainage at the top surface only, the case being one involving residual hydrostatic excess; there may be double drainage and an artesian condition. The boring data must be turned to in deciding which of the two above cases holds. If the past pressure curve falls to the right of the static intergranular curve, a case of precompression exists.

For Fig. 10·13 (*a*) the maximum past pressure is approximately 3 kg per sq cm. This figure was defined in Section 12·3 as holding for a sample from elevation −90, at which point the intergranular pressure from Table 12·1 is 3.03 tons per sq ft. Thus it appears that a simple static condition holds for this case.

In principle the method of comparison explained above is simple. In actual practice the maximum past pressure values obtained are of low probable accuracy and are frequently erratic. If the structure of the samples has been disturbed to an appreciable degree during or after sampling, the pressures obtained by this method tend to be too low. Even if samples are in the best of condition, the variable nature of soil precludes the possibility of a high degree of accuracy, and this method must be classified as one giving rough indications, at best. Much value must be attached to the method, nevertheless.

Analyses based on the more complicated cases and on combinations of cases are sometimes required, but they are involved and would require too lengthy a discussion for detailed treatment herein. In the illustrative example which is given in this chapter a simple static case is assumed.

12·12   The Pressure Increment

The pressure increment may now be defined as the difference between the average preloading intergranular pressure and the average ultimate intergranular pressure. According to the Terzaghi theory its value is equal to the average initial hydrostatic excess pressure. The following items may contribute to the pressure increment:

1. Pressures transmitted to the clay by construction of buildings or by other imposed loads.

2. Residual hydrostatic excess pressures.

3. Pressure changes caused by changes in the elevation of the water table above the compressible stratum.

4. Pressure changes caused by changes in the artesian pressure below the compressible stratum.

The pressure induced by building loads is the most obvious of these items and in general the most important. The methods generally used for determination of such pressures are those outlined in Chapter 11. The next section will be devoted to an example of computations of this type.

If residual hydrostatic excess pressures exist in a buried stratum below a proposed building, they must be combined with the excess pressures caused by the weight of the building to give the initial hydrostatic excess pressures of the consolidation process that will take place.

Any decreases in the water pressures at either the top or the bottom of the clay stratum will cause increases in hydrostatic excess pressures. This can best be explained by examples, and two will be given. If all the artesian pressure in Fig. 12·2 (c) is relieved, allowing the water pressure below the clay to drop to the value holding in simple case (a), the pressure represented by the space between lines D and B becomes hydrostatic excess and, after consolidation, the intergranular pressure shown in case (a) is attained. If pumping is started above and below the stratum in case (a) and continued permanently at a rate sufficient to relieve all water pressure at the boundaries of the stratum, and if any decrease in the weight of the water above the clay is neglected, the pressure diagram represented by the space between lines *A* and *O* would become initial hydrostatic excess and would be equal to the pressure increment of the consolidation process that would take place.

12·13   Example of Pressure Increment Computations

The computation of the stresses transmitted to a buried clay stratum by the weight of a building is likely to be a long and tedious task. In order that basic principles may not be obscured by details, a very simple structure of rather impractical column spacing will be used as a numerical example.

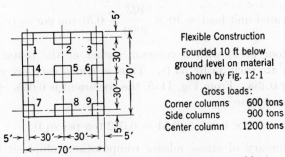

Flexible Construction
Founded 10 ft below
ground level on material
shown by Fig. 12·1

Gross loads:
Corner columns   600 tons
Side columns   900 tons
Center column   1200 tons

Fig. 12·4   Building used in the illustrative problem.

The geological section of Fig. 12·1 is assumed to hold for this example. The building and its column loads are shown in Fig. 12·4. It will be assumed that the building is relatively flexible and therefore that the column loads are not appreciably affected by differential settlements. The data ultimately wanted are the amounts and rates of settlements at the center column and at a corner column of the building.

Since the elevation of load application is 10 ft below ground surface, the effective depths to points at which stresses are computed is measured from elevation −10. The depths at which stresses are to be determined are here arbitrarily taken as those to the top, the midpoint, and the bottom of the clay stratum.

In Chapter 11, two elastic solutions of stress distribution were presented, the Boussinesq and the Westergaard solutions. The Westergaard solution will be used in this analysis.

The computations comprise two parts: first, the stress decreases caused by the removal of material in excavating for the foundation; second, the stress increases caused by the column loads.

For the computations of pressure release due to excavation the most convenient method uses the chart of Fig. 11·5. As an example, the stress release below the center of the building at the mid-depth of the clay is determined as follows:

Elevation -90, $z = 80$ ft

Unit weight of excavated soil $= \dfrac{G(1 + w)}{1 + e} \gamma_w = \dfrac{2.70 \times 1.06}{1.75} \times$

$62.5 = 102$ lb per cu ft

Excavated unit load $= 10 \times \dfrac{102}{2000} = 0.51$ ton per sq ft

The four areas with a common corner at the center of the building are each 35 by 35 ft. Thus m and n each are equal to $35/80$ or 0.438. From Fig. 11·5, the coefficient is 0.045. Finally, the stress release is

$$4 \times 0.045 \times 0.51 = 0.092 \text{ ton per sq ft}$$

A summary of stress release computations obtained by this procedure is given in Table 12·2.

In order to determine the stresses caused by the building weight at each of the six points under study the stresses induced at the point by each of the nine individual columns must be obtained and summed.

The stress computations are relatively simple in this problem if the column loads may be assumed to be point loads. In Section 11·4 it has been shown that such an assumption is reasonable when the dimensions of the loaded areas are less than one third of the depth. The extreme individual case herein is that of the stress thrown to the surface of the clay at a depth of 40 ft by the center footing which has a bearing area that is roughly 15 ft square. It is seen that the ratio is in this instance slightly greater than one third, but that it is less than one third for all other depths. Therefore no important error will result if point loads are assumed, as in this analysis.

For example, the computation of the stress increase at the mid-

TABLE 12·2 TABULATION OF COMPUTATIONS OF STRESS RELEASE CAUSED BY EXCAVATION

(Pressures in tons per square foot; $q = 0.51$ ton per sq ft)

Below Column	Quadrants	Area, feet	At El. −50 ($z = 40'$)			At El. −90 ($z = 80'$)			At El. −130 ($z = 120'$)		
			m, n	Coeff.	$\Delta\sigma$	m, n	Coeff.	$\Delta\sigma$	m, n	Coeff.	$\Delta\sigma$
5	4	35 × 35	0.875, 0.875	0.103	0.210	0.438, 0.438	0.045	0.092	0.292, 0.292	0.024	0.049
9	1	65 × 65	1.625, 1.625	0.159		0.812, 0.812	0.096		0.542, 0.542	0.060	
	1	5 × 5	0.125, 0.125	0.005		0.062, 0.062	0.001		0.042, 0.042	0.000	
	2	65 × 5	1.625, 0.125	2 × 0.026		0.812, 0.062	2 × 0.010		0.542, 0.042	2 × 0.006	
				0.216	0.110		0.117	0.060		0.072	0.037

TABLE 12·3 TABULATION OF COMPUTATIONS FOR STRESSES INDUCED BY
COLUMN LOADS

(Stresses in tons per square foot)

Below Column	Column Nos.	Load, tons	r, feet	At El. −50 ($z = 40'$)			At El. −90 ($z = 80'$)			At El. −130 ($z = 120'$)		
				r/z	N	QN	r/z	N	QN	r/z	N	QN
5	1, 9, 3, 7	4 × 600	$30\sqrt{2}$	1.06	0.054	130	0.53	0.163	391	0.353	0.228	547
	2, 4, 6, 8	4 × 900	30	0.75	0.103	370	0.375	0.219	790	0.25	0.267	962
	5	1200	0	0	0.318	382	0	0.318	382	0	0.318	382
					$\Sigma QN =$	882			1563			1891
				$\frac{1}{z^2}\Sigma QN =$		0.552			0.244			0.132
9	1	600	$60\sqrt{2}$	2.12	0.010	6	1.06	0.054	32	0.707	0.113	68
	2, 4	2 × 900	$30\sqrt{5}$	1.68	0.019	34	0.84	0.085	153	0.56	0.153	275
	5	1200	$30\sqrt{2}$	1.06	0.054	65	0.53	0.163	196	0.353	0.228	274
	3, 7	2 × 600	60	1.50	0.025	30	0.75	0.103	124	0.50	0.173	208
	6, 8	2 × 900	30	0.75	0.103	186	0.375	0.219	394	0.25	0.267	481
	9	600	0	0	0.318	191	0	0.318	191	0	0.318	191
					$\Sigma QN =$	512			1090			1497
				$\frac{1}{z^2}\Sigma QN =$		0.320			0.170			0.104

depth of the clay strata below column 9, due to the load of column 2, is determined as follows:

El. −90, $z = 80$ ft, load = 900 tons

Horizontal distance $r = \sqrt{(30)^2 + (60)^2} = 67.1$ ft, $\dfrac{r}{z} = \dfrac{67.1}{80} = 0.84$

From the Westergaard curve of Fig. 11·2, the coefficient is 0.085, and the stress induced is

$$\frac{QN}{z^2} = \frac{900 \times 0.085}{(80)^2} = \frac{76.5}{(80)^2} = 0.0120 \text{ ton per sq ft}$$

All stress increases caused by column loads are tabulated in Table 12·3. All pressures which are needed in the final computations are summarized in Table 12·4; they are based on data from Tables 12·1 to 12·3 inclusive.

TABLE 12·4   TABULATION OF FINAL PRESSURE ANALYSIS DATA

(Pressures in tons per square foot)

p_1		El. −50	El. −90	El. −130	Average
		1.930	3.030	4.130	3.030
Below Col. 5	from excavation	−0.210	−0.092	−0.049	
	from column loads	+0.552	+0.244	+0.132	
	$\Delta p = p_2 - p_1$	0.342	0.152	0.083	0.172
	p_2				3.202
	$p_a = \frac{1}{2}(p_1 + p_2)$				3.116
Below Col. 9	from excavation	−0.110	−0.060	−0.037	
	from column loads	+0.320	+0.170	+0.104	
	$\Delta p = p_2 - p_1$	0.210	0.110	0.067	0.120
	p_2				3.150
	$p_a = \frac{1}{2}(p_1 + p_2)$				3.090

Sufficient data are now available for the computation of pressure increments and final pressure values. In the theoretical treatment p_1 and p_2 were assumed constant throughout the thickness of the stratum. In this example, these pressures vary with depth, and the use of average values must be resorted to. Another approximation is thus added, but for the general run of analyses this will not be the source of any appreciable inaccuracy.

The determination of an average pressure when top, center, and bottom values are known is made easily and accurately by the use of Simpson's rule:

$$p_{av} = \tfrac{1}{6}(p_t + 4p_m + p_b) \qquad (12\cdot2)$$

in which p_{av} denotes the average pressure with respect to depth, and p_t, p_m, and p_b denote respectively the pressures at the top, mid-depth, and bottom of the stratum. Average values of p_1 and p_2 computed on this basis appear in the last column of Table 12·4.

The soil properties obtained in laboratory tests are plotted against the average pressures of the increments, $\frac{1}{2}(p_1 + p_2)$, as stated in Section 10·14 and shown by Fig. 10·13. When such plots are entered to obtain soil properties the average pressure of the increment in nature must be known; this pressure is given as the final pressure value for each column represented in Table 12·4.

The completion of the computations given in Table 12·4 concludes the pressure analysis.

From Table 12·4 it may be noted that the average pressure increment differs from the increment at the mid-depth of the stratum by only about 10 per cent. Moreover, the stratum analyzed above is relatively thick; this difference would be much smaller in a relatively thin stratum. It may be concluded that it will be satisfactory in many cases, and perhaps in practically all cases, to carry out pressure computations for the mid-depth elevation only, and the results may be considered to be representative of average conditions in the stratum as a whole.

12·14 Estimate of Settlements

Once data from laboratory tests and from the pressure analysis are available, the settlements are easily obtained.

The thickness which the solid matter of a double-drainage stratum would have if it could be segregated may be expressed

$$2H_0 = \frac{2H_1}{1 + e_1} = \frac{2H_2}{1 + e_2}$$

in which $2H_1$ and $2H_2$ are initial and final values of actual, double-drainage thickness and e_1 and e_2 are the corresponding average void ratios. These expressions may be written

$$2H_1 = 2H_0(1 + e_1) \quad \text{and} \quad 2H_2 = 2H_0(1 + e_2)$$

whence

$$2H_1 - 2H_2 = 2H_0(e_1 - e_2)$$

This expression represents the change in thickness which is equal to the total or ultimate settlement, ρ_u. Therefore

$$\rho_u = \frac{2H_1}{1 + e_1} (e_1 - e_2) \tag{12·3}$$

It is more convenient, however, to work in terms of pressure changes and the compressibility than in terms of void ratio changes.

In place of $e_1 - e_2$ the expression $a_v(p_2 - p_1)$, given by equation 10·5, may be substituted, or the expression derived below may be used.

The numerical value of the slope of the curve of the logarithm of pressure versus void ratio in Fig. 10·13 (a) was defined in Section 10·6 as the compression index, and its value may easily be obtained from the figure. For the case under consideration there is no precompression, and therefore the slope of the portion of the curve at pressures beyond the precompression range is desired. This slope is equal to the void ratio change per logarithmic cycle on the straight line portion of the curve, and for this case its value is 0.40. An expression for this slope is

$$C_c = -\frac{de}{d(\log_{10} p)} \quad \text{or} \quad de = -C_c \times d(\log_{10} p)$$

Since

$$d(\log_{10} p) = \frac{\log_{10} \epsilon}{p} dp = \frac{0.435 dp}{p}$$

the void ratio differential may be written

$$de = -\frac{0.435 \, C_c \, dp}{p}$$

giving

$$e_1 - e_2 = \frac{0.435 \, C_c(p_2 - p_1)}{\frac{1}{2}(p_2 + p_1)}$$

It may be noted that $0.435 C_c/p$ in the above equation equals the coefficient of compressibility.

The compression index C_c is often a constant but not necessarily so. If the curve is not a straight line, the above equations are still valid as long as C_c is taken as the numerical value of the slope of the curve at the pressure $\frac{1}{2}(p_2 + p_1)$.

Insertion of the above expression into equation 12·3 gives

$$\rho_u = \frac{2H_1}{1 + e_1} \frac{p_2 - p_1}{\frac{1}{2}(p_2 + p_1)} 0.435 C_c \qquad (12 \cdot 4)$$

By the use of a C_c value of 0.40, pressure data from Table 12·4, and data from Figs. 12·1 and 10·13 (a), the ultimate settlement at column 5 is found to be

$$\rho_u = \frac{80 \times 12}{2.08} \times \frac{0.172}{3.116} \times 0.435 \times 0.40 = 4.4 \text{ in.}$$

and by a similar computation for column 9 the ultimate settlement is found to be 3.1 in.

As a final consideration in the determination of ultimate settlements a possible qualification of the results should be mentioned. It is shown in Fig. 10·14 and explained in the third paragraph of Section 10·15 that the position of the curve of pressure versus void ratio depends somewhat on durations of loading increments but that the slope of the curve is essentially independent of the durations. On this basis the ultimate settlements given above are those reached after the load due to the added pressure Δp has been in place as long as the period during which p_1 acted prior to construction. The initial load may in some cases have acted for many centuries, whereas the life of the building may be relatively short, and it is possible that an appreciable final portion of the ultimate compression may not occur within the ordinary life of the building. The effect is greatest in cases like the example given, in which the pressure increment is relatively small. Neglecting it is, of course, a conservative procedure in all cases.

12·15   Time-Settlement Predictions

Settlement predictions are usually presented in the form of curves showing settlement in inches versus time in years. The data needed for the final predictions are the ultimate settlement, as obtained in the previous section, the theoretical consolidation function given by curve I of Fig. 10·10, the values of the coefficient of consolidation, and the thickness of the stratum and data on drainage conditions at the stratum boundaries.

The following assumptions are used in this prediction. The ultimate settlement in nature is assumed to be entirely the result of primary compression; in other words, it is assumed that there is no secondary compression in nature. The coefficient of consolidation as obtained in the laboratory test is assumed to hold for the slow consolidation of the thick layer in nature. A complete discussion of the validity of these assumptions cannot be included here.* However, settlements predicted on this basis are larger than the actual values, mainly because of effects of plastic lag which are not accounted for and which retard the settlement. In extreme cases, and especially in cases of very small load increments, the plastic lag may retard the settlement

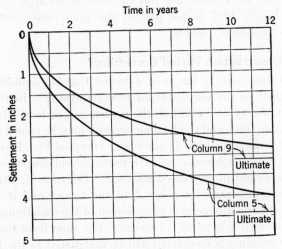

FIG. 12·5 Time-settlement curves.

to such a degree that for decades the predicted settlements are many times the actual values. However, considerably more research is needed before methods that account for this factor can be developed.

From Fig. 10·13 (a), the coefficient of consolidation for the average pressures of 3.1 tons per sq ft is found to be 0.0035 sq cm per sec. The thickness of the stratum is the dimension $2H$, and it equals 80 ft.

From the basic consolidation expression

$$T = \frac{c_v t}{H^2}$$

the following expression for time in years may be written

$$t_{\text{years}} = T \frac{H^2}{c_v} = T \frac{(40 \times 30.5)^2}{0.0035 \times 31.5 \times 10^6} = 13.5T$$

* These assumptions are discussed in detail in references 138 and 150.

The computation of points on the settlement curve will be illustrated by the determination of the point for 40 per cent consolidation for column 5. The ultimate settlement is 4.4 in., and the settlement at 40 per cent consolidation is $0.40 \times 4.4 = 1.8$ in. At 40 per cent consolidation, Fig. 10·10 gives the value of the time factor T as 0.126, and the time is $0.126 \times 13.5 = 1.7$ years. Figure 12·5 is the plot of the time versus settlement curves for columns 5 and 9.

12·16   Construction Period Correction

Up to this point it has been assumed that the building load was applied to the clay stratum instantaneously. In the construction of a typical building the application of load requires a considerable time, and the loading progress may be shown graphically by a diagram such as the upper curve of Fig. 12·6. The net load does not become positive until the building weight exceeds the weight of excavated material. The time at which this occurs is represented by point A of the figure, and it will be assumed that no appreciable compression of the underlying strata will occur until this point is reached. The time from this point until the building is completed will be designated as the *loading period,* and the loading diagram in this interval will be approximated by a straight line, as shown in Fig. 12·6 by the dashed line AB. It is frequently assumed that the excavation and the replacing of an equivalent load have no effect on settlement. Actually some rebound and some recompression always occur during this period, and they can be studied in detail, but often they are not considered to be of sufficient importance.

An approximate method for the prediction of building settlements during construction was advanced some years ago by Terzaghi, and was later extended by Gilboy. This method is based on the assumption, furnished largely by intuition, that at the end of construction the settlement is the same as that which would have resulted in half as much time had the entire load been acting throughout. For predicting settlements during the loading period this assumption was extended to the following: When any specified percentage of the loading period has elapsed, the load acting is approximately equal to this percentage of the total load; at this time the settlement may be taken as this percentage times the settlement at one-half the time in question from the curve of time versus settlement under instantaneous loading. This method has been found to be in close agreement with theoretical solutions which have been derived since it was proposed.

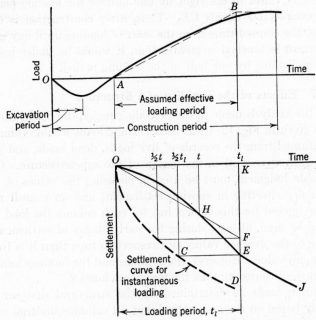

FIG. 12·6 Graphical determination of the settlement curve during the loading period.

The time-settlement curve for the given case, on the basis of instantaneous loading, is assumed to be line OCD of Fig. 12·6, zero time being measured from point A. According to the assumption stated above the settlement at time t_l is equal to that at time $\frac{1}{2}t_l$ on the instantaneous curve. Thus from point C on the instantaneous curve, point E is obtained on the corrected curve.

At any smaller time t the settlement determination is as follows: The instantaneous curve at time $t/2$ shows the settlement KF. At time t the load acting is t/t_l times the total load, and the settlement KF must be multiplied by this ratio. This may be done graphically as indicated in the figure. The diagonal OF intersects time t at point H, giving a settlement at H which equals $(t/t_l) \times KF$. Thus H is a point on the settlement curve, and as many points as desired may be obtained by similar procedure.

Beyond point E the curve is assumed to be the instantaneous curve CD, offset to the right by one half of the loading period; for example, DJ equals CE. Thus, after construction is completed, the elapsed time from the start of loading until any given settlement is reached is greater than it would be under instantaneous loading by one half of the loading period.

12·17 Effects of the Rigidity of a Structure

In the analysis made in the preceding pages, the list of column loads given in Fig. 12·4 was used. These loads would ordinarily be obtained from the records of live loads, dead loads, and wind loads that were used in the design of the superstructure. Considerable judgment must be used in choosing the values of load which are effective in causing settlement, and no overall rules can be quoted for this choice, but for each column the load that should be used, at least during the early stages of settlement, is nearer to the average value with respect to time than it is to the maximum value. However, the columns and the footings must be designed, of course, to take the maximum loads.†

Column loads as determined by the structural designer are usually based on the assumption that all columns undergo equal settlement. In a structure with timber framing or with brick bearing walls throughout, or in any large, relatively flexible structure, considerable magnitudes of unequal settlement may occur without causing major changes in the distribution of load to the various footings, and for such cases this assumption is reasonable. However, in structures which are not large and which are of concrete or steel framing the settlement of any individual footing leads to a considerable readjustment in the load on this and adjacent footings.

This important action is analogous to that in a continuous bridge with several supports. The principle is illustrated by the uniformly loaded elastic beam with three supports shown in Fig. 12·7. The magnitude of the center reaction depends greatly

† Further discussion of this point is given in Section 19·34.

on the elevation of the center support relative to the end supports. All three supports are at the same elevation in (c); a subsidence of the center support, as represented in (d), causes a decrease in the reaction at this support, with the reactions at the outer support increasing in magnitude.

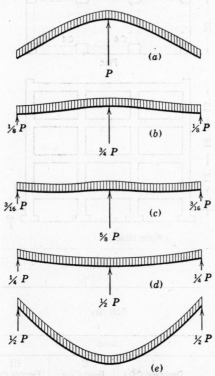

FIG. 12·7 Beam with three supports, showing relationship between reactions and relative elevations of supports.

In a structure that is framed in concrete or steel, it is possible for the structural designer to determine the changes in column loads in terms of the amounts of differential settlements. Such analyses, however, are lengthy and involved and are seldom available for use in settlement analyses. Thus in settlement analyses it is common to use the values of column loadings which would hold if there were no differential settlement. The assumption of flexible construction is always on the side of safety since

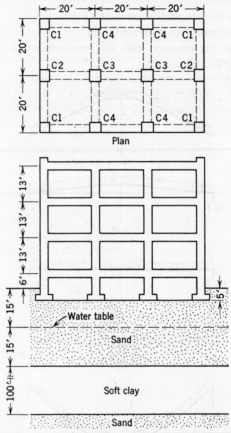

| | I | | II | | III | |
| | Designed Case | | Rigid Case | | Flexible Case | |
Column Number	Load (Tons)	ρ (In.)	Load (Tons)	ρ (In.)	Load (Tons)	ρ (In.)
C1	**131**	**1.9**	**233**	**2.1**	**84**	**1.8**
C2	123	2.7	76	2.1	158	2.6
C3	**257**	**2.9**	**125**	**2.1**	**291**	**3.2**
C4	142	2.4	129	2.1	152	2.5
AV. ρ		**2.5**		**2.1**		**2.5**

Fig. 12·8 Comparison of settlement and load distributions for various degrees of rigidity of a structure.

it leads to greater differential settlements than actually occur. The effect of rigidity therefore is definitely a desirable one, both with reference to the building as a whole and with reference to local irregularities. If a certain footing happens to be founded above an undiscovered pocket of compressible soil, it is inevitable that this footing will tend to undergo a relatively large settlement, and if there is flexible construction the settlement might well be of detrimental magnitude. In rigid construction the start of settlement at this footing immediately transfers much of the footing load to the adjacent footings, thus greatly relieving all undesirable effects.

The analysis of the building shown in Fig. 12·8 ‡ illustrates the effects of rigidity. Comparisons of loads and settlements are given in the figure for three cases: first, the building as designed in concrete framing; second, the case which would result if heavy trusses were framed into the lower story to prevent all differential settlement; third, the case obtained under perfect flexibility. The significance of the comparisons of loads and settlements is most evident for interior and corner columns, and for these columns the data are given in heavy type. The data from these three cases must of course be taken as qualitative only, since the numerical values depend greatly on design details which are not given in the figure. It is interesting to note that for this 60 ft by 40 ft building with concrete framing the settlements and loads are considerably nearer to those for flexible construction than to those for completely rigid construction. Nevertheless the rigidity of this concrete design is sufficient to lead to a corner column load which is more than 50 per cent greater than that occurring in the flexible case.

A clearer understanding of the subject may be obtained by consideration of the two types of buildings that are founded above a compressible foundation and shown in Fig. 12·9.

The flexible building shown in (a) will exert on the soil immediately below it a pressure distribution which is approximately uniform; it is shown by curve (1). This pressure distribution, according to concepts presented in Chapter 11, will cause a bell-

---

‡ From a thesis by R. H. Wingate, reference 172, abstracted in reference 134.

shaped pressure distribution at the surface of the buried compressible stratum as shown by curve (2). Under this pressure
distribution the surface of the compressible stratum will undergo
a settlement pattern of the shape shown by curve (3). If the soil
above is of much better quality as a foundation material than
the soil of the compressible stratum, it is reasonable to assume

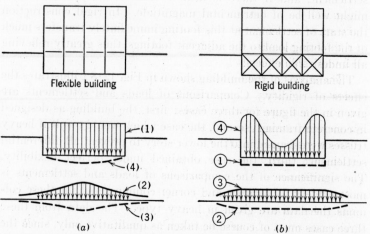

Fig. 12·9 Settlement patterns and pressure distributions below buildings
underlain by buried compressible strata.

that the compressible stratum is the source of practically all the
settlement, and the settlement pattern at the foundation level is
curve (4), which is similar to curve (3).

For the rigid building shown in (b), the settlement pattern is
known, and thus the curves must be considered in reverse order
as compared to (a). The building must settle uniformly and
must cause an approximately uniform compression of the buried
clay stratum, as shown in curve (2). For uniform compression
of the stratum the stress must be about uniform, as shown in
curve (3). By reverting to (a) and noting that pressure distribution curve (2) results from the uniform pressure distribution
curve (1), it may be deduced that in (b) the surface pressure
distribution required to cause distribution curve (3) is of the
form of distribution curve (4).

From these deductions the following conclusions may be

drawn: (a) If an approximately uniform load is applied to the soil above a buried compressible stratum, greater settlement occurs at the center than at the edges of the loaded area; (b) if a rigid foundation mat undergoes settlement because of compression of a buried stratum, the stress near the edges of the loaded area is greater than that near the center. The important subject of stress distribution patterns below foundations is discussed in greater detail in Section 19·29.

The differential settlement which occurs in the case shown in Fig. 12·9 (a) must result in distortion of the framing. Plastered walls would offer a slight resistance to such distortion but not enough to have appreciable effect in preventing it. Therefore such walls would be likely to undergo severe cracking. In the case shown in (b) with the rigid foundation the upper stories are not subject to distortion, to cracks in plastering, or to secondary stresses in framing members. However, if the soil reactions are carried by slabs at the bottom of the trussed basement framing, it must be noted that the pressures on the outer portions of these slabs are large. It is evident that these outer slabs would be likely to be overstressed if the design were based on the assumption of a uniform soil reaction, as it often is in structural design.

12·18   Effects of Horizontal Drainage

From the data of Table 12·4 it may be noted that the hydrostatic excess pressures at any given depth below columns 5 and 9 are not alike and, therefore, that horizontal components of gradient exist and horizontal drainage occurs.

The size of the building relative to the depth and the thickness of the clay stratum has a considerable effect on the importance of the horizontal drainage, the effect being greatest when the building dimensions are relatively small. This effect also depends greatly on the relative magnitude of the soil properties in the horizontal and vertical directions.

An investigation of the effect of horizontal drainage, which has been made by J. P. Gould (66), is based on the simple building shown in Fig. 12·4, in which the effects of horizontal drainage are relatively large because of the relatively small dimensions

of the building. In this investigation determinations were made
both for the assumption of equal coefficients of permeability in
the horizontal and vertical directions and for the assumption of

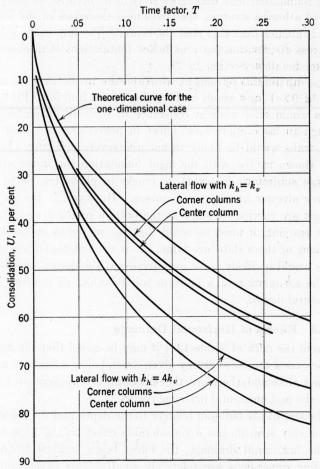

Fig. 12·10 Effect of lateral flow on consolidation.

the horizontal coefficient equal to four times the vertical coefficient.

The results of this investigation are shown in Fig. 12·10. It
may be concluded from the data of this isolated case that the
settlement may in extreme cases proceed at a rate that is as

much as two or three times as fast when radial drainage occurs as it would when one-dimensional drainage occurs, but in the majority of cases the effect of radial drainage may be of much less importance. The effect of radial drainage is somewhat greater at the center column than it is at corner columns, but the difference is not large.

12·19   Discussion of Accuracy in the Settlement Analysis

Remarks have been made in this chapter and in Chapter 10 concerning assumptions which are rough approximations of actual conditions. A logical treatment of the analysis cannot be concluded without a review of the more important of these approximations.

Assumptions made for the interpretation of the geological profile, for example values used for strata thicknesses, may lead to large errors if they are incorrect. These, however, are errors in data rather than items for which the soundness of the analysis can be criticized. When soil properties are determined from tests on partially disturbed samples, their use may introduce large errors into estimates of amounts and speeds of settlements. Since no sample is truly undisturbed, this source of inaccuracy is present to some degree in every analysis, but it also is an inaccuracy in data rather than in method of analysis.

In numerous instances variable functions have been treated as if they were constant, and average values of the variables have been used. It is believed that in all these instances the inaccuracies which are introduced are of minor importance and are of much smaller orders of magnitude than those associated with the factors which are discussed in the following paragraphs.

Two of the main sources of inaccuracy have been discussed in the immediately preceding sections. The effects of rigidity of structure can be taken into account if the details of the design of the superstructure are known. An analysis including such considerations is long and complex, and such refinements are not often justifiable in settlement analyses.

Conditions of one-dimensional compression and one-dimensional drainage are usually assumed in consolidation theory, in the laboratory test, and in settlement analyses. In the laboratory test these assumptions are practically true. If the settlement of a building in nature results from the compression of a deeply buried clay stratum, it is probable that the resistance to horizontal dislpacement of the clay is so large that the compression is essentially one-dimensional. Thus the ultimate settlement as determined under the one-dimensional assumption may be accepted as correct. However, the assumption of one-dimensional drainage may be far from valid, as the special case considered in the previous section shows. This special case shows that this factor can be considered in the analysis, but the amount of work required generally makes such a precedure prohibitive.

The final factor of importance which is neglected in the settlement analysis is the effect of the plastic bond, which has been described in Section 10·15. This effect is reviewed briefly in the next section.

In conclusion it may be stated that settlement analyses usually give results which at best are crude estimates. However, as long as the accuracy is not misrepresented, there can be little question that the crude estimate is much more valuable than the pure guess which often is the only alternative.

12·20 The Effect of the Plastic Bond

It has been stated in Section 10·15 that the effects of plastic resistance in the standardized laboratory test are not of sufficient magnitude to invalidate the values of the soil coefficients obtained.

When strata in nature undergo consolidation the plastic effects may be more important. The larger thickness of natural strata is a favorable factor since it leads to slower compression and smaller plastic resistances than occur in laboratory tests. However, small load increment ratios are common in nature, and therefore the plastic resistance is of greater relative importance than in tests. Moreover, because the duration of action of the preloading pressure in nature may often be hundreds or thousands of years, plastic bond is an important phenomenon.

Terzaghi has described and discussed the practical significance of a bond which gives natural clays the strength to carry small load increments with smaller compressions than his theory indicates (150). The research mentioned in Section 10·15 proves that this phenomenon occurs not only in nature but also in all laboratory specimens and even in remolded specimens. It is possible, moreover, that plastic bond occurs to greater degree under natural conditions.

The main conclusion of this discussion is that a small load increment, applied in nature to a clay mass that previously has been under an essentially constant pressure for ages, is likely to cause more compression of a secondary nature and less consolidation or compression of a primary nature than has hitherto been supposed. If the load increment is very small it is possible that it will cause practically no hydrostatic excess pressure, and the compression will therefore be secondary compression. In such a case the settlement that does occur may take place so slowly that it cannot be observed.

At present no method is available for estimating the amount of the plastic bond existing under natural conditions.

12·21 Settlement Records

Settlement records § offer the one real test of the accuracy of a settlement analysis, and the obtaining of such records should be a required final step of any analysis. However, settlements progress slowly, construction organizations are disbanded, interest lags, and after the completion of construction many other conditions contribute to make difficult the maintenance of such records. Actually they have been kept in too few cases. The development of better methods of analysis, with more accurate predictions of settlement in the future as their aim, depends greatly on careful comparisons of settlement records with predicted settlement values. Thus every engineer who has charge of a settlement analysis on any important structure should feel it his responsibility to see that settlement records are obtained.

The commonest method of observing settlements uses periodic lines of levels, run with an engineer's level and observing a representative group of reference points. When more accurate records are desired, special leveling devices, similar to one described by Terzaghi (146), may be used. In any case a dependable bench mark must be available, and in a locality where there is a deep, buried clay layer bench marks that are not subject to settlement

§ For examples see references 46, 146, 154, and 35.

often are not available. Satisfactory bench marks must be founded on solid ground, preferably on ledge. A permanent bench mark that extends to ledge at a depth of 120 ft below

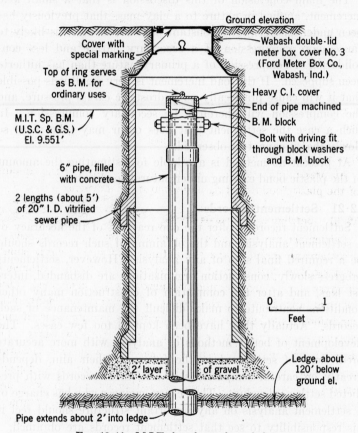

FIG. 12·11 M.I.T. bench mark to ledge.

ground surface was established in Cambridge, Massachusetts, in 1927; it is shown in Fig. 12·11.

12·22 Approximate Comparisons

The fundamental principles discussed under consolidation theory and settlement analysis may sometimes be put to practice in relatively simple problems. One such case occurs when settlement observations have been carried out on an existing building and it is desired to predict the settlement of a second building from a comparison of conditions. Naturally, the accuracy of the prediction for the proposed building will depend to a large degree on the accuracy and completeness of the data available for the comparison. It often happens that such data are meager but, if any dependability may be placed on them, an idea of the settlement of the proposed structure can be obtained. A second type of simple comparison is useful in the interpretation of the results of a settlement analysis. Numerous assumptions will have been made in such an analysis, and sometimes when an assumption must be made it is hard to decide which of two or more choices is the most reasonable. As a result it is often desired to know what change there would be in the settlement if an assumption were revised.

Simple comparison problems which involve only one or two factors make excellent exercises for the development of a clear understanding of the principles of consolidation, and a number of examples will be given in this section. Practical comparison problems may go deeply into all possible factors, or they may study only a single factor. If no settlement records are available in a locality, the engineer must resort to theoretical analyses for predictions of settlement. On the other hand, if settlement data for nearby structures are available, the most dependable prediction of settlement that can be obtained must be based on a combined study of the results of theoretical analyses and of the results of comparison studies in which the settlement records and data of all structures and clay strata involved are used.

Before the examples are presented, a summary of factors affecting settlement and of basic consolidation relationships will be given. The settlement of a building constructed above a compressible clay stratum depends upon the following:

I. Δp, the average increase in the intergranular pressure in the compressible stratum. The magnitude of Δp depends on the net building loads and the relative elevations and the locations of the points of load application. If there is any residual hydrostatic excess, it also is included in Δp.

II. H, which depends on the thickness of the compressible stratum and the drainage conditions.

III. t, the time interval since the application of the load. It has been shown that after construction is completed this time may be measured from the middle of the loading period.

IV. The coefficients of compressibility and consolidation of the soil, both of which are functions of the average intergranular pressure and may be determined from laboratory tests.

In the predicting of the settlement of one structure from the settlement of another, the estimate being based on the relative conditions of the two cases, a good deal of judgment is required in the setting up of the relative conditions. However, in the problems given below it must be assumed that the relative conditions are known. If it is attempted to make such comparisons by mere substitution in formulas, there is a strong possibility that incorrect interpretation of the meaning of the formulas may lead to erroneous results. The theoretical relationships that apply for such comparisons and that are given below must be thoroughly understood, and there is considerable inherent danger in blind use of these equations.

The fundamental laws of consolidation may be expressed as follows:

(1) $$\rho = U\rho_u$$

(2) $$\rho_u = \frac{\Sigma H}{1 + e}\, a\, \Delta p$$

(3) $$T = \frac{\pi}{4} U^2 \quad \text{when} \quad U < 60 \text{ per cent}$$

(4) $$T = \frac{c_v t}{H^2}$$

The term ΣH in expression (2) is the stratum thickness, equal to H for a single-drainage stratum and $2H$ for a double-drainage stratum. Comparisons can always be based on double drainage, and a subsequent adjustment can be made to take care of cases of single drainage and cases in which there are several drainages.

Following are a number of examples of simple approximate comparisons.

EXAMPLE I. The loading period for a structure extended from January, 1930, to January, 1932. In January, 1935, the average settlement was 5 in. It is known that the ultimate settlement will exceed 1 ft. Estimate the settlement in January, 1940.

Time t is measured from the middle of the loading period, that is, from January, 1931. Thus 5 in. of settlement occurred in 4 years, and it is desired to know what settlement will occur in 9 years.

All factors of the above expressions are constant in this comparison except ρ, t, T, and U. Therefore expressions (1), (3), and (4) give

$$\rho:\rho' = U:U' \qquad U:U' = \sqrt{T}:\sqrt{T'} \qquad \sqrt{T}:\sqrt{T'} = \sqrt{t}:\sqrt{t'}$$

in which terms with and without primes represent quantities for the required case and the given case, respectively, and

$$\rho:\rho' = \sqrt{t}:\sqrt{t'} \quad \text{or} \quad 5:\rho' = \sqrt{4}:\sqrt{9}$$

whence the settlement in January, 1940, was $7\frac{1}{2}$ in. Since the ultimate settlement was given as greater than 1 ft, the $7\frac{1}{2}$ in. obtained probably represents less than 60 per cent consolidation and cannot be above 60 per cent by a sufficient amount to invalidate expression (3).

EXAMPLE II. Observations show 4 in. of settlement in 3 years for building A, and it is known that the ultimate settlement will be about 1 ft. Building B and its underlying clay layer are, as far as is known, very similar to A with the single exception that the clay layer below B is 20 per cent thicker. It may also be assumed that the average pressure increase is alike for the two cases. Estimate the ultimate settlement of building B and also the settlement in 3 years.

From (2),

$$\rho_u:\rho_u' = H_0:H_0' \quad \text{or} \quad 12'':\rho_u' = H_0:1.2H_0$$

and ρ_u', the ultimate settlement for building B is 14.4 in.

From (4),

$$T:T' = \frac{t}{(H_0)^2} : \frac{t'}{(H_0')^2} = \frac{3}{(H_0)^2} : \frac{3}{(1.2H_0)^2} \quad \text{or} \quad \frac{T}{T'} = (1.2)^2$$

From (3),

$$T:T' = (U)^2:(U')^2 = (1.2)^2 \quad \text{or} \quad \frac{U}{U'} = 1.2$$

From (1),

$$U:U' = \frac{\rho}{\rho_u} : \frac{\rho'}{\rho_u'}$$

and since

$$\frac{U}{U'} = 1.2 \quad \text{and} \quad \frac{\rho_u}{\rho_u{}'} = \frac{1}{1.2}$$

it follows that $\rho = \rho'$. Thus at any time the settlements of buildings A and B are alike, as long as U is less than 60 per cent. Each undergoes 4 in. of settlement in 3 years.

It is of unusual interest to find that two strata of different thicknesses, but with all other conditions alike, will show the same time-settlement curve as long as both are less than 60 per cent consolidated. Each of the curves of settlement versus time for the two buildings of this example will follow the same parabolic curve to its 60 per cent consolidation point. The curve for A is parabolic to a settlement of 60 per cent of 12 in.; for B it is parabolic to 60 per cent of 14.4 in. For settlements greater than 7.2 in. the curves separate, and the ultimate settlements are 12 in. for A and 14.4 in. for B.

EXAMPLE III. The settlement analysis for a proposed structure indicates 3 in. of settlement in 4 years and an ultimate settlement of 10 in. This analysis is based on the assumption that the underlying clay layer is drained at both its top and bottom surfaces. However, there are some indications that there may be no drainage at the bottom. In alternate A it is to be assumed that there is no bottom drainage. For this alternate estimate determine the ultimate settlement and the time required for 3 in. of settlement.

The ultimate settlement is independent of drainage conditions, and it equals 10 in. for alternate A, just as it did for the original estimate.

Let the single-drainage stratum of alternate A be designated as stratum A. Imagine a double-drainage stratum twice as thick as stratum A, with its upper half indentical to stratum A, and assume the lower half to have the same loading condition and to be in every way a mirror image of the upper half; designate it as stratum A2. The time-settlement data for the various strata may now be recorded as follows:

Original estimate: 3 in. in 4 years

Stratum A2, according to the principle demonstrated by Example II:
   3 in. in 4 years

Stratum A, since it is exactly a half of stratum A2: $1\frac{1}{2}$ in. in 4 years

As in Example I:

$$\rho:\rho' = \sqrt{t}:\sqrt{t'} \quad \text{or} \quad 1.5:3 = \sqrt{4}:\sqrt{t_2}$$

whence a 3-in. settlement will take place in 16 years in alternate A.

EXAMPLE IV. One of the borings at the site for which the original estimate of Example III was made showed thin sand strata at points about one third and two thirds of the way through the clay stratum

Assuming that these two thin strata are completely drained but that other conditions are as in the original estimate, determine, as alternate B, the time required for 3 in. of settlement.

First assume that the average Δp for the entire clay layer is constant throughout the height and that it may be used as the Δp for each of the three partial heights. This might lead to appreciable errors in estimates for the top and bottom thirds individually, but in estimates for the entire stratum the errors in the top third will approximately balance those in the bottom third.

Since the initial portion of the time settlement curve was shown by Example II to be independent of the stratum thickness, each third would settle 3 in. in 4 years and the entire clay layer would settle 9 in. in 4 years, if 9 in. is less than 60 per cent of the ultimate settlement. However, the ultimate settlement of the entire layer is only 10 in., and therefore a modified procedure will be used.

The settlement in 1 year for the original estimate may be computed as in Example I. The relationship is $3:\rho' = \sqrt{4}:\sqrt{1}$ and $1\frac{1}{2}$ in. of settlement occurs in 1 year.

It may now be noted that each of the thirds will settle $1\frac{1}{2}$ in. in 1 year, the three sections together will settle $3 \times 1\frac{1}{2} = 4\frac{1}{2}$ in. in 1 year, and a check shows that this is less than 60 per cent of the ultimate settlement. The required time t' is $4.5:3 = \sqrt{1}:\sqrt{t'}$, whence the time required for 3 in. of settlement in alternate B is $\frac{4}{9}$ year.

EXAMPLE V. The laboratory data for the original estimate of Example III were from tests on a few samples. Subsequent tests on additional samples give what are believed to be more accurate determinations of the soil coefficients and show that the coefficient of compressibility is 20 per cent smaller and the coefficient of consolidation is 30 per cent smaller than originally obtained. Basing alternate C on these more accurate test data, but otherwise using the data of the original estimate, determine the ultimate settlement and the time for 3 in. of settlement.

From (2),

$$\rho_u:\rho_u' = a:a' \quad \text{or} \quad 10:\rho_u' = a:0.8a$$

whence the ultimate settlement ρ_u' is 8 in.

On the basis of $\rho = \rho' = 3$ in., from (1),

$$U:U' = \rho_u':\rho_u = 0.8$$

from (3),

$$\sqrt{T}:\sqrt{T'} = 0.8$$

from (4),

$$T:T' = c_e t:c_e' t' \quad \text{or} \quad (0.8)^2 = (c_e \times 4):(0.7c_e \times t')$$

whence in alternate C the time required for 3 in. of settlement is 9 years.

EXAMPLE VI. An alternate design of the structure for which the original estimate of Example III applies proposes a taller building which would increase the net building load by 25 per cent. On the basis of this heavier load, all other conditions being as in the original estimate, determine as alternate D the ultimate settlement, the settlement in 4 years, and the time required for 3 in. of settlement.

In the absence of any data to the contrary it must be assumed that there is no residual hydrostatic excess in the clay stratum of this problem. Therefore, if the same foundation plan and similar distributions of load hold for the original estimate and the alternate, it follows that $\Delta p' = 1.25 \Delta p$. The average pressure will be increased slightly and a somewhat smaller coefficient of compressibility will result, but for this small increase the variation in the coefficient may be neglected.

From (2),

$$\rho_u : \rho_u' = \Delta p : \Delta p' \quad \text{or} \quad 10 : \rho_u' = p : 1.25p$$

and the ultimate settlement for alternate D is 12.5 in.

In the determination of the settlement in 4 years, $t = t'$ and, from (4) and (3), $T = T'$ and $U = U'$; then from (1),

$$\rho : \rho' = \rho_u : \rho_u' \quad \text{or} \quad 3 : \rho' = 10 : 12.5$$

or in 4 years the settlement in alternate D is 3¾ in.

From (4),

$$\rho : \rho' = \sqrt{t} : \sqrt{t'} \quad \text{or} \quad 3¾ : 3 = \sqrt{4} : \sqrt{t'}$$

whence the time for 3 in. settlement in alternate D is 2.5 years.

It may be noted that a simultaneous solution of equations (1) to (4) inclusive could be used if desired to determine a general equation for settlement. It is recommended, however, that use of such an expression be avoided. For students, its use would be at the expense of the development of a clear understanding of the various relationships. Its limitations would not be understood by one who is not familiar with the theory, and incorrect applications might frequently result.

PROBLEMS

1. A revision of the settlement analysis covered in the text is desired. The revisions in data are: the gross load on each column is to be reduced 100 tons; the building is to be founded 6 ft below ground level; the loading period will be 2 years. All other data may be accepted as unchanged, and the analysis may be based on pressure data at the center of the clay stratum only. Curves like those in Fig. 12·5 are desired.

2. A tower footing that is 10 ft square will rest at a depth of 5 ft below ground surface and it will carry a net load of 500 tons. Dense sand exists at the site to a depth of 30 ft below ground surface. Below this sand is a 10-ft layer of peat for which the consolidation characteristics may be assumed to be given in Fig. 10·13 (*d*). Below the peat is impervious ledge. The effective overburden pressure at the middle of the peat stratum before construction may be assumed to be 1.2 tons per sq ft. Estimate the settlement that the tower will undergo as a result of compression of the peat.

3. A stratum of clay is 50 ft thick, and the intergranular overburden pressure at its surface is 1 kg per sq cm. The average consolidation characteristics of this clay may be assumed to be represented by Fig. 10·13 (*c*). The clay at present is just consolidated under the existing overburden. A permanent 5-ft lowering of the water table is to take place within the soil above the clay. Determine the time-settlement curve for this change of loading, assuming that there will be no change in water content in the soil above the water table.

4. *Settlement Analysis.*

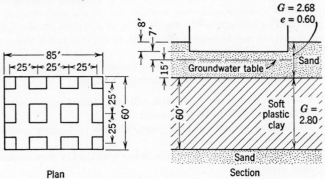

Plan   Section

PROB. 12·4.

The following data are to be assumed.

Gross loads: corner columns 500 tons, side columns 700 tons, interior columns 1100 tons

Clay just consolidated under original overburden

The straight line portion of the compression curve given by $e = 1.20 - 0.36 \log_{10} p$, in which p is in tons per square foot

Load increment in tons per square foot	1 to 2	2 to 4	4 to 8
Coefficient of consolidation in 10^{-4} sq cm per sec	19	20	22
Primary compression ratio	0.70	0.68	0.65

Construction schedule: start of excavation, May 1, 1948; net load of zero, July 1, 1948; completion, January 1, 1950

All transmitted stresses are to be estimated by use of the Westergaard equations.

(*a*) On the basis of the stress values at the mid-depth only, determine settlement curves for interior and corner columns. Neglect the construction period in this estimate.

(*b*) For the interior column only, make estimates of final settlements by using stress values at (1) mid-depth only, (2) top and bottom of clay only, (3) top, mid-depth, and bottom of clay.

(*c*) For the interior column only, determine the settlement curve corrected for construction period, using the curve of part (*a*) for the uncorrected curve.

5. A stratum of clay is 80 ft thick and is just consolidated under its present overburden. At the top of this stratum the intergranular pressure and the hydrostatic pressure are 3000 and 1000 lb per sq ft, respectively. To furnish a supply of water it is proposed to pump water from a sand stratum that underlies the clay. What ultimate settlement would occur at ground surface if the pressure in the water below the clay were to be permanently reduced by 1000 lb per sq ft by pumping?

6. The preliminary settlement analysis for a proposed building, to be founded above a compressible clay stratum, indicates a settlement of 3 in. in 5 years and an ultimate settlement of 12 in. at a typical interior column. The estimated average increment of pressure in the clay below this column is 0.133 tons per sq ft.

Data that have recently been obtained indicate the following variations from the assumptions used in the preliminary analysis:

(*a*) A 3-ft lowering of the water table will take place during construction, and this change is likely to be permanent.

(*b*) The loading period will be 2 years, whereas no loading period was considered in the previous estimate.

(*c*) The compressible clay stratum is 20 per cent thicker than assumed in the original analysis.

Obtain estimates of the ultimate settlement, the settlement at the middle and at the end of the loading period, and the settlement 2 years after the completion of the building.

Chapter 13

STRENGTH THEORY

13·1 General Discussion

Slopes of all kinds, including river banks and sea coast bluffs, hills, mountains, and man-made cuts and fills, stay in place only because of the shearing strength possessed by the soil or rock of which they are composed. In contrast water has no static strength in shear and, therefore, the surfaces of all bodies of water are level.

Stability analysis in soil mechanics includes all studies which attempt to determine whether or not the shearing strength is sufficient to prevent danger of failure. Basically, such studies consist of comparisons between all forces which tend to cause failure—such as weights and the force of seeping water—and the resisting forces provided by the shearing strength.

Two of the greatest contributions of soil mechanics to engineering are the development of better basic understanding of slope stability and the building up of improved methods of stability analysis. The all-important factor underlying such analysis is an understanding of shearing strength of soils.

This chapter deals with theoretical considerations of shearing strength, and contains a general treatment of such subjects as friction between solid bodies, stress at a point, intrinsic pressure, and theories of strength. In Chapter 14 the common types of shearing tests on soils are outlined, and shearing strength in granular soil is discussed. The shearing strength of cohesive soils is the subject of Chapter 15.

13·2 Friction between Solid Bodies

In Fig. 13·1 (a) a body rests on a horizontal surface. The force P_n represents the total vertical force acting on the body, and includes the weight of the body. The reaction to force P_n is force P_r. These vertical forces make available a friction force P_f, which may be expressed

$$P_f = P_n \tan \phi = P_n f \qquad (13 \cdot 1)$$

The angle ϕ is called the angle of friction, and f the coefficient of friction. The characteristics ϕ and f are properties of the mate-

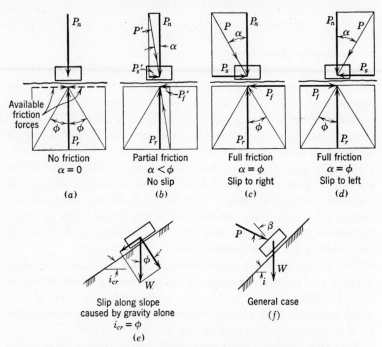

FIG. 13·1 Illustrations of friction and the criterion of slip.

rials which are in contact; for most materials they are approximately constant and are independent of the forces acting. The force P_f does not come into action unless it is required to resist an applied horizontal force; in Fig. 13·1 (*a*) this force does not act.

In (*b*) a small horizontal force $P_s{'}$ has been applied to the body. The resultant of P_n and $P_s{'}$ is force P' which is at angle α to the normal to the interface between the body and the plane on which it rests. The angle α is called the angle of obliquity of force P'; it depends on the forces acting and not on properties of the materials present. To resist force $P_s{'}$ the force $P_f{'}$ is summoned into action;

this force P_f' is a part of the available friction P_f. Since P_f' is less than P_f and α is less than ϕ, there is no slip between the body and the plane.

In (c) a horizontal force P_s, which is just equal to P_f, has been applied. The entire friction force P_f now comes into play to resist P_s; angles α and ϕ are equal; and slip or sliding to the right is incipient. Similarly in (d) slip is incipient but in the opposite direction since the applied force is to the left. The friction force here, as always, acts in the direction opposing the motion.

The simple cases given above point out the following fundamentals: The amount of available friction depends directly on the pressure and on the friction angle; if either pressure or friction angle is zero there is no friction. If the obliquity of the applied stress on a surface is less than the friction angle, only a part of the friction acts and there is no danger of slip. The friction angle is the limiting value of the obliquity; when the obliquity is equal to ϕ, all friction is acting and slip is imminent. The criterion of slip is therefore an obliquity equal to the friction angle.

These fundamentals may be extended to other cases of applied forces. In (e) a body, which is acted on only by gravity, rests on a plane at a slope which has been gradually increased until it has reached the critical slope i_{cr} at which slip just occurs. The figure shows that i_{cr} is equal to ϕ. This relationship holds, however, only if the weight and the reaction to the weight are the only forces acting.

In (f) a body of weight W is in addition acted on by a resultant force P which is at an obliquity β to the plane on which the body rests. This plane is at slope i. In this case

$$\tan \alpha = \frac{W \sin i - P \sin \beta}{W \cos i + P \cos \beta}$$

and slip will occur if α is numerically equal to ϕ; the slip will be in the downhill direction if the expression above is positive and in the uphill direction if it is negative.

The condition of incipient slip for all solid bodies in contact may now be expressed

$$\frac{P_s}{P_n} = \frac{P_f}{P_r} = \tan \phi = f \qquad (13 \cdot 2)$$

For solid bodies which are in contact but which have no adhesion or bond between them the term friction is synonymous with the terms shearing strength and maximum shearing resistance. In most soils the friction represents an important part of the shearing strength, but other phenomena also contribute to the shearing strength, particularly in certain fine-grained soils.

13·3   Internal Friction within Cohesionless Granular Masses

In sands and in other cohesionless granular materials the resistance to sliding on any plane through the material is similar to that discussed above in that it depends on the direct pressure existing on this plane and on the friction angle, which in this case is called the angle of internal friction. However, the frictional resistance in sands is somewhat more complex than that between solid bodies, since it is partly sliding friction and partly rolling friction. Resistance to shear is also offered in sands by the phenomenon known as interlocking, which is generally considered to be a part of the frictional resistance.

The expression for the force required to overcome all frictional resistance and cause slip on a plane through a mass of granular material is of the same form as equation 13·2 and may be written

$$P_s = P_n \tan \phi \tag{13·3}$$

In this expression P_n must be defined as the normal force on the plane subject to slip. The angle of internal friction, ϕ, has values in any given sand which vary appreciably with the density of the sand, the amount of interlocking that occurs being determined by the density. This angle also varies somewhat with the magnitude of the direct pressure. However, for a given sand at a given density, the friction angle is so close to constant that in the derivation of fundamental concepts of shear it is reasonable to consider it constant.

Since slip within a soil mass is not restricted to any specific plane, the relationships which exist between the stresses on the various planes through a given point must be known before shear in sands can be considered in any detail.

13·4 Stress at a Point

In the consideration of the stresses on all planes through a point, the various planes will in general be found to have both direct stress and shearing stress acting on them. The direct stress, which is designated by σ, is the normal component of force per unit of area across the plane; the shearing stress, which is designated by τ, is the tangential or shearing component of force per unit of area.

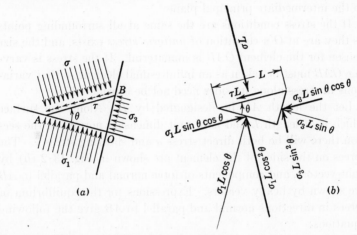

Fig. 13·2 Element considered in the derivation of the expressions for stress at a point.

In all soil studies, pressures are considered positive direct stresses and tensions negative.

A principal plane is a plane having no shearing stress and therefore having an obliquity angle of zero. It is a fundamental principle of mechanics that three principal planes exist through any point. These three planes always intersect each other at 90 degrees. In order of decreasing magnitude of direct stress these planes are known as the major, the intermediate, and the minor principal planes.

In Fig. 13·2 (a), O represents any point within a stressed mass; OA represents the major principal plane on which the stress acting is the major principal stress σ_1, and OB represents the minor principal plane on which the stress acting is the minor principal stress σ_3. The intermediate principal plane is the plane of the figure. It is desired to know the stress conditions on any plane normal to the sketch, the location of this plane being defined by its angle θ to the major principal plane. Other planes through point O which are not normal to the plane of the figure need not be considered because, as will be seen later, critical values, such as the maximum and minimum values of normal and shearing stresses and stress obliquities, always occur on planes normal to the intermediate principal plane.

If the stress conditions are the same at all surrounding points as they are at O a condition of *uniform stress* exists, and the size chosen for the element OAB is immaterial. If the stress is varying, OAB must be taken as an infinitesimal element so that variations in stress along its sides need not be considered.

Let the length AB be designated by L. Along the surface which is of length L and is of unit dimension normal to the section there will be both direct stress σ and shearing stress τ. The forces on the sides of the element are shown in Fig. 13·2 (*b*) by light vectors, and components of force normal and parallel to AB are shown by heavy vectors. Expressions for the equilibrium of forces in directions normal and parallel to AB give the following equations:

$$\sigma = \sigma_1 \cos^2 \theta + \sigma_3 \sin^2 \theta = \sigma_3 + (\sigma_1 - \sigma_3) \cos^2 \theta$$
$$\tau = (\sigma_1 - \sigma_3) \sin \theta \cos \theta \tag{13·4}$$

It is seen that the normal and shearing stresses on any plane which is normal to the intermediate principal plane may be expressed in terms of σ_1, σ_3, and θ.

13·5   The Mohr Diagram

All details that pertain to stress at a point may be represented graphically by a plot known as the Mohr diagram (103). This diagram is of the utmost value in the study of stress conditions.

If a plot is made with normal stresses used as abscissas and shearing stresses as ordinates, and if points are plotted to represent stress coordinates for all possible values of θ as given by equations 13·4, it is found that the locus of these points is a circle, as shown in Fig. 13·3 (*a*). This circle has its center on the σ axis, and cuts it at abscissas of σ_3 and σ_1. Any point on the circle represents the coordinates of stress on some plane; point C in the figure is for the same θ value as used in Fig. 13·2 (*a*). This circle is called the Mohr circle.

The Mohr diagram also permits an excellent visualization of the orientations of the various planes. Through point D, the coordinate of which is the major principal stress, let a line be drawn parallel to the known orientation of the major principal

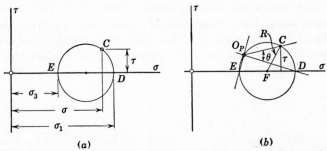

(*a*)   (*b*)

FIG. 13·3   The Mohr circle for the stress condition illustrated in Fig. 13·2.

plane, which is given by OA of Fig. 13·2 (*a*). This line is shown in Fig. 13·3 (*b*). Its intersection with the Mohr circle is the point designated by O_P; it is called the origin of planes. It is seen that a line which is drawn through point O_P and at right angles to $O_P D$ must pass through point E. Therefore, this line through point E, the coordinate of which is the minor principal stress, is parallel to the minor principal plane. Moreover, *any line through O_P, parallel to any arbitrarily chosen plane, intersects the circle at a point the coordinates of which are the stress components on that plane.*

This relationship may be proved as follows. The expression for shearing stress in equations 13·4 may, if the radius of the Mohr circle is denoted by R, be written

$$\tau = R \sin 2\theta$$

In Fig. 13·3 (*b*), the lines representing τ and R for the plane represented by point C are marked, and it is seen that angle CFD must equal 2θ. Since angle CFD is a central angle and $CO_P D$ is an inscribed angle cutting the same circular arc, and since central angles are twice as large as corresponding inscribed angles, it follows that angle CO_PD must equal θ. This is the relationship which was to be proved.

On plane AB in Fig. 13·2 (a), the shear is shown acting in the counterclockwise sense, and in Fig. 13·3 this shear is represented by a positive ordinate. Thus it is seen that counterclockwise shears are positive.

A number of basic relationships, which are sometimes derived mathematically in textbooks on mechanics, may be observed directly from the Mohr diagram. Among these are the following:

1. The maximum shearing stress, often called the principal shearing stress, has a magnitude of $\frac{1}{2}(\sigma_1 - \sigma_3)$, which equals the radius of the Mohr circle. The principal shearing stress occurs on planes with θ values of 45 degrees. These relationships are shown in Fig. 13·4 (a).

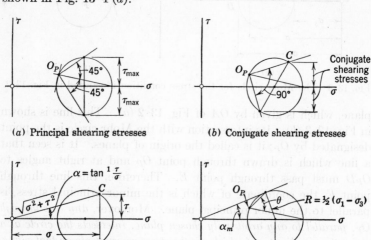

(a) Principal shearing stresses   (b) Conjugate shearing stresses

(c) Obliquity and resultant stress   (d) Maximum obliquity

FIG. 13·4 Fundamental relationships demonstrated by the Mohr diagram.

2. Shearing stresses on planes at right angles to each other are numerically equal but are of opposite sign. These stresses, called conjugate shearing stresses, are shown in Fig. 13·4 (b).

3. The resultant stress on any plane has a magnitude expressed by $\sqrt{\sigma^2 + \tau^2}$ and has an obliquity which is equal to $\tan^{-1}(\tau/\sigma)$. This is shown in Fig. 13·4 (c).

4. The maximum of all the possible obliquity angles on the various planes is called the maximum angle of obliquity, and is designated by α_m. This angle may be constructed by drawing a line which passes through the origin and which is tangent to the Mohr circle, as shown in Fig. 13·4 (*d*). The coordinates of the point of tangency are the stresses on the plane of maximum obliquity, and it is obvious that the shear on this plane is less than the principal shear. However, it is seen that on the plane of principal shear there is an obliquity which is slightly smaller than α_m. Since a limiting obliquity is the criterion of slip, it may now be noted that it is the plane of maximum obliquity and not the plane of principal shear which is most liable to failure.

All important stress relationships can be derived from the Mohr diagram, and most of them are more easily obtained from the diagram than by any other means. Among the commonly used relationships are

$$\sin \alpha_m = \frac{\sigma_1 - \sigma_3}{\sigma_1 + \sigma_3}$$

$$\frac{\sigma_1}{\sigma_3} = \frac{1 + \sin \alpha_m}{1 - \sin \alpha_m} \qquad (13·5)$$

$$\theta_{cr} = 45° + \tfrac{1}{2}\alpha_m$$

$$\sigma_{cr} = \sigma_3(1 + \sin \alpha_m)$$

In these expressions θ_{cr} and σ_{cr} are the θ and σ values for the plane of maximum obliquity.

13·6 Intergranular Pressure, Intrinsic Pressure, and Cohesion

If loads are applied to a mass of any material they will cause stresses within the mass. If the mass is a saturated soil the stresses produced will be a combination of intergranular stress and hydrostatic excess stress. As will be shown later, it is difficult on some occasions to evaluate the intergranular stresses in soils under shear, even though the applied loads may be accurately known. This difficulty need not be considered at this point, however, since the present problem is only to outline interrelationships which must hold between intergranular stresses. It should be noted, however, that the Mohr diagram in its basic form represents intergranular stresses only.

Materials which can be called solid have strength which cannot be attributed to any visible source of pressure. This condition often may be described as a result of a pressure which was exerted on the material at some time in the past, the effects of which have in some way been retained.

Supercooled liquids, one of which is steel, provide one example of retained pressure. Such materials were once in molten form. During the subsequent cooling, shrinkage occurred, more and more crystals were formed, and pressures between crystals increased until, when the material was finally cooled, an internal pressure of the order of millions of pounds per square inch was reached.

A stiff clay, loaded and compressed in past ages by overlying strata, provides another example of retained pressure. When a specimen of such a soil is removed from the ground and protected from evaporation or increase in water content, a large portion of the intergranular pressure is retained by capillary action at the surface of the specimen. In this condition the pore water is in tension as explained in Section 8·6, and the pressure on the sample is capillary pressure. The shearing strength which is caused by capillary pressure is sometimes called apparent cohesion. In some clays most of this pressure is lost in a short time if the specimen is placed under water, because submergence destroys the surface menisci, the sample swells, and the tension in the water soon is dissipated. A simple but common test to determine the degree to which this process occurs is called the slaking test, which consists simply in visually noting how fast and to what degree the sample slakes, or falls apart, when placed below water. The strength lost during a slaking test is apparent cohesion or strength due to capillary pressure.

Some clays in such a test lose practically all their intergranular pressure, and others lose practically none. In those which lose only a minor portion of their strength, pressure must be retained by some type of bond in the adsorbed water adjacent to the points where grains touch or nearly touch. Water in this form is highly plastic and will flow, but the flow is at a very slow rate. If a submerged specimen is given sufficient time, the retention of pressure contributed by this bound water may gradually be lost, but the adjustment may require decades, whereas only minutes or hours are required for apparent cohesion to disappear. This relatively permanent type of strength is called true cohesion and is said to be caused by intrinsic pressure. A clay which actually has started to pass into the category of shale may have a large amount of true cohesion.

Many modern concepts relative to intrinsic pressure are of hypothetical nature but it may at least be said that, when loads are applied to a solid, some type of intrinsic attraction or bond either exists or comes into action to resist the relative displacement of adjacent particles. The shearing strength which any material possesses by virtue of its intrinsic pressure is given the general name *cohesion*. Since failure will not result unless additional stresses are applied there will seldom be a failure in which cohesion is the entire shearing strength.

The cohesion is sometimes described as equal to $p_i \tan \phi$, where p_i is the intrinsic pressure and ϕ is the friction angle. This simplified relationship is often used in the explanation of fundamental concepts. This expression may be reasonably correct, but it must be recognized that p_i is not a constant for a given soil. The total intergranular pressure is equal to the intrinsic pressure plus the applied intergranular pressure, but while the stresses are being applied during a shear test on any given specimen it is likely that the intrinsic pressure gradually decreases. However, this decrease need not be considered unless knowledge of stress-strain relationships is desired, since it is probable that only the intrinsic pressure which remains when rupture impends affects the shearing strength. Further explanation of these concepts requires the presentation of a number of fundamental ideas which are discussed in Chapter 15.

For preliminary and approximate studies in which simplified conditions are adopted it often is assumed that intrinsic pressures are equal on all planes; thus a Mohr diagram of intrinsic pressures is a point-circle.

13·7 The Mohr Strength Theory

On any plane the shearing stress may be expressed

$$\tau = \sigma \tan \alpha$$

If the obliquity angle α is at its maximum or limiting value ϕ, the shearing stress is also at its limiting value, which is the shearing strength and which for a cohesionless soil may be expressed

$$s = \sigma \tan \phi \qquad (13 \cdot 6)$$

If it is assumed that the angle of internal friction ϕ is a constant, the shearing strength may be represented by a pair of straight lines at slopes of plus and minus ϕ through the origin

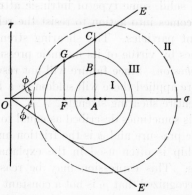

FIG. 13·5 Diagram illustrating the Mohr strength theory.

of the Mohr diagram. A line of this type is called a Mohr envelope. In Fig. 13·5, lines OE and OE' are Mohr envelopes.

If the stress at a given point within a specimen of sand is represented by Mohr circle I, it may be noted that every plane through this point has a shearing stress which is smaller than the shearing strength. For example, on the plane subject to a direct stress OA, the shearing stress AB is smaller than the shearing strength AC. Under this stress condition there is no possibility of failure. On the other hand it would not be possible to apply the stress condition represented by Mohr circle II to this sample because it is not possible for shearing stresses to be greater than the shearing strength.

Mohr circle III in this figure is tangent to the Mohr envelope at point G. The plane having the direct stress OF has the shearing stress FG and also has the shearing strength FG. Other values pertaining to this plane can be obtained by the use of equations 13·5 under the special conditions here obtaining of α_m equal to ϕ. Failure threatens to occur on this plane, and in fact it will occur unless an increase occurs in the magnitude of the direct stress on the danger plane.

The example given above explains the Mohr rupture theory. In brief, this theory may be expressed by the statement that any Mohr circle within the Mohr envelope represents a stable condition, whereas any circle tangent to the envelope represents a condition wherein failure threatens on the plane represented by the point of tangency. The Mohr envelope should be thought of as a property of the material and as independent of the stresses imposed on the material. The Mohr circle depends only on the stresses caused by the loading, and it is independent of what the material may be.

It is to be noted that σ and s in equation 13·6 are equal respectively to the direct stress and to the shearing stress which causes failure, and that both of these stresses act on the incipient failure plane. To emphasize that this direct stress must be that on the failure plane, it is sometimes designated by σ_f, and the strength is expressed $\sigma_f \tan \phi$. The shearing strength is largely friction which is caused by pressure σ_f, and the frictional strength should not be considered to be caused by any other pressure. However, since the relationships at failure between direct stress values on various planes are known, the strength may be expressed in terms of any desired direct stress. The common direct stress relationships prevailing when failure is incipient may be derived from the Mohr diagram. They are

$$\sigma_f = \sigma_3(1 + \sin \phi) = \sigma_1(1 - \sin \phi) = (\sigma_1 - \sigma_3)\frac{\cos^2 \phi}{2 \sin \phi}$$

The principal stress difference, appearing in the final expression, is called the *compressive strength*. From these expressions

$$s = \sigma_f \tan \phi = \sigma_3 \tan \phi(1 + \sin \phi) = \sigma_1 \tan \phi \, (1 - \sin \phi)$$

$$= (\sigma_1 - \sigma_3)\tfrac{1}{2} \cos \phi \tag{13·7}$$

and for various values of ϕ the shearing strength may be expressed as follows, all stresses in these expressions being values that hold at the point of incipient failure:

When $\phi = 25$ degrees,

$$s = 0.47\sigma_f = 0.66\sigma_3 = 0.27\sigma_1 = 0.45(\sigma_1 - \sigma_3)$$

When $\phi = 30$ degrees,

$$s = 0.58\sigma_f = 0.87\sigma_3 = 0.29\sigma_1 = 0.43(\sigma_1 - \sigma_3)$$

When $\phi = 35$ degrees,

$$s = 0.70\sigma_f = 1.00\sigma_3 = 0.30\sigma_1 = 0.41(\sigma_1 - \sigma_3)$$

When $\phi = 40$ degrees,

$$s = 0.84\sigma_f = 1.38\sigma_3 = 0.30\sigma_1 = 0.38(\sigma_1 - \sigma_3)$$

It may be noted that the Mohr strength theory contains the assumptions that the magnitude of the intermediate principal stress has no effect on the strength, and that no variables other than the pressure have bearing on the shearing strength. Only with these assumptions can the strength be represented on the plot by a single pair of lines. Actually the shearing strength does depend somewhat on the intermediate principal stress as well as on the density, the structure, the speed of distortion during the shearing process, and other variables. However, most of these factors have minor effects.

If the friction angle is constant, the Mohr envelope is a straight line. Actually the friction angle decreases slightly with increasing pressure in some materials, and therefore the Mohr envelope is slightly curved. When the friction angle varies there are other small variations from the simplified relationships which have been derived above, but such variations are important only in detailed, theoretical studies of shearing strength. Among such variations is the occurrence of failure on planes having obliquities which are slightly smaller than the maximum obliquity and having θ angles which differ somewhat from $45 + \frac{1}{2}\phi$.

The Mohr strength theory has its limitations, but it explains stress and strength concepts in soils in such a satisfactory manner that no other strength theories will be discussed herein.*

* For a discussion of strength theories see reference 127.

13·8   The Mohr Strength Theory for Concrete and Steel

The Mohr strength theory may be used to demonstrate a number of fundamental concepts related to failure. Diagrams for the two commonest engineering materials, concrete and steel, will be used for such demonstrations.

For simplicity the idealized form of the Mohr strength theory will be adopted, with the friction angle ϕ assumed constant under all conditions and for all types of intergranular load. The intrinsic pressure often is assumed to be constant for all planes. For use in this section an even broader assumption regarding intrinsic pressure will be made, and it will be assumed to be constant under all conditions of loading; this assumption may not hold for soils but it may be reasonable for concrete and steel. Therefore in these considerations the total direct stress will be considered to consist of the sum of the applied direct stress, which varies for different planes, and a constant intrinsic pressure.

If two specimens of concrete are tested, one in compression and the other in tension, and both tests are carried to failure, the data from these tests and the use of the simplifying assumptions stated above permit the determination of the Mohr envelope for concrete.

The compression test would normally be run on a cylindrical specimen. When this test reaches failure, the applied stress is an axial compression equal to the compressive strength f_c, and it is also the applied major principal stress. Since the load in such a test is applied in one direction only, the intermediate and minor applied principal stresses are zero. Each of the total principal stresses is greater than these values by the intrinsic pressure p_i, which is still unknown.

This test may be represented by Mohr circle I of Fig. 13·6. The circle is drawn through the origin of applied stresses O_A with a diameter f_c. The total stresses are measured from O_T, the origin of total stresses, which is at the unknown distance p_i to the left of O_A.

In the tension test the specimen would normally be the familiar briquette with large ends to permit the application of tension by the jaws of the testing machine. At failure a tension which is equal to the tensile strength f_t is the only applied stress. Thus the three applied principal stresses are f_t and two stresses equal to zero, with f_t negative and thus obviously the smallest of the three values. Therefore, f_t is the applied minor principal stress. The Mohr circle for this test is circle II of Fig. 13·6 with a σ_3 value of $-f_t$ and a diameter equal to f_t. It is much smaller than circle I, since the tensile strength of concrete is always a small fraction of the compressive strength.

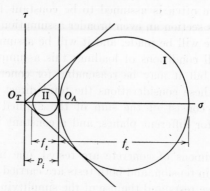

FIG. 13·6 Mohr diagram for concrete.

The Mohr envelope must be tangent to all Mohr circles that represent failure and, under the assumption of a straight line envelope, a straight line may be drawn tangent to the two circles in the figure; thus O_T is located and the intrinsic pressure and the friction angle of the concrete are determined.

Similar tests in tension and compression may be run on steel, and the Mohr circles for the failure conditions of these tests are shown in Fig. 13·7. It is known that the compressive strength of steel is only slightly greater than the tensile strength; thus circle I is only slightly larger than circle II. After the envelope has been drawn tangent to the circle it is seen that the angle of internal friction is very small and the intrinsic pressure very large. For iron and nickel Terzaghi (page 109 of reference 143) quotes intrinsic pressures of about 4.8 million lb per sq in.

The tension failure in steel is the familiar "cup and cone" shape, which gives a failure plane which is at an angle of approximately 45 degrees to the major principal plane. This agrees with the Mohr strength theory, according to which the angle should be 45 + ½ϕ.

A strong case can be developed, even in metals, for the general validity of the Mohr strength theory. According to this theory all failures are failures in shear; they result whenever the obliquity reaches the angle ϕ and occur on planes at 45 + ½ϕ to the major principal plane. However, in concrete and iron and other brittle materials the failure planes do not occur at 45 + ½ϕ

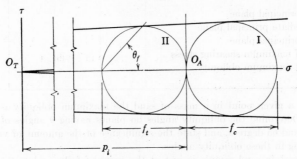

FIG. 13·7 Mohr diagram for steel.

to the major principal plane, possibly because of local stress irregularities around gradually developing failure cracks. The Mohr theory is used only to a limited degree in the study of metals.

For soils, however, the Mohr strength theory in all respects shows reasonable agreement with the observed action at failure, and this theory is a very useful tool in stress and strength studies in soil mechanics.

PROBLEMS

1. At a given point within a sand deposit the major, intermediate, and minor principal stresses are 5, 3, and 2 tons per sq ft, respectively. Construct the Mohr diagram, and from it scale the direct and shearing stresses and the obliquity angles on planes having θ values of 30, 45, 60, and 75 degrees.

2. At a given point in a steel beam there is a compression of 5000 lb per sq in. on the vertical plane, and the shearing stress is 1000 lb per sq in. There is no direct stress on the longitudinal plane. Construct the Mohr diagram of applied stresses, and from it scale the applied stresses on the

principal plane and the angles these planes make with the horizontal plane.

3. A 1-ft cube within a stressed soil mass has direct stresses of 6 tons per sq ft on its top and bottom faces, 5 tons per sq ft on one pair of vertical faces, 4 tons per sq ft on the other pair of faces, and no shear on any face. Copy the following table and determine and insert numerical values in all spaces.

	σ	τ	α	θ
Major principal plane				
Intermediate principal plane				
Minor principal plane				
Plane of maximum shearing stress				
Plane of maximum obliquity				

4. At a given point in a mass of sand the maximum obliquity is 32 degrees. Determine the obliquity angles on planes having θ angles of 57, 59, 61, 63, and 65 degrees, and state the significance of the amount of variation occurring in these obliquity angles.

5. A certain sand sample is just at the point of failure when the major principal stress and the minor principal stress are equal, respectively, to 3.9 and 1.0 tons per sq ft. Construct the Mohr diagram and determine the direct and shearing stresses and the obliquity angles on the plane of maximum shear and on the plane of maximum obliquity.

SHEAR TESTING METHODS
SHEARING CHARACTERISTICS OF SANDS

14·1 General

Before entering the discussion of shearing strength of soils and the factors upon which this strength depends, it is desirable that testing methods and a number of general considerations of action during shear be covered. Most of these general items refer equally to shear in cohesionless soils and to shear in cohesive soils. The latter part of this chapter is devoted to discussion of the strength of cohesionless soils. A treatment of the subject of shear in cohesive soils requires so many additional concepts that it is relegated to the next chapter.

14·2 The Direct Shear Machine

Until a few years ago the only type of apparatus in common use for determining shearing strengths of soils was the direct shear machine.

In the direct shear type of apparatus a shear box is used which consists of two parts, called the upper frame and lower frame. This box holds the sample, half of which is within either frame. A normal load applied to the top of the sample causes a pressure across the plane of separation between the upper and the lower frames. The sample is subjected to rupture at the plane of separation. Rupture may be induced by application of a force to one frame in a direction parallel to the plane of separation, while the other frame is anchored in position. This force, called the shearing force, is increased either gradually or in steps, and it causes a relative motion between the upper and the lower frames which is called the shearing displacement.

A direct shear machine is illustrated in Fig. 14·1. In this apparatus * the platform scale is mounted on wheels which run

* A more detailed description is given in reference 54.

on a track within the framework. A constant-speed motor causes
the scale and lower frame to move to the right at an essentially
constant speed. The upper frame, which does not move, is held
in place by a horizontal arm, the force required to hold this arm
being furnished by readings on a proving ring. Vertical load is
applied by the platform scale and is transmitted through the

Fig. 14·1   Direct shear apparatus.

yoke which bears on the cover of the sample container. The
scale beam may be kept level at all times by a take-up jack at
the bottom of the yoke. The top and bottom surfaces of the
soil sample bear on detachable covers or holders which fit within
the frames. Holders with rough surfaces are used for some soils;
for other soils holders containing teeth which project slightly
into the sample are more satisfactory. For tests in which rapid
drainage of pore water is desired, porous stone holders are used.
When a submerged condition is desired during testing, a pan
which is filled with water and which surrounds the shear box is
used. The shearing displacement, which furnishes an indication
of the amount of shearing strain within the sample, is given by

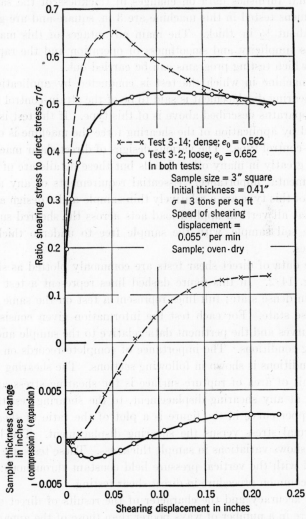

FIG. 14·2 Plots of typical direct shear tests (Ottawa standard sand).

readings of a horizontal extensometer dial. A vertical extensometer dial furnishes data on changes of thickness of the sample. Specimens tested in this machine are 3 in. square and are generally about ½ in. thick. The main advantages of this machine are its simplicity and smoothness of operation and the rapidity with which testing programs can be carried out.

A machine in which the test is conducted by application of the shearing displacement is said to be of the strain-control type; the apparatus described above is of this type. If the test is conducted by application of the shearing force the machine is of the stress-control type. The various designs of direct shear machines differ greatly in many other details but these details are of little fundamental importance. Essential requirements of any apparatus of this type are a relatively thin sample and a design assuring that all vertical applied load acts across the sheared surface of the soil sample, with the sample free to undergo thickness changes.

The data of direct shear tests are commonly plotted as shown in Fig. 14·2. In this figure dashed lines represent a test on a sand in dense state; full lines represent a test on the same sand in loose state. For each test the information given consists of two curves and the pertinent data relative to the sample and the testing conditions. The importance of complete records on testing conditions is shown in following sections. The shearing force per unit of area of rupture surface is the shearing stress and is equal, at any shearing displacement, to the shearing resistance. The upper curve in the figure is a plot of the ratio of shearing to normal stress versus the shearing displacement. The lower curve shows variations in sample thickness. These tests are conducted with the vertical pressure held constant throughout; this is the common procedure in direct shear testing.

The accuracy and the character of the results of direct shear tests are in a number of ways poorer than those of the apparatus discussed in the next section. Direct shear testing has the disadvantage that lateral pressures and stresses on planes other than the plane of shear are not known during the test. However, the simplicity of this test, both in its operation and in the understanding of its meaning, is an important advantage.

14·3 The Cylindrical Compression Apparatus

This type of apparatus for testing soils in shear is frequently called a triaxial machine.

In this apparatus, the sample is cylindrical, and its cylindrical surface is covered by a rubber membrane. The ends of the sample bear on porous stones. Fluid pressure, applied within

FIG. 14·3 Cylindrical compression apparatus.

the chamber which contains the sample, gives an essentially uniform stress over all surfaces of the sample. Failure is caused by the application of an additional axial thrust. Thus the minor principal stress is equal to the chamber pressure, and the major principal stress is the chamber pressure plus the intensity of axial thrust.

The sample is usually saturated and a connection to a graduated glass tube is provided through the base of the chamber. Volume changes are furnished by observations of the amount of water entering or leaving the sample.

A cylindrical compression apparatus † is shown in Fig. 14·3.

† The apparatus in Fig. 14·3, the specimens in Fig. 14·4, and the tests in Figs. 14·5 and 14·6 are the work of H. A. Fidler (55).

The specimens tested in this machine are 1.4 in. in diameter and 3 in. or more in length, but recent machines of the same type are designed to test samples that are 2.8 in. in diameter and about 7 in. in length. Photographs of typical sand samples after testing in this apparatus are shown in Fig. 14·4. In dense samples a clearly defined rupture plane commonly occurs and is at an angle to the axis of the sample which agrees reasonably well with the Mohr rupture theory. At the other extreme, in very loose samples failure occurs by a symmetrical bulging. In Fig.

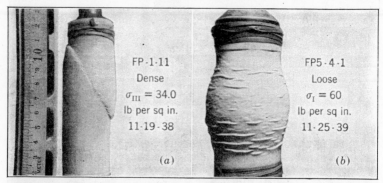

FP-1-11
Dense
$\sigma_{III} = 34.0$
lb per sq in.
11-19-38
(a)

FP5-4-1
Loose
$\sigma_I = 60$
lb per sq in.
11-25-39
(b)

Fig. 14·4   Failed specimens from cylindrical compression tests (Fort Peck sand).

14·4 (b) the wrinkles are the result of the axial shortening of the sample. At the bulge the rubber sheath has been stretched tangentially, but the rubber is so thin that the force required to cause this stretching is generally considered to be negligible. For application of axial compression in this type of machine either stress-control or strain-control methods may be used. The apparatus of Fig. 14·3 operates on the strain-control principle. The measure of the axial compression occurring during a test on this machine is indicated by readings of a revolution counter attached to the screw transmitting the compression.

The simplest and most commonly used test in this type of apparatus is the one in which the lateral pressure is held at a constant value. Tests of this type are called constant-σ_3 tests, and examples of plotted data are given in Fig. 14·5. Another type of test which can be conducted on this apparatus is the constant-volume test. Change in volume may be prevented during testing by continuous changing of the lateral pressure; for example, if the standpipe level starts to rise, indicating that the sample is starting to decrease in volume, this volume change

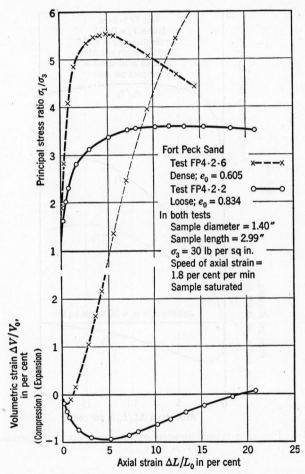

FIG. 14·5 Plots of typical cylindrical compression tests.

tendency may be counteracted by a decrease in the lateral pressure. An example of plotted data from a constant-volume test is given in Fig. 14·6. The constant-volume test is not so simple as the constant-σ_3 test, either in its operation or in the ease of understanding its significance. It is a test which is valuable, however, because shear at constant volume gives the best representation that can be obtained of the action of large saturated

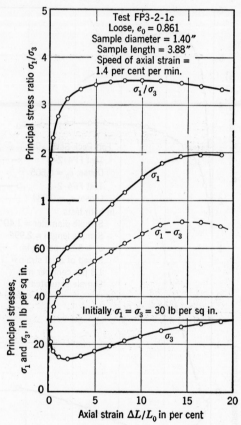

Fig. 14·6 Plot of a typical constant-volume cylindrical compression test (Fort Peck sand).

sand masses when sheared too fast to permit the escape of the pore water.

The following are the main advantages of the cylindrical compression method of testing. The stress conditions, although not absolutely constant throughout the sample, are nearer to constant than in other types of apparatus. All stress values are known with fair accuracy throughout a test, and accurate determinations of volume changes are obtainable. For fundamental research on soils, for cases in which the tests are in the hands of careful and experienced technicians, and for testing programs in which the time required for individual tests is not a controlling factor, this type of apparatus is generally recognized as the best now available.

14·4 General Characteristics of Test Data

A similarity in the shapes of the upper curves of Figs. 14·2 and 14·5 is noticeable even though different coordinate values are used. Shearing tests on clays also give plots which are of this same general shape.

During the early stages of all shear tests, while gradual increase in strain is occurring, there is also a gradual increase in shearing stress and in the obliquity of stress. The obliquity of stress, as explained in the previous chapter, is given at any time during a direct shear test by

$$\tan \alpha_s = \frac{\tau}{\sigma} \qquad (14\cdot1)$$

where α_s is the obliquity on the plane of shear. In the cylindrical compression test the maximum obliquity at any instant is given by the expression

$$\sin \alpha_m = \frac{\sigma_1 - \sigma_3}{\sigma_1 + \sigma_3} = \frac{\dfrac{\sigma_1}{\sigma_3} - 1}{\dfrac{\sigma_1}{\sigma_3} + 1} \qquad (14\cdot2)$$

At the maximum ordinate in each of the upper plots of the various shear tests of Figs. 14·2, 14·5, and 14.6, the obliquity of stress and the ratios τ/σ and σ_1/σ_3 all reach their maximum values. This point is designated in this book as the *peak point*.

The friction angle is at a maximum value at the peak point, and in general it decreases somewhat thereafter, as will be explained later. The slight curvature of Mohr envelopes for soils lead to a number of different ways of computing friction angles, but differences between them are small and of minor practical interest. A value for the peak-point friction angle, ϕ_m, from direct shear test data, is given by

$$\tan \phi_m = \left(\frac{\tau}{\sigma}\right)_m \qquad (14 \cdot 3)$$

in which $(\tau/\sigma)_m$ is the maximum value of τ/σ. An evaluation of ϕ_m from the cylindrical compression test data may be obtained by use of the expression

$$\sin \phi_m = \frac{\left(\dfrac{\sigma_1}{\sigma_3}\right)_m - 1}{\left(\dfrac{\sigma_1}{\sigma_3}\right)_m + 1} \qquad (14 \cdot 4)$$

in which $(\sigma_1/\sigma_3)_m$ is the maximum value of σ_1/σ_3.

In the final stages of the tests the ordinates appear to be approaching an asymptote or ultimate value. Expressions for the ultimate friction angle, designated by ϕ_u, for the two types of test, are

$$\tan \phi_u = \left(\frac{\tau}{\sigma}\right)_u \qquad (14 \cdot 5)$$

and

$$\sin \phi_u = \frac{\left(\dfrac{\sigma_1}{\sigma_3}\right)_u - 1}{\left(\dfrac{\sigma_1}{\sigma_3}\right)_u + 1} \qquad (14 \cdot 6)$$

When large strains have been reached in tests of conventional types, non-uniform conditions have distorted the samples to such a degree that the dependability of test results is relatively low. It is commonly acknowledged that satisfactory test data at the ultimate point cannot be obtained in cylindrical compression tests because localized failures have occurred, and they prevent uniform action in the sample as a whole. In direct shear testing ultimate point data are somewhat more dependable.

When there is no danger of confusion between the friction angles ϕ_m and ϕ_u, the designation ϕ without subscript is often used for the peak-point friction angle. In later chapters of this book this designation is adopted; it is also commonly used in soil mechanics literature.

14·5 Mohr Diagrams for Conventional Shear Tests

A Mohr circle may be drawn to show the stress conditions at any time during a cylindrical compression test. During a conventional test at constant σ_3, the value of σ_1 increases and the circle increases in radius until the peak point is reached. At this

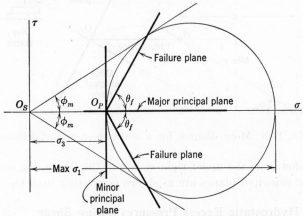

Fig. 14·7 Mohr diagram for a cylindrical compression test at failure.

point the stress conditions are shown by the circle of Fig. 14·7. The angle between the σ axis and a tangent to the circle is the maximum obliquity angle, and it would be equal to the peak-point friction angle if the Mohr envelope were a straight line; in any case this angle is a close approximation of the friction angle. In this type of test the major principal plane is horizontal; thus the origin of planes O_P is as shown. The failure plane is at angle θ_f to the horizontal; it may be noted that this angle is approximately the same as that in the photograph of Fig. 14·4 (a).

The peak-point values of the stresses τ and σ, which act on the failure plane in a direct shear test, may be plotted on a Mohr diagram to give point A of Fig. 14·8. If it is again assumed that the Mohr envelope is a straight line through the origin of stresses, it follows that the maximum obliquity occurs on the failure plane. Thus the line from the origin to *A* must be tangent to the Mohr circle, and the circle may be constructed on this basis. Since failure is on the horizontal plane, the origin of planes may be obtained by drawing a horizontal line through *A*, giving O_P. For a specimen subjected to shear and distortion as shown in the

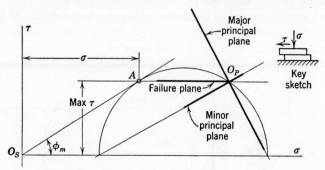

FIG. 14·8   Mohr diagram for a direct shear test at failure.

small sketch on the upper right corner of the figure, the orientations of principal planes are as shown emanating from O_P.

14·6   Hydrostatic Excess Pressures during Shear

Up to this point little has been said on the subject of neutral pressures in the pore water of the soil during shear. In the discussions of strength theory and of laboratory tests it presumably has been considered that no pressures of this type existed in the soils in question.

Actually, hydrostatic excess pressures may occur in large sand masses in nature. However, in most types of apparatus used for laboratory tests on small soil specimens the high permeability of sand prevents their occurrence in appreciable magnitude. In clays such pressures are often of much importance, as explained in Chapter 15.

If hydrostatic excess pressures of unknown magnitude are present in any shearing test, the unknown neutral pressure *u* occurs on every plane. If the investigator is not aware that this excess pressure exists, his work contains a constant error in all normal intergranular stresses, which has the effect of displacing the origin of stresses to the left. Since friction can be caused only by intergranular pressure it should be evident that, with such displacement, true values of the friction angle can no longer be obtained from the Mohr diagram.

14·7 The φ-Obliquity Condition and the Failure Condition

The state that is attained at the peak point and that continues as the ultimate point is approached is characterized by a number of important conditions: The σ_1/σ_3 ratio and the maximum τ/σ ratio do not increase with increase of strain. At any time within this interval all available shearing resistance that is possible under the existing intergranular pressures has been mobilized, the shearing stress on the critical plane is equal to the shearing strength, and the Mohr circle is tangent to the Mohr envelope. In this book this state is called the φ-obliquity condition.

For the simple loading conditions used in conventional tests, wherein either the direct stress on the failure plane or the minor principal stress is maintained at a constant value, failure is occurring when a φ-obliquity condition holds. In certain cases that are of practical importance, however, there may be a φ-obliquity condition without failure.

Since the shearing strength is equal to $\sigma \tan \phi$, two requirements for failure must be recognized. The first and more obvious one is the existence of a φ-obliquity condition. The second requirement for failure is that the intergranular direct stress on the plane of incipient failure be at or approximately at the maximum value that it will attain.

The commonest practical example, in which failure is not reached until the direct stress approaches its maximum value, occurs when shear takes place under constant volume or under conditions wherein the volume changes that tend to occur are partially prevented. The action of a sand in constant-volume shear, as illustrated in Fig. 14·6, may be used as an example. Governed by the constant-volume condition, σ_3 begins to increase in this test at about 2 per cent axial strain and is still increasing at 19 per cent axial strain. A φ-obliquity condition has virtually been reached at 5 per cent strain and has definitely been reached at 10 per cent strain, as is shown by the upper curve. Yet the strength, as shown by the curve of $\sigma_1 - \sigma_3$, continues to increase until an axial strain of 15 per cent is reached. In other words, at 10 per cent strain, and perhaps less, the Mohr circle touches the Mohr envelope and a ϕ-obliquity condition exists. With further strain, the Mohr circle becomes larger, still touching the Mohr envelope but at continuously larger stress values. If the shearing strength is defined as equal to the maximum shearing stress that can be applied, and if failure is considered to be reached only when the shearing stress on the critical plane is equal to the shearing strength, failure in this example does not occur until the strain equals 15 per cent.

Actually, the value of the friction angle and the slope of the Mohr envelope tend to decrease slightly over the duration of the ϕ-obliquity condition, as the upper curve of Fig. 14·6 shows. In addition, test data, such as are shown by this figure, are of relatively low accuracy when the strain is as large as 15 per cent. These points are not of fundamental importance, but they must be considered in detailed studies of this type of test.

14·8   Non-Uniform Stress and Strain Conditions; Progressive Failure

If the loading on a large mass of soil in nature is gradually increased until failure is incipient, the conditions will seldom, if ever, be uniform over an entire incipient rupture surface, and failure will not be reached at all points at the same time. The shearing strains that occur will not be uniform, and concentrations of shearing stress will tend to take place at points of maximum strain, causing rupture to start at these points. Subsequently the rupture will progress through the mass, somewhat analogous to the tearing of a piece of paper.

The ideal laboratory shear test for soils would be one with uniform stress and uniform strain throughout the sample. Actually, such a condition is not possible, since non-uniform conditions of stress and strain occur in all types of tests, and failures are always, to a degree, progressive. It is believed that conditions in cylindrical compression specimens are more nearly uniform than those in direct shear. However, cylindrical samples are subjected at their top and bottom surfaces to friction which prevents lateral strain. Therefore, bulging occurs at the center of the sample, and this in itself proves that conditions are not uniform.

For an explanation of progressive action let it be assumed that the solid curve of Fig. 14·9 represents the curve of stress versus strain that would be obtained under some given condition of loading in an ideal test, this ideal test having uniform stress and uniform strain throughout the specimen. This curve may be called a *true stress-strain curve*, and it should be valid at a point

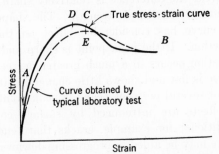

Fig. 14·9 Relationship between a true stress-strain curve and a curve from a typical test.

in a soil mass that is subjected to variable stress and strain, provided the soil conditions and the condition of loading at this point conform to the corresponding conditions in the ideal test. Let it now be assumed that a specimen of this soil is tested to failure in a direct shear test. In this test it is known that there is a large amount of variation from uniform strain and, therefore, the true peak-point stress, represented by point D, cannot be in effect at any given time on more than a small portion of the failure surface. When the specimen as a whole reaches incipient failure, the various points on the failure surface may have strains varying, possibly, all the way from the small strain represented by point A to the large strain represented by point B, the strain represented by point E being the average value. The stress represented by point E is a mean of weighted ordinate values from portion ADB of the true curve. In the figure point E is the peak point of the average curve, and this peak point must always have a smaller ordinate than peak point D of the true curve.

The degree to which progressive action occurs is represented by the difference between stresses at points D and E. This difference is large in some cases and small in others, and it is dependent on a number of factors. The most important contributing factor is the difference between the true peak-point strength and the ultimate strength. This difference is relatively large in dense sands and small in loose sands. Clays that have structure of the type that is destroyed by remolding may have true peak-point strengths that are much greater than the ultimate strength, whereas the difference is relatively small in soft clays with little natural structural strength. The shape of the true stress-strain curve has considerable effect on the amount of progressive action. If the peak point is sharp and well defined, progressive action occurs to a much greater degree than it does when the curve is flat and shows little change in strength over a strain range of several per cent near the peak point. In nature, progressive effects are introduced by surface conditions and weather conditions; for example, cracks that tend to form at ground surface may be aided in progressing downward by evaporation or by action of water or frost.

It must be realized that there is progressive action during all shear failures, both in nature and in laboratory tests. Only by the merest of chances, however, will the degree to which progressive action occurs in any given case in nature be the same as that in any given type of testing apparatus. Any assumption to the effect that progressive effects need not be considered because they occur both in nature and in laboratory tests is definitely unsound. In investigations in which progressive effects occur to greater degree in shear tests than in nature, the average shearing strengths in nature are somewhat greater than laboratory determinations of peak-point values. In cases in which the progressive effects are greater in nature than in laboratory tests, the average strengths in nature must fall somewhere between peak-point values and ultimate values from test data. Information as to which of these two cases holds in any given problem would be valuable if it could be obtained but, unfortunately, present knowledge of soil action often is not sufficient to give it. Actually, it is fairly common practice to use peak-point values from laboratory tests for analyses of problems in nature. The above discussion shows that this procedure is conservative in some cases and is on the unsafe side in other cases and, without doubt, there are occasions in which it is not reasonable. On the other hand the use of ultimate values is generally far too conservative. Any intermediate course must at present be based mainly on judgment.

In any type of shear test, points which are but a fraction of an inch apart may have relatively large differences in stresses and strains. In spite of this non-uniformity, the average action of the sample in the test is the only action that can be considered, since it is the nearest approach to the true stress-strain condition obtainable. In a large mass of homogeneous soil in nature any two points in the failure zone that are not more than a few feet apart normally would have relatively small differences in strain conditions. It is not known whether or not this difference between natural conditions and test conditions is significant.

It is common in considerations of stability to distinguish between failure at individual points and failure of the mass as a whole. An analogous situation exists in the design of steel structures, in which the members are usually designed so that an allowable fiber stress is nowhere exceeded; thus the design aims to guard against failure at every point. In an entirely different design procedure that is sometimes used and that is known as *limit design*,‡ certain zones may pass beyond the elastic range and into a state of plastic flow as long as the structure as a whole has a reasonable margin of safety against failure. In most types of soil analysis, limit design is used. However, in qualitative studies, concepts of failure at a point are often mentioned. For example, an understanding of the action of footings § requires the concept that there is failure at points just below the edge of a rigid footing on the surface of a sand deposit even when it is under a very small fraction of the total load the footing can safely carry.

14·9 Factors Contributing to Shearing Strength in Sands

The shearing strength in sand may be said to consist of two parts, the internal, frictional resistance between grains, which is a combination of rolling and sliding friction, and a second factor

‡ For examples see references 165 and 136.
§ See Section 19·7 for further explanation.

for which the most common name is *interlocking*. Interlocking contributes a large portion of the strength in dense sands; this phenomenon does not occur in very loose sands. The gradual loss of strength after the peak point is passed, illustrated by the dense tests of Figs. 14·2 and 14·5, may be attributed to a gradual decrease in interlocking which takes place because the sample is decreasing in density. The angle of internal friction, in spite of its name, does not depend solely on internal friction, since a portion of the shearing stress on a plane of failure is utilized in overcoming interlocking.

Interlocking can best be explained by considerations of strain energy. Sands generally are undergoing increase in volume when the ϕ-obliquity condition is reached, and the part of the shearing stress that is acting to overcome interlocking may also be said to be supplying the energy that is being expended in volume increase.

As an example the data of the test on dense sand, represented in Fig. 14·2, will be used. The shearing strength at the peak point of this test is 0.645×3 or 1.94 tons per sq ft. At this point the sample thickness is increasing, the ordinate increasing from 0.0059 to 0.0076 in. between abscissa values of 0.05 and 0.06 in., which represents a rate of 0.0017 in. of thickness increase per 0.01 in. of shearing displacement. For the occurrence of the expansion, which is resisted by the applied normal pressure, energy must be supplied in some way. The amount of energy used during the expansion of the sample is the product of the thickness increase and the direct load σA on the top and bottom surfaces of the sample. Since there are no changes in the horizontal dimensions of the sample, the stresses on the vertical sides of the sample do no work. If the portion of the shearing stress that acts to supply the energy of expansion is designated by s_e, the energy supplied is the product of the shearing displacement and the shearing force $s_e A$. Setting the expression for energy that is used equal to that for the energy that is supplied and inserting the numerical values quoted above gives

$$3A \times 0.0017 = s_e A \times 0.01$$

whence

$$s_e = 0.51 \text{ ton per sq ft}$$

which is about 26 per cent of the total shearing stress.

In this example the coefficient of friction is 0.645, the portion of this value that is contributed by friction being 0.475 and the portion contributed by interlocking, or resistance to volume increase, being 0.17. The corresponding divisions of the shearing strength are 1.43 and 0.51 tons per sq ft, respectively. A shearing stress of 1.94 tons per sq ft is required to bring the sample to the state of incipient failure, but once it is at this point the shearing stress that would be required to hold it, with neither additional shearing strain nor rebound of shearing strain, is only 1.43 tons per sq ft.

All factors which contribute to strength, interlocking included, occur in soils that are being tested in the laboratory. Therefore, laboratory tests are representative of natural conditions if they are conducted under the approximate pressure and density conditions that hold in the soil in nature. The fundamentals upon which the Mohr theory is based are not invalidated by the occurrence of interlocking; the Mohr envelopes merely have larger ordinates and steeper slopes for dense than for loose soils.

14·10 Discussion and Data on Friction Angles in Granular Soils

In the oldest and simplest procedure for obtaining the friction angle of a dry, granular soil, the angle of repose of a small pile of the material is observed. Actually, the angle of repose is the friction angle under a pressure of practically zero, but it tends to differ from the angle of internal friction under ordinary pressures for several reasons. A pile of the material cannot be in equilibrium unless the least stable grains at its surface are in equilibrium; thus the angle of repose is determined by the least stable grains. The angle of internal friction refers to internal conditions, and therefore it depends on an average condition of all grains; for this reason it tends to be somewhat larger than the angle of repose. The surface of a pile of sand is likely to be in a slightly looser state than the interior; therefore, the friction angle in the surface zone where the angle of repose is determined will tend to be smaller than that of the mass as a whole. In addition, the angle of repose includes little or no strength due to interlocking. On the other hand sands seldom are perfectly clean and dry, and thus they generally tend to possess a small amount of cohesion. For shearing strengths at ordinary inter-

granular pressures this small cohesion may be of entirely inappreciable magnitude, but at the surface of a sand pile where
intergranular pressures approach zero it may make the grains
capable of standing at a somewhat steeper repose angle. Thus
the angle of repose is at best a crude approximation of the angle
of internal friction, and in truly cohesionless soils it generally
is appreciably smaller than the friction angle.

The ideal way to test for the angle of internal friction of sands
would be to subject samples to tests in which uniform stress and
strain conditions are maintained. However, no type of test meets
this ideal requirement, and with the possible exceptions of a few
elaborate investigations on special, complicated apparatus ‖ the
two types of apparatus which have been described supply the best
shear data obtainable.

Figure 14·10 shows data on the peak-point friction angle from
a series of direct shear tests on Standard Ottawa sand at various
loads and densities. The density of the sample is represented
on this chart by the initial void ratio under the normal pressure
used during the test. If the peak-point void ratio were used instead of the initial value, there would be less dependence of the
friction angle on the pressure, but dependable void ratios are not
easily obtained at the point of failure in this type of test.

Friction angles obtained from a series of tests on washed Fort
Peck sand by cylindrical compression apparatus, in which tests
under constant lateral pressure were used, are shown in Fig.
14·11.

These two illustrations are sufficient to show that, from the
practical viewpoint, ranges in friction angles are not large. Comparison studies (140) have been made which show that differences in results obtained by the different types of apparatus are
also of minor importance. A small number of tests suffices to
indicate friction angle values with sufficient accuracy for most
practical problems, and it undoubtedly is true that estimates
made by experienced soil engineers, on the basis of visual inspection, furnish values which are sufficiently accurate for many
analyses.

The peak-point friction angle of a given granular soil under

‖ For example see references 87 and 76 or 79.

the conditions existing in conventional tests depends considerably on the initial void ratio of the test and in smaller degree on the pressure. From the limited amount of data available on ulti-

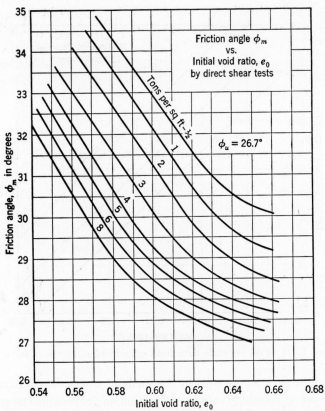

Friction angle ϕ_m
vs.
Initial void ratio, e_0
by direct shear tests

Tons per sq ft-½

$\phi_u = 26.7°$

Friction angle, ϕ_m, in degrees

Initial void ratio, e_0

FIG. 14·10 Friction angle data from direct shear tests (Ottawa standard sand).

mate friction angles it appears that this angle is practically a constant for any given granular soil.

The angles of internal friction for soils in general depend to some degree on a number of factors that are properties of the grains. A greater value of friction angle occurs in soils with sharp grains than in soils with smooth grains. The mineralogical content of the grains has some effect on the value of the friction angle. Uniform sands tend to have smaller friction angles than sands with a wide range of grain sizes.

Because of the difficulty of testing soils which contain large particles relatively little is known about friction angles of coarse

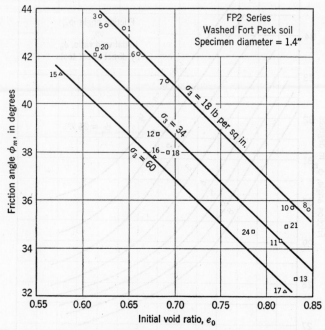

FIG. 14·11 Friction angle data from cylindrical compression tests.

materials, such as the soils in the shells of hydraulic-fill dams.¶ However, it is usually safe to use friction angles obtained on such materials with the coarsest particles removed.

Studies of the magnitude of the angle of internal friction of submerged sands, in which tests are run at a sufficiently slow speed to allow the pore water to escape as fast as the void ratio changes tend to occur, indicate results which vary only slightly from those on perfectly dry sand. This disproves an old belief that water, acting as a lubricant, causes lower values of friction angle when the soil is submerged. However, in submerged soil

¶ For description see Section 18·4.

masses the intergranular pressures are reduced by buoyancy and, since strengths depend directly on intergranular pressures, the strengths are less for the submerged condition. Questions regarding accuracy of determinations of shearing strength values of sands seldom reside in the values of friction angle used, but are due usually to questions relative to the magnitude of the intergranular pressure.

The friction angles in a sand may be slightly different under rapid and under slow shear because of dynamic phenomena, but this difference is believed to be so small that it is of no real importance.

If a fine-grained granular soil is partially saturated, apparent cohesion is present. Therefore, soils of this type must be either dry or submerged if they are to be classed as cohesionless materials.

14·11 Partial Liquefaction during Shear at Constant Volume

In Chapter 7 quicksand and seepage forces were defined, and it was pointed out that a saturated granular soil is in a fluid state if no intergranular pressures exist within it. This fluid state is commonly called *liquefaction*. It was demonstrated that the introduction of an upward gradient with a magnitude of $(G - 1) \div (1 + e)$ causes the state of complete liquefaction that is commonly called *quicksand*. An upward gradient of smaller magnitude reduces the intergranular pressure, giving *partial liquefaction*, a condition that occurs when a portion of the existing intergranular pressure is transferred into water pressure.

Another common example of partial liquefaction results when a loose, saturated sand is subjected to shearing strain with escape of pore water prevented. Such a condition is likely to occur in a large mass of such a material if the shearing strains occur rapidly; it may be obtained in the laboratory by the use of sealed samples. Typical values for the volume of water which tends to escape from or be drawn into laboratory specimens are shown in Fig. 14·5. Between the start of the test and the peak point the volumes of escaping water are about −3 per cent of the total volume for the dense sample and +0.5 per cent for the loose sample. On the basis of the ultimate point, the corresponding volumes are somewhat over −8 per cent for the dense sample and perhaps about -0.5 per cent for the loose sample. If these changes of water volume were prevented, stresses inevitably would be thrown into the water. The dense sample would attempt to expand and thereby throw tension into the water. Therefore the intergranular pressure would be larger, and on occasion many times larger, than the total pressure, and the sample would show a larger shearing strength than that which occurs in the test shown in the figure. The loose sample would attempt to undergo volume decrease and thereby throw pressure into the water. Thus only part of the applied pressure would continue to be intergranular pressure, and there would be partial liquefaction. This action is borne out by the constant-volume test on loose soil represented in Fig. 14·6, in which the value of σ_3, which is initially 30 lb per sq in., is smaller at all other times during the test, indicating that partial lique-faction would occur in this soil under any loading in which the applied σ_3 remains constant or increases.

Shear tests of the type shown in Fig. 14·6 are sufficiently significant to make the figure worthy of considerable study. The test of this figure is so conducted as to maintain constant volume, and in the test there is no pore pressure; however, constant volume is the significant condition, and the test is conducted with no water pressure simply because this is the most convenient way of maintaining constant volume. The curves show the relation-ships between strains and intergranular stresses for constant-volume shear, and for the given soil and the given initial condi-tions these curves are valid for shear at constant volume, whatever the water pressures may be. All amounts by which externally applied principal pressures are greater than the values shown in the figure are carried by the water. At any given value of axial strain during such a test there are definite values of the inter-granular principal stresses $\bar{\sigma}_1$ and $\bar{\sigma}_3$, the expressions for these stresses, if water pressure exists, being

$$\bar{\sigma}_1 = \sigma_{1t} - u_w$$

$$\bar{\sigma}_3 = \sigma_{3t} - u_w \qquad (14\cdot7)$$

$$\bar{\sigma}_1 - \bar{\sigma}_3 = \sigma_{1t} - \sigma_{3t}$$

in which σ_{1t} and σ_{3t} are the applied principal stresses and u_w is the water pressure. If the externally applied lateral pressure were to be held constant and equal to 30 lb per sq in., the neutral pressure would be the difference between the 30-lb-per-sq-in. line and the σ_3 curve of the figure; at any strain an equal difference would exist between the externally applied vertical pressure and the σ_1 curve of the figure. The intergranular $\bar{\sigma}_1 - \bar{\sigma}_3$ and the applied $\sigma_{1t} - \sigma_{3t}$ are alike under all conditions. If the applied σ_{3t} were gradually increased during the test, a steadily increasing amount of pressure would be added to the pore water.

The above statements are not strictly true, of course, unless the pore fluid is incompressible. Actually, water is slightly compressible and gas, which is often present in submerged soils, is a source of some compressibility. Moreover, complete freedom from drainage seldom occurs in a soil mass. The constant-volume condition during shear is thus a limiting one. However, many examples occur in nature which are a close approach to this limiting condition, and in all such instances the effects of small amounts of compressibility or drainage are so hard to evaluate that information on the behavior under constant volume must be accepted as the best obtainable representation of actual conditions.

An important conception relative to rates of drainage from soil masses is furnished by the consolidation theory. It has been demonstrated that for masses of similar shape the time required to allow any given percentage of the total drainage is proportional to the square of the length of the longest drainage path. This explains why drainage may be nearly complete throughout typical laboratory tests on sand samples even though no definite efforts are made to cause drainage, whereas in large sand masses the drainage occurring within a short period of time may be insignificant.

Since the degree of liquefaction depends on the values which the combined pressures attain during loading, no general statement of the degree of liquefaction for the case represented by Fig. 14·6 can be given. However, the shearing strength of this sample may be obtained from the data of the figure. Comparisons of such values can be made with the strength which would exist under the pressures attained during loading if the soil were free to undergo volume change. The difference is a measure of the degree of liquefaction.

14·12   Critical Void Ratios

Dense sands generally attain greater strengths when volume changes are prevented during shear, and loose sands lose strength. It would appear that there must be some intermediate density at which there is neither gain nor loss. The void ratio at which prevention of volume change leads to no strength change is called the *critical void ratio*.

However, a given soil under various conditions of loading may have a wide range of critical void ratios. Only if sheared under a completely specified set of loading conditions does a given soil have a definite value of critical void ratio.

In addition dynamic conditions are present in the great majority of problems in which critical void ratio concepts may be applied, since it is unusual for a large sand mass to be stressed to failure in shear without drainage, unless the shearing load is applied suddenly. Examples are given by cases in which the loads are caused by an earthquake, or by blasting, or by the shock attending a sudden local failure at some point of weakness. Any loading of this type is of dynamic nature, and when it threatens to cause a liquefaction failure it is sometimes referred to as *trigger action*.

In constant-volume tests there is no trigger action, and it is probable that no laboratory test which uses a small sample can be devised to represent the effect of sudden shocks. Possibly the sudden shock causes adjacent grains to jump out of contact with each other, and thereby produces conditions that cannot be represented by static tests. On the other hand, it may be that constant-volume shear tests in the laboratory are reasonably representative of certain cases in nature that are attended by trigger action. At least, it should be realized that the effect of shocks is not known and that all laboratory constant-volume test results and all data on critical void ratios obtained from such tests can be accepted as representation of sudden liquefaction conditions in nature only to that degree to which such conditions in nature are free of the dynamic effects that are not present in the laboratory tests.

14·13 Laboratory Determination of Certain Critical Void Ratios

The use of laboratory determinations of critical void ratio for investigations relative to danger of liquefaction in masses of loose granular soil was first proposed by A. Casagrande (155). His proposed type of critical void ratio will be designated herein as the *Casagrande critical void ratio*. His arbitrarily chosen

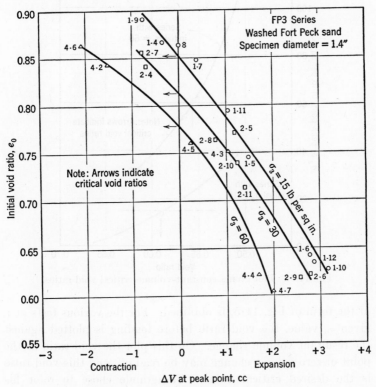

FIG. 14·12 Plot giving constant-σ_3 critical void ratios.

conditions of loading represent his early concepts of conditions that should give conservative results.

Values of Casagrande critical void ratios are determined by series of constant-σ_3 cylindrical compression tests of conventional type with individual tests at a number of σ_3 values and at various densities. The void ratio of each specimen is determined before it is placed under lateral pressure for testing. For each specimen the resultant volume change between the start of the test and the peak point, as given by conventional data plots

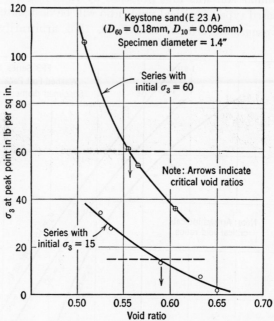

FIG. 14·13 Plot giving constant-volume critical void ratios.

of the form of Fig. 14·5, is obtained. For the various tests at a given σ_3 value, the void ratio before loading is plotted against the resultant volume change. On this plot the void ratio at the point of zero volume change may be read off, and this void ratio is the desired critical value. Casagrande chose to refer his critical void ratio to the void ratio before loading, because the natural void ratios which would be compared with the critical values obtained from tests would normally be the values occurring before loading.

The type of critical void ratio that is represented by Fig. 14·12 (taken from reference 55) is called the *constant-σ_3 critical void ratio*. It differs from the Casagrande critical void ratio in one important respect; this relatively small difference illustrates the care that must be used in defining any critical void ratio. In the determination of the constant-σ_3 critical void ratio the recorded initial void ratio of each test is the value holding at the start of the test just after the σ_3 value of the test has been applied, whereas the Casagrande critical void ratio is based on the void ratio before loading. The constant-σ_3 critical void

TABLE 14·1   CRITICAL VOID RATIOS

Franklin Fall Sand (E1-A)

σ_3 at Beginning of Test and at Peak Point, lb per sq in.	Type of Critical Void Ratio [1]		
	Casa-grande	Constant σ_3	Constant Volume
15	0.84	0.81	0.77
30	....	0.74	0.69
60	0.74	0.69	0.65
120	....	0.63	0.59

[1] All based on cylindrical compression starting from $\sigma_1 = \sigma_3$ and extending to peak point.

ratios at σ_3 values of 15 and 60 lb per sq in. are given by Fig. 14·12 as 0.85 and 0.78, respectively.

Since liquefaction is a phenomenon associated with shear at constant volume, the *constant-volume critical void ratio*, which is represented by Fig. 14·13, may be in some ways considered to be a more rational type than either of those previously described. To obtain this critical void ratio, series of constant-volume, cylindrical compression tests are run at various initial-σ_3 values and at various densities. For the several tests at each initial-σ_3 value the σ_3 value attained at the peak point is plotted against the void ratio of the test. At the point where the ordinate equals the initial-σ_3 value, the abscissa is the constant-volume critical void ratio. Values of this type of critical void ratio for initial-σ_3 values of 15 and 60 lb per sq in. are given as 0.59 and 0.56, respectively, by the figure.

Values of constant-σ_3 and constant-volume critical void ratios differ by relatively small amounts. A comparison of the three types of critical void ratio considered above is given for one sand in Table 14·1.

The use of critical void ratios that are based on ultimate data instead of on peak-point data has also been suggested, but values based on the peak-point data are generally preferred because they are more conservative and may be obtained with greater accuracy.

14·14 Final Comments on Critical Void Ratios and Shear at Constant Volume

The magnitude of the critical void ratio is dependent on every detail of the loading conditions, as the following comments indicate. If shear starts with $\bar{\sigma}_1$ and $\bar{\sigma}_3$ alike, the critical void ratio is larger, other things being equal, than it is when shear starts with $\bar{\sigma}_1$ greater than $\bar{\sigma}_3$. If $\bar{\sigma}_3$ decreases during shear, the critical void ratio is larger than if $\bar{\sigma}_3$ increases during shear. If failure in shear is assumed to have occurred as soon as the peak point is reached, the critical void ratio is smaller than it is when large strains are permitted, and the ultimate point is attained before failure is considered to have occurred. If $\bar{\sigma}_2$ is approximately equal to $\bar{\sigma}_3$ during shear, it is probable that the critical void ratio is larger than it is when $\bar{\sigma}_2$ more nearly approaches equality to $\bar{\sigma}_1$.

It is probable that quantitative determinations of the critical void ratios that hold for given soils on given projects cannot now be obtained in view of the present limited knowledge of stress conditions in nature. Moreover, the dependability of critical void ratios that are determined by laboratory tests may be severely questioned, since these values are based on conditions that may differ greatly from those holding for liquefaction caused by sudden shock.

Relative values of critical void ratio may be used advantageously, however, and any one of the several types of critical void ratio that have been proposed may be adopted arbitrarily. If several soils have been tested and the natural void ratio and some given type of critical void ratio have been obtained for each soil, the difference between the critical void ratio and the natural void ratio of each soil may be used as a relative measure of the danger of liquefaction in that soil. If the natural void ratio of one soil is larger than the arbitrarily chosen type of critical void ratio, for example, whereas the natural void ratio of a second soil is smaller than the critical void ratio, then it is probable, although it is not absolutely certain, that the use of the second soil is to be preferred on a project in which danger of liquefaction exists. However, these considerations prove neither that the first soil is unsatisfactory nor that the second soil is satisfactory; it merely is known that the preference lies with the second soil.

It is possible that certain concepts pertaining to shear at constant volume are of greater significance in connection with liquefaction than usually realized and, therefore, brief mention of a few such concepts will be made. The shearing strength of any soil is under all conditions dependent in large degree on the void ratio at failure. When volume changes are free to occur, the strength depends on the void ratio and the pressures prevailing when failure is reached, and it is essentially independent of the pressures that existed before failure was attained. In constant-volume shear, in either cohesionless or highly cohesive soils, the void ratio is determined by the type of structure, whether loose or dense, and by the pressures that acted on the sample before the start of failure in shear. The strength in constant-volume shear is a predetermined quantity, the only pressures that can be construed as affecting this strength being the pressures that brought the sample to its void ratio. The magnitude that individual applied pressures have attained when failure is reached affect only the stress condition in the pore water. From this point of view the concept of critical void ratio is not an especially satisfactory one, because the critical void ratio is, basically, an attempt to associate undrained strength with the applied pressures existing at failure. Perhaps a better point of view is one similar to that used for clays in undrained shear, wherein the strength is expressed directly in terms of either the density or the pressures existing before shearing. In sands, however, this point of view must be modified to account for trigger action or any other dynamic effects that are found in nature but not reproduced in laboratory tests.

PROBLEMS

1. For the two direct shear tests shown in Fig. 14·2, compute the friction angle and the coefficient of friction at the peak point and compute approximate values of these quantities at the ultimate point.

2. *Direct Shear Test.*

Sample: Franklin Falls Sand (E1-B), fairly dense.

Initial dimensions: 3 in. square by 0.442 in. thick, initial void ratio 0.668.

Time Elapsed, minutes	Vertical Load, pounds	Horizontal Displacement Dial, 10^{-4} in.	Thickness Change Dial, 10^{-4} in.	Horizontal Load, pounds
0	506	3500	1400	0
0.5		3472	1395	80
1.		3397	1385	162
2.		3324	1381	228
3.		3120	1391	321
4.		2828	1414	372
5.		2510	1430	398
6.		2162	1438	392

Compute the data needed and plot the conventional curves for this type of test.

3. For the two cylindrical compression tests shown in Fig. 14·5, compute the friction angle and the coefficient of friction at the peak point. Also make rough estimates of the values of these quantities at the ultimate point. Construct Mohr circles for the stresses prevailing at the peak point and at the final plotted point of each test.

4. *Cylindrical Compression Test.*

Sample: Fort Peck Sand (FP4-2-6), dense.

Initial dimensions: Area, $A_0 = 1.545$ sq in.; length, $L_0 = 2.80$ in.; void ratio 0.605.

The area at any time during the test is to be taken as $A_0/(1 - \Delta L/L_0)$. (Data observed during the test are given on page 361.) Obtain the necessary data and plot stress-strain curves for this test.

5. Draw Mohr circles for the stress conditions prevailing in the test shown in Fig. 14·6 at axial strains of 2, 5, 10, 15, and 19 per cent. Note on each circle whether or not it represents a ϕ-obliquity condition. Label the line that represents the shearing strength of the specimen for the conditions of this test.

6. Determine the relative portions of the coefficient of friction that are caused by true friction and by interlocking in the test on loose sand repre-

TABLE FOR PROBLEM 4

Time Elapsed, seconds	Chamber Pressure, lb per sq in.	Counter Reading (giving ΔL), 10^{-3} in.	Buret (giving ΔV), cc	Axial Deviator Load, pounds
0	30	200	2.00	0
	(constant)	205	1.91	41
		210	1.86	84
45		224	1.92	144
		240	2.13	177
90		278	2.80	207
		319	3.66	218
		359	4.56	221
240		402	5.40	218
		508	7.30	202
460		603	8.09	183

sented in Fig. 14·2. Compare these values with those obtained in the text for the test on dense sand.

7. (a) If a completely saturated sample of the soil represented by Fig. 14·6 were tested at the same void ratio as in that test, if no drainage were allowed, and if the chamber pressure were maintained constant at 30 lb per sq in., what would be the values of the pore water pressure u and the total applied major principal stress σ_{1t} at axial strains of 2, 5, 10, and 15 per cent?

(b) If the test were run as in (a) except for a steady chamber pressure increase of 1 lb per sq in. for each 1 per cent of axial strain, what would be the values of the pressures asked for in (a)?

8. (a) From the data given in Fig. 14·5, what would appear to be the approximate value of the constant-σ_3 critical void ratio? List the conditions for which this critical void ratio applies.

(b) If critical void ratios based on ultimate values instead of peak values were used, what would be the approximate value of this type of critical void ratio? List the conditions for which this value applies.

Chapter 15

SHEARING STRENGTH OF COHESIVE SOILS

15·1 Importance and Complexity of Shearing Strength Data

In the majority of troublesome stability problems the soils involved are cohesive materials. Therefore, it may be stated that the importance of an understanding of the fundamentals of shearing strength will apply in greatest degree to cohesive soils. There probably is no phase of soil mechanics which has greater need of logical treatment and of freedom from blind use of rule-of-thumb methods. In fact no physical property of cohesive soil is more complex than the shearing strength. This property depends on many factors, and the individual factors are themselves complicated but, in addition, they are interrelated to such a degree that it is extremely difficult to understand their combined action.

It is a simple task to place a clay specimen in a shearing apparatus and cause a shear failure. A numerical value of shearing strength, which has acceptable precision, may readily be obtained if proper technique, a representative sample, and satisfactory apparatus are used. The point which has too often been insufficiently appreciated by testing engineers is that the shearing strength, both in the laboratory specimen and in the clay in nature, is dependent on a number of variables.* Before meaning can be attached to shearing strengths determined in the laboratory, the engineer who is to interpret the test results must have at his command an understanding of the factors or variables on which the strength is dependent, and he must make adjustments for every factor which occurs differently in the test than in nature. Of course, the test conditions should be chosen to reproduce natural conditions as closely as possible. However,

---

* For example see reference 74.

exact reproduction of all natural conditions is not obtainable.

Actually, test conditions and natural conditions are often too involved to permit complete comparison. Fundamental research on shearing phenomena during the last two decades or so has led to a much improved understanding of the various phases of the subject, but today it must be admitted that certain factors are still only partially understood. The problem of estimating from laboratory test data the shear strength which exists under natural conditions is one that probably will always be among the most complex in soil engineering, and its solution will always be subject to many pitfalls. However, it may now be claimed that most of the important phenomena affecting shearing strength are sufficiently well understood to allow the presentation of a rational outline of such phenomena. Understanding of these basic physical factors is a first prerequisite to an ability to deal with shear strength problems.

The presentation herein starts from a highly idealized expression for shearing strength and, step by step, revises this oversimplified expression toward a form which is as rational and complete as it possibly can be. The material in Chapter 14 on shear testing apparatus, general aspects of shear test data, concepts of failure, progressive action, and so on may be viewed as introductory to this presentation. In the discussion which follows, various factors are first explained as they occur in tests in which drainage is complete and in which no hydrostatic excess pressures exist. Later the effects of complete prevention of drainage are considered, and partial drainage is discussed. When possible, inherent differences between laboratory and natural conditions are explained. After the treatment of fundamentals the essential differences in results obtained by apparatus of the direct shear and cylindrical compression types are considered, and Coulomb's Law, which is a widely used empirical expression for strength, is presented.

It must be recognized that there may be factors still unknown that affect the shearing strength. Moreover, since some factors covered herein are still not completely understood, the discussion consists, to a degree, of merely current impressions of the most probable action; these impressions, however, serve at least as working hypotheses.

Throughout the presentation the clay considered is a truly homogeneous material. In any group of representative samples from a given, relatively homogeneous clay deposit there inevitably will be differences in the properties of the various samples, because actual clays are never truly homogeneous. Detailed considerations of these variations are necessary in important laboratory investigations, but they are beyond the scope of this chapter.

The subject of this chapter simply cannot be resolved into simple form, and attempts to do so have left what some soil engineers consider undesirable and even dangerous impressions relative to the shearing strengths that clays possess. For this reason it is inevitable that the discussion in the following pages include complex concepts, and as a whole this material will probably be found by the reader to be more difficult to understand than other chapters of this book. The importance of the subject, the need of a rational attitude toward it, and the need of an outline which attempts to cover all main points are believed sufficient reason for the inclusion of the material in the form chosen.

15·2   Reference List of Items Affecting the Shearing Strength of Clays

No outline of the factors on which shearing strength depends can be set up which is both simple and in all respects satisfactory. The following list of items is given as a reference list rather than as an outline. Figures in parentheses refer to the sections in this and the preceding chapter in which the item is discussed.

FUNDAMENTAL FACTORS AFFECTING SHEARING STRENGTH

Friction angle	(14·4, 14·7, 15·4)
Intergranular pressure	(15·4)
Intermediate principal stress	(15·6)
Cohesion	(15·9, 15·10)
Structural strength	(15·11)
Speed of shear	(15·12, 15·13)
Colloidal phenomena	(15·13)
Degree of progressive action	(14·8, 15·22)

15·3 Fissured Clays and Intact Clays

Terzaghi (147) has suggested that clays may be divided into two categories, fissured clays and intact clays. Very stiff clays invariably contain fissures; that is, they are filled with small joints or cracks. These stiff clays have such high shearing strength that questions seldom arise regarding the adequacy of their strength to prevent failure. The real problems in such clays occur when water enters the cracks, perhaps after they have been opened slightly by additional stresses imposed by a change of loading, and leads to slaking and the formation of a soft clay matrix within the joint system. Shearing investigations on such stiff clays are relatively unimportant, and studies should tend, rather, toward the setting up of methods to prevent the entrance of the water which leads to loss of strength. In cases where disintegration does take place, shearing investigations, if made, should usually be on the soft matrix material which, on its own merits, might be classified as an intact clay.

Intact clays may be defined as clays which are free of joints and fissures. The discussion in the following sections will apply mainly to intact clays.

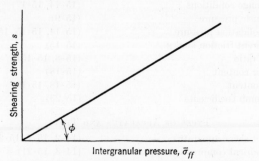

Fɪɢ. 15·1 Idealized form of Mohr envelope.

15·4 Idealized Initial Expression

The starting basis for this development is the expression for the idealized Mohr envelope, illustrated by Fig. 15·1, which may be stated

$$s = \bar{\sigma}_{ff} \tan \phi \qquad (15·1)$$

In this chapter double subscripts will be needed to differentiate between the numerous types of stress that will be discussed and, for example, f will be used as a second subscript to designate a stress acting when failure is occurring. In the above expression s is the shearing strength, $\bar{\sigma}_{ff}$ is the intergranular pressure normal to the surface of failure when failure is occurring, and ϕ is the *true friction angle.*† The significance of the designation of ϕ as the true friction angle appears later. The angle ϕ as used here may be either a *peak-point friction angle* or an *ultimate friction angle;* considerations regarding which should be used are similar to those outlined for sands in Section 14·8.

15·5 Non-Isotropic Effects

It is likely that most stratified soils have somewhat smaller shearing strengths parallel to the strata than they do across the

† Some investigators prefer to consider that clays do not have friction angles. Whether or not this view is shared, it must be recognized that the shearing strength s is proportional to the intergranular pressure $\bar{\sigma}_{ff}$. If it is desired to avoid the designation of friction angle, the angle ϕ may be defined as the slope of the envelope of Fig. 15·1.

strata.‡ In some varved clays this difference may be large. However, in clays having only a moderate degree of stratification there is little evidence of much strength variation on different planes, and in stability analyses pertaining to such soils this variation usually is not considered.

15·6 Effect of the Intermediate Principal Stress

Practically all testing by the cylindrical compression type of apparatus has been under axial compression with σ_2 and σ_3 equal, both being lateral pressure. During direct shear tests practically no information is available on the σ_2 values which occur. They, of course, fall somewhere between σ_1 and σ_3, but in such tests even the σ_1 and σ_3 values are known only when the sample has reached the ϕ-obliquity condition.

According to the idealized Mohr strength theory, the shearing strength is independent of the value of σ_2. Very little evidence can be cited, but it is generally believed that the shearing strength actually depends somewhat on σ_2, the friction angle being perhaps of the order of magnitude of 10 per cent greater when σ_2 equals σ_1 than it is when σ_2 equals σ_3. The Mohr envelope obtained from cylindrical compression tests thus has the smallest possible slope, as far as effects of σ_2 on the strength are concerned, whereas the envelope obtained by direct shear tests may have a slope somewhat greater than the minimum.

15·7 Drained Shear Tests

To obtain a curve of the type shown in Fig. 15·1, a series of tests of the type that will herein be called *drained tests* § may be run. When direct shear apparatus is used for such a series

‡ For an example of test data on this subject see page 92 of reference 80 and for a treatment of the theory of the non-isotropic case see reference 31.

§ The earliest presentation of results of fast and slow tests in the literature is reference 30. In reference 80 strength envelopes for fast and slow tests are presented by M. J. Hvorslev. In reference 24 shearing investigations of outstanding value are described by A. Casagrande, and three types of tests are proposed for investigations of shearing strength of clays: the (S)-*test* or slow test is the type designated above as the drained test; the (Q_c)-*test* or *quick-consolidated test* is the type discussed in Section 15·14 and called the *consolidated-undrained test;* the (Q)-*test* or *quick test* is the type discussed in Section 15·18.

of tests, the values of direct stress and shearing stress that occur on the horizontal plane when the ϕ-obliquity condition is reached in each individual test are plotted as abscissa and ordinate on the Mohr plot. A line through these points is the Mohr envelope. An example of this envelope is Fig. 15·2. When a series of drained tests is obtained by the use of cylindrical compression apparatus, a Mohr circle is plotted for the stresses acting when the ϕ-obliquity condition is reached in each test. A sketched

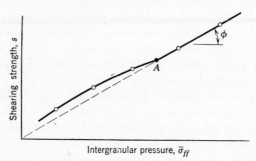

Fig. 15·2   Mohr envelope obtained from drained, direct shear tests.

line which is tangent to these circles is the strength envelope. This case is illustrated by Fig. 15·3.

The deviation from a straight line at small pressures in Figs. 15·2 and 15·3 is caused by cohesion and is explained in subsequent sections. At higher pressures the envelope may deviate somewhat from a perfectly straight line, but in clays this deviation is usually so small that for all practical purposes this portion of the envelope may be assumed to be a straight line.

A condition of complete drainage can be most closely approached in testing by the use of small samples which drain freely at their surfaces. Slow speed testing is often resorted to in tests of this type but the slow speed should be viewed as merely an aid to drainage; the drainage requirement here is fundamental, the speed incidental.

Explanations of fundamentals are somewhat simpler when referred to direct shear tests than when referred to cylindrical compression tests and, therefore, the direct test is usually mentioned first when tests are referred to in this chapter. However, the cylindrical compression type is at present generally conceded to give the more dependable data, as is indicated by the fact that the curved portion of the envelope is clearly defined by cylindrical compression tests whereas it is poorly defined by direct

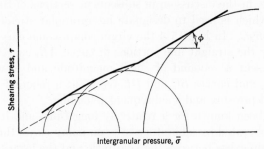

Fɪɢ. 15·3   Mohr envelope obtained from drained, cylindrical compression tests.

shear data.   Further comments on comparative results for the two types of test and discussion of the details of the action during drained tests are given later.

15·8   The Mechanics of Drained Shear Tests

For an understanding of the behavior of saturated clays in shear the first requirement is a knowledge of the compressions that take place in drained shear tests and the modified amounts of compression and shearing strength that occur when a sample has been precompressed.   An explanation of these phenomena requires the consideration of a number of related phenomena which will be discussed in this and the next section.

In Fig. 15·4 the curve labeled σ_c represents the relationship of the consolidation pressure σ_c to the void ratio; it is similar to curves presented in Chapter 10.   This curve could be accepted as that occurring in either one-dimensional consolidation or in uniform consolidation, since the curves for the two cases are essentially the same.   However, uniform consolidation will be assumed herein in order to simplify the discussion, and σ_c is therefore the consolidation pressure when the major and minor principal consolidation stresses, designated by σ_{1c} and σ_{3c}, are equal.   In one-dimensional consolidation σ_{3c} is slightly smaller than σ_{1c}, and all shearing stresses that exist are small. In a sample that is just consolidated, the consolidation pressure σ_c is an intergranular pressure. However, intergranular pressures tend to change during shear, and at incipient failure they can differ considerably from the σ_c values that existed at the start of the shearing process. Therefore, in the discussion in subsequent sections of this chapter the bar which is used to designate intergranular stresses will not be used on σ_c. In Fig. 15·4 the virgin compression curve is represented by the straight line portions of curve AB, curves XY and YZ represent a rebound of small magnitude and a subsequent reloading, and curves BC and DE represent a rebound to zero or to a small pressure and a subsequent reloading.

It has been known for a relatively long time, and it has been well corroborated by laboratory tests on many clays, that a linear relationship exists between the void ratio and the logarithm of the compressive strength of a given clay. As long as there is no structural disturbance this relationship appears to be independent of all other variables. This straight line curve is always essentially parallel to the σ_c line; it is shown in Fig. 15·4 by the heavy dashed line labeled $\bar{\sigma}_{1f} - \bar{\sigma}_{3f}$, the subscript f signifying stresses at the point of failure. For any soil for which the compressive strength $\bar{\sigma}_{1f} - \bar{\sigma}_{3f}$ and the true friction angle ϕ are known it may be noted that the intergranular principal stresses $\bar{\sigma}_{1f}$ and $\bar{\sigma}_{3f}$, the intergranular pressure on the failure plane $\bar{\sigma}_{ff}$, and the shearing strength s may be computed by the use of the following expressions that were given previously as equations 13·7.

$$s = \bar{\sigma}_{ff} \tan \phi = \bar{\sigma}_{3f} \tan \phi (1 + \sin \phi) = \bar{\sigma}_{1f} \tan \phi (1 - \sin \phi)$$

$$= (\bar{\sigma}_{1f} - \bar{\sigma}_{3f}) \tfrac{1}{2} \cos \phi \qquad (15·2)$$

Curves for these stresses are shown in the figure by parallel dashed lines and are labeled by their respective stresses. All stresses represented can be intergranular stresses only, with the exception of $\bar{\sigma}_{1f} - \bar{\sigma}_{3f}$, which equals $(\bar{\sigma}_{1f} + u) - (\bar{\sigma}_{3f} + u)$, or $\sigma_{1t} - \sigma_{3t}$ at failure. All dashed lines on the figure represent stresses which hold at the point of incipient failure.

Because of the variable nature of soils the curves of the types discussed in the two preceding paragraphs seldom are exactly the same for any two samples from a given deposit. The inevitable differences between the various samples from a given deposit introduce irregularities that must be considered carefully and that must be analyzed in any thorough laboratory investigation in such a way as to eliminate irregular scattering from the true trends.|| This process of elimination cannot be discussed in

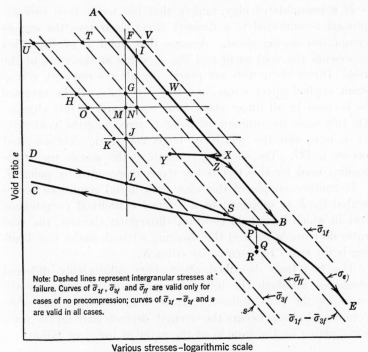

Note: Dashed lines represent intergranular stresses at failure. Curves of $\bar{\sigma}_{1f}$, $\bar{\sigma}_{3f}$ and $\bar{\sigma}_{ff}$ are valid only for cases of no precompression; curves of $\bar{\sigma}_{1f} - \bar{\sigma}_{3f}$ and s are valid in all cases.

Various stresses – logarithmic scale

FIG. 15·4 Plot of void ratio versus pressures and strengths.

any great detail herein, but it can be stated that a main requirement of this important process is the choice of *representative* samples for use in the important tests. Sometimes it is desirable to run simple classification tests on large numbers of samples, the tests most commonly used being visual tests, grain-size analyses, Atterberg limits, natural water content determinations, and unconfined compressive strength tests. From the results of one or more of these simpler types of tests it often is possible to

|| Some discussion of this problem is given in Harvard Reports, reference **24.**

discard samples with irregular or extreme characteristics and to choose a limited number of samples that are reasonably representative of the soil deposits being studied. Such a choice of samples should exhibit much less scattering than would normally be encountered.

If a consolidated clay sample that has never been precompressed is subjected to a drained direct shear test, the sample compresses during shear. Assume that point F of Fig. 15·4 represents the void ratio and the σ_c value at the start of the test. Direct shear tests are practically always run with a constant applied direct stress, and this procedure will be assumed to be used in all direct shear tests mentioned in this chapter. On this basis the ordinate of point G represents the void ratio at failure, and the relatively large void ratio decrease that occurs is FG. The shearing strength of the sample under the loading used for this test is the stress represented by point H.

If another sample of this clay with initial conditions represented by F is subjected to a drained cylindrical compression test in which $\bar{\sigma}_3$ is held constant throughout the test, the void ratio decrease is FJ and the shearing strength under this loading is the stress represented by point K.

The two tests described above have appreciably different strengths, although the initial consolidation pressure was the same for the two specimens. It is seen, therefore, that when complete drainage occurs the strength depends only on the pressures acting on the sample at the point of incipient failure.

15·9 The Mechanics of Drained Shear Tests on Clays Having Precompression and Cohesion

The case of a precompressed specimen will now be considered. Assume that a sample has at some time in the past been consolidated to point B of Fig. 15·4, that the load was later removed, and that more recently the sample has been reloaded to point L. If a specimen of this sample is subjected to a direct shear test in which drainage of water into or out of the sample occurs freely, it is found that the specimen expands. In consolidation tests the expansion or unloading curve always falls well below the virgin compression curve and, similarly, it is reasonable to expect that a drained specimen that is precompressed and is expanding in a shear test may come to equilibrium at a smaller void ratio than would a similarly loaded specimen that is not precompressed. Thus, the void ratio attained at failure is represented by the ordinate of point M, which is smaller by GM than that value which would be attained if the sample had not been precompressed. According to this reasoning precompression is the cause of a smaller void ratio at failure than would otherwise exist, and this greater density gives the additional strength represented by the abscissa difference of points H and O. This additional strength is the cohesion. If desired it may be considered that the precompression introduces an additional pressure MN, which is the pressure equivalent of the additional compression GM, but this pressure exists as intrinsic pressure and not as applied direct stress. The intrinsic pressure and the cohesion it causes appear here as equal distances on the plot because of the logarithmic scale; actually the cohesion is equal to $p_i \tan \phi$.

A direct shear test on a specimen with initial conditions represented by point I would have the $\bar{\sigma}_{ff}$ value represented by point N and would have the shearing strength represented by point O, which is the strength obtained in the test with initial conditions represented by point L.

The additional strength, which usually is attributed to cohesion, is actually caused in part by resistance to volume increase, in the manner explained for cohesionless soils in Section 14·9. Volume increases which are taking place at failure cause somewhat greater values of shearing strength along the curved portion of the envelopes of Figs. 15·2 and 15·3, whereas volume decreases cause a lowering of the shearing strength along the straight line portions of these envelopes.

The Mohr diagram of Fig. 15·5 shows Mohr circles for the failure conditions of the three direct shear tests that have been considered; the circles labeled I, II, and III correspond to the tests starting with conditions represented by points F, L, and I of Fig. 15·4. Circles I and II are for the same $\bar{\sigma}_{ff}$ value, but circle II represents a case containing cohesion AB and intrinsic pressure BC. Circles II and III represent cases having the same void ratio, the same compressive strength, and the same shearing strength, but circle II has $\bar{\sigma}_{1f}$, $\bar{\sigma}_{3f}$, and $\bar{\sigma}_{ff}$ values which are smaller than those of circle III by the magnitude of the intrinsic pressure. Therefore, it is seen that the dashed lines representing the strengths s and $\bar{\sigma}_{1f} - \bar{\sigma}_{3f}$ in Fig. 15·4 are valid for both precompressed soils and soils that have not been precompressed, but the dashed lines representing the stresses $\bar{\sigma}_{1f}$, $\bar{\sigma}_{3f}$ and $\bar{\sigma}_{ff}$ are valid only for soils having no precompression.

The curved portion of the envelope of Fig. 15·2 represents shearing strengths that are affected by precompression, but the exact location of point A is not definitely known. A direct shear

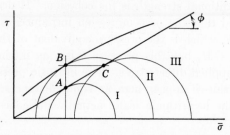

Fig. 15·5 Mohr circles representing results of drained, direct shear tests on a given clay with and without precompression.

test starting at the pressure and void ratio of point B of Fig. 15·4 would have a strength that would probably plot beyond the curved portion of the envelope. Since point S is a small distance below the $\bar{\sigma}_{ff}$ line, a direct shear test with starting conditions represented by that point must undergo a small amount of expansion; there must be some cohesion, and the strength must plot on the curved portion of the envelope. A test with the starting conditions of point P would show void ratio decrease during shear, but some precompression has occurred in this instance and, therefore, there may be a small amount of cohesion; thus the void ratio attained at failure may be that of point R rather than Q. The stresses at points B and S are represented by σ_B and σ_S, respectively, in Fig. 15·10. It is possible that the curved portion of the envelope extends to somewhat larger pressures than shown in curve I of this figure, but the amount of cohesion in this questionable zone is probably too small to be of practical significance.

The shearing strength of a precompressed specimen may be expressed as the cohesion plus strength values such as are given in equation 15·2, and for any type of test it may be written

$$s = c + \bar{\sigma}_{ff} \tan \phi = (p_i + \bar{\sigma}_{ff}) \tan \phi \qquad (15 \cdot 3)$$

It should be noted, however, that the cohesion is a variable quantity, its magnitude depending considerably on the amount of the precompression.

Drained tests on undisturbed samples give directly the effect of any precompression of the clay and furnish directly Mohr diagrams of the types shown by Figs $15 \cdot 2$, $15 \cdot 3$, $15 \cdot 5$, and $15 \cdot 10$. The effects of precompression are not very large for cases of drained shear, and in general the magnitude of the cohesion is small. The cohesion is shown to exaggerated scale in Fig. $15 \cdot 5$, and it usually is more of the general magnitude indicated in Fig. $15 \cdot 10$.

15·10 The Possibility of Cohesion Being Temporary

It is possible that the cohesive strength, represented by the humps on the envelopes in Figs. $15 \cdot 2$ and $15 \cdot 3$, is of temporary nature. The plastic flow during a shearing process which occurs over a period of many years may dissipate some of the effects of previous compression, and thus remove part and possibly all of the cohesion. In clay embankments which must be stable for many generations this possibility should be recognized. However, in embankments which are maintained only during a short construction period, the strength known as cohesion may safely be assumed to exist.

15·11 Structural Strength

Many clays are stiff in the undisturbed state, but become very soft after being subjected to remolding without change of water content. The simple demonstration of this loss of stiffness as produced by squeezing a piece of clay of this type between the fingers, was mentioned in Section $4 \cdot 7$. The process of remolding a clay specimen by squeezing it is in effect simply the imposing of repeated applications of shearing strain. The amount of structural disturbance that is caused by remolding depends on the magnitude of the imposed shearing strain, and complete remolding may require a large amount of strain, aided perhaps by reversals of strain. However, an appreciable amount of remolding may occur in a shear test which is carried to a relatively large shearing strain, as shown by the decreased strength be-

tween points *A* and *B* in Fig. 15·6, which represents a drained
direct shear test under constant applied direct stress. In addition, an appreciable amount of remolding is often caused during
sampling, even though the best-known sampling procedures are
used.

It should be noted that peak point *A* on a curve such as that
shown in Fig. 15·6 is caused by a different phenomenon than
that which causes the peak points observed in shear tests on
sand. In sands the high strength that occurs at the peak point
is due in part to the stress required to supply the energy being
expended in volume increase.
In this case the strength becomes smaller at large strains
when the rate of volume change
becomes smaller, as explained
in Section 14·6. In drained
tests on clays that have little
or no precompression, decrease
of volume is occurring at the
peak point. In this respect the
typical volume changes that occur during drained shear tests
in clays are the cause of decreases rather than increases in shearing strength. The high strength at the peak point in clays is the
result of structural strength, and the decrease in strength that
occurs after the peak point is passed in a shear test is the result
of decreasing structural strength due to remolding.

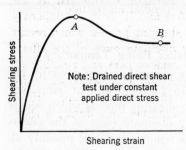

Note: Drained direct shear
test under constant
applied direct stress

Shearing stress

Shearing strain

Fig. 15·6 Typical curve of stress
versus strain for shear in clay.

Some clays possess large amounts of structural strength, others
much smaller amounts. Even completely remolded clays, which
have been consolidated since remolding, possess a small amount
of structural strength.

The true nature of structural strength is not known, but it is
believed that the general shapes of envelopes discussed in the
foregoing sections apply qualitatively to all materials, whether
or not they possess high structural strength. The envelope simply has larger ordinates if there is high structural strength. The
structure is an essentially independent variable, and testing
should be restricted to samples whose structure is as near the
natural structure as possible.

The testing of samples in the undisturbed state so that their structural strength will be properly reflected is now widely and correctly recognized to be of paramount importance. However, it is commonly believed that structural strength in some clays may be considerably greater in nature than it is in even the best of test specimens. This can be explained only by the fact that the structural strength is so susceptible to disturbance that the stress changes and shearing strains which occur in the most refined of sampling methods are sufficient to destroy a part of this strength. It is difficult to understand why a clay, when subjected to failure in nature, can lose much less structural strength than it does in sampling and in being later subjected to failure in the laboratory, and especially so if it has been sampled by methods which soil engineers trust sufficiently to call *undisturbed sampling*. This unfortunate condition apparently exists, however, if the latest and best of sampling methods are not used, and probably it exists to a smaller degree in the best samples now obtainable. When and if it occurs, any allowance that is made to account for this lost strength must be based largely on judgment. Neglecting this loss of strength gives results which, at least, are on the safe side.

15·12 Effects of Speed of Shear

All viscous materials and all plastic materials exhibit a resistance to shearing strain that varies with the speed at which the shearing strain occurs. The plastic structural resistance to distortion in clays, called herein the *plastic resistance*, is an example. Figure 15·7 shows the compressive strength of a remolded Boston blue clay of given water content under various speeds of compression (from Ninth Report, reference 137), the variations in strength in this figure being due entirely to variations of plastic resistance. Relatively little testing has been done on this property, and therefore data on its magnitude are meager. Because of the effects of speed of shear, data such as those given by Fig. 15·2 should be viewed as strictly valid only for a certain given speed of shear, but Fig. 15·7 indicates that the effects of speed are not large.

Data have been obtained (138) which indicate that the plastic resistance at any given speed of shear in a given clay at various densities is approximately proportional to the intergranular pressure. On the basis of this relationship and the assumption that the plastic resistance depends only on the intergranular pressure

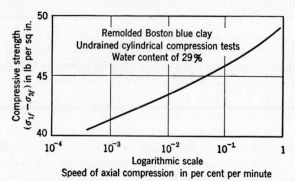

FIG. 15·7   Effect of speed of shear on the compressive strength of clay.

and the speed of shear, equation 15·3 may be extended to the following expression:

$$s = (\bar{\sigma}_{ff} + p_i)\left[\tan\phi + f\left(\frac{\partial \epsilon_s}{\partial t}\right)\right] \qquad (15\cdot4)$$

in which ϵ_s designates the shearing strain. The function of speed of shearing strain which appears in this equation may be obtained from data of the type given in Fig. 15·7.

15·13   Effects of Colloidal Phenomena

During recent years much progress has been made in colloidal physics and colloidal chemistry toward better understanding of the phenomena which affect the action of materials containing particles of colloidal size. There probably are numerous ways in which these colloidal phenomena affect the shearing strength of clays, and it has been claimed, and in all probability correctly so, that too little attention has been paid to colloidal hypotheses by soil engineers. It is likely that a number of subjects that have been discussed in previous sections are largely dependent on such phenomena.

Structural strength, which in many clays has had untold ages for development, has been variously referred to by such names as bond, congealing, the development of preferred orientations of molecules, and the squeezing of adsorbed water films from between fine mineral particles. Probably the prospects of a true explanation of the physical nature of structural strength depend in large degree on an understanding of colloidal phenomena.

The loss of structural strength during shearing strain or, as it is often called, the loss of strength due to remolding, is of great practical significance. It is possible that this phenomenon is merely a change of type or degree of adsorption at particle surfaces. Since no physical explanation of this loss is available, it is not surprising that controversy exists regarding whether or not the structural strength lost during conventional testing procedures is reasonably representative of corresponding losses during shear in natural clay deposits.

Data presented by Hvorslev (80) demonstrate that some of the structural strength that is lost by remolding action is in time recovered. Hvorslev called this action *thixotropic regain.* Recent shear research (Ninth Report, reference 137), has shown that when a remolded clay specimen is carried to the ϕ-obliquity condition and then held without change of strain for a day or two, it shows increased strength when again sheared. In addition, a very slow drainage of water from a sample during shear may lead to a greater strength increase than can be attributed to the increased density alone. These items probably are examples of change of type or degree of adsorption.

There may also be colloidal phenomena which have considerable effect on the shearing strength of clays, but which have not been mentioned in these pages because they are unknown or because their importance is not appreciated.

The effect of speed of shear on the strength is believed to be caused by the viscous or plastic characteristics of material in the adsorption zones in the vicinity of points of contact or near contact of clay particles. Thus this effect is a colloidal phenomenon, and it is of sufficient importance to justify a detailed discussion.

The following hypothetical explanation of plastic resistance and of time relationships was first presented (138) for one-dimensional compressions, but it may be extended to the action of clays in shear. If a drained clay sample is maintained under any given system of constant applied direct and shearing stresses that do not cause failure, it gradually approaches an ultimate shape and an ultimate void ratio at which there is static equilibrium. Ages may be required to reach this state of equilibrium, but when it is reached the applied stresses are equal to static internal resistances and they have values that are free of plastic resistance and all other time effects. During the approach to equilibrium, however, the applied stresses are made up in part of the stresses required to overcome the plastic resistance. The plastic resistance is usually considered to depend mainly on the speed of strain although possibly it depends also on such factors as changes in type or degree of adsorption. As the clay specimen approaches the static state, the strains continuously decrease in speed and the plastic resistance decreases in magnitude; however, the speed becomes almost imperceptibly small when the plastic resistance is still quite large and the strains and the void ratio still have a considerable change to undergo before they reach the static state. Secondary compression, as it occurs in consolidation tests, is a good illustration of this condition. From these concepts it appears that a clay that has reached static equilibrium in nature after the lapse of many centuries and is suddenly subjected to stress increases of relatively small magnitude may be expected immediately to exert a plastic resistance that is equal to the stress increase, and it is possible that the speed of distortion required for the exerting of this amount of plastic resistance may be too small to be noticeable. In such a case the plastic resistance cannot be distinguished from a bond, and the occurrence of bonds of this type is possible both when the shearing stresses are small and when they are relatively large.

Understanding of colloidal phenomena and related phenomena which affect the shearing strength of soils is in its infancy, and it may always be incomplete. Thus it may always be necessary in soil engineering to test clays without thorough knowledge of the physical phenomena that govern their action. In all cases, however, the test conditions chosen should be as representative of natural conditions as possible. In this connection it should be realized that work in developing improved testing procedures and in setting up better methods for the interpretation of test data may be aided greatly by the insight on the action of small particles that is given by a familiarity with the most recent concepts on colloidal phenomena.

15·14 Consolidated-Undrained Shear Tests

It is far too difficult and time-consuming to make a general practice of conducting tests which are completely drained. Moreover, in clay, under natural conditions occurrences of shear with distinctly limited drainage are much more common than drained cases.

A second type of shear test, and one which is very important, is that in which a completely saturated sample is initially consolidated to some given pressure and then sheared with no drainage allowed. It is called the *consolidated-undrained test.*

The case in nature that is represented by this type of test is that in which a completely saturated clay mass originally has intergranular pressures of known magnitude, and in which this mass, if subjected to shear failure, is sheared at a speed at which essentially no drainage can occur. If the mass is large, shear can take place at a relatively slow speed with practically no drainage.

The original pressure system to which a clay is consolidated in nature is more likely to be one in which there is a considerable difference between the major and the minor principal stresses, σ_{1c} and σ_{3c}, than it is to be one in which these stresses are approximately equal. For the laboratory test, however, it is common to use either uniform consolidation or one-dimensional consolidation, a procedure which is sometimes on the conservative side and sometimes on the unsafe side. The discussion herein, as in Section 15·8, will be based on uniform consolidation, and consideration of the effects of other consolidation conditions will be limited to brief general statements that will be made at the end of Section 15·15.

The applied lateral pressure used in cylindrical compression tests of the consolidated-undrained type and the applied vertical pressure used in direct shear tests of this type are often arbitrarily maintained constant and equal to the consolidation pressure. However, the magnitude of these constant applied pressures during undrained tests is not significant if the clay is completely saturated, the consolidation pressure being the only significant pressure.

In the undrained test there usually is pressure in the pore water when failure is reached. Under the usual testing conditions, however, the magnitude of these pressures cannot be determined and, therefore, the intergranular pressures are not known. For this reason the shearing strength in this type of test cannot be expressed or plotted as a function of the intergranular pressure at failure. This situation explains the requirement of the use of expressions for strength in terms of the consolidation pressure. It is only in special testing apparatus that pore-water pressures can be observed. An example of a test in which pore-pressure data are obtained is shown in Fig. 15·9; this example will be used for reference in connection with certain concepts that are discussed later, but it should be recognized as a special type of test.

15·15 The Mechanics of Consolidated-Undrained Shear Tests

Figure 15·4 will be used to explain the details of consolidated-undrained tests. First, however, comments are required on two items shown by this figure.

The dashed lines representing stresses at failure are believed to be essentially independent of whether failure is reached in drained shear, in undrained shear, or in some other type of shear, and it will be assumed herein that these lines are valid for all types of shear.¶

In undrained tests the position of the virgin-σ_c line of Fig. 15·4 relative to the lines representing the various stresses at failure is an important factor. Since the $\bar{\sigma}_{1f}$ curve and the virgin-σ_c curve are parallel in a plot of this type, the expression $\log \bar{\sigma}_{1f} - \log \sigma_c$ has the same value for undrained shear tests at all void ratios and the ratio $\bar{\sigma}_{1f}/\sigma_c$ is constant. Since the ratio $\bar{\sigma}_{1f}/\sigma_c$ has significance for undrained tests only, any reference to this ratio in the following pages indicates that undrained tests are being considered. In the figure, $\bar{\sigma}_{1f}$ is shown as slightly greater than σ_c and, therefore, the ratio $\bar{\sigma}_{1f}/\sigma_c$ in this case is slightly greater than unity. Recent

¶ This assumption is used by A. Casagrande in a working hypothesis described in reference 24. Actually resistances to volume increase and probably other phenomena have some effect on the positions of these lines.

research indicates that in numerous clays the ratio $\bar{\sigma}_{1f}/\sigma_c$ is roughly equal to unity, but in some clays it is considerably smaller and in other clays considerably greater than unity.* For any clay it is possible to determine this ratio from the data of a conventional consolidation test and a conventional drained shear test, but a larger number of tests are required for a dependable determination. More detailed data on this ratio and related characteristics are obtainable from undrained shear tests in which pore pressure values are observed.

If an undrained shear test is conducted in either direct shear or triaxial apparatus on a completely saturated sample that initially has the σ_c and void ratio values represented by point F of Fig. 15·4, there is no void ratio change during the test, and the stresses $\bar{\sigma}_{1f}$, $\bar{\sigma}_{ff}$, and s that are reached at failure are shown respectively by points V, T, and U. Similarly an undrained test starting from conditions represented by point W has final $\bar{\sigma}_{ff}$ and s values that are represented by points G and H.

Expressions for shearing strength, based on the $\bar{\sigma}_{1f}$ and $\bar{\sigma}_{ff}$ expressions of equations 15·2, may be written in the form

$$s = \bar{\sigma}_{ff} \tan \phi = \sigma_c \left[\frac{\bar{\sigma}_{1f}}{\sigma_c} (1 - \sin \phi) \right] \tan \phi \qquad (15 \cdot 5)$$

The expression in terms of $\bar{\sigma}_{ff}$ can be used only if the intergranular pressure at failure is known. The final expression contains, first, the term σ_c, which is known for any consolidated undrained test. The ratio $\bar{\sigma}_{1f}/\sigma_c$ and the true friction angle ϕ are constants for a given soil that has not been precompressed and, therefore, the bracketed term is a constant. The bracketed expression cannot be evaluated from the results of undrained tests alone, unless pore pressure data are observed, but its value is of the order of magnitude of 0.5 in some clays. It follows that in some clays the $\bar{\sigma}_{ff}$ values in undrained shear tests are approximately equal to $\frac{1}{2}\sigma_c$. A simple and convenient form of expression for the relationship between the shearing strength and the consolidation pressure for the case of undrained shear is

$$s = \sigma_c \tan \phi_a \qquad (15 \cdot 6)$$

* The use of a value of unity for this ratio is proposed in a method for interpreting test data given by P. C. Rutledge in reference 125. Procedures based on the use of this ratio are suggested in reference 126.

in which ϕ_a is called an *apparent friction angle*. From the relationship between σ_c and $\bar{\sigma}_{ff}$ stated above, it is seen that tan ϕ_a for some clays is approximately equal to ½ tan ϕ.

In Fig. 15·8 results are shown for both undrained and drained shear tests. Mohr circle I represents the intergranular stresses at failure in a drained direct shear test which initially had the conditions represented by point F of Fig. 15·4. Thus the shearing strength represented by point A of Fig. 15·8 is that given by point H of Fig. 15·4. The true strength envelope is the straight line that is tangent to circle I and that passes through point A of Fig. 15·8. According to the discussion in the previous para-

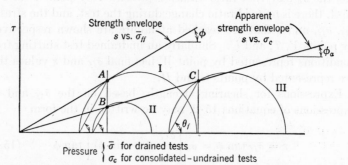

Pressure $\begin{cases} \bar{\sigma} \text{ for drained tests} \\ \sigma_c \text{ for consolidated-undrained tests} \end{cases}$

Fig. 15·8   Mohr diagram illustrating true and apparent strength envelopes for a clay with no precompression.

graph an undrained shear test that has the initial conditions represented by point F of Fig. 15·4 may show roughly one-half as much shearing strength as the drained test with the same initial conditions. The shearing strength obtained in the undrained test is represented by point U of Fig. 15·4, and if this strength is plotted against the consolidation pressure in Fig. 15·8 point B is obtained. Similarly, an undrained test that starts with conditions represented by point W of Fig. 15·4 gives the shearing strength represented by point H of Fig. 15·4 and point C of Fig. 15·8. The shearing strength and all other intergranular stresses for the case represented by point C are the same as those represented by point A; the use of points such as C with σ_c for abscissas is simply a substitute procedure that is adopted when intergranular pressures are not known. The straight line through points B and C has a slope of ϕ_a and is called an *apparent envelope.*

Mohr circles for the undrained tests are shown in Fig. 15·8, but points B and C are the only points on these circles that have significance in relation to the apparent envelope. The reason for this is that any point on the apparent envelope may be located by multiplying the abscissa of the corresponding point on the true envelope by a constant, which sometimes has a value of roughly one-half, but points on an apparent Mohr circle are obtained by adding to the abscissa of the corresponding point on the true Mohr circle a constant pressure, which is the pore-water pressure at failure if the applied pressure on the plane of failure equals σ_c. Because of this situation apparent envelopes are not tangent to apparent Mohr circles, as the figure shows, and it would be somewhat unsafe to assume a condition of tangency. To aid in obtaining a thorough understanding of the apparent envelope it may be noted that ordinates of the apparent envelope are shearing strengths or limiting values of shearing stress on planes of failure, and that shearing strengths can be associated with no other plane than the failure plane; therefore, a strength envelope of any type must cut Mohr circles at points representing stresses on failure planes, the locations of these points on Mohr circles being defined by the angle θ_f. This angle is shown in the figure; it is the angle between the major principal plane and the failure plane. Theoretically it is equal to $45° + \frac{1}{2}\phi$, and actually its value is of the order of 60 degrees in the majority of clays.

An apparent envelope is easily plotted from the data of a series of undrained direct shear tests, since the shearing strengths are given directly by such tests. The construction of the apparent envelope from data given by a series of undrained cylindrical compression tests is somewhat complicated because the shearing strengths are not given directly by such tests. However, the shearing strengths of the various tests of such a series may be determined by use of the expression.

$$s = \tfrac{1}{2}(\sigma_{1f} - \sigma_{3f}) \cos \phi$$

in which the compressive strength $\sigma_{1f} - \sigma_{3f}$ is directly available from the test data and the value of ϕ may be obtained from the data of a drained test, or sometimes it may be estimated with sufficient accuracy for use in this expression.

On some occasions apparent envelopes are expressed in terms of applied pressures. Such a procedure is possible for any case in which the applied pressure bears a definite relationship to the consolidation pressure, the commonest example being the usual undrained direct shear test in which the applied direct stress is constant and equal to the consolidation pressure. It should be realized, however, that if the applied direct stress were increased instead of held constant, there would be no changes in the strengths and in the intergranular pressures at failure; the pressure increase would be entirely taken up by an increase in pore-water pressures that would be of the same magnitude on all planes. Therefore, full significance is not given to the consolidated-undrained case in saturated soils when strength expressions in terms of applied pressure are used. It should also be noted that, although this case is designated as initially consolidated, it applies equally well to all instances of undrained shear which start with an intergranular stress that is equal to σ_c, even though the soil initially may be only partially consolidated.

The use of the assumption of uniform consolidation with σ_{1c} equal to σ_{3c} in the foregoing discussion has served the purpose of simplifying the general explanations given. It should now be noted that the ratio $\bar{\sigma}_{1f}/\sigma_{1c}$ in some cases depends considerably on the principal stress ratio of the consolidation pressures σ_{1c}/σ_{3c}. In brief, for soils in which $\bar{\sigma}_1$ remains approximately constant during shear, the value of $\bar{\sigma}_{1f}/\sigma_{1c}$ is not dependent on the value of σ_{1c}/σ_{3c}, and the concepts outlined in the preceding pages may be accepted as given. For soils in which $\bar{\sigma}_1$ changes appreciably during shear a more complicated situation exists, and for analyzing this case the shearing strength may be expressed $\sigma_{1c} \tan \phi_a$, in which ϕ_a is a more general form of apparent friction angle, with $\tan \phi_a$ equal to s/σ_{1c}. The major consolidation pressure σ_{1c} is equal to or slightly larger than the vertical overburden pressure † in many actual clay deposits, and approximate determinations of its in situ values are often possible. For soils in which $\bar{\sigma}_1$ increases during shear the ratios $\bar{\sigma}_{1f}/\sigma_{1c}$ and s/σ_{1c} decrease with increasing values

† For considerations of vertical overburden pressures see Chapter 16.

of the ratio σ_{1c}/σ_{3c}. ‡ In such soils typical tests initially consolidated to σ_c would give no data on $\bar{\sigma}_1$ variations, and they would
give values of tan ϕ_a that are too large and are thus unsafe for
any ratio of σ_{1c}/σ_{3c} that exceeds unity. Conversely, for soils in
which $\bar{\sigma}_1$ decreases during shear the results obtained might be too
conservative.

15·16 Consolidated-Undrained Shear Tests on Precompressed Clays

If undrained tests are run on specimens having the initial
conditions represented by points *B*, *S*, and *L*, respectively, of
Fig. 15·4, the shearing strengths obtained will not differ greatly
because the void ratios of the three specimens are not greatly

‡ An example of this condition and of the value of information on $\bar{\sigma}_1$ variations, as given by pore pressure data, is furnished by the test represented in
Fig. 15·9. If failure is considered to be reached when $\bar{\sigma}_1 - \bar{\sigma}_3$ attains its
maximum value at the $\Delta L/L_0$ value of 10 per cent, $\bar{\sigma}_{1f}/\bar{\sigma}_{3f}$ equals 3.57, ϕ equals
34°, and s equals $\frac{1}{2}(\sigma_{1f} - \sigma_{3f})$ cos ϕ or 10.1 lb per sq in. This shearing strength
holds for consolidation to a σ_c value of 23.7 lb per sq in., and it also holds for
other consolidation pressure systems such as σ_{1c} and σ_{3c}, respectively, equal to
29.5 and 7.6 lb per sq in., which is the condition holding when $\Delta L/L_0$ equals
5 per cent. On this basis the following table illustrates data obtainable from
this test:

For Initial Consolidation to			$\dfrac{s}{\sigma_{1c}} = \tan \phi_a$
σ_{1c}	σ_{3c}	σ_{1c}/σ_{3c}	
23.7	23.7	1.0	0.43
27.8	18.5	1.5	0.36
26.0	10.4	2.5	0.39
26.2	7.7	3.4	0.39
31.6	8.3	3.8	0.32
34.2	9.5	3.57	0.295

The tan ϕ_a value of 0.43 is the only one that can be obtained in ordinary
tests. For σ_{1c}/σ_{3c} values of less than about 3.5 in this soil the tan ϕ_a values
are between 0.43 and 0.36, representing possible variations in tan ϕ_a of approximately 15 per cent; for consolidation to pressure systems approaching
that occurring at failure, tan ϕ_a approaches 0.295, which is a 31 per cent
variation from the value obtained in this instance in ordinary tests.

different. This indicates that the apparent envelopes which represent undrained shear tests on completely saturated, precompressed clays have the shape of curve II of Fig. 15·10. The envelope has a very flat slope at consolidation pressures that are

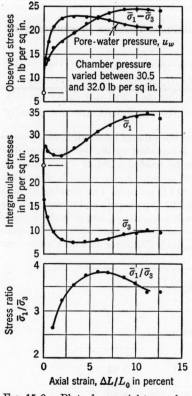

Boston Blue Clay (undisturbed)
South Boston Navy Yard (U-T3)
Previously consolidated to 23.7 lb per sq in. with $\sigma_1 = \sigma_3$.
Specimen length 6.5 in.; diameter 2.8 in.
Speed of axial strain 0.3 per cent per min (approx.)

FIG. 15·9   Plot of a special type of undrained, cylindrical compression test in which pore-pressure values are observed.

considerably smaller than the maximum intergranular pressure that has existed on the sample in the past.

The pressures σ_B, σ_S, and σ_L that appear in Fig. 15·10 are the pressures at points B, S, and L, respectively, in Fig. 15·4. Figure 15·10 shows that an *undrained* test starting with conditions represented by point B of Fig. 15·4 would show roughly one-half as much shearing strength as a *drained* direct shear test under an applied pressure equal to σ_B. Since point S of Fig. 15·4 is practically on the $\bar{\sigma}_{ff}$ line, a *drained* direct shear test under a pressure equal to $\bar{\sigma}_S$ would undergo practically no void ratio change, and the strength in such a test would therefore be essentially the same as that in an *undrained* test with initial consolidation to σ_S. In Fig. 15·10 it is seen that the two curves show approximately equal strengths at pressure σ_S. An *undrained* test

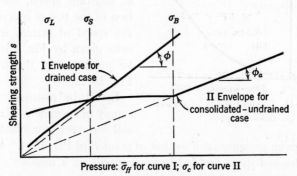

Fig. 15·10 Relationship of Mohr envelopes for the drained and the consolidated-undrained cases.

starting at point L of Fig. 15·4 would show a much larger shearing strength than would be obtained in a *drained* direct shear test under a pressure equal to σ_L, since the drained specimen would expand during testing. This relationship is also represented in Fig. 15·10. It is a point worthy of careful note that a highly precompressed soil may exhibit many times as much shearing strength in an undrained test as it does in a drained test.

15·17 General Discussion of Time Effects

The speed of shear affects the shearing strength of a given clay in two distinctly different ways. The first and better known of the two is the effect of speed of shear on the amount of drainage that can take place before failure. The second is the effect of speed on the magnitude of the plastic resistance. Combinations of the two types of time effects must be given careful consideration in planning laboratory tests if the tests are to be reasonably representative of conditions in nature.

Two types of curves are used to aid in the following explanation of combined time effects. The curve of one-dimensional consolidation versus time is a familiar one, and the commonly used semi-logarithmic form that was shown in Fig. 10·12 is also given in Fig. 15·11. It is known that most of this curve falls within two cycles of logarithmic time scale. The second curve presents

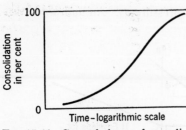

the plastic resistance relationship. If a sample is sheared at constant speed, the duration of the test is inversely as the speed of strain, and results given by Fig. 15·6 may be presented in the form of Fig. 15·12.

FIG. 15·11   General shape of consolidation curves.

Let it be assumed that a supply of specimens of a given soil has been consolidated to some given pressure such as that of point F of Fig. 15·4. A series of *undrained* shear tests at various speeds on a number of these specimens gives the relationship between shearing strength and duration of test which is of the form of Fig. 15·12 and which is shown by curve I of Fig. 15·13. A series of *drained* shear tests, run on a number of specimens at various speeds with applied pressures on the failure plane equal to σ_c, gives curve II. It must

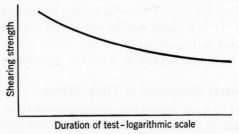

FIG. 15·12   Effect of the duration of the test on the shearing strength.

be assumed that extremely small specimens are used in the drained tests of short duration so that a completely drained condition can be obtained.

It is known from consolidation theory that the portions of the ultimate drainage quantity and the ultimate increase of intergranular pressure, which occur in any given time in a clay stratum that is free to drain at its surface, are dependent on the dimensions of the mass. It is also known that any given portion of the ultimate drainage occurs in a time that is about proportional to the square of the stratum thickness. Therefore, a very small specimen, which is failed in shear in 1 minute in a direct

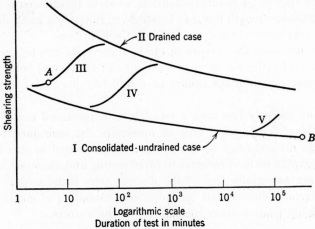

FIG. 15·13   Time effects on the shearing strength.

shear test in which drainage occurs at the surfaces of the specimen, may undergo practically no drainage before failure, but a similar specimen, which is sheared in 1 hour, may be almost completely drained before failure. The strength at some arbitrarily chosen point within such a sample is represented in Fig. 15·13 by curve III, which is similar in shape to the curve of Fig. 15·11. Let it be assumed that the point chosen is at the center of the sample where consolidation proceeds at the slowest rate. Since it is doubtful if a satisfactory test can be conducted in less than about 5 minutes, point A may be said to represent the smallest strength that can be observed on this sample.

A similar representation for a larger size of sample under similar conditions is given by curve IV. Since this curve is about one cycle to the right of curve III, the sample represented requires about ten times as long for any given degree of drainage and therefore it has a thickness that is slightly greater than three times as large.

A point not far from the drained surface of a large clay mass in nature might be represented by a curve such as V. The curve representing conditions near the center of the mass might be many cycles to the right of curve V. Thus there exists the possibility that a point such as *B* represents the average shearing strength for the clay in its natural condition, whereas point *A* represents the smallest strength that can be observed in tests on small direct shear specimens which drain freely at their surfaces.

The drainage that occurs in direct shear tests can be greatly restricted by the use of impervious blocks above and below the specimen, but drainage cannot be completely prevented in such tests.

There recently has been a trend toward increased use of the cylindrical compression type of apparatus for undrained tests, because drainage can be almost entirely prevented in this type of apparatus without recourse to rapid testing and, therefore, such tests are essentially free of the discrepancies mentioned above. This trend indicates that improved understanding of conditions invariably leads to more rational testing procedures.

15·18 Effect of Small Variations from Complete Saturation; Strength Envelopes of the Constant-*w* Type

All discussion up to this point refers to completely saturated clays. However, many clays in their natural state have a small percentage of their void space occupied by air or other gases. Because of the compressibility of this gas it is possible for appreciable void ratio changes to take place during undrained shear.

The effect of a small air content can best be represented by a strength plot of the type shown in Fig. 15·14. This curve shows the shearing strength as a function of the applied pressure on the failure plane for a given clay at a *given value of water content*, and it is called the *envelope* for the *case of constant water content*. The applied pressure in this connection includes both intergranular pressure and neutral pressure. A plot of this type may be obtained from a series of tests run at various applied pressures on a group of specimens, all of which are consolidated under the same pressure, or such a plot may be obtained from tests on a group of specimens from an undisturbed sample at its natural water content.§

In clays that are not completely saturated, the shearing strength depends on both the consolidation pressure and the applied pressure. The constant-w envelope gives the shearing strength as a function of the applied pressure on the failure plane for an arbitrarily chosen consolidation pressure or water content. Such series of tests must be supplemented by consolidated-undrained tests to give the relationship between the shearing

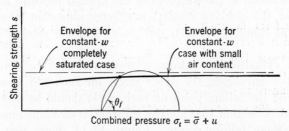

FIG. 15·14   Strength envelope for the case of constant water content.

strength and the consolidation pressure, and in this case the consolidated-undrained tests must be run under definite values of applied pressure, the simplest choice being applied pressures on the failure plane that are equal to the consolidation pressure. When envelopes of the two types have been obtained for any given clay, estimates of shearing strength may be made for undrained shear under any pressure conditions.

The shearing strength of a completely saturated clay specimen with a given water content is independent of the magnitude of the applied pressures; the straight, dashed line in Fig. 15·14 is a constant-w envelope for such a condition. The constant-w envelope for the same soil at the same water content but with a given small quantity of gas within the pore water is shown by a heavy line in the figure. At large applied pressures the gas occupies a relatively small volume; thus, the void ratio is slightly larger

§ The consolidation pressure is the same, therefore, for all points on the plot, and it is this type of test, on samples at natural water content and thus under no consolidation except that existing in nature, that A. Casagrande has designated the unconsolidated-undrained test. (See footnote in Section 15·7.)

and the shearing strength is slightly smaller than for the saturated condition. At small applied pressures the gas occupies a relatively large space, and the shearing strength is less than that for the saturated clay by a considerable amount. The volume of the gas bubbles depends on the pressure in the gas. However, the relationships between the applied pressure, the gas volume, and the shearing strength are not simple, because the curvature of bubble surfaces causes the pressure in the gas to be larger than the pressure in the pore water and because some of the gas may go into solution in the water when the applied pressure is large. Moreover, the shearing strength is affected somewhat by surface tension at contacts between soil grains and the menisci of gas bubbles.

When cylindrical compression tests are used to determine constant-w envelopes, the Mohr circle for each test should be drawn and the failure point on each circle should be located as explained in Section 15·15. The constant-w envelope must pass through these failure points. Figure 15·14 shows that much larger errors would be involved, if this type of envelope were drawn tangent to the Mohr circle, than the errors in the apparent envelope of the consolidated-undrained case.

15·19 Effect of Relatively Large Air Contents

There are cases in which considerable amounts of air exist in the pores of a soil. An outstanding example is the typical rolled-fill embankment, which is compacted in such a way that entrapped air often occupies more than 10 per cent of the pore space.

Tests on rolled-fill materials should be conducted on disturbed rather than on undisturbed specimens, since the structure of such materials is disturbed during excavating and placing, but otherwise testing procedures are essentially the same as those discussed in the foregoing pages. Such a material may be investigated by series of drained tests, by series of consolidated-undrained tests (with the applied pressure on the failure plane at failure approximately equal to the consolidation pressure), and by series of constant-w tests. However, it may be found that the curves of shearing strength versus applied pressure practically coincide for these series.‖ This indicates that practically no neutral pressures

‖ An example of this situation is given by tests reported in reference 161.

occur in such a soil, because the large volume of compressible pore space make it nearly as compressible without drainage as it is with complete drainage.

It should be realized, however, that rolled fills may reach practically complete saturation in time. Therefore, for determinations of the dependable, permanent shearing strength it may be necessary to saturate specimens completely and test them in this state.

15·20 Determinations of In Situ Shearing Strengths

The investigations described in preceding sections are those needed for extensive information on the shearing strength of a given clay over a wide range of pressure conditions and for various conditions of drainage and precompression.

The information actually wanted for the general run of projects on which investigations are made is the shearing strength at the various points of a soil mass under existing or anticipated conditions. This information can be obtained from the investigations mentioned in the previous section if the specimens tested are representative of the soil at all parts of the mass under consideration. A somewhat different procedure that may be used, however, consists of tests on a number of undisturbed samples from various points within the mass, the aim of the tests being to determine only the shearing strength of each sample at its natural water content. This strength is the undrained, in situ shearing strength, which will herein be called simply the *in situ shearing strength*. For certain investigations, such as those involving undrained shear in very heterogeneous deposits, the determination of in situ strengths is the more direct approach to the problem.

In the following paragraphs, determinations of the in situ shearing strength will be discussed. This discussion will also serve as a means of presenting a number of fundamental considerations that are important in all shearing strength investigations. No specific testing procedure is the ideal one for determination of the in situ strength of a clay specimen. Several testing procedures that give information on the in situ strength will be described, and comments will be given relative to the advantages and undesirable features of each. Before testing procedures are described, however, a few of the basic phenomena that must be considered in comparing the results of various types of test will be explained.

It is probable that the best grade of samples now obtainable reach the laboratory at essentially their in situ water contents, but it should be recognized that some disturbance of structure and loss of structural strength have probably occurred in every sample tested.

In the process of sampling soils that occur at considerable depths below the free water surface, the pore-water stress passes from compression to tension. In many soils this tension causes dissolved gases to come out of solution, and thereby introduces swelling of the sample. Thus, without change of water content there may be a somewhat increased void ratio as compared to the in situ value. If a sample is later placed under uniform pressure in the laboratory, the pore water is again under pressure and the gas is compressed, but even if the gas redissolves it is possible that it will do so at a very slow rate.

There is a possibility that the water content may increase in the center of such samples by the phenomenon known as *internal swelling*. If the surfaces of a sample are disturbed slightly more than the interior, the clay becomes slightly softer at the surface; thus it has at the surface a smaller intergranular pressure and a correspondingly smaller numerical magnitude of tension than at the center of the specimen. Even though the sample is completely sealed from overall water content change, the gradients due to this difference in pore pressures cause migration of water from the outer portions to the center of the sample.

The three tests that will be considered in this discussion are the test under in situ pressure and natural water content, the test with reconsolidation to the in situ pressure, and the unconfined compression test at natural water content.

The *test under in situ pressure and natural water content* is often used to obtain information on the in situ shearing strength. In it the specimen is placed before testing under the in situ pressure, which is the total overburden pressure (intergranular plus neutral pressure) to which the soil was subject in nature before sampling. No drainage of water from the specimen is allowed during this pressure application, and the shearing test is run with no drainage allowed. The shearing strength obtained in this type of test tends to be too small, since strength may have been lost by structural disturbance during sampling, by internal swelling, and by expansion due to escape of gas from solution. The effect of the escape of gas is decreased, however, by the application of the in situ pressure before the test is run; this effect may be minimized by allowing the specimen to stand under pressure for as long a time before testing as is practicable.

In the *test with reconsolidation to the in situ pressure* the specimen is placed under the intergranular or effective overburden pressure that existed in nature and allowed to drain. After this reconsolidation the test is run with no drainage allowed. The soil in this test has the natural consolidation pressure, but it has less structural strength and it has a smaller void ratio than exist in nature. The shearing strength in a test of this type is greater than that in the test described in the previous paragraph by the strength increase introduced by reconsolidation. This increase leads to a shearing strength which may be either somewhat larger or somewhat smaller than the in situ strength, but it is likely that the reconsolidated test approximates the in situ strength more closely than any other type of test.

The test that has been most commonly used for in situ strength determinations is the *unconfined compression test at natural water content*. An empirical procedure that has become common in the interpretation of this test is the use of one half of the compressive strength as the shearing strength. The compressive strength as given by this type of test may be considerably smaller than that obtained in the test under in situ pressure and natural water content, since any gas that exists in the pores occupies a considerably larger volume. In addition, the lack of a confining pressure offers a somewhat greater possibility of minute fissures opening slightly as the test progresses and removing certain tendencies for the sample to act as a unit, and thereby allowing a greater degree of progressive failure. The use of $\frac{1}{2}(\sigma_{1f} - \sigma_{3f})$ for the shearing strength, serves to counteract the tendency toward too small a value of shearing strength, since the theoretical expression for the strength is $\frac{1}{2} \cos \phi (\sigma_{1f} - \sigma_{3f})$. This test is more empirical in nature than those previously discussed, but it is much simpler, it has been used much more than the others,

and there have been many more investigations into its dependability by its use in connection with analyses of actual shear
failures in nature. For these reasons some engineers are con-
vinced that this is the best type of test for general use.

15·21   Characteristic Differences between Results of Direct Shear and Cylindrical Compression Tests

A number of differences between the results of the two common
types of shear testing apparatus have already been stated or implied. As stated in Section 15·6, larger relative values of intermediate principal stress tend to give somewhat larger shearing
strength values in direct shear tests than are obtained in cylindrical compression tests. On the other hand progressive action occurs to a greater degree in direct shear tests than in cylindrical
compression tests, as stated in Section 14·8, and on this basis
strengths obtained in direct shear tests tend to be smaller than
those obtained in cylindrical compression tests. Failure must
occur on a definite plane in direct shear tests and, therefore,
strength values from such tests on isotropic soils tend to be somewhat larger than those from cylindrical compression tests in
which failure tends to occur on the weakest plane; this is especially true in soils containing minute fissures or any other such
tendency toward definite planes of weakness. In direct shear
tests in which an undrained condition is desired it is likely that
complete prevention of drainage will not be obtained; thus the
strength values obtained may be too large in a soil that is not
precompressed and may be too small in a highly precompressed
soil.

In a cylindrical compression test a small element of the specimen undergoes change in shape as shown in Fig. 15·15 (a); full
lines indicate the initial shape and dashed lines the final shape.
The planes within the soil which initially are principal planes
remain principal planes throughout the shearing process. This
type of strain, in which there is no rotation of principal planes,
is sometimes called *pure shear*. In a direct shear test the change
in shape of a small element of the specimen is as shown in Fig.
15·15 (b). The major principal planes are horizontal at the outset of the test, but during the shearing process they rotate through
an angle of roughly 60 degrees to reach the orientation shown

in Fig. 14·8. This type of strain is sometimes called *simple shear*. The essential difference between simple shear and pure shear is in the rotation or absence of rotation of principal planes. As far as is known, rotations have no appreciable effects on strengths, but an understanding of the two basic types of shear is needed for a clear visualization of the strain systems that occur in various types of soil problems.

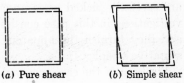

(*a*) Pure shear   (*b*) Simple shear

FIG. 15·15 Types of shear.

The differences mentioned above are the ones that are the most widely recognized at present, but future investigations may point out other differences that exist between the conditions of these two types of test and that cause appreciable differences in the shearing strength values they furnish. Relatively little dependable data which furnish quantitative demonstration of these differences are available at the present time.

15·22 Final Discussion of Determinations of Strength Envelopes

When investigations are being made for a given project at which a large mass of saturated clay will not be able to undergo an appreciable amount of drainage in case shear failure occurs, the shearing strength investigation will probably follow one or the other of the procedures reviewed in the two following paragraphs.

When the soil profile at a site shows highly irregular conditions and no clearly defined strata, it is likely that best results will be obtained simply by determination of the in situ shearing strength of each sample that it obtained. The strength values may then be inserted on the profile at the points from which the samples were taken to give a visual picture of the variations. In addition, the in situ strengths may be plotted against estimated in situ vertical pressures. If the points on such a plot are at all consistent with each other, an average apparent envelope can be chosen. If there is no noticeable trend toward greater strengths at greater pressures, then, no matter how consistent or how irregular the various points may be, an average strength, assumed to be constant and represented by a straight line envelope parallel to the σ axis, is the most reasonable choice.¶

When the main feature of the soil profile is a single, relatively homogeneous, saturated clay stratum, the testing program can usually be carried out to best advantage on a few samples that are carefully picked as representative of the stratum. The investigations in this case consist of consolidated-undrained tests, and they furnish the apparent envelope for each of the representative samples.

For both of the cases covered in the preceding paragraphs, the final results are apparent envelopes of the type of curve II of Fig. 15·10, the ordinates being the consolidation pressure.

For the common case of a clay in which a certain small amount of undissolved gas is present in the pore water, the determination of envelopes of the constant-water-content type is required in addition to the apparent envelopes.

For the case of a soil mass which drains completely, the laboratory investigations should consist of drained tests. Regardless of how uniform or how irregular the soil may be, the final results of the investigation will usually be in the form of an envelope of shearing strength versus the intergranular pressure on the plane of incipient failure.

The above discussion is based on the assumption that the entire mass is to be considered a single soil. If two or more distinctly different soil types exist in the mass, or if there are definitely different average characteristics in two or more portions of the soil profile, the section may be considered in its idealized form to consist of two or more soils.

¶ This horizontal type of envelope is not of uncommon occurrence. In reference 150 Terzaghi has called attention to the fact that the void ratio in many clays does not vary appreciably and, therefore, the strength does not vary with depth. In the closure discussion of reference 32, A. Casagrande has presented results of thorough investigations of Boston clays, showing that void ratios and, similarly, shearing strengths are approximately the same in the upper and lower portions of the deposit; he demonstrates that this condition is the result of precompression in the upper zones, caused by drying in past ages when the surface of the clay was above water. It is probable that precompression by drying at the surface of clay deposits is of more common occurrence than usually realized and, when the clay is underlain by a relatively pervious stratum with its pore water under usual pressures, precompressions of this type will not extend to the bottom of the clay.

In addition to the cases considered above, numerous combined and intermediate cases may occur. In addition to shearing strength investigations it may be necessary to carry out consolidation investigations for cases of partial drainage. Such cases present difficulties because drainage is often complete at the top surface or the top and bottom surfaces, whereas the degree of drainage at the center of the mass will vary greatly.

15·23 Coulomb's Empirical Law

After the strength envelope for a given soil under given conditions has been determined, a simplification is often introduced.

Let it be assumed that the envelope of Fig. 15·16 has been accepted as one that furnishes a satisfactory representation of average conditions within a soil mass. The abscissa of this plot is the effective pressure σ_e. The effective pressure is the intergranular pressure on the failure plane for cases of complete drainage, and it is the consolidation pressure, or under certain conditions it could be the applied pressure, for undrained cases in completely saturated or nearly saturated soils. For cases of partial drainage the effective pressure might represent pressures intermediate between consolidation pressures and intergranular pressures. It also is conceivable that under certain conditions some investigators might desire to express the shearing strength in terms of one of the principal stresses in accordance with equation 15·2, in which case the effective pressure might be an effective or a total principal stress. In short, the effective pressure has many possible meanings, and its meaning in any given case is greatly dependent on the conditions.

An envelope of the type shown in Fig. 15·16 may be closely approximated by a straight line for any given pressure range. In the range between pressures σ_a and σ_b a straight line that is a close representation of the envelope of this figure is shown by a heavy dashed line. Such a line could be represented by the empirical equation

$$s = A + \sigma_e B \qquad (15 \cdot 7)$$

in which A and B represent respectively the intercept at zero pressure and the slope of the straight line.

An equation which is of the form of equation 15·7 and which

has been widely used is commonly called Coulomb's Law.   It may be written

$$s = c_e + \sigma_e \tan \phi_e \tag{15·8}$$

in which c_e and ϕ_e usually are called, respectively, the *effective cohesion* and the *effective friction angle*.   Equations 15·7 and 15·8 must be viewed as empirical, and they are obviously the same except for different notations for coefficients.   It may well be claimed that it is poor policy to use the terms cohesion and

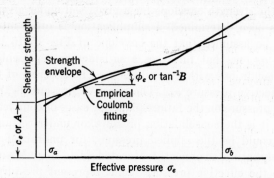

FIG. 15·16   Plot illustrating the rational interpretation of Coulomb's Empirical Law.

friction angle in this empirical sense for the coefficients A and B. However, this procedure is in such common use that it must be accepted.

The rational use of Coulomb's Law requires an understanding of the many complex factors affecting the shearing strength of clay; this important fact should be recognized by all engineers who use the expression.   It is of special importance that it be realized that c_e and ϕ_e are not constant soil properties but are empirical coefficients which may vary over wide ranges for a given soil under the various possible conditions of precompression, drainage, and other variables.   When the coefficients c_e and ϕ_e for a given case are determined by one organization or one department of an organization and are passed on to some other organization or department for use in stability analyses, it is essential that all data pertinent to the case be given with the coefficients.

Curves of the type shown in Fig. 15·16 are representative, in their simplest form, of the strength of a given soil when it has been subjected to a given magnitude of precompression. At different depths in a given soil deposit there usually are different amounts of precompression; thus a different envelope may hold for each different depth. Sometimes, however, the variation with depth is not large within a given deposit, and the envelope that is valid for an average depth may sometimes be accepted as representative of the entire strata.

A relatively thick clay layer in which the magnitude of the precompression varies considerably with depth is fairly common. Such a layer may be subdivided into several strata, for each of which a different envelope applies, and the use of several envelopes on this basis is sometimes the approach that must be used. If all of this group of envelopes is shown on one plot, however, and each envelope is shown by heavy lines over the range of pressures that may be expected to occur within the zone to which the envelope applies, it often is found that a composite envelope can be chosen which is reasonably representative of the entire clay layer.

When several different soils occur in a given soil mass it often will be necessary to use a different strength envelope for each soil. On occasions, however, the strata may have approximately the same characteristics, and it may be possible, as in the case covered in the previous paragraph, to determine a composite envelope that applies for the entire mass.

Coulomb's Law will be used in a number of types of analyses in the following chapters. Unless otherwise stated the effective pressure σ_e in all cases covered herein will represent either the intergranular pressure acting on the failure plane at the time of failure, or the pressure to which the soil has been consolidated before being subjected to shear, the pressure in either case being an intergranular pressure. In general, statements will not be made regarding which of these two meanings applies, since the application is generally the same for either meaning and the presentation of methods of analyses would only be confused by discussion of such subjects.

Procedures used in subsequent chapters should in no way be taken to imply that Coulomb's Law can be used correctly without previous, careful consideration of the factors discussed in this chapter, and it should be realized that in all cases the accuracy of stability analyses depends to a very large degree on the accuracy of the strength characteristics used in them.

PROBLEMS

1. In each of the following cases state which test, X or Y, should show the greater shearing strength. Except for the difference stated below the two tests are in each instance alike and on clay samples which are alike.

(*a*) The tests are run with no drainage allowed, and test Y is run much faster than test X.

(*b*) Sample Y is preconsolidated to a larger pressure than sample X; the pressures during the tests are alike for the two cases.

(*c*) Neither sample is preconsolidated; test X is allowed to drain during shear and test Y is not allowed to drain.

(*d*) Both samples are highly preconsolidated; test X is not allowed to drain and test Y is allowed to drain.

(*e*) Test Y is on a sample that is essentially in the undisturbed state and test X is on a specimen with appreciably disturbed structure but with the same void ratio as Y.

2. Investigations on a certain stiff clay show a somewhat lower shearing strength in drained tests than occur in tests with drainage prevented. Give an explanation of this behavior.

3. Laboratory tests on specimens from a completely saturated sample of clay have given the following data:

(*a*) The sample has in the past been precompressed to 2 tons per sq ft.

(*b*) A specimen tested in direct shear under a direct stress of 6 tons per sq ft, with complete drainage allowed, shows a shearing strength of 3.5 tons per sq ft.

(*c*) A specimen which is first consolidated to 6.0 tons per sq ft and then subjected to a direct shear test, in which no drainage occurs, shows a shearing strength of 1.75 tons per sq ft.

Compute the true friction angle and the apparent friction angle for the undrained case. Present carefully drawn sketches of the Mohr envelopes which you would expect to obtain from extensive series of undrained and drained tests on this sample.

4. Cylindrical compression tests have been run on specimens from a large sample of clay. Data are given below. In tests 1 to 4 inclusive, the tests were run so slowly that complete drainage may be assumed. In tests 5 to 8 inclusive, no drainage was permitted.

Test No.	1	2	3	4	5	6	7	8
$\sigma_1-\sigma_3$ at failure	4.47	1.67	0.95	0.37	3.31	1.55	1.33	1.19
$\bar{\sigma}_3$ at failure	2.46	0.89	0.36	0.06				
σ_c					4.81	2.31	1.31	0.53

Plot strength envelopes for this soil.

5. State Coulomb's Empirical Law for the shearing strength of a clay, explain its relationship to strength envelopes, and give the warnings that may be necessary to prevent incorrect understanding of this expression.

Chapter 16

STABILITY OF SLOPES

16·1 General Discussion of Stability

At all locations where the ground is not level there are forces acting which tend to cause movement of soil from high points to low points. The most important of such forces is the component of gravity that acts in the direction of probable motion. Also important, but not so well recognized, is the force of seeping water. Earthquakes occasionally contribute large forces.

These forces cause shearing stresses throughout the soil, and a mass movement occurs unless the shearing resistance on every possible surface through the mass is of sufficient magnitude to withstand these shearing stresses. The shearing resistance of the soil depends on factors discussed in Chapters 14 and 15, and also, on occasions, on such items as strength of roots, ice, and other materials which must be severed if there is to be a mass movement.

Near the ground surface the shearing strength of the soil may differ greatly during the various seasons of the year. Some surface soils swell during the rainy season, and during this season they have much lower strength than during the dry season. In cold countries where frost heaving occurs the soil may have a greatly lowered strength after the spring thaw. The study of strength changes of these types is difficult, and in many types of soils quantitative analyses of stability are possible only when the failure zone extends well into the ground. Deep in the ground there normally are some seasonal variations but they are sufficiently small to permit reasonably accurate estimates of the strength. The strengths which should be used in any analysis are of course those holding at the most unfavorable season of the year.

16·2   Effects of Water on Stability

The various effects of flowing or seeping water are generally recognized as very important in stability problems, but often these effects have not been properly identified.

It has already been mentioned that seepage occurring within a soil mass causes seepage forces, which have a much greater effect on stability than is commonly realized.

Erosion on the surface of a slope may be the cause of the removal of a certain weight of soil, and may thus lead to increased stability as far as mass movement is concerned. On the other hand, erosion in the form of undercutting at the toe may increase the height of the slope, or decrease the length of the incipient rupture surface, thus decreasing the stability.

When there is a lowering of the groundwater or of a free water surface adjacent to the slope—for example, in a drawdown of the water surface in a canal—there is a decrease in the buoyancy of the soil which is in effect an increase in the weight. This increase in weight causes increases in shearing stresses, that may or may not be in part counteracted by increases in shearing strength, depending on whether or not the soil is able to undergo the compressions which the load increase tends to cause. The ruling factor with reference to these compressions is the consolidation, which is still another effect of water. If a large mass of soil is saturated and is of low permeability, practically no volume changes will be able to occur except at a very slow rate, and in spite of increases of load the strength increases may be inappreciable.

Shear at constant volume may be accompanied by a decrease in the intergranular pressure and an increase in the neutral pressure, as shown in Fig. 14·6. A failure may be caused by such a condition, in which the entire soil mass passes into a state of liquefaction and flows like a fluid. A somewhat similar action may occur in certain thin strata of weakness within the mass, and may produce failure on the weak strata.

The various effects that have been cited in the foregoing paragraphs are sometimes said to be caused by *lubrication*. This term may be acceptable in some instances, but often it does not describe the true action adequately. A more rational point of view results if the various phenomena are explained in terms of inter-granular and neutral pressures; swelling, for example, is simply volume increase which leads to decreased intergranular pressure. Thus the general term lubrication is seldom used in this book.

16·3   Soil-Creep

Near the ground surface on any hillside or any earth slope the soil is subjected to cycles of expansion and contraction. These cycles may be due to temperature variation, to alternate wetting

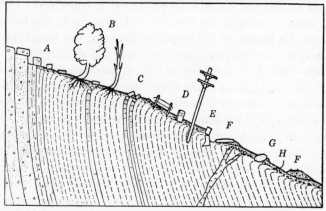

Fig. 16·1   Common evidences of creep. *A*, moved joint blocks; *B*, trees with curved trunks concave upslope; *C*, downslope bending and drag of bedded rock, weathered veins, etc., also present beneath soil elsewhere on the slope; *D*, displaced posts, poles, and monuments; *E*, broken or displaced retaining walls and foundations; *F*, roads and railroads moved out of alignment; *G*, turf rolls downslope from creeping boulders; *H*, stone line at approximate base of creeping soil. *A* and *C* represent *rock-creep;* all other features shown are due to *soil-creep*. Rather similar effects may be produced by some types of landslides. (Reproduced from Sharpe, *Landslides and Related Phenomena,* by permission of Columbia University Press.)

and drying, and in cold climates to frost heaving and subsequent thawing. During expansion the soil rises in opposition to the force of gravity; during contraction the soil subsides, aided by gravity. The net result is a slow motion in the downhill direction. The movement is somewhat analogous to that of a brick placed on a tin roof which has a slight pitch. There is no slipping, but over a period of weeks or months the brick may be observed to be moving slowly down the roof.

The depth of the creep zone may vary from a few inches to perhaps several feet, depending on the soil properties and the weather conditions. The creep will be the more pronounced the greater the volume changes that occur in the soil, and for this reason it is most noticeable in soils that are highly compressible and that also have relatively high permeability.

The phenomenon known as creep does not in general involve rupture or failure of a slope. Whether or not creep is considered a lack of stability depends largely on the exact definition chosen for the word stability.

Engineers must be concerned with creep because of its effect on pipe lines, on bench marks, and on roads, railroads, and walls which are on or just at the foot of a slope. The common evidences of creep are shown in Fig. 16·1.

16·4 Slides Not Readily Susceptible to Analysis

There are a number of types of slides which are of interest to engineers but which engineers find difficult if not impossible to analyze quantitatively. The reason is that the shearing strengths involved cannot be determined with any reasonable degree of accuracy. A few types of such slides are discussed briefly below.

On a slope with heavy vegetation the creep will be resisted somewhat by tension in the roots. This tension increases gradually, sometimes for years, until some individual root fails in tension. If the surrounding roots are unable to carry the extra load this throws upon them, a landslide is likely to result. This type of spontaneous landslide is commonest in tropical countries where the creep tends to be large and also where vegetation is heavy.

There are flow slides or flow failures of numerous types. A granular soil which is looser than the critical density by a sufficient amount may pass into a state of complete liquefaction if failure once starts, or it may be thrown into a liquid state by some shock, such as an earth tremor. A clay of the type which shows large loss of strength when remolded may similarly pass into a virtually fluid state once a failure starts. Flow slides of these types occur rapidly, and the mass which moves may continue to flow to low ground a considerable distance away. Analyses for the determination of critical void ratios in sands, and investigations of strengths by undrained tests on clays may be used in some cases for quantitative studies of such slides, but satisfactory accuracies in such studies are not always obtainable.

Many interesting examples of flow slides of various types come

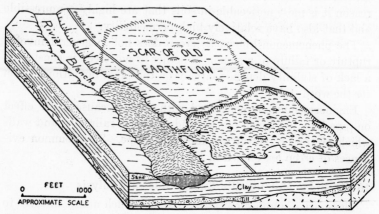

FIG. 16·2 Example of earthflow. Earthflow of 1898 near St. Thuribe, Rivière Blanche, Quebec. A large area of the terrace surface moved into the river through a 200-foot gap, leaving an irregular depression 15 to 30 ft deep containing large blocks of clay stranded there when movement ceased. When visited in 1935 the site of this earthflow had assumed much the appearance of the prehistoric earthflow scar immediately adjoining it on the north. Clay blocks and scarps had weathered to rounded hummocks or gentle slopes, and the river had removed the earthflow dam. The road and fences had been reconstructed many years before, and the land had been returned to farming. (Drawn in part from map of Wilson and MacKay and photographs by Dawson; reproduced from Sharpe, *Landslides and Related Phenomena*, by permission of Columbia University Press.)

from all parts of the world. In sands which naturally have very loose packing any sudden occurrence of strain may lead to almost complete liquefaction, occasionally in slopes as flat as 5 or 10 degrees, and may cause slides of large extent. It is reported that the coast of Holland is especially susceptible to slides of this nature. In masses of rock on the side slopes of glacial valleys in Switzerland flow slides known as *müren* occur, and it is said that they carry quantities of rock long distances down the valley.

Figure 16·2 shows an unusual earthflow which was probably initiated by a small failure in relatively stiff soil at the river bank.

The various types of flow slides have been studied by geologists, and classifications have been proposed. However, these classifications are not very adaptable to engineering uses. In geological terminology rapid flow slides are often termed *earthflows* or *mudflows*. Flow slides that occur slowly and that are commonest in cold climates or at high altitudes and often are associated with frost action are termed *solifluction*.*

Slopes in fissured clays, which have been subjected to softening by water as discussed in Section 15·2, can seldom be analyzed for stability with any satisfactory degree of accuracy.

16·5 General Considerations and the Idealized Conditions Used in Analyses

The engineer must deal with many practical problems in which earth slopes are involved and in which it is important that he have as good information as can be obtained regarding the stability of the slopes. Common examples include the slopes in both cut and fill along railroads and highways, the banks of canals or other streams, the slopes of earth dams, slopes maintained during many types of construction operations, and natural slopes which are adjacent to valuable properties.

Such slopes can be analyzed for stability and reasonable results can be obtained if the geological cross section is known and if the shearing strength can be determined with satisfactory accuracy. Cases will arise in which the accuracy of results is limited by lack of knowledge of strata thicknesses and of groundwater elevations and pressures. However, in the great majority of thorough analyses the accuracy of the results depends mainly on the accuracy with which the shearing strength can be predicted. There are times when shearing strengths can be determined with good accuracy, but the discussion in Chapter 15 indicates that there are cases in which a high degree of accuracy is not possible.

Many factors introduce complications into stability analyses. Most embankments contain heterogeneous soils, often of several

* Such slides are discussed in detail in reference 129.

types. In most cases there are a number of questions that cannot be answered regarding the variables that affect the shearing strengths of the soils. The boundary conditions which define the flow net and thus determine the neutral pressures are sometimes known only roughly.

These and other complications usually necessitate the use of a simplified cross section that is as nearly representative of the actual, average cross section as can be obtained, but that is free of minor irregularities and other unimportant details. At the same time it often is necessary to adopt simplified, average soil characteristics which are as good a representation of the actual variable characteristics as can be obtained. Those steps which bear on the choice of the simplified section and the simplified soil characteristics are always important in stability analysis work. These steps are independent, however, of the actual carrying out of the analysis.

From this point on, simplified conditions only will be considered, since the main object herein is to explain methods of attack once the conditions are known. It should be realized that the time required for actual analyses, in which many small details enter and numerous alternate possibilities often need consideration, may be many times that indicated by the simple examples which follow.

Simplified conditions and assumptions that are used in the cases treated in this chapter follow:

1. An average or typical cross section is used. It is assumed that no shearing stresses act on the plane of the section and, therefore, that a two-dimensional case exists. The mass that is analyzed is of unit dimension in the direction normal to the section, and the section is assumed to be made up of uniform soils, each having constant properties. In most cases the entire mass is assumed to be composed of one type of uniform soil.

2. It is assumed that the shearing strength of each individual soil occurring in the cross section may be represented by an expression in the form of Coulomb's Empirical Law:

$$s = c_e + \bar{\sigma} \tan \phi_e$$

wherein c_e and ϕ_e are the effective cohesion and the effective friction angle, respectively, that apply for each soil under the existing conditions. As explained in Section 15·23, the normal pressure $\bar{\sigma}$ in all cases considered herein is intergranular pressure on the failure plane, but it may be either the intergranular pressure at failure or the pressure to which the soil has been consolidated, depending on whether drainage does or does not occur under the existing conditions.

3. It is assumed that the groundwater conditions and pressures, as represented by a given flow net, are known. The intergranular pressure used in the shearing strength expression is obtained by deducting the neutral pressure, which is given at any point by the flow net, from the total pressure existing at that point.

All stability analyses are based on the concept that an embankment fails unless the resultant resistance to shear on every surface traversing the embankment is greater than the resultant of all shearing forces exerted on that surface by the mass above. The surface which is most liable to fail is called the *critical surface*. Determination of its location is sometimes simple, but sometimes it requires a tedious process of successive trials. Sometimes there is a sharply defined surface of rupture, as with brittle clays and dense sands. On other occasions failure occurs throughout a zone of plastic flow, this often being the case in soft clays. This point needs no further discussion, however, since any one of the many failure planes through a zone that is in the plastic state serves satisfactorily as the critical surface.

The commonest type of stability analysis consists in brief of the following steps: The resultant of all forces acting on the mass above the critical surface is determined. Included in this resultant force are the weight of the mass, the force due to water effects, and sometimes certain other forces. Herein this resultant force is called the *actuating force*. If there is to be stability, a resultant *resisting force* must exist which is of sufficient magnitude to counterbalance the actuating force. The available resisting force is made up of the total cohesion on the critical surface, the resultant of all normal pressure acting across this surface onto the mass above, and all friction that this pressure is capable of developing. The sum of the cohesion and the friction per unit of area at any point is the shearing strength, which is expressed by Coulomb's Empirical Law. The main step of the analysis is the comparison of the magnitudes of the actuating force and the available resisting force.

It will be assumed that before failure can occur the shearing strains at all points of the critical surface must be large enough to mobilize all available shearing strength. On this basis considerations of magnitudes of shearing strains are unnecessary in stability analyses. Progressive effects of the type discussed in Section 14·8 will occur, but it will be assumed that allowance has been made for this by the use of sufficiently conservative values of coefficients in Coulomb's Law.

16·6 Factors of Safety

Much criticism has been leveled in the past at improper use of *factors of safety* and the incomplete definitions that have sometimes been given for such factors. However, any quantitative stability analysis must make use of some measure of the degree of safety. It must be realized that many types of failure are possible with respect to a system as a whole and also that many types are possible with respect to individual points or individual parts of the system. It thus appears that there is no such thing as *the* factor of safety and that when *a* factor of safety is used its meaning should be clearly defined. For this reason considerable care will be used in defining the factors of safety used herein.

As an example let it be assumed that an embankment is to be designed of soil that under the given conditions has the strength characteristics

$$c_e = 600 \text{ lb per sq ft}; \quad \phi_e = 15 \text{ degrees}$$

In order to give a margin of safety it is specified that the working values must be smaller than those given above. The working values may be defined as the largest values that may be developed or mobilized; for all practical purposes it may be supposed that the soil cannot withstand greater shearing stresses than those represented by the working values. In order to present as general a case as possible it will first be assumed that different margins of safety are desired for the two components of shearing strength, and the working values for this example will be taken as

$$c_d = 400 \text{ lb per sq ft}; \quad \phi_d = 12 \text{ degrees}$$

When the embankment has been constructed according to these specifications the shearing stress on the critical surface may be written

$$\tau = c_d + \bar{\sigma} \tan \phi_d \qquad (16 \cdot 1)$$

in which c_d is the average value of developed cohesion and ϕ_d is the average value of developed friction angle. Actually the shearing resistances do not develop to like degree at all points of an incipient failure surface. The shearing strains vary considerably, and the shearing stresses may be far from constant, in accordance with progressive action, as discussed in Section $14 \cdot 8$. However, the above expression is correct on the basis of average conditions.

The factors of safety that are used in the considerations given above may be expressed

$$F_c = \frac{c_e}{c_d} \quad \text{and} \quad F_\phi = \frac{\tan \phi_e}{\tan \phi_d} \qquad (16 \cdot 2)$$

in which F_c is the average factor of safety for the cohesional component of strength and F_ϕ is the average factor of safety for the frictional component of strength. In this example

$$F_c = \frac{600}{400} = 1.5 \quad \text{and} \quad F_\phi = \frac{0.268}{0.212} = 1.26$$

Let it now be assumed that an embankment has been designed on this basis and that the average value of direct intergranular pressure on the critical surface through the embankment is 2300 lb per sq ft. On this basis the average shearing strength on the critical surface is

$$600 + 2300 \times 0.268 = 1216 \text{ lb per sq ft}$$

and the average value of shearing stress on the critical surface is

$$400 + 2300 \times 0.212 = 889 \text{ lb per sq ft}$$

It may now be noted that the values of F_c and F_ϕ that were used for the design are not the only possible combination of these factors for this embankment. A combination of F_c and F_ϕ values that would usually be preferable to the one considered above is that in which the two factors have the same value. This combination may be defined as follows. For the case in which equal values of F_c and F_ϕ are desired, F_c and F_ϕ are designated by F_s and

$$F_s = \frac{c_e}{c_d} = \frac{\tan \phi_e}{\tan \phi_d} = \frac{s}{\tau} \qquad (16\cdot3)$$

in which F_s is the *factor of safety with respect to shearing strength*. Its value in the example is

$$F_s = \tfrac{1\,2\,1\,6}{8\,8\,9} = 1.37$$

Of the unlimited number of possible combinations of F_c and F_ϕ values that could apply in this case a few follow.

| F_c | 1.00 | 1.26 | 1.37 | 1.50 | 2.20 |
| F_ϕ | 2.13 | 1.50 | 1.37 | 1.26 | 1.00 |

It should be mentioned that the location of the critical surface through any given embankment is not exactly the same for different combinations of F_c and F_ϕ, but this detail is of little importance in the present considerations.

In the final combination of values given in the above table F_c equals 2.20 and F_ϕ equals unity. The value 2.20 may be defined as the ratio between the actual cohesion and the cohesion required for stability with full friction mobilized, this ratio sometimes being called the *factor of safety with respect to cohesion*. According to an important relationship, which will be demonstrated in subsequent sections, the cohesion required for stability is directly proportional to the height of the slope. From this it may be concluded that the factor of safety with respect to cohesion is equal to a more significant quantity called the *factor of safety with respect to height*. This factor is designated by F_H, and it is the ratio between the *critical height* and the *actual height*, the critical height being the maximum height at which it is possible for the slope to be stable. This case may be expressed as shown below.

For the case in which F_ϕ is arbitrarily taken equal to unity, F_c becomes equal to F_H and

$$F_H = \frac{c_e}{c_d} \quad \text{and} \quad \tau = \frac{c_e}{F_H} + \bar{\sigma} \tan \phi_e \qquad (16\cdot4)$$

The cross section of the example used in this section would be thrown into a condition of incipient failure if the shearing strength

were suddenly divided by F_s or 1.37. Failure would also be incipient if the cohesional strength were suddenly divided by 2.20, or
if the height were suddenly multiplied by F_H, which equals 2.20.
These statements can be reworded to give alternate definitions
of safety factors that in some respects are preferable to those
previously given. For example, F_s may be defined as the factor
by which the shearing strength would have to be divided to give
the condition of incipient failure.

The general formulas which are developed later in this chapter
are relationships between the height and the inclination of the
slope, the unit weight of the soil, and the developed average values
of the soil coefficients c_d and ϕ_d. Factors of safety do not appear
in these expressions. However, when c_d and ϕ_d values have been
determined by an analysis of the cross section and c_e and ϕ_e values
have been obtained by laboratory investigations, factors of safety
may be computed by the use of expression $16 \cdot 2$, $16 \cdot 3$, or $16 \cdot 4$.
If c_d and ϕ_d are thought of merely as average developed values,
then it must be recognized that an approximation is introduced
into results of analyses by fluctuations above and below the average
values. However, this approximation is due only to variations
of distributional nature, and it is of minor importance, as explained
in the discussion of distributional assumptions in Section $16 \cdot 16$.
It may be noted that when the viewpoint of the previous paragraph is adopted and use is made of the alternate definition of
safety factor suggested therein, c_d and ϕ_d are not subject to fluctuations.

The value 1.37 for the factor of safety with respect to shearing
strength may appear to be small when compared with safety
factors used in designs in steel and other structural materials.
When the low degree of dependable accuracy in shearing strength
determinations in soils is considered, this value may appear even
smaller. It is a typical value, however, and many embankments,
which according to engineering experience are safe, have safety
factors smaller than this value. The fact that the usual margin
of safety that can be specified in stability analyses is often no
larger than the probable amount of inherent error in the procedures
used is alone sufficient to show that soil mechanics is not an exact
science.

16·7   Infinite and Finite Slopes

The analysis of two types of cross sections will be covered in considerable detail in this chapter. These two types will be designated as the *infinite slope* and the *simple slope*.

The term *infinite slope* is used to designate a constant slope of unlimited extent which has constant conditions and constant soil properties at any given distance below the surface of the slope. In the cases considered the soil will often be assumed to be ho-

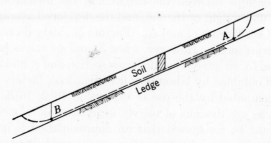

Fᴵɢ. 16·3 Slope of great extent which usually may be considered an infinite slope.

mogeneous, but an infinite slope may consist of numerous strata of different soils as long as all strata boundaries are parallel to the surface of the slope. Any vertical column of soil within the infinite slope is thus by definition the same as any other vertical column in all respects.

No slope exists that truly extends infinitely without variation, but at many sites there are slopes of considerable extent, over which the conditions on all verticals may be adequately represented by an average condition. Such a case may be studied on the infinite slope basis, which consists in treating a vertical column of the material as typical of the entire mass. An example of such a slope is shown in Fig. 16·3. Any mass movement of this slope usually involves dimensions parallel to the slope which are many times greater than the depth to ledge. The boundary of a possible failure mass is indicated by a dashed line. The typical column, shown shaded, may be taken as representative of the entire mass for ordinary estimates. For detailed studies it may sometimes be necessary to introduce a small correction to care for conditions at the extremities of the rupture surface where the depth is not constant.

Slopes which are of finite extent are illustrated by Fig. 16·13 and subsequent figures. In such slopes the statics of the entire failure mass must be considered, the relationships are more complex, and analyses are more involved.

The simple case, in which the ground is level at the foot of the slope and at the top of the slope and the sloping surface is of constant inclination, is illustrated by Fig. 16·14; it is called the *simple slope*.

16·8   Conjugate Stresses within the Infinite Slope

In Fig. 16·4, AB is the surface of a slope of infinite extent, with an inclination i, and made up of homogeneous soil. At any two points that are at equal depths, such as C and D, the stress conditions must be the same. Thus the stresses at various depths on

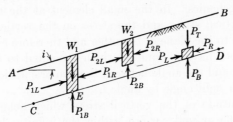

Fig. 16·4   Conjugate stresses in the infinite slope.

any vertical plane must be the same as those at corresponding depths on any other vertical plane.

Consider a column of soil bounded by the ground surface, a plane parallel to the ground surface, and two vertical planes. Assume unit length in the third dimension. The four forces which act on this column and which must be in equilibrium are the weight W_1, the total force across the base of the column P_{1B}, and the total forces P_{1L} and P_{1R} across the sides of the column. For reasons stated above, forces P_{1L} and P_{1R} are of the same magnitude and must have parallel lines of action. The line of action of vector W_1 must pass through point E, the mid-point of the base. Since stresses are alike at C and D and at all intermediate points, P_{1B} is made up of a constant base pressure and therefore it also passes through E. The summation of the moments of the four forces about point E must equal zero, but only P_{1L} and P_{1R} exert moments about this point; thus P_{1L} and P_{1R}, which were previously shown to have the same magnitude, are now seen to give counterbalancing moments. It may be concluded that P_{1L} and P_{1R} must have a common line of action which is parallel to ground surface. Since P_{1L} and P_{1R} just balance each other it follows that W_1 and P_{1B} also are equal and opposite. Thus all the four sides of the column of soil considered and all the four forces acting on the column have directions which are either vertical or parallel to the slope. The column shown in the figure with forces designated by subscripts 2 is similar to the first except for its depth. The small element shown to the right is the difference between the two columns, and it represents a typical element at any depth. All forces and all sides of these figures are also either vertical or parallel to the slope.

The characteristics of conjugate stresses are explained in textbooks on mechanics. In the small element at the right in Fig. 16·4 the vertical stress and the stress on the vertical plane are each parallel to the plane of the other and therefore are conjugate stresses. Both have obliquities which are equal to the angle of inclination i, and the angle between the two orientations of planes differs from a right angle by angle i.

The magnitude of the vertical stress which acts on a plane parallel to the ground surface within the infinite slope may be easily expressed. The weight above the surface AB in Fig. 16·5 is $\gamma zb \cos i$, and this weight divided by the area b over which it acts gives

$$p_v = \gamma z \cos i \qquad (16 \cdot 5)$$

Acting on the vertical plane with a line of action parallel to the ground surface is the lateral pressure p_l which is conjugate to p_v. This pressure has a wide range of possible values, as shown in the following section.

The above discussion is valid for any soil. It holds for a dry soil, in which all forces considered are intergranular forces and γ in equation 16·5 is the dry unit weight. It applies equally well to a mass which is saturated throughout and has seepage occurring throughout. Under such conditions the forces considered are a combination of intergranular and neutral forces, the pressure p_v of equation 16·5 is a combined pressure, and the unit weight value in this expression is the total unit weight γ_t.

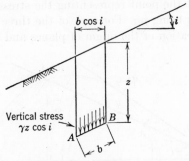

FIG. 16·5 Representative element used for the derivation of the expression for vertical stress.

16·9 The Range of Possible Lateral Pressures in a Cohesionless Infinite Slope without Seepage

The range of possible lateral pressures may be determined from the Mohr diagram. The determination for the simple case of cohesionless soil without seepage is explained in this section. Cohesive soil and soil in which seepage occurs are discussed in subsequent sections.

In Fig. 16·6 the distance OA represents the vertical stress p_v, as expressed by equation 16·5 for some given depth below the surface of a 25-degree slope. The line OA is at a slope of 25 degrees, since p_v has the obliquity i. Strength envelopes for a friction angle of 35 degrees are also shown in the figure. The Mohr stress circle for the given point must have its center on the σ axis and must pass through point A; the only other requirement is that the stress circle must not cross the strength envelope. The circle meeting these requirements and having the smallest possible value of minor principal stress is that shown with its center at point C_1, the one with the largest possible value of minor principal stress is that shown with its center at point C_3; the other circle shown is one of the infinite number of possible intermediate cases.

The origin of planes for each of the circles may be obtained by the method presented in Section 13·4. Through point A, which represents the stress p_v, a line is drawn parallel to the plane on which p_v acts, which is at the slope i, to intersect the Mohr circle at the origin of planes O_P. A vertical through the origin of planes cuts the circle at the point representing the stress on the vertical plane, this stress being p_l. For each of the three Mohr circles in Fig. 16·6 the location of the origin of planes and the p_l value are

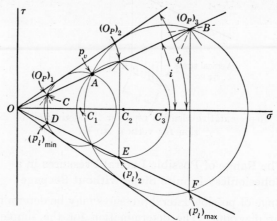

FIG. 16·6 Mohr diagram illustrating the range of possible lateral pressures in the infinite slope.

shown. The maximum and minimum values of p_l are so labeled. At each origin of planes the orientations of principal planes are indicated by short full lines emanating from the origin. For the two limiting cases the orientations of failure planes are shown by short dashed lines.

The minimum lateral pressure $(p_l)_{min}$ is known as the *active pressure*. The maximum lateral pressure $(p_l)_{max}$ is known as the *passive pressure*. The significance of active and passive pressures will be discussed in considerable detail in Chapter 17.

The ratio between the magnitudes of the conjugate stresses is called the conjugate ratio. A general expression for the conjugate ratio may be determined from the Mohr diagram. In Fig. 16·7 this ratio is OB/OA which equals OB'/OA; also

$$\frac{OB}{OA} = \frac{OD - DB'}{OD + DA}$$

whereas

$$OD = OC \cos \alpha$$

$$DA = DB' = \sqrt{r^2 - (DC)^2}$$

$$r = OC \sin \alpha_m$$

and

$$DC = OC \sin \alpha$$

The substitution of these expressions into the initial expression for OB/OA and the use of the identity $\cos^2 \alpha = 1 - \sin^2 \alpha$ gives

$$\frac{OB}{OA} = \frac{\cos \alpha - \sqrt{\cos^2 \alpha - \cos^2 \alpha_m}}{\cos \alpha + \sqrt{\cos^2 \alpha - \cos^2 \alpha_m}} \qquad (16 \cdot 6)$$

Equation $16 \cdot 6$ is the general expression for the ratio between the smaller and the larger of any pair of conjugate stresses.

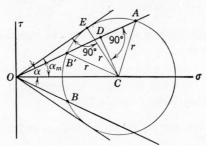

FIG. 16·7 Mohr diagram used for the derivation of the conjugate ratio.

When the above equation is applied to the infinite slope case, α becomes the slope i, and when applied to the limiting or ϕ-obliquity case, α_m becomes equal to ϕ. Moreover, in Fig. $16 \cdot 6$

$$\frac{OC}{OA} = \frac{OA}{OB}$$

and

$$OC = OD = (p_l)_{\min}; \quad OA = p_v; \quad OB = OF = (p_l)_{\max}$$

giving

$$\frac{(p_l)_{\min}}{p_v} = \frac{p_v}{(p_l)_{\max}} \qquad (16 \cdot 7)$$

The left- and the right-hand sides of equation 16·7 are conjugate ratios for the active and passive cases, respectively. In both of these cases a ϕ-obliquity condition exists, and therefore they are represented by the conjugate ratio of equation 16·6 with the modification stated below that equation; the following equation results:

$$\frac{(p_l)_{\min}}{p_v} = \frac{p_v}{(p_l)_{\max}} = \frac{\cos i - \sqrt{\cos^2 i - \cos^2 \phi}}{\cos i + \sqrt{\cos^2 i - \cos^2 \phi}} \qquad (16 \cdot 8)$$

For the special case in which the angle i equals zero, the conjugate stresses become principal stresses and the conjugate ratio becomes the principal stress ratio. This special form of equation 16·8 is a much more familiar expression to the average engineer than the general equation. For this special case of *zero slope*, the conjugate ratio is

$$\frac{1 - \sin \phi}{1 + \sin \phi} \quad \text{or} \quad \tan^2 (45 - \tfrac{1}{2}\phi) \qquad (16 \cdot 9)$$

16·10 The Significance of the Range of Possible Lateral Pressures

If as typical values a friction angle of 35 degrees and a vertical pressure p_v of 1 ton per sq ft is assumed, it is found from equation 16·8 that when i equals 25 degrees

$(p_l)_{\min} = 0.40$ ton per sq ft   and $(p_l)_{\max} = 2.5$ tons per sq ft

and when i equals 0 degrees

$(p_l)_{\min} = 0.27$ ton per sq ft   and $(p_l)_{\max} = 3.7$ tons per sq ft

An understanding of the reason for these large ranges of lateral pressures and of the conditions under which each of the limiting values occur is most important in soil mechanics. The case of i equal to zero will be considered in the following discussion, since the explanation is somewhat easier for this simple case.

Assume that two cubes of sand have a friction angle of 35 degrees and assume a pressure of 1 ton per sq ft acting initially on all faces. These cubes are shown by full lines in Fig. 16·8. Assume now that the lateral pressure of cube (a) is decreased; conditions corresponding to a cylindrical compression test run under decreasing lateral pressure will result. When the lateral pressure has been reduced to 0.27 ton per sq ft, a ϕ-obliquity condition is reached and it is known from the discussion of this type of test that the vertical dimension of the cube must have decreased and the lateral dimension must have increased. Similarly, if the lateral pressure is increased on the other cube while the vertical pressure remains constant, a ϕ-obliquity condition will be reached when the lateral pressure is 3.7 tons per sq ft. Meanwhile the lateral dimensions must decrease and the vertical dimension must increase as shown in (*b*).

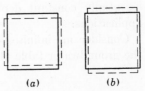

(*a*)   (*b*)

Fig. 16·8 Diagrams showing the distortions required for (*a*) active and (*b*) passive conditions.

From these considerations the following conclusions may be stated. If a ϕ-obliquity condition exists in a soil mass and the lateral pressures are smaller than the vertical pressures, lateral expansion and vertical compression must have occurred during the history of the soil. If there is a ϕ-obliquity condition and the lateral pressure is larger than the vertical pressure, lateral compression and vertical expansion must have occurred in the past.

In detailed analyses of slopes that have failed the concepts explained above are very valuable. They are also of prime importance in retaining wall studies; they will be considered further in Chapter 17. In Fig. 16·6 the orientations of failure planes for the two limiting cases are shown by dashed lines at points $(O_P)_1$ and $(O_P)_3$. Failure on these orientations of planes would have to be accompanied by lateral strains of the types described above, and these strains would have to extend to infinite depth.

Actually, the failures of infinite slopes that are considered in this chapter are of the type shown in Fig. 16·3, and the main portions of the failure surfaces are essentially parallel to ground surface. On these failure surfaces the obliquity of stress is the angle i. Therefore, in the usual considerations of stability it may be said that an infinite slope in granular soil with no seepage is stable if i is less than ϕ. In connection with this criterion it is not necessary to consider the strains that have occurred. A cohesive slope may be stable with i greater than ϕ, but in this case certain depth limitations must be considered.

16·11   Stresses within an Infinite Cohesionless Slope with Seepage Occurring

The treatment of the seepage case given in this section can be justified solely because it serves as a means of explaining a number of important concepts relative to seepage and neutral pressures. However, many natural slopes exist in cohesionless soil where the slopes are of considerable extent and have groundwater tables at essentially constant depths; thus this case has many practical applications.

Consider an infinite, cohesionless slope of inclination i with the groundwater table at ground surface, as shown in Fig. 16·9.

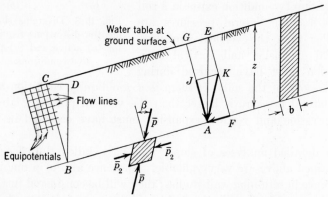

FIG. 16·9   Stresses in an infinite slope with seepage throughout.

According to equation 16·5 the combined vertical pressure on planes parallel to the slope is $\gamma_t z \cos i$, whence the normal component of p_v is $\gamma_t z \cos^2 i$ and the shearing component is $\gamma_t z \sin i \cos i$.

If the same conditions are to exist at all vertical lines, it is necessary that all flow lines be parallel to ground surface. Assuming that the soil either is isotropic or, if non-isotropic, that the maximum permeability is in the direction parallel to the slope, it follows that equipotential lines are normal to the slope. Line BC is an equipotential line of length $z \cos i$ and the pressure head at B is the distance BD, equal to $z \cos^2 i$. Thus the neutral pressure at depth z is $\gamma_w z \cos^2 i$. Subtraction of this pressure from the combined direct pressure on surface AB gives the intergranular direct pressure $(\gamma_t - \gamma_w) z \cos^2 i$. Thus

$$\bar{\sigma} = \gamma_b z \cos^2 i$$

$$\tau = \gamma_t z \sin i \cos i \qquad (16 \cdot 10)$$

in which $\bar{\sigma}$ and τ are the components of intergranular stress on the plane parallel to the surface of the slope.

If the combined resultant pressure on surface AB is shown by vector EA, which is of length z, other stresses are as follows: the combined normal stress is GA; the intergranular normal stress is GA times γ_b/γ_t or approximately one-half GA, and it is represented by JA; the shearing stress is entirely intergranular, and it is represented by FA; the resultant intergranular stress on plane AB is KA.

According to the definition of conjugate stresses, the stress which is conjugate to KA must act on a plane parallel to KA; it is stress $\bar{p}_2$ in the figure. For this case in which seepage occurs parallel to the slope throughout the mass the magnitude of the resultant intergranular pressure $\bar{p}$ of Fig. 16·9 and its obliquity β may be expressed

$$\bar{p} = \gamma_b z \cos i \sqrt{1 + \sin^2 i \left[\left(\frac{\gamma_t}{\gamma_b} \right)^2 - 1 \right]}$$

and $\qquad (16 \cdot 11)$

$$\beta = \tan^{-1} \left[\frac{\gamma_t}{\gamma_b} \tan i \right]$$

The ranges of values of the conjugate intergranular pressure $\bar{p}_2$, of the intergranular pressure $\bar{p}_l$ on the vertical plane, and of pressures on all other planes through the slope shown in Fig. 16·9 are given by the Mohr diagram of Fig. 16·10.

Under the conditions represented in Fig. 16·9, stability is not possible unless angle β is less than the friction angle, ϕ. As an example, let it be assumed that a certain saturated, cohesionless soil has a total unit weight of 120 lb per cu ft and a friction angle of 35 degrees. In this soil the steepest infinite slope that can be stable, when there is seepage throughout, is given by equation 16·11 as

$$i = \tan^{-1} \frac{120 - 62.5}{120} \tan 35 = 18\tfrac{1}{2}°$$

16·12   Alternative Solution in Terms of Seepage Forces

In Section 9·18 it was demonstrated that the resultant of gravity and seepage forces could be determined in either of two ways: by a combination of total weight and boundary neutral force or by a combination of submerged weight and seepage force.

In the previous section the first of these methods was utilized, because the total weight and the neutral pressure at the plane in

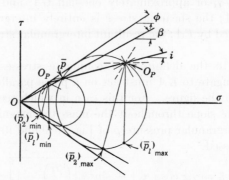

Fig. 16·10   Mohr diagram showing the ranges of lateral pressures and conjugate pressures in an infinite slope with seepage throughout.

question were considered. In order to show that the procedure used takes full account of the effects of seepage, the determination in terms of seepage forces will now be demonstrated.

It was shown in Section 9·18 that the seepage force per unit of volume is expressed by $i_h\gamma_w$, the hydraulic gradient here being designated by i_h to distinguish it from the slope i. The hydraulic gradient in the example of the previous section is $\sin i$. Assuming unity for the dimension b in Fig. 16·9, the volume of the shaded column is $z \cos i$, and the total seepage force in this volume is $\gamma_w z \sin i \cos i$. This force is in the downhill direction parallel to the surface AB. The submerged weight is $\gamma_b z \cos i$. Its component normal to AB is $\gamma_b z \cos^2 i$, which is the direct component of intergranular pressure on AB. The component parallel to AB is $\gamma_b z \sin i \cos i$, which combines with the seepage force $\gamma_w z \sin i \cos i$ to give the shearing component of intergranular pressure $\gamma_t z \sin i \cos i$. These components agree with equations 16·10.

16·13 Stability of Cohesive Infinite Slopes

In an infinite slope with no seepage the pressure on a plane parallel to the surface is equal to $\gamma z \cos i$ and was represented by OA in Fig. 16·6. This stress is similarly represented by OA in Fig. 16·11. The direct stress on this plane is represented by OD and the shearing stress by DA.

In a cohesive soil with a shearing strength that is expressed by

$$s = c_e + \bar{\sigma} \tan \phi_e$$

the strength envelope may be represented by the line BC of Fig. 16·11. According to this line the shearing strength is DC when the direct stress is OD.

If i is less than ϕ_e, the two lines of the types shown in Fig. 16·11 do not intersect and failure cannot occur on planes parallel to ground surface. If i is greater than ϕ_e, as in Fig. 16·11, the shearing stresses on planes parallel to the slope are smaller than the shearing strengths when the depths are small, and at these depths there is no danger of failure. This relationship is illustrated by shearing strength DC, which is larger than shearing stress DA. However, at some critical depth there are equal values of shearing strength

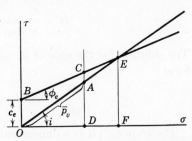

Fig. 16·11 Mohr diagram illustrating the limited depth within which there is stability in a clay slope, when the slope angle is greater than the effective friction angle.

and shearing stress, as represented by FE, and failure is incipient. At depths greater than this critical value the figure indicates that the shearing stresses would be greater than the shearing strengths, but this is not possible. Therefore, it may be concluded that the slope may be steeper than ϕ_e as long as the depth of soil is less than the critical depth, and ledge or some other material with a sufficiently large strength exists below the soil. Similarly, if there is seepage throughout the mass, the angle β of Figs. 16·9 and 16·10 may be larger than ϕ_e, if the depth of the soil is less than the critical depth.

Expressions for the stability condition in an infinite slope of clay of depth H will now be set up. Equation 16·1 gives the shearing stress as

$$\tau = c_d + \bar{\sigma} \tan \phi_d$$

For the case of *no seepage* and *no neutral pressure* the stress components on a plane at depth H and parallel to the surface of the slope are

$$\tau = \gamma H \sin i \cos i \quad \text{and} \quad \bar{\sigma} = \gamma H \cos^2 i$$

Substitution of these stress expressions in the equation above and rearrangement give as the expression for the cohesion needed for stability

$$c_d = \gamma H \cos^2 i(\tan i - \tan \phi_d)$$

whereas an expression for allowable height is

$$H = \frac{c_d}{\gamma} \frac{\sec^2 i}{\tan i - \tan \phi_d}$$

The solution for the case of *no seepage* may also be written in the form

$$\frac{c_d}{\gamma H} = \cos^2 i(\tan i - \tan \phi_d) \tag{16·12}$$

The term $c_d/\gamma H$ is a dimensionless expression called the *stability number*. This dimensionless number is proportional to the required cohesion and is inversely proportional to the allowable height. The main value of this form of expression is that the stability number may be considered to be a composite variable which reduces the number of variables in simple stability equation to three and thus allows the use of simple charts for representations of stability relationships. Actually equation 16·12 is so simple that a chart would be of little value in this case but, for some types of slopes, charts may be used to good advantage.

If there is *seepage* parallel to the ground surface *throughout* the entire clay mass, with the free water surface coinciding with the ground surface, the components of stress on planes parallel to the surface of the slope are given as equations 16·10; by setting z equal to H and by substitution of these expressions into equation

16·1 and simplifying, the stability expression obtained is

$$\frac{c_d}{\gamma_t H} = \cos^2 i \left(\tan i - \frac{\gamma_b}{\gamma_t} \tan \phi_d \right) \qquad (16 \cdot 13)$$

If the top flow line is parallel to the slope but is at a depth of H_1 vertically below ground surface and the unit weight within height H_1 is designated by γ_1, and if c_d and ϕ_d represent the developed strength of the soil at any depth H that is greater than H_1, the stability number for depths greater than H_1 is

$$\frac{c_d}{\gamma_t H} = \cos^2 i \left[\left(1 - \frac{H_1}{H} \frac{\gamma_t - \gamma_1}{\gamma_t} \right) \tan i \right.$$

$$\left. - \left(\frac{\gamma_b}{\gamma_t} + \frac{H_1}{H} \frac{\gamma_1 - \gamma_b}{\gamma_t} \right) \tan \phi_d \right] \qquad (16 \cdot 14)$$

The assumption that all vertical columns of soil are alike throughout the failure mass is often an acceptable one. On some occasions, however, a correction to cover differences in forces across the vertical planes above points A and B of Fig. 16·3 is desirable. If failure is incipient, the lateral pressure has an active or minimum value on the vertical plane through A and a maximum or passive value on the vertical plane through B. The magnitudes of these maximum and minimum pressures are given by equation 16·8 or by similar relationships discussed in more detail in Chapter 17. The difference between the total uphill lateral thrust at B and the total downhill lateral thrust at A acts to help prevent failure and aids the shearing strength in counteracting the total shearing force on the incipient failure surface between A and B.

16·14 Introduction to the Circular Arc Method of Analysis

The considerations in previous sections have referred to slopes of great extent and to failures which occur along surfaces parallel to the slope. A more common problem is one in which the slope is of finite extent and in which failures occur on curved surfaces. The most widely used method of analysis of homogeneous, isotropic finite slopes is the Swedish method based on circular failure surfaces. It is believed that this method was first used by K. E. Petterson in the study of the failure of a quay wall in Goeteberg in 1915 or 1916.

Numerous slope failures that had occurred along Swedish railroads led to the setting up of an elaborate program in that country in 1920 or earlier for the investigation of slope stability. This work was carried out by the Swedish Geotechnical Commission (132). From boring data the shapes of the failure surfaces of numerous slides were determined, and one of the main contributions of the program was the information that actual failure surfaces generally do not deviate greatly in shape from circular cylinders. This finding is the main justification of the method of analysis proposed by this commission; it was developed by W. Fellenius (52, 53) and others and is now widely used. In this method failure surfaces are assumed to be of cylindrical shape, and they appear on cross sections as circular arcs. There are many possible circular arcs through a cross section, and the location of the critical, or most dangerous, arc must usually be determined by methods of trial.

The Swedish investigations included comparisons of shearing strength determinations of actual failures, based on circular arc analyses, with laboratory determinations of shearing strength obtained by direct shear tests on representative samples, and they found reasonable agreement between these determinations.†
Thus it was shown for the first time that it is sometimes possible to obtain reasonably accurate predictions of stability from analyses based on laboratory determinations of shearing strengths.

16·15 Explanation of the Method of Slices

The method of slices was developed by W. Fellenius. It is based on the statical analysis of the mass above any trial failure arc, with this mass considered to be made up of vertical slices.

Before the method and its assumptions can be truly understood a clear picture is required of all forces entering the analysis, and these forces will be explained in some detail. Seepage

---

† The information that may be obtained from studies of slope failures is also illustrated by reference 56.

forces are included in the following explanation, although in its original form the slices method did not account for seepage.

Let it be assumed that the circular arc on the section of Fig. 16·12 (*a*) is an arbitrarily chosen trial arc. This section is assumed to be of homogeneous soil through which a steady state of seepage is occurring as represented by the equipotential lines, which are shown by dashed curves. This section has been arbitrarily divided into five vertical slices of equal width.

From the equipotential lines the neutral pressure may be determined at any point on the section. For example, at point N in Fig. 16·12 (*a*) the pressure head is MN. Point S is determined by setting the radial distance NS equal to MN. A number of points obtained in the same manner as S give the curved line through S which is a *pressure head diagram*. On the sides of the slices pressure head diagrams are also shown.

In Section 9·18 it was proved that the actuating force may be taken as either the combination of total weights and boundary neutral forces or the combination of submerged weights and seepage forces. In the analyses in this chapter the former is used. Thus the forces acting on any slice are its total weight, the neutral forces acting on its sides and on its base and the resultant intergranular forces on its sides and on its base. In this example the developed strength characteristics ϕ_d and c_d are assumed to be constant over the circular arc, and the intergranular forces on the base thus consist of the cohesion, the normal component of intergranular force P_N, and the frictional resistance that is developed by P_N and that is equal to $P_N \tan \phi_d$.

In (*b*) vector polygons are given which show all forces for all slices. For purposes of explanation any slice may be used, since notations are the same for each slice except for subscript, and the discussion applies equally well to any slice. The total weight of any slice is equal to the volume multiplied by unit weight $[(G + e)/(1 + e)]\gamma_w$ and is represented by vector AB. The neutral force across the base is represented by vector BC, which acts normal to the arc. The combined neutral force on the two sides of the slice is represented by vector CD, acting horizontally. For the steady seepage case with the flow net

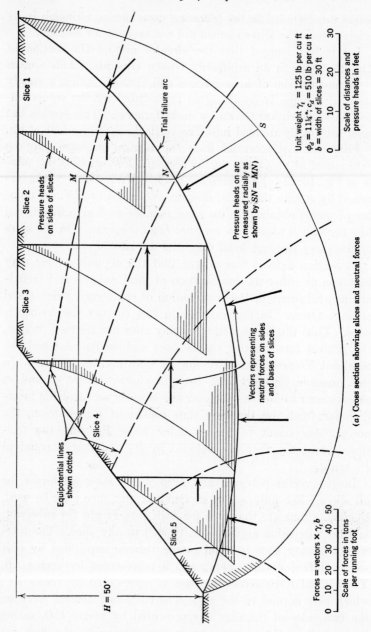

Unit weight γ_t = 125 lb per cu ft
ϕ_d = 11¼°; c_d = 510 lb per cu ft
b = width of slices = 30 ft

Scale of distances and pressure heads in feet

0   10   20   30

Slice 1

Trial failure arc

Pressure heads on sides of slices

Slice 2

M

N

S

Pressure heads on arc (measured radially as shown by $SN = MN$)

Slice 3

Vectors representing neutral forces on sides and bases of slices

Equipotential lines shown dotted

Slice 4

$H = 50'$

Slice 5

Forces = vectors × $\gamma_t b$

Scale of forces in tons per running foot

0   10   20   30   40   50

(a) Cross section showing slices and neutral forces

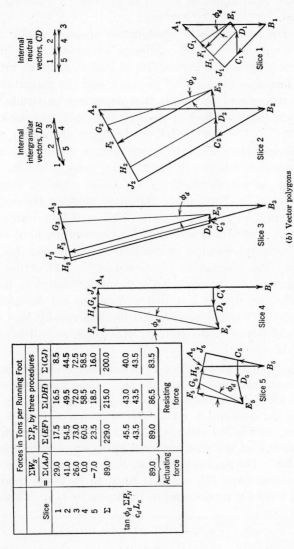

	Forces in Tons per Running Foot				
	ΣW_s	ΣP_N by three procedures			
Slice	$= \Sigma(AJ)$	$\Sigma(EF)$	$\Sigma(DH)$	$\Sigma(CJ)$	
1	29.0	17.5	16.5	8.5	
2	41.0	54.5	49.5	44.5	
3	26.0	73.0	72.0	72.5	
4	0.0	60.5	58.5	58.5	
5	−7.0	23.5	18.5	16.0	
Σ	89.0	229.0	215.0	200.0	
$\tan\phi_d \Sigma P_N$		45.5	43.0	40.0	
$c_d L_a$		43.5	43.5	43.5	
	89.0	89.0	86.5	83.5	
	Actuating force		Resisting force		

(b) Vector polygons

Fig. 16·12 Stability analysis by the slices method.

known, vectors BC and CD are completely defined, and from the pressure head diagrams shown in (a) these vectors may be determined.

Vector DE represents the combination of intergranular force on the two sides of the slice. Different lateral strain conditions of the type discussed in Section 16·10 lead to different magnitudes of forces on the sides of the slice, and the magnitude of the force represented by DE is thus dependent on strains and stress-strain characteristics of the soil; it is therefore statically indeterminate. The vectors DE in the figure are merely arbitrarily chosen values that are reasonable; to obtain a solution some assumption relative to these forces must be made.

Reverting to considerations of the entire mass, it may be noted that the total weight of the mass must be transmitted across the rupture arc. The sum of all boundary forces, including both neutral and intergranular components, must equal the total weight, regardless of the distribution among the several slices. The assumption mentioned at the end of the previous paragraph is, therefore, an assumption relative to distribution only and thus it is called a distributional assumption. Fortunately the various possible distributions usually lead only to minor differences in the stability conditions, as will be demonstrated later.

The remaining forces are the normal and tangential components of the intergranular forces across the arc. These forces are represented by EF and FA and are commonly designated by P_N and P_S. Once the assumption giving DE is chosen and point E is thus known, EF and FA can be determined. The requirement for equilibrium is that the shearing force P_S be supplied by friction and cohesion. The figures show that P_S is supplied by the sum of the frictional force FG, which is equal to $P_N \tan \phi_d$, and the cohesional force C_d, represented in the figure by GA. This may be written

$$P_S = P_N \tan \phi_d + C_d$$

With respect to the mass as a whole the requirement for stability is expressed in terms of the equilibrium of moments about the center of the circle. In the case under consideration boundary neutral pressures exist only on the circular arc and introduce no moment. Thus the actuating movement is the moment of the total weight. If weight AB is separated into shearing and normal components AJ and JB, designated respectively by W_S and W_N, the normal component has no moment, and the actuating moment may be written $R\Sigma W_S$, in which R is the radius and the moment is clockwise.

For a correct consideration of the equilibrium of individual slices, forces CD and DE, which act on the sides of slices, must be included. However, relative to the mass as a whole they form closed polygons, as shown in the diagrams at the upper right in (b), and the summation of their moments must be zero. Force EF also has no moment about the center of the circle. Thus the only other forces introducing moment are FG and GA. Forces FG give a moment which may be expressed $R\Sigma(FG)$, or $R\tan\phi_d\Sigma P_N$. Forces GA give the moment $R\Sigma(GA)$, or Rc_dL_a, in which L_a is the length of the arc. These moments are counterclockwise, and together they form the resisting moment.

Equating the actuating and resisting moments gives the expression of moment equilibrium,

$$R\Sigma W_S = R\tan\phi_d\Sigma P_N + Rc_dL_a \qquad (16\cdot15)$$

All terms in this expression are moments, and therefore they are vector quantities. If the equation is divided by R it becomes

$$\Sigma W_S = \tan\phi_d\Sigma P_N + c_dL_a \qquad (16\cdot16)$$

The terms of this equation have the dimensions of forces, but since they are tangential summations they are not vector quantities in the ordinary sense.

In equation $16\cdot16$ the only term which depends on the distributional assumption and thus the only term which offers any difficulty in the analysis is ΣP_N. If the resultants of lateral intergranular pressures DE are correct as shown in Fig. $16\cdot12$ (b), the vectors EF, representing P_N, are correct. The table in the figure shows that the force polygons are in equilibrium if vectors EF are accepted as representing forces P_N. For each running foot of slope the actuating force W_S equals 89 tons; the resisting force ($\tan\phi_d\Sigma P_N + c_dL_a$) equals 0.199×229 tons + 510 lb per sq ft $\times$ 171 ft, which also equals 89 tons.

Fellenius proposed the use of the assumption that the lateral forces are equal on the two sides of each slice. This is not simply an assumption relative to the distribution, since in addition it involves other factors which cannot be fully explained without an unduly long discussion. A small amount of study shows that it gives conditions in individual slices which are entirely incorrect. For example, it indicates that slices 1 and 2 have much less resisting force than is required for equilibrium, and that slices 4 and 5 have much more resisting force than needed. However, these inconsistencies counteract each other to a large degree and for the mass as a whole this assumption, which is the characteristic assumption of the slices method, gives fairly reasonable results. In analyses of the type shown in Fig. 16·12, where the effects of seepage are included, there are two possible interpretations of the Fellenius assumption. These interpretations are considered separately in the two following paragraphs.

In the first interpretation it is assumed that the lateral intergranular forces are in balance on the sides of each slice. According to this assumption forces DE all become equal to zero and ΣP_N becomes $\Sigma(DH)$. As shown in the table, this summation equals 215 tons and gives a resisting force about 3 per cent smaller than the value of 229 tons obtained by taking ΣP_N equal to $\Sigma(EF)$.

In the second interpretation it is assumed that the lateral combined forces are in balance on the sides of each slice. On this basis combinations of forces CD and DE all become zero and ΣP_N becomes $\Sigma(CJ)$, which in this example equals 200 tons and gives a resisting force about 6 per cent smaller than that obtained in the original determination.

The use of the second interpretation does not require the determination of the neutral pressures on the sides of the slices, and thus it saves a considerable amount of labor. Since it gives conservative results, it is probably the more satisfactory procedure for general use.

16·16 Graphical Analyses Based on the Slices Method

The stability analysis for any given trial arc, using the method of slices and the assumption that the combined lateral force on the two sides of each slice are equal, may now be summarized. The choice of vector scale and of numerous other details is arbitrary, and with respect to such details this outline is only one convenient way of carrying out the analysis.

First let it be assumed that a given section is being analyzed to determine factors of safety. Divide the trial failure mass into an integral number of slices of equal width. For each slice lay off the weight vector as shown by AB in Fig. 16·13. If the slice is of homogeneous soil the height of the slice serves as a convenient

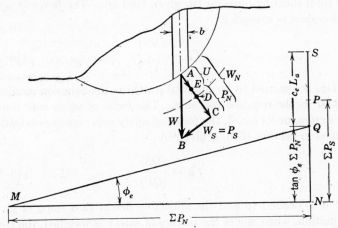

FIG. 16·13 Details of the procedure in graphical analyses by the slices method.

vector; on this basis forces are obtained if vectors are multiplied by $\gamma_t b$, where γ_t is the combined unit weight and b is the width of the slice. A radial line is drawn through A and a line perpendicular to it through B, giving CB or W_S, which is equal to P_S, as the shearing component of weight, and AC or W_N as the combined normal component of weight. The dashed line is the pressure head curve, AD being the pressure head at point A. The neutral force across the base of the slice is $(AD)\gamma_w b'$ where b' is the arc distance along the base of the slice. Dividing this force expression by $b\gamma_t$ gives $AD \times (\gamma_w/\gamma_t) \times (b'/b)$ as the neutral force vector AE. Vector EC represents P_N. The summations ΣP_S and ΣP_N are obtained by adding individual values for all slices, and they are plotted as NP and NM, respectively, in the lower diagram of the figure. By laying off the angle ϕ_e as shown, the distance NQ, equal to $\tan \phi_e \Sigma P_N$, is obtained. The total cohesion, equal to $c_e L_a$, may be represented vectorially by

$$(QS) = \frac{c_e L_a}{\gamma_t b} \tag{16·17}$$

Distance NS represents the total shearing resistance and NP the total shearing force for the given trial arc. The *factor of safety with respect to strength* is

$$F_s = \frac{(NS)}{(NP)} \tag{16·18}$$

If ϕ_d is assumed to be equal to ϕ_e, QS is the cohesion available and QP is the required cohesion. The *factor of safety with respect to cohesion*, or its equal, the *factor of safety with respect to height*, as defined in Section 16·6, is given by

$$F_H = \frac{(QS)}{(QP)} \tag{16·19}$$

If it is desired to find the allowable height of a slope of given inclination, when one of the factors of safety is specified, the steps as far as the plotting of ΣP_N, ΣW_S, and ϕ_e are the same as before. The same vector scale may be used, the only difference being that H is not known and, therefore, the distance represented by dimension b is not known. With dimensions NP and NQ known and with a known value for a factor of safety, whether it is F_s or F_H, the use of the appropriate one of equations 16·18 or 16·19 gives the data needed to plot point S. Equation 16·17 may be rearranged to give the following expression

$$b = \frac{c_e}{\gamma_t} \frac{L_a}{(QS)}$$

in which c_e and γ_t are known and $L_a/(QS)$ is the ratio of two distances appearing in Fig. 16·13; this ratio may be taken from the figure although the distances themselves are not known. Dimension b may now be evaluated, and once its value is known the scale of the figure and the height H are easily obtained. The value obtained for H is the allowable height for the given trial circle, and various circles must be tried until the one showing the smallest allowable height is obtained.

For the soil mass analyzed in this section, it is assumed that the circle passes through the toe of the slope and that cohesion is effective over the entire rupture arc. Water pressures in this section occur only along the arc. Possible variations from these assumed conditions are of considerable importance in many instances, and a number of items of this type are covered in later sections.

16·17   The Friction-Circle Method

A trial circular rupture arc is shown in Fig. 16·14; its radius is designated by R. A concentric circle of radius $R \sin \phi$ is also shown. Any line tangent to the inner circle must intersect the main circle at an obliquity ϕ. Therefore, any vector representing an intergranular pressure at obliquity ϕ to an element of the rupture arc must be tangent to the inner circle. This inner circle is called the *friction circle* or the ϕ *circle*. The friction-circle method of slope analysis

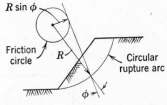

Fig. 16·14   The friction circle.

is a convenient approach for both graphical and mathematical solutions. It is given this name because the characteristic assumption of the method refers to the ϕ circle.

The forces considered in this method of analysis are shown in Fig. 16·15. The actuating forces may be considered to be the total weight W and the resultant boundary neutral force U; they are shown in (a). The weight vector and its line of action may be determined in a number of ways. The vector U may be determined by graphical methods from the pressure head diagram. Graphical methods for determining these forces are explained later. Once obtained, their vector sum may easily be determined. Vector B represents the resultant actuating force.

Figure 16·15 (b) shows cohesive resisting forces acting tangentially on each element of arc. Let the length of arc AB be designated by L_a, the length of chord AB by L_c. The algebraic sum of all cohesional forces along the arc is $c_d L_a$. However, if two small cohesion forces such as C_2 and C_5 are divided into components parallel and normal to the chord AB, the parallel components are directly additive, and the normal com-

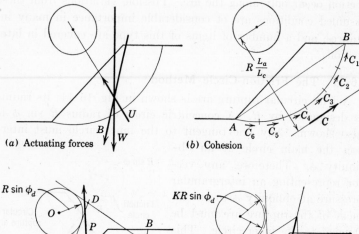

(a) Actuating forces   (b) Cohesion

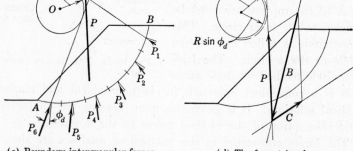

(c) Boundary intergranular forces   (d) The force triangle

FIG. 16·15 The forces in stability analyses by the friction-circle method.

ponents give only a counterclockwise moment. Thus the vector sum of all cohesive forces is $c_d L_c$, because components normal to the chord cancel, and vector C, which is of magnitude $c_d L_c$ and represents the total cohesion, is a force which acts parallel to the chord AB. Its line of action may be determined by moment considerations. The moment of the total cohesion is given by the expressions

$$c_d L_a R = c_d L_c a$$

whence a, the moment arm of vector C, is

$$a = R \frac{L_a}{L_c}$$

It is seen that the line of action of vector C is independent of the magnitude of c_d.

The intergranular forces shown acting along the arc in Fig. 16·15 (c) are at an obliquity ϕ_d to the circular arc and thus they have lines of action which are tangent to the ϕ_d circle. The vector sum of any two small forces such as P_1 and P_6 has a line of action which passes through point D, missing tangency to the ϕ_d circle by a small amount. The resultant of all intergranular forces must, therefore, miss tangency to the ϕ_d circle by an amount which is not large. Let the distance of the resultant intergranular

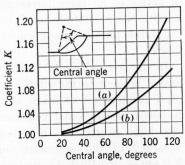

FIG. 16·16 The coefficient K of the friction-circle assumption.

force P from the center of the circle be designated by $KR \sin \phi_d$. The magnitude of K is statically indeterminate, and it depends on the distribution of intergranular stress along the arc. Any assumption relative to it is therefore a distributional assumption. The value also depends on the central angle AOB. For any assumed pattern of stress distribution, along an arc having a given central angle, the value of K can be obtained. For two simple types of stress distribution, plots of K versus central angle are given in Fig. 16·16; curve (a) is for uniform pressure and curve (b) is for the distribution having zero values at the ends of the arc and sinusoidal stress variation between. If it is assumed that all intergranular force across the arc is concentrated at the point of action of the resultant vector, K equals unity regardless of the value of the central angle. In typical examples the actual distribution is not symmetrical, but otherwise it bears quite close resemblance to the sinusoidal variation. Therefore, curve (b) can probably be accepted as giving values of K that are sufficiently accurate for most analyses.

The graphical solution based on the concepts explained above is simple in principle. For the three forces B, C, and P of Fig. 16·15 (d) to be in equilibrium, P must pass through the intersection of the known lines of action of vectors B and C. The line of action of vector P must also be tangent to a circle of radius KR sin ϕ_d. The value of K may be estimated by the use of curve (b) of Fig. 16·16, and the line of action of force P may be drawn as shown in Fig. 16·15 (d). Since the lines of action of all three forces and the magnitude of force B are known, the magnitudes of P and C may easily be obtained by the force parallelogram construction that is indicated in the figure.

In the original use of the friction-circle method vector P was drawn tangent to the circle of radius R sin ϕ_d; thus the value of K originally was taken as unity. The use of the value of K based on sinusoidal variation does not change the results to any large degree, but it is easily obtained and improves the accuracy of the procedure somewhat. The circle of radius KR sin ϕ_d is called the *modified friction circle*.

16·18 Graphical Solutions by the Friction-Circle Method

Three graphical steps are needed for a graphical solution by the friction-circle method. These three steps are the determination of the weight vector W, the determination of the neutral force vector U, and a final trial procedure which is required because the angle ϕ_d usually is not directly known. This final trial procedure is not especially complicated, but it leads to trials of the second order, since it must be used on each of the various trials of circular arcs.

The weight vector may be determined, if desired, by planimetering the area. Its line of action is vertical through the center of gravity of the area. The center of gravity may be determined by cutting a piece of cardboard to the shape of the failure mass and balancing the cardboard model on a sharp point. As an alternate method the following, simple, all graphical procedure is available. For simplicity in the explanation a homogeneous section with straight lines for exterior boundaries is used. This method is shown in Fig. 16·17, and its description follows.

The weight of mass ACB is W; it is equal to W_1, the weight of the sector AOB, minus $W_2 + W_3$, the weights of triangles AOC and COB. The unit weight will be designated by γ_t, radii OA and OB by R, and arc length AB by L_a. Weights W_1, W_2, and W_3 are equal respectively to $\frac{1}{2}\gamma_t R(L_a)$, $\frac{1}{2}\gamma_t R(CD)$, and $\frac{1}{2}\gamma_t R(CE)$,

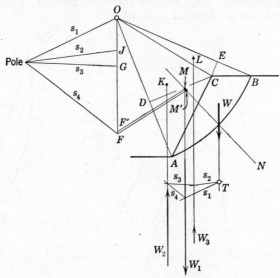

FIG. 16·17 Graphical determination of the weight vector.

and W is equal to $\frac{1}{2}\gamma_t R(L_a - CD - CE)$. The lengths in parentheses are used for vector distances, making vector distances multiplied by $\frac{1}{2}\gamma_t R$ equal to corresponding forces. Vector W_1 is of length L_a and is shown by OF in the force polygon $OFGJO$; it acts through the center of gravity of the sector which is point M. Point M is located on line ON, which bisects the central angle, and distance OM equals $\frac{2}{3}R(L_c/L_a)$. Distance CM' is set equal to $\frac{2}{3}R$, distances OF' and OF are equal to L_c and L_a respectively, and the drawing of $F'M$ parallel to FM' locates point M. Similarly vectors W_2 and W_3, of lengths CD and CE, respectively, are shown by GF and JG in the force polygon, and they have lines of action which pass through points K and L. Points K and L are the centers of gravity of the triangular areas and may be located by intersections of median lines, that is, lines from an apex to the middle of the opposite side. The pole location is chosen arbitrarily and rays s_1 to s_4 are drawn to each point on the force polygon; ray s_3, for example, is through point G, which is the junction between the vectors representing W_2 and W_3. Below the section the string s_3, which is parallel to the above-mentioned ray s_3, runs from force W_2 to W_3. The other strings are drawn on the same basis, giving the *string polygon*. This polygon furnishes point T, which is on the vertical line of action of force W.

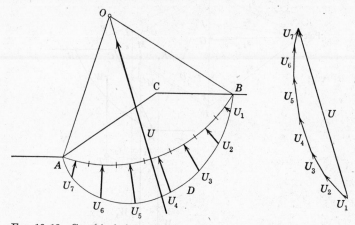

Fig. 16·18   Graphical determination of the boundary neutral force.

The neutral force vector acting across the circular arc may be determined without difficulty from a pressure head diagram of the type shown in Fig. 16·12 (a). This determination is shown in Fig. 16·18, and its description follows.

Arc AB is the trial failure arc, and line ADB is the pressure head diagram obtained as shown in Fig. 16·12 (a); radial distances from the arc to this line are pressure heads. The arc is divided into n equal sections each of length L_a/n. It is assumed that the average pressure head on each section is the head at the center point of the section, and that the resultant water force across the section acts at the mid-point. The force across section 1 is $h_1\gamma_w(L_a/n)$, and it is represented by vector U_1 of length h_1; thus forces are equal to vectors multiplied by $\gamma_w(L_a/n)$. The vectors are summed as shown at the right, giving the resultant vector U, which must act through point O since neutral pressures are everywhere directed toward O. The scale of vectors used in the final analysis is the one previously used in Fig. 16·17. If vector U of Fig. 16·18 is multiplied by $\gamma_w(L_a/n)$, the force U is obtained, and if this force is divided by $\frac{1}{2}\gamma_t R$, the vector to the desired scale is obtained; thus the vector shown in Fig. 16·18 is to be multiplied by $(2/n)(\gamma_w/\gamma_t)(L_a/R)$ to transfer it to the scale of Figs. 16·17 and 16·19.

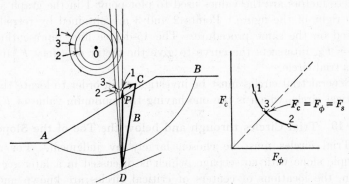

FIG. 16·19 Graphical trial method for determining the factor of safety with respect to strength.

The vector scale introduced above is the one most commonly used and generally the most convenient; however, any desired vector scale may be used. Figures 16·17 and 16·18 are simple cross sections, but the procedures that have been outlined may be used with minor modifications on relatively complicated sections.

The graphical procedure requiring the use of trial ϕ_d values is shown in Fig. 16·19; its explanation follows.

Vector B is the resultant actuating force. Point D is the intersection of the lines of action of vectors B and C. An arbitrary first trial using any reasonable ϕ_d value, which will be designated by ϕ_{d1}, is given by the use of circle 1 of radius $KR \sin \phi_{d1}$. Subscript 1 is also used for all other quantities of the first trial. Vector P_1 is drawn through D tangent to circle 1. Vector C_1 is parallel to chord AB, and point 1 is the intersection of vectors C_1 and P_1. The developed cohesion equals $c_{d1}L_c$ and also equals vector C_1 multiplied by $\frac{1}{2}\gamma_t R$. Thus

$$c_{d1} = \frac{\gamma_t R}{2L_c} C_1$$

After c_{d1} has been evaluated the factors of safety with respect to the frictional and cohesional components of shearing strength may be determined from the expressions

$$F_{\phi 1} = \frac{\tan \phi_e}{\tan \phi_{d1}} \quad \text{and} \quad F_{c1} = \frac{c_e}{c_{d1}}$$

These factors are the values used to plot point 1 in the graph at the right of the figure. Points 2 and 3 are obtained by retrials based on the same procedure. The 45-degree line, representing $F_c = F_\phi$, intersects the curve to give the factor of safety F_s for this trial circle.

Several trial circles must be investigated in order to locate the critical circle, which is the one having the minimum value of F_s.

16·19   Trial Circles through and below the Toe of the Slope

Trial circles must be chosen largely by judgment. For a simple slope with no seepage, which is discussed in a later section, the locations of centers of critical circles are known and

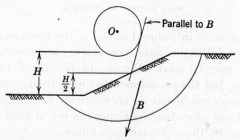

Fɪɢ. 16·20   Illustration of an approximate requirement relative to locations of critical circles that pass below the toe of the slope.

are given in Table 16·2. These data may be of some small aid in choosing the first trial in complicated sections with seepage occurring.

In homogeneous sections with steep slopes and in all slopes in soils that have high friction angles, the critical circle passes through the toe of the slope. However, for flat slopes in soils in which the shearing strength does not increase with depth and for steep slopes where the underground has a lower shearing strength than the embankment, the circle may pass below the toe of the slope. For a section of homogeneous soil it can be demonstrated that, if there is no seepage and the critical circle passes below the toe, a vertical line tangent to the friction circle must intersect the slope at mid-height. If there is seepage, no corresponding rigorous rule exists, but a line parallel to the resultant actuating force B and tangent to the friction circle should cut the slope near the mid-height point. This condition is illustrated by Fig. 16·20, and it may be used as a guide in the analysis of trial circles that pass below the toe.

16·20 Considerations of Tension Cracks

The Mohr circles in Fig. 16·21 show stresses at failure at various depths below the surface of an infinite slope of cohesive soil. Point A_1 represents the pressure acting vertically on the plane parallel to the surface of the slope at a relatively large depth. According to principles already illustrated in Fig. 16·6, point B_1

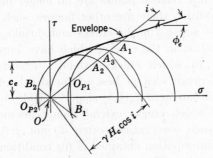

FIG. 16·21 Mohr diagram illustrating the tension zone at the surface of an infinite cohesive slope.

represents the active pressure on the vertical plane at this depth. Similarly, A_2 represents the stress on the plane parallel to the surface of the slope and point B_2 represents the active stress on the vertical plane at a smaller depth. Since point B_2 falls to the left of the origin of stresses, the normal component of the lateral stress at this depth is tension. Thus it is seen that the lateral stresses near the surface of a cohesive slope are tensions when failure impends.

Below a certain depth, tension is not possible. This limiting depth may be determined by constructing the Mohr circle that passes through the origin of stresses O and is tangent to the strength envelope. Point A_3 on this circle represents the stress on the plane parallel to the ground surface, this stress being $\gamma H_c \cos i$, in which H_c is the limiting depth. The radius of this Mohr circle is equal to $\frac{1}{2}\gamma H_c$ and it also is equal to $c_e \tan(45 + \frac{1}{2}\phi_e)$, whence

$$H_c = \frac{2c_e}{\gamma} \tan\left(45 + \frac{1}{2}\phi_e\right) \qquad (16\cdot20)$$

Within the zone in which the clay is under tension, cracks are likely to exist and, if there are no cracks, there is an ever-present possibility of their developing. For this reason the cohesional portion of the shearing strength cannot be depended upon in this zone.

The expression given above for the maximum depth of the tension zone is valid only for the infinite slope, wherein conditions are the same on all vertical planes. After the first cracks have occurred, all vertical planes are no longer under like conditions. In addition there are other factors, such as expansion caused by frost action ‡ in the cracks and shrinkage of the clay due to evaporation in the cracks, which have important effects on the depth to which cracks extend. Therefore, equation $16\cdot20$ gives a rough idea at best of the depth of the zone of cracking within an actual clay slope. Field observations of the depths to which cracks extend should be made whenever possible, but such observations often do not give satisfactory data, and the information obtained is for conditions at the time of observation only. The questionable action and the questionable depth § of the tension zone have considerable bearing on the limited dependability of many stability analyses, and the action within the tension zone is a subject that is worthy of much study.

When a value for the depth of the tension zone has been estimated, it is not difficult to make a satisfactory allowance for its effect on the stability analysis. Simple revisions which need no detailed explanation may, if desired, be made in the

‡ For discussions of frost action see references 12, 118, and 133.

§ Terzaghi states, on page 146 of reference 148, "On the basis of the results of model tests on gelatin [he] assumes that the depth of the tension zone does not exceed one-half the height of the bank, provided the tension is due to gravity and not due to excessive shrinkage."

procedures given in Sections 16·16 and 16·18. However, the depth of the zone of cracking can seldom be accurately known, and a procedure that usually is satisfactory retains the assumption of uniform cohesion but uses a reduced value of cohesion. For example, if only 70 per cent of the trial rupture arc is outside the estimated zone of cracking, the average cohesion may be assumed equal to 70 per cent of the value which otherwise would be used.

16·21 Procedures for the Case of Partial Submergence

When partial submergence exists because of a pond or a stream adjacent to a slope, the resultant boundary neutral force includes water pressures on the surface of the slope in addition to the water pressures across the rupture arc, whereas only the latter were present in the slopes treated in Sections 16·15 and 16·17.

A modification of the slices method to allow for this condition is shown in Fig. 16·22. The failure mass is here assumed

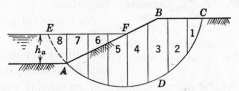

Fig. 16·22 The case of partial submergence.

to include area *AEF*, which is within the water. Therefore, the weight of water above line *AF* must be included in the weights of slices 5 to 8 inclusive. Slices 5 to 7 require no further revision of the procedure outlined in Section 16·5. Along the base of slice 8 there is no shearing strength; thus *EA* is not included in the arc length L_a in the cohesion determination, and the normal component of weight of slice 8 does not enter the friction determination. However, the tangential component of the weight of slice 8 must be included in ΣW_S. It acts in a counterclockwise, or resisting, sense; thus it is negative relative to values of W_S for slices 1 to 4, inclusive, and it gives appreciable aid to the stability.

In the friction-circle method this water condition may be

cared for as follows: The neutral resultant thrust across AF is the static force $\frac{1}{2}\gamma_w h_a^2 \csc i$, acting normal to AF at a point one third of the distance from A to F. This exterior neutral force must be added vectorially to the radially directed neutral force across the arc to give the resultant boundary neutral force. This neutral force is then added vectorially to the total weight as shown in Fig. 16·15 (a) to give the total actuating force.

16·22 Earthquake Considerations

Earthquakes may cause the failure of earth embankments which under ordinary conditions would be amply safe. However, relatively little is known of the forces introduced by earthquakes. A quake actually imposes displacements rather than forces, and the forces resulting from the displacements are dependent in a complicated way on dynamic stress-strain relationships of the embankment materials.

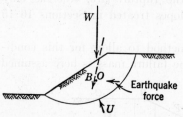

FIG. 16·23 Consideration of the earthquake force as a body force.

An empirical procedure that has been used in regions that are subject to earthquakes consists in assuming that the quake imposes a horizontal acceleration of sinusoidal variation, with an amplitude that is equal to some given per cent of gravity. This probably is a crude allowance at best for buildings and, even if valid for buildings, it is not necessarily reasonable for earth embankments. The per cent of gravity which best represents the case probably depends much on the specific conditions, but a value of 10 per cent has sometimes been used.

If it is assumed that a maximum horizontal acceleration of 0.1 gravity is reasonable for the earthquake allowance in an earth embankment, an idea of quake effects can easily be obtained. In Fig. 16·23 the actuating forces are the total weight W, the boundary neutral force U, and the quake force that is equal to $0.1W$ and acts horizontally through the center of gravity of the failure mass. The resultant of these three forces is the body force B.

In addition the soil properties c_e and ϕ_e are likely to have different values under earthquake conditions than they have under normal conditions. Failures caused by quakes are likely to occur suddenly, allowing no drainage of water from the mass even in highly pervious soils. In addition greater degrees of progressive failure may occur, since successive shocks may cause cracks gradually to progress deeper into the ground. Sands in loose state may be susceptible to liquefaction, and a violent earthquake surely represents the condition most likely to cause this state.

Because of the danger they present, earthquake effects deserve much study. As in almost all studies of dynamic soil action, however, the physical relationships involved are complex, and progress toward a satisfactory understanding of such problems has been limited.

16·23 Solutions for Simple, Finite Slopes without Seepage

The procedures given in Sections 16·15 to 16·20 inclusive have broad applicability. Solutions by these methods can be obtained for embankments under wide ranges of conditions, but such solutions often require much time.

Solutions for simple cross sections of homogeneous soils, within which no seepage is occurring, may be obtained somewhat more easily and, once obtained, they may be made available in the form of relatively simple charts. A number of solutions that have been presented in the past in the form of equations or charts are mainly of academic interest, since they contain questionable assumptions and have no practical advantages over more logical methods. The highly mathematical treatments known as the Résal-Frontard method (122, 60) and the Jáky method (82) fall into this category and thus are not discussed herein. Simple slope analyses based on plane failure surfaces, on circular failure surfaces, and on spiral failure surfaces are presented in following sections.

16·24 The Culmann Method

The Culmann method (40) is based on the assumption that failure occurs on a plane through the toe of the slope. Figure 16·24 represents the type of section to which this analysis

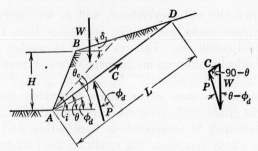

Fig. 16·24 Elements of the Culmann method.

applies. The forces that act on the mass above a trial failure plane, at an inclination defined by the angle θ, are also shown in the figure. The expressions for the weight and the total cohesion are, respectively,

$$W = \tfrac{1}{2}\gamma LH \csc i \sin (i - \theta)$$

and

$$C = c_d L$$

The use of the law of sines in the force triangle, shown at the right of the figure, gives

$$\frac{C}{W} = \frac{\sin (\theta - \phi_d)}{\cos \phi_d}$$

The substitution herein of the above expressions for C and W and rearranging gives

$$\left(\frac{c_d}{\gamma H}\right)_\theta = \frac{1}{2} \csc i \sin (i - \theta) \sin (\theta - \phi_d) \sec \phi_d$$

in which the subscript θ indicates that the stability number is for the trial plane at the inclination θ.

The most dangerous plane is that with the maximum stability number. This maximum value may be obtained by setting the first derivative with respect to θ of the above equation equal to zero. This operation gives

$$\theta_c = \tfrac{1}{2}(i + \phi_d)$$

and

$$\frac{c_d}{\gamma H} = \frac{1 - \cos (i - \phi_d)}{4 \sin i \cos \phi_d} \tag{16·21}$$

The angle θ_c is the critical value of θ, and it is the slope of the plane that is shown by a dashed line in Fig. 16·24. In accordance with the above expression this plane bisects the angle between the slope and a line at an inclination of ϕ_d. According to equation 16·21 the stability is not affected by the value of angle δ. However, this is an incorrect concept which is inherent in the questionable assumption of plane failure.

Values given by equation 16·21 are tabulated in column (3) of Table 16·1, and these values allow comparisons with other determinations described later. Since the assumption of plane failure represents a limited choice of failure surfaces, the results must be on the unsafe side, and the stability numbers shown by this method are too small when compared with other data of Table 16·1.

The Culmann method is mainly of interest because it serves as a test of the validity of the assumption of plane failure, which is used in various types of stability analysis. In some cases this assumption is reasonable and in others it is questionable. If it is assumed that the final columns of Table 16·1 are the best results obtainable (as they will later be shown to be), it may be concluded that the plane assumption leads to generally acceptable accuracies if the slope is vertical or nearly so, but it does not give satisfactory accuracy for flat slopes.

16·25 Solutions for Simple Slopes without Seepage Based on Circular Failure Surfaces

Solutions have been obtained for this simple case and are available in the form of charts and tables which give the stability number directly for any given values of friction angle and slope angle. A considerable amount of labor is required to obtain such charts but, once obtained, solutions by their use are simple indeed. These solutions are strictly valid only for the simple homogeneous finite slope with the types of cross sections shown in Fig. 16·25 and for cases involving no seepage, but they may also be used for rough determinations and preliminary solutions of more complex cases.

The first general solution of this type was made by Fellenius (53) and was published in 1928. This solution was based on the slices method and was carried out by graphical trial procedure. A general solution based on the friction-circle method, using a mathematical trial method, was made by the author (139) and published in 1937. These two general solutions show such close agreement that neither can be adjudged preferable. The mathematical solution is more precise and thorough, how-

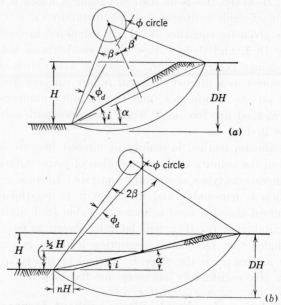

FIG. 16·25 Elements of the friction-circle method.

ever, especially in the determinations of locations of critical circles. Stability numbers obtained by these two methods are given in columns (4) and (5) of Table 16·1.

The critical circle for steep slopes passes through the toe of the slope with the lowest point on the failure arc at the toe of the slope; this is shown by key sketch (*A*) in Fig. 16·26. This condition holds throughout zone *A* of this figure, which is a chart of stability numbers. In zone *B* the low point of the critical circle is not at the toe of the slope, and three cases that will be considered are shown in key sketch (*B*). For small slope angles or small friction angles the critical circle may pass below rather than through the toe of the slope, as is shown in case 2. For all ranges in which this case holds, stability numbers are given in the chart by long dashed curves. Stability

TABLE 16·1 STABILITY NUMBERS FOR HOMOGENEOUS SIMPLE SLOPES
WITHOUT SEEPAGE—BY SEVERAL METHODS

(1) i	(2) ϕ_d	(3) Culmann (Plane)	(4) Slices	(5) ϕ Circle	(6) Logarithmic Spiral
90	0	0.250	0.261	0.261	0.261
	5	0.229	0.239	0.239	0.239
	15	0.192	0.199	0.199	
	25	0.159	0.165	0.166	0.165
75	0	0.192	0.219	0.219	0.219
	5	0.171	0.196	0.195	
	15	0.134	0.154	0.152	
	25	0.102	0.118	0.117	
60	0	0.144	0.191	0.191	0.191
	5	0.124	0.165	0.162	0.162
	15	0.088	0.120	0.116	0.116
	25	0.058	0.082	0.079	0.078
45	0	0.104	(0.170) [1]	(0.170)	(0.170)
	5	0.083	0.141	0.136	
	15	0.049	0.085	0.083	
	25	0.023	0.048	0.044	
30	0	0.067	(0.156)	(0.156)	(0.156)
	5	0.047	(0.114)	(0.110)	
	15	0.018	0.048	0.046	
	25	0.002	0.012	0.009	0.008
15	0	0.033	(0.145)	(0.145)	(0.145)
	5	0.015	(0.072)	(0.068)	(0.068)
	10	0.004		(0.023)	

[1] All values given are for the critical circle through the toe of the slope. When there is a more dangerous circle which passes below the toe, values are shown in parentheses. For data on circles below the toe see Table 16·2.

numbers for the most dangerous circles passing through the toe are given by solid lines in the chart both when there is and when there is not a more dangerous circle that passes below the toe; where a solid line does not appear in the chart the most dangerous circle passes below the toe, and the most dangerous circle through the toe does not have a perceptibly different stability number. Table 16·2 presents stability numbers with additional data relative to the location of the critical circle; the key to variables α, β, n, and D is given by Fig. 16·25. The chart and the table show that the differences between stability numbers, as given by the solid and long dashed curves, are of no practical importance unless the friction angle is less than 5 degrees.

Sometimes the investigations of shearing strengths of soil samples from a given embankment show no consistent tendency toward increased strength at greater distances below ground surface. This case is discussed further in Section 16·31; it is usually given the somewhat misleading designation of $\phi = 0$ case. Whether the name is satisfactory or not the case wherein the shearing strength is assumed constant is an important one, and it is represented in stability charts by a zero friction angle. For this case the critical circle passes below the toe for slopes with inclination of less than 53 degrees. Theoretically the critical slope for this case is at an infinite depth. In slopes encountered in practical problems, however, the depth to which the rupture may pass is usually limited by ledge or other underlying strong material. Thus the stability number for the zero-ϕ case is greatly dependent on the limiting value of the depth. To represent this condition the variable used is the ratio of depth of failure mass to height of slope; it is designated by D and is shown in Fig. 16·25.

For various values of D and for the zero-ϕ case the chart in Fig. 16·27 supplements Fig. 16·26. The coordinates used in Fig. 16·27 allow a reasonably simple presentation of a number of items of practical information. As shown by the key sketches, circles passing below the toe are represented by full line curves and n values are represented by short dashed lines. Cases wherein there are loadings outside the toe, which prevent the circle from passing below the toe, are represented by long dashed lines.

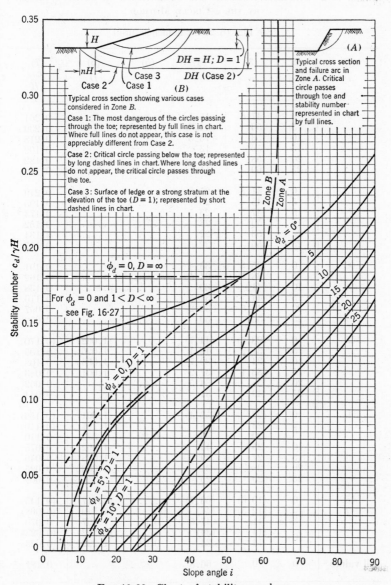

FIG. 16·26 Chart of stability numbers.

Stability of Slopes

TABLE 16·2   STABILITY NUMBERS AND OTHER DATA ON CRITICAL CIRCLES
BY THE ϕ-CIRCLE METHOD

(See Fig. 16·25 for nomenclature.)

(1) i	(2) ϕ_d	(3) α	(4) β	(5) n	(6) D	(7) $\dfrac{c_d}{\gamma H}$
90	0	47.6	15.1	....	.....	0.261
	5	50	14	....	.....	0.239
	10	53	13.5	....	.....	0.218
	15	56	13	....	.....	0.199
	20	58	12	....	.....	0.182
	25	60	11	....	.....	0.166
75	0	41.8	25.9	....	.....	0.219
	5	45	25	....	.....	0.195
	10	47.5	23.5	....	.....	0.173
	15	50	23	....	.....	0.152
	20	53	22	....	.....	0.134
	25	56	22	....	.....	0.117
60	0	35.3	35.4	....	.....	0.191
	5	38.5	34.5	....	.....	0.162
	10	41	33	....	.....	0.138
	15	44	31.5	....	.....	0.116
	20	46.5	30.2	....	.....	0.097
	25	50	30	....	.....	0.079
45	0	(28.2) [1]	(44.7)	....	(1.062)	(0.170)
	5	31.2	42.1	....	1.026	0.136
	10	34	39.7	....	1.006	0.108
	15	36.1	37.2	....	1.001	0.083
	20	38	34.5	....	.....	0.062
	25	40	31	....	.....	0.044
30	0	(20)	(53.4)	....	(1.301)	(0.156)
	5 {	(23)	(48)	....	(1.161)	(0.110)
		20	53	0.29	1.332	0.110
	10	25	44	....	1.092	0.075
	15	27	39	....	1.038	0.046
	20	28	31	....	1.003	0.025
	25	29	25	....	.....	0.009
15	0	(10.6)	(60.7)	....	(2.117)	(0.145)
	5 {	(12.5)	(47)	....	(1.549)	(0.068)
		11	47.5	0.55	1.697	0.070
	10 {	(14)	(34)	....	(1.222)	(0.023)
		14	34	0.04	1.222	0.023
All values [2]	0	0	66.8	∞	∞	0.181

[1] Figures in parentheses are values for most dangerous circle through the toe when a more dangerous circle, which passes below the toe, exists.
[2] A critical value at infinite depth.

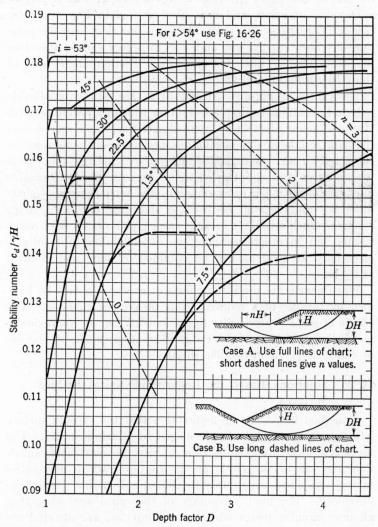

FIG. 16·27   Chart of stability numbers for the case of zero friction angle and limited depth.

If there is ledge or other strong material at the elevation of the toe of the slope, the case is represented in Fig. 16·27 by a D value of unity, and it is also covered in Fig. 16·26 by case 3. For D equal to unity and ϕ greater than zero the solution has been carried out only for 15-degree slopes; therefore the short dashed lines for the larger friction angles are of short length in Fig. 16·26.

The charts in Figs. 16·26 and 16·27 are strictly applicable only to the extremely simple section for which they were derived. However, many slopes that approximate the simple section and that are composed of more or less heterogeneous soils may be subjected to an approximate analysis by entering the charts with average values. The choice of average or representative values requires much discrimination, and retrials using slightly different values should be used to show the effects of slight changes. Such estimates in some cases give no more than rough results, but in other instances the dependability of results is essentially as good as can be obtained by long and detailed analyses.

When charts are used, the effects of cracks can best be handled by the use of a reduced value of average cohesion. The effects of seepage are harder to account for, but an approximate method of accounting for seepage in solutions made by the use of charts is given in Section 16·30.

16·26 Solutions Based on Logarithmic-Spiral Failure Surfaces

A method based on the assumption that the rupture surface is a logarithmic spiral was developed by Rendulic (121). The use of the logarithmic spiral is in some ways more inconvenient than the use of the circle as the rupture surface, but satisfactory graphical procedures for the spiral method have been developed. The main advantage of the spiral method is that all intergranular forces with the obliquity ϕ_d are directed toward the center of the spiral. Because of this condition the analysis is statically determinate without an assumption relative to the pressure distribution.

The logarithmic-spiral method has been investigated, and a mathematical trial solution has been developed by the author which gives the stability numbers in column (6) of Table 16·1. These values are almost exactly the same as those by the ϕ-circle method and, in addition, the failure surfaces according to the two methods almost coincide. Thus the two methods give essentially identical results for simple slopes, and it would appear reasonable to believe that the agreement is about the same for more complex sections.

16·27 Definitions of Four Special Cases

In order to explain a number of important concepts it will be assumed that the slope shown in Fig. 16·28 and subsequent figures is subjected, in succession, to a number of different sets of conditions. First, it will be assumed to be submerged and just consolidated under the forces acting for such a condition, giving case I, the *submerged case*. Secondly, it will be assumed that all surrounding water is suddenly removed, giving case II, the *instantaneous, complete drawdown case*. Thirdly, it will be assumed that a constant supply of groundwater reaches the slope and that eventually a steady state of seepage is reached, with seepage occurring within a large part of the incipient failure mass, giving case III, the *steady seepage case*. No specific set of boundary conditions will be named, since the considerations in this case refer to a wide range of conditions of steady-state seepage. Fourthly and finally, it will be assumed that the groundwater supply becomes exhausted and the top flow line recedes, but that the entire soil mass remains essentially saturated by capillarity and eventually reaches complete consolidation under the new loading with the resultant of the water pressures on the incipient failure surface practically equal to zero. This gives case IV, the case of *zero boundary neutral force*.

It will be shown that these four cases in the order mentioned generally represent either unchanged or successively greater average intergranular pressures within the mass. For this reason it is possible for the same values of effective friction angle and effective cohesion to be valid for the successive cases under the condition of shear without drainage. If case I were to occur subsequent to case IV, some precompression would then exist, and the effective strength coefficients might be changed.

For very slow shear, leading to essentially complete drainage, case II is not possible. However, the following discussion is applicable to cases I, III, and IV for the condition of complete drainage, under which condition the same effective soil characteristics could hold for the three cases.

The four cases will be discussed in order, and each will be treated in considerable detail. The discussions apply to any trial circle and all conclusions reached apply to any circle; therefore the conclusions must be valid for the critical circle. The values of cohesion considered are the resultant cohesion needed for stability and the actual resultant cohesion. When the explanations require mention of a safety factor the factor of safety with respect to height will be used. In this discussion the difference between the ϕ circle and the modified ϕ circle will be disregarded. It will be assumed that the soil is completely saturated.

16·28 Case I, the Submerged Case

For the submerged case the forces which enter the analysis are shown in Fig. 16·28. The total weight of the soil may be written

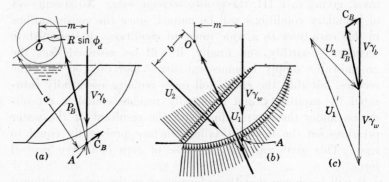

Fig. 16·28 The submerged case.

$V\gamma_t$, or $V(\gamma_b + \gamma_w)$, as explained in Section 7·2. The submerged weight $V\gamma_b$ is the only actuating force in the submerged case. The remainder of the true total weight $V\gamma_w$ is a weight which certainly exists but is here just supported by the boundary neutral or buoyancy forces U_1 and U_2, which are shown by both vectors and distribution diagrams in (b). Force triangles are shown in (c).

Moment equilibrium for the forces shown in (a) is expressed:

$$V\gamma_b m = P_B R \sin \phi_d + C_B a \qquad (16 \cdot 22)$$

Moment equilibrium for the force system shown in (b) may be written

$$V\gamma_w m = U_2 b \qquad (16 \cdot 23)$$

or, in words, the moment of the buoyed weight $V\gamma_w$ is just balanced by the moment of water pressures across the surface of the slope. It may be noted that the left-hand side of equation $16 \cdot 22$ may, if desired, be written

$$V\gamma_b m + V\gamma_w m - U_2 b \quad \text{or} \quad V\gamma_T m - U_2 b \qquad (16 \cdot 24)$$

The factor of safety with respect to height in this case is

$$(F_H)_1 = \frac{Ca}{C_B a} = \frac{Ca}{V\gamma_b m - P_B R \sin \phi_d} \qquad (16 \cdot 25)$$

in which C without subscript represents the actual total cohesion.

Solutions for simple submerged slopes are easily handled by the use of the stability charts of Figs. $16 \cdot 26$ and $16 \cdot 27$. In such solutions the submerged unit weight must be used for the unit weight value in the stability number. The submerged unit weight is equal to $[(G - 1)/(1 + e)]\gamma_w$, and for most soils its value falls between 50 and 70 lb per cu ft.

16·29   Case II, the Instantaneous, Complete Drawdown Case

The sudden drawdown case considered in this section is the extreme case of *instantaneous* removal of all impounded water from a *completely submerged* slope.

Drawdowns at actual dams and embankments can never be spoken of as truly instantaneous. Complete drawdowns do not often occur, since the water level before drawdown is seldom exactly at the top of an embankment, and the height of drawdown is seldom as large as the height of the slope. However, a drawdown may be considered instantaneous if no appreciable drainage is able to take place in the vicinity of the incipient rupture surface during the drawdown period. A complete drawdown is an extreme case, yet its occurrence is possible and its consideration is necessary. There are situations in which case II may be accepted as a reasonably close approximation of actual conditions. In other instances solutions based on case II are of considerable value because they define an upper limit.

The change in actuating force introduced by a sudden drawdown may be considered to be merely the removal of force U_2 of Fig. 16·28. The removal of this force causes a more severe loading condition, because the moment of force U_2 no longer balances that of weight $V\gamma_w$, as stated in equation 16·23. Therefore, the total

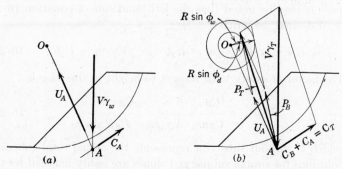

FIG. 16·29 The drawdown case.

actuating force may be considered to be the total weight $V\gamma_t$, which is of the order of twice the actuating force $V\gamma_b$ of the submerged case. The increase in actuating force causes no increase in shearing strength, however, because the strength cannot increase unless water escapes from the pores of the soil.

The forces entering the sudden drawdown analysis may be considered to be the combination of the forces of the submerged case, shown in Fig. 16·28 (a), and the force system consisting of $V\gamma_w$ and the forces required to balance it, shown in Fig. 16·29 (a). The suddenly applied force $V\gamma_w$ can introduce no intergranular pressure and can develop no friction and, therefore, the force U_A, acting across the arc, must be a neutral force and must pass through point O. The figures show that the additional required cohesion C_A is considerably larger than C_B of the submerged case. The point of concurrency of the forces of both Figs. 16·28 (a) and 16·29 (a) is point A.

The combination of the two force systems mentioned above is

the total force system of the drawdown case; it is shown in Fig. 16·29 (*b*). The resultant of $V\gamma_b$ and $V\gamma_w$ is $V\gamma_t$, that of C_B and C_A is C_T; these two combinations are determined by simple addition. The vector sum of force P_B, which is tangent to the ϕ_d circle, and force U_A, which passes through point O, is force P_T.

A circle may be drawn which has its center at O and which is tangent to force P_T, as shown in the figure. It is called the *weighted friction circle* or the ϕ_w *circle*; its radius is $R \sin \phi_w$, the angle ϕ_w being the angle of obliquity of force P_T to the rupture arc. Setting the moment of force P_T about point O equal to the moments of its constituents, P_B and U_A, gives

$$P_T(R \sin \phi_w) = P_B(R \sin \phi_d)$$

whence

$$\sin \phi_w = \frac{P_B}{P_T} \sin \phi_d \qquad (16\cdot26)$$

This equation is not satisfactory for the determination of ϕ_w because the value of the ratio P_B/P_T is not easily obtained. However, a simple, approximate expression which may be used in its place with very little sacrifice of accuracy is

$$\phi_w = \frac{\gamma_b}{\gamma_t} \phi_d \text{ (approx.)} \qquad (16\cdot27)$$

The expression for moment equilibrium for this case is

$$V\gamma_t m = P_T R \sin \phi_w + C_T a \qquad (16\cdot28)$$

The factor of safety with respect to height is

$$(F_H)_{\text{II}} = \frac{Ca}{C_T a} = \frac{Ca}{V\gamma_t m - P_T R \sin \phi_w} \qquad (16\cdot29)$$

Solutions for the limiting case of instantaneous complete drawdown for simple slopes may be made directly by the use of the charts in Figs. 16·26 and 16·27. In such solutions the values applying for unit weight and friction angle are the total unit weight γ_t, which has values that fall between 110 and 130 lb per cu ft for most soils, and the weighted friction angle ϕ_w, which may be determined by the use of equation 16·27.

16·30   Case III, the Steady Seepage Case

After a drawdown, whether it is sudden or relatively slow, seepage occurs. If sufficient time is allowed, consolidation under the new force system takes place and, if the boundary conditions remain constant, a steady state of seepage eventually is reached. The amount of time required for consolidation depends on the permeability of the soil and on the drainage facilities. In a saturated embankment of impervious clay consolidation is likely to take place very slowly.

The steady seepage case, as understood herein, has complete consolidation. Partial consolidation gives an intermediate case between cases II and III. In case III the resultant seepage force depends on boundary conditions and is especially dependent on the location of the top flow line. Thus no rigorous general solution is possible, and an exact solution requires the use of the flow net which holds for the given conditions. However, it may be shown that the case of steady seepage is in general slightly more stable than the sudden drawdown case, and thus the stability number for the sudden drawdown case may often be used as a conservative approximation of the stability number under steady seepage.

For an analysis of forces let it be assumed that a protracted period of heavy rainfall has maintained the free water surface just at ground level, thus preventing the existence of a capillary fringe. This condition gives seepage throughout the slope, and it is the most unfavorable of steady seepage cases. This steady seepage case is represented in Fig. 16·30. In (b) the resultant actuating force B is either the submerged weight $V\gamma_b$ plus the resultant seepage force J or the total weight $V\gamma_t$ plus the resultant boundary neutral force U_{III}, as explained in Sections 9·18 and 16·15. The three forces B, C_{III}, and P_{III} have their point of concurrency at A_{III} in (a). Point A_{III} is located to the left of point A of the previous cases and, therefore, vector P_{III} has a line of action which is more nearly vertical than the lines of action of vectors P_B and P_T of cases I and II. Consolidation under the seepage force J causes increases in intergranular pressures, and the direction of action of this force shows that the largest increases occur over the lower portion of the incipient rupture arc.

Meanwhile decreases in neutral pressures take place and the largest decreases occur over the lower portion of the arc. Therefore neutral force U_{III} must have a line of action that cuts the rupture surface somewhat higher than it is cut by U_A of case II, and U_{III} must have a slope that is somewhat flatter than the slope of U_A. The force polygon of case II, from Fig. 16·29 (b), is shown by dashed lines in Fig. 16·30 (b) to aid in comparing the force systems of cases II and III.

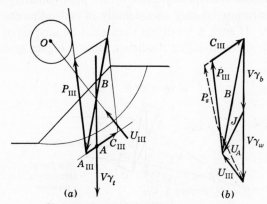

Fig. 16·30 The steady seepage case.

Figure 16·30 (b) shows a required cohesion in case III which is smaller than that in case II. Pure reasoning shows this to be logical, since drainage of water from the mass after a drawdown must mean added shearing strength and, therefore, a smaller required cohesion. Exceptions to this relationship are possible under unusual conditions (for instance, when artesian pressures develop after drawdown), but in general it would appear that the adjustment to the steady seepage case leads to somewhat greater stability.

When the top flow line is below ground surface, a still safer condition exists, since force U_{III} is smaller and, therefore, force C_{III} is smaller than in the case illustrated by Fig. 16·30. When there is a capillary fringe above the top flow line, the body force is given by the vector sum of forces $V\gamma_t$ and U or by the vector sum of buoyed W, seepage force J, and the capillary force which is exerted on the grain structure by the water within the capillary fringe; in the latter case the buoyed weight is based on unit weight γ_t above and γ_b below the free water surface. If seepage occurs in only a small portion of the mass above the critical surface, the case approaches case IV.

16·31   Case IV, the Case with Zero Resultant Boundary Neutral Force

Cases in which the resultant neutral forces across the incipient failure surfaces are equal to zero, or are approximately equal to zero, are encountered only occasionally in embankments of saturated clay. If such a condition does exist at any given time, it may not be the controlling condition, since a higher groundwater

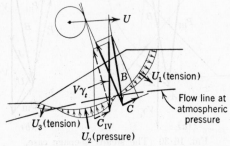

FIG. 16·31   A case that may be approximated by the case of zero boundary neutral force.

table and fairly large magnitude of seepage force may be present during some other season of the year. However, there are instances in which case IV can reasonably be assumed, and frequently occurring examples of cases falling between cases II and IV can be solved approximately by interpolations between results based on these two special cases.

For determining how closely the conditions in any given instance conform to case IV, some idea of the magnitude of the pore-water stresses is needed. It is possible to determine these stresses from bore holes. If no water enters at the base of the hole, there is no water pressure. However, it must be realized that in fine clays the water may enter a bore hole too slowly to give satisfactory indications of this type.

A case in which the resultant boundary neutral force is small is represented in Fig. 16·31. The forces acting are shown by full line vectors. The force in the water across the critical surface is made up of forces U_1 and U_3, which represent tension, and force U_2, which represents pressure. The vector sum of these three forces is the resultant boundary neutral force U, which is here a small force acting in an approximately horizontal direction and directed away from the center of the circle. The vector sum of forces $V\gamma_t$ and U is the actuating force B. A solution by the ϕ-circle method gives force C as the required cohesion.

If the boundary neutral force is disregarded, the conditions conform to case IV. For this special case $V\gamma_t$ is the actuating force, the ϕ-circle method gives the dashed line vectors, and force C_{IV} is obtained as the required cohesion. The figure shows that forces C and C_{IV} are approximately equal in this instance. Therefore, it may be concluded that case IV can reasonably be assumed to approximate the actual case represented in this figure.

Stability analyses for case IV are easily obtained for simple slopes by the use of the charts in Figs. 16·26 and 16·27. For this case the unit weight value that applies is γ_t which is the total unit weight of the essentially saturated soil, and the friction angle that applies is the developed angle ϕ_d.

According to the previous section the steady seepage case is more stable than the sudden drawdown case. According to the considerations of this section the case with a small zone or no zone of seepage within the failure mass is considerably more stable than the case with steady seepage throughout the mass. If the free water surface within the embankment is well below the critical surface, all boundary water stresses are tensions and a still more stable condition exists. As first steps in any preliminary study in which any of these conditions must be considered, solutions based on cases II and IV are valuable.

16·32   Example of Solutions for the Special Cases

A simple slope of 40-ft height has an inclination of 45 degrees. The soil is saturated and highly impervious. At present the slope is completely submerged, but it is known that a rapid, complete drawdown will take place in a short time and, eventually, the water table may recede to an average level somewhat below the toe of the slope.

There is apprehension that the slope may fail when the draw-down occurs. Therefore, factors of safety for this case are wanted and comparable values of present and eventual factors of safety are also desired.

Laboratory tests on specimens in which no drainage is permitted furnish the following average soil characteristics:

$$\gamma_t = 130 \text{ lb per cu ft}$$

$$c_e = 600 \text{ lb per sq ft}$$

$$\phi_e = 20 \text{ degrees}$$

DETERMINATIONS OF FACTORS OF SAFETY WITH RESPECT TO HEIGHT

Submerged Case. For $\phi = 20$ degrees and $i = 45$ degrees Fig. 16·26 gives the stability number 0.062.

$$0.062 = \frac{c_e}{F_H \gamma_b H} = \frac{600}{F_H \times (130 - 62.5) \times 40}$$

whence $F_H = 3.58$.

Sudden Drawdown Case.

$$\phi_w = \frac{130 - 62.5}{130} \times \phi_d = 10.4 \text{ degrees}$$

and for $\phi = 10.4$ degrees and $i = 45$ degrees, Fig. 16·26 gives 0.106 for the stability number.

$$0.106 = \frac{600}{F_H \times 130 \times 40}$$

whence $F_H = 1.09$.

Zero Boundary Neutral Case. The stability number is the same as in the submerged case, and

$$0.062 = \frac{600}{F_H \times 130 \times 40}$$

whence $F_H = 1.86$.

DETERMINATIONS OF FACTORS OF SAFETY WITH RESPECT TO STRENGTH

Submerged Case. Since the unknown F_s appears in both $c_d = c_e/F_s$ and $\tan \phi_d = \tan \phi_e/F_s$, a trial method of solution must be used. If F_s equals 2.0, the allowable height may be determined as follows:

$$\phi_d = \tan^{-1}\left(\frac{\tan \phi_e}{F_s}\right) = \tan^{-1}\left(\frac{\tan 20}{2}\right) = 10.3 \text{ degrees}$$

For $\phi = 10.3$ degrees and $i = 45$ degrees, Fig. 16·26 gives 0.106 for the stability number.

$$0.106 = \frac{600}{2 \times 67.5 \times H}$$

whence $H = 42$ ft, if $F_s = 2.0$.

If $F_s = 2.1$, $\tan^{-1}\left(\frac{\tan 20}{2.1}\right) = 9.8$ degrees, and the chart gives 0.109 for the stability number.

$$0.109 = \frac{600}{2.1 \times 67.5 \times H}$$

whence $H = 38.8$ ft, if $F_s = 2.1$.

Since H actually equals 40 ft, interpolation gives $F_s = 2.06$.

Drawdown Case. The trial procedure is again required. Let the trial value be $F_s = 1.06$. From the previous solution for the drawdown case $\phi_w = 10.4$ degrees. Here $\tan^{-1}\left(\frac{\tan 10.4}{1.06}\right) = 9.8$ degrees, and for $\phi = 9.8$ degrees and $i = 45$ degrees the chart gives 0.109 for the stability number.

$$0.109 = \frac{600}{1.06 \times 130 \times H}$$

whence $H = 40$ ft, showing that the trial value was correct; therefore $F_s = 1.06$.

Zero Boundary Neutral Case. Let the trial value be $F_s = 1.38$. For this case $\tan^{-1}\left(\frac{\tan 20}{1.38}\right) = 14.8$ degrees, and for $\phi = 14.8$ degrees and $i = 45$ degrees the stability number is 0.084.

$$0.084 = \frac{600}{1.38 \times 130 \times H}$$

whence $H = 40$ ft, showing that the assumption was correct; therefore $F_s = 1.38$.

Case	F_H	F_s
I. Submerged	3.58	2.06
II. Sudden drawdown	1.09	1.06
IV. Zero boundary neutral force	1.86	1.38

16·33 Constant Strength and the So-Called ϕ = 0 Case

In some embankment investigations it is found that the shearing strength can be represented almost as closely by a constant value as it can by some form of Coulomb's Law with strength varying linearly with pressure. A common example is the non-homogeneous embankment wherein the scattering of strength values at various points within the mass makes it difficult to establish any definite tendency toward variation of strength with depth.

There are also cases in which the shearing strength definitely increases with pressure and depth, but in which it is possible to obtain a reasonably accurate estimate of the average pressure $\bar{\sigma}_{av}$. If this average pressure is used in the expression

$$s_{av} = c_e + \bar{\sigma}_{av} \tan \phi_e \qquad (16 \cdot 30)$$

and if the average shearing strength s_{av} is assumed to be the shearing strength throughout, the results sometimes are as good as those obtained when working with a variable strength. However, if some trial arcs go deeper into the ground than others in such a case, poor results may be obtained unless larger values of s_{av} are used for the arcs that penetrate to the greater depths.

All types of stability analysis are much simpler when the shearing strength is assumed to be constant, as is suggested above, and this simplified approach has much merit and is entirely reasonable if correctly used. In addition it is often advantageous to make check computations by this simple procedure when analyses that are known to be more accurate have been made in which variable strength has been assumed.

Solutions for cases of constant shearing strength may be made for simple slopes by the use of stability charts, by considering the effective cohesion to be the average shearing strength, and by considering the friction angle to be zero. Graphical solutions may also be conducted on a similar basis.

The procedure discussed above has had considerable use and has come to be called the $\phi = 0$ case. This designation definitely is a misnomer, and it may well be argued that it should be discontinued. However, most of the undesirable aspects of the use of this name are avoided if it is realized that the true friction angle of a soil is never zero and that this case is merely an example of substitution of an average value for a variable quantity.

If an accurate average pressure is used in equation $16 \cdot 30$, the results of analyses based on circular failure surfaces are the same as those obtained when a variable pressure is used, because the resisting moments are the same, $R \tan \phi_e \Sigma \bar{\sigma} dA$ being equal to $R \tan \phi_e \bar{\sigma}_{av} A$. It should be mentioned that the major principal plane is actually at an angle of, roughly, 60 degrees to the failure

plane in most soils, rather than at the 45-degree angle implied
by the expression $\phi = 0$; this factor would require consideration
in certain types of stress distribution analyses, but it does not
affect the procedure or the data of the types of stability analyses
than are commonly used.

16·34   The Effect of Stratification on the Shape of Failure Surfaces

If stratification exists in an embankment, as it does to some
degree in the majority of natural soils, there is a tendency for
rupture arcs to deviate from the usual approximately circular
arc, following the strata somewhat as illustrated in Fig. 16·32.
This action results because the shearing strength parallel to the
strata is usually smaller than the shearing strength across the
strata.

An approximate method that may be used in investigations

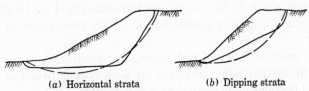

(*a*) Horizontal strata   (*b*) Dipping strata

Fig. 16·32   Shapes of failure surfaces in stratified soils.

dealing with stratified soils consists, first, of laboratory tests to
obtain the shearing strengths on planes parallel to the strata;
then the stratification is ignored, the shearing strengths that
have been obtained are assumed to be valid for all surfaces
through the embankment, the assumption of circular failure arcs
is used, and the analysis is carried through according to the usual
procedures.   The explanation of the reasonably accurate results
obtained by this method may be obtained by reference to Fig.
16·32.   It is known that any two trial failure surfaces that are
close together have practically the same safety factors; thus the
small differences in position between the circular arcs and the
actual failure surfaces in the figure will not have an appreciable
effect on the results.   The shearing strengths that are assumed
to exist along the circular arc are the correct strengths along the
strata, and the portions of the actual rupture surfaces that fol-

low the strata are over 50 per cent in (*a*) and about 75 per cent in (*b*); thus the strengths assumed are essentially correct for more than one half of the rupture surfaces. The portions of the actual failure surface that are not parallel to the strata are the shallower parts; therefore their pressures and shearing strengths are relatively small and they are the portions in which strength loss due to surface cracks occurs. These considerations are the basis of the conclusions that the approximate method explained above is slightly conservative if there is a moderate amount of difference between the shearing strengths across the strata and parallel to the strata, and that it may be quite conservative if the shearing strengths across the strata are relatively large.

In some materials, such as varved clays and shales, the shearing strength across the strata may be many times greater than it is parallel to the strata; in such materials the approximate method given above should not be used. In these highly stratified materials a dip in the strata, as illustrated in Fig. 16·32 (*b*), gives a much greater possibility of failure than exists in level strata.

The great majority of soils have some stratification, and it is quite likely that failure surfaces are somewhat flattened in their central portions more often than is generally realized.

PROBLEMS

1. A certain surface that passes through an embankment and that is believed to be the surface most liable to failure has a length of 50 ft. The shearing force on this surface is 32.5 tons per running ft of embankment. Tests indicate that the shearing strength of the soil may be represented by the expression $\bar{\sigma} \tan 10° + 1000$ lb per sq ft. The average value of $\bar{\sigma}$ on the given surface is 4500 lb per sq ft. Determine the safety factors relative to strength and height.

2. An embankment of dry sand, weighing 105 lb per cu ft, has a surface that extends for several hundred feet at a slope of 4 to 1 (4 horizontal to 1 vertical). The friction angle of the sand is 34 degrees. Sketch a Mohr diagram showing stresses at a depth of 10 ft, and from the diagram determine the largest and smallest stresses that are possible on the vertical plane at this depth. Check your results by formula.

3. Assume that the embankment of Prob. 2 has been completely saturated and that the top flow line coincides with the ground surface. Draw the Mohr diagram of stresses at a depth of 10 ft, and from it determine the

range of intergranular pressures possible on vertical planes. Comment on the stability of the embankment.

4. A 20-degree slope of great extent is subject to seepage throughout with the top flow line coinciding with the ground surface. The true unit weight of the soil is 120 lb per cu ft. Consider a column of soil of 1 sq ft horizontal area and 10 ft high, determine magnitudes and directions of the following forces acting on it, and show the relationship existing between these forces: true weight, buoyant weight, boundary water force, and seepage force.

5. At a depth of 10 ft below the surface of a saturated 20-degree slope of great extent there is no pressure in the pore water. The soil within this 10-ft depth is a clay that is essentially saturated by capillarity, and thus there is seepage throughout this zone. The true unit weight of the soil is 120 lb per cu ft. Consider a column of soil of 1 sq ft horizontal area and 10 ft high, determine the following forces and their components normal and parallel to the surface of the slope, and demonstrate the relationship between these forces: true weight, buoyant weight, boundary water force, seepage force, and capillary force at ground surface.

6. A slope of great extent is to be constructed of cohesionless soil, and it will occasionally be subject to seepage throughout with the free water surface at ground surface. The soil has a friction angle of 33 degrees. It has been specified that the slope must have a safety factor of 1.5 with respect to strength. What is the maximum inclination that the slope may have?

7. Construct a stability chart with coordinates as in Fig. 16·26, this chart to be applicable to cases represented by both equations 16·12 and 16·13. On a corner of the sheet sketch the cross section for which the chart is applicable.

8. A 20-degree slope of great extent is composed of clay of 12-ft depth with ledge below. The clay has properties as follows: effective cohesion 500 lb per sq ft; effective friction angle 15 degrees; true unit weight, 120 lb per cu ft. Determine the factors of safety relative to strength and depth for this slope, (a) if there is no water pressure at the bottom of the clay layer; (b) if the free water surface coincides with the surface of the clay.

9. A stability analysis by the method of slices for a 45-degree slope which is 28 ft high gives the following data on forces on the most dangerous circular arc: algebraic sums of forces in pounds per running foot are 32,800 for shearing forces, 61,700 for total normal forces, and 13,100 for neutral forces; the length of the rupture arc is 64.5 ft. Laboratory tests have furnished values of 15 degrees for effective friction angle and 420 lb per sq ft for effective cohesion. Determine (a) the factor of safety with respect to shearing strength, (b) the factor of safety with respect to cohesion for the given circular arc.

10. Make a graphical analysis based on the method of slices for a 38-degree slope and a developed friction angle of 10 degrees, assuming that no seepage is occurring. Use the critical arc as given by data in Table 16·2

and use a 2-in. height of slope. Obtain the stability number and compare with the value given by Table 16·1.

11. Make the graphical analysis called for in Prob. 9, using the same cross section and the same arc as a trial failure surface and obtaining similar results, but base the analysis on the assumption that seepage is occurring and that the equipotential lines of the flow net are as given in Fig. 16·12 (a).

12. Make the analysis called for in Prob. 9, using the ϕ-circle method instead of the method of slices.

13. Make the analysis called for in Prob. 10, using the ϕ-circle method.

14. Revise equation 16·21 so that it applies to a slope that is subject to earthquakes. Use all asumptions underlying this equation, but add as quake allowance a horizontal force that equals 10 per cent of the weight of the failure mass.

15. It is planned to cut a 70-degree slope 40 ft high, measured vertically, in soil having a unit weight of 130 lb per cu ft, an effective cohesion of 800 lb per sq ft, and an effective friction angle of 15 degrees. Neglecting all possibility of seepage through the embankment, determine the factor of safety with respect to height. Give an opinion as to whether the slope may be considered safe (a) if there is no seepage, (b) if seepage occurs throughout the major portion of the mass.

16. A 45-degree simple slope is composed of soil with an effective cohesion of 400 lb per sq ft, an effective friction angle of 18 degrees, and a unit weight of 130 lb per cu ft. Determine the critical height of this slope for the special cases of sudden drawdown and zero boundary neutral pressure, and discuss the value of these special cases for obtaining an indication of the critical height for a case in which a steady state of seepage is occurring throughout most of the embankment.

17. Along the circle shown the cohesion required to maintain equilibrium of the slope indicated by solid line is 500 lb per sq ft. For this case the area of the mass is 1700 sq ft, and its centroid is at point X. If the slope is cut back parallel to itself to the position shown by dashed lines, what will be the cohesion required along the same circle? The effective friction angle of the soil is to be assumed equal to zero.

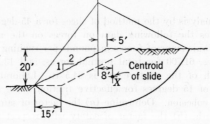

PROB. 16·17.

18. Laboratory tests on a certain soil give the following data: $\gamma_t = 135$ lb per cu ft; $c_e = 450$ lb per sq ft; $\phi_e = 12$ degrees. The bank of a canal con-

sists of this soil; this bank is at a 2 to 1 slope, has a height of 30 ft, and for this analysis may be considered completely submerged. A removal of the water in the canal is to occur in the near future, and eventually the free water surface will recede to just below the bottom of the canal. Determine factors of safety with respect to strength and height, and discuss their applicability to present and future stability conditions in this slope.

19. A cut 30 ft deep is to be made in a deposit of highly cohesive soil that is 60 ft deep and is underlaid by ledge. The shearing strength is essentially constant throughout the depth at 500 lb per sq ft. The unit weight of the soil is 120 lb per cu ft. It has been specified that the factor of safety with respect to strength must be 1.25. How flat should the side slopes of the cut be made?

Chapter 17

LATERAL PRESSURES
STABILITY OF RETAINING WALLS

17·1 Lateral Pressures, Their Practical Importance and the Role of Soil Mechanics in Their Determination

One of the most widely used applications of soil mechanics relates to the investigation of the stability of walls that resist lateral earth pressures. In general the civil engineer will make only occasional use of some of the types of analyses outlined in the foregoing pages, whereas it is likely that he will frequently be called on to estimate lateral pressures and analyze some type of retaining wall.

Lateral pressure data are used in the design of many types of structures and structural members, common examples being retaining walls of the gravity and other types, sheet pile bulkheads, basement walls of buildings and other walls that retain earth fills, and sheeting of pits and trenches. Often the lateral pressures are statically indeterminate and are therefore difficult to evaluate, and in many instances lateral pressures cannot be estimated with the accuracy the engineer usually likes to maintain. In this connection soil mechanics plays an important role, since knowledge of the fundamental relationships between strains, time effects, and lateral pressures in soils not only contributes to more accurate pressure estimates but it can also give the engineer much information regarding which cases allow reasonably accurate estimates and which cases contain factors that preclude accurate determinations.

17·2 Fundamental Relationships between the Lateral Pressures and the Strains within a Backfill

By means of tests on a large scale model retaining wall Terzaghi (145, 141) demonstrated in 1929 that the lateral force on a wall varies as the wall undergoes lateral movement. The relationship between the force and the movement is shown in Fig. 17·1. The ordinate of point A represents the force on a wall which has been held rigidly in place while a sand backfill has been placed behind it. If the wall undergoes movement in the direction away from the backfill, the force decreases and after a small movement reaches a minimum value at point B. If the wall is forced against the backfill, the force between the wall and the fill increases, reaching a maximum value at point C.

An explanation of Fig. 17·1 has been given in Chapter 16. At point B the thrust on the wall is the *active thrust*, and at point C the thrust is the *passive thrust*. It has been shown in Section 16·10 that the active pressure is equal to roughly one quarter of the vertical pressure, and the passive pressure is equal to roughly four times the vertical pressure at any depth. Since the lateral pressure would equal the vertical pressure if the material were a fluid, ratios of the type illustrated by the above-mentioned approximate values of 1/4 and 4 are sometimes called *hydrostatic pressure ratios*.

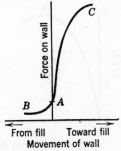

Fig. 17·1 Effect of movement of a wall on the lateral thrust.

Under the condition of no movement of the wall the soil has undergone no strains in the past except the slight vertical compression caused by the placing of overlying soil. The lateral pressure for this condition is called the *lateral pressure at rest*. Hydrostatic pressure ratios for lateral pressures at rest in sands have been determined by a number of experimental methods. Terzaghi (141) has quoted typical values of 0.45 to 0.50 for loose sands and 0.40 to 0.45 for dense sands. In clays the corresponding ratios may be about twice as large as these values.

The considerations of the slope of infinite extent in Sections 16·8 to 16·10 inclusive explain the variations of thrust shown in Fig. 17·1. However, the case of the infinite mass differs from the case of the yielding wall in two respects, both of which are of outstanding practical importance. The first difference results from frictional forces which develop at the wall and cause deviation from the infinite slope characteristic of like stresses on all vertical planes. The second difference results from wedge action which leads to arching unless the wall yields in a particular manner. These two important items will be discussed separately.

For an explanation of friction on the wall reference will be made to the cylindrical compression test, described in Section 14·3. While the ratio σ_1/σ_3 in this type of test is building up to its maximum or ϕ-obliquity value, which is approximately equal

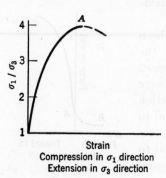

Strain
Compression in σ_1 direction
Extension in σ_3 direction

Fig. 17·2 General form of stress-strain curve.

to 4, the sample compresses in the σ_1 direction and expands in the σ_3 direction, as shown in Fig. 17·2. This relationship holds while σ_1/σ_3 is increasing regardless of other conditions; it is independent of such details as whether or not σ_3 is constant. When the lateral pressure is approaching the active pressure within an infinite slope, the soil is expanding laterally, σ_3 is decreasing, and σ_1 is essentially constant. The most significant point in the present connection,

however, is that meanwhile the soil is compressing vertically. If a wall is adjacent to the soil, the wall height is a fixed dimension, and thus the soil bearing against the wall must, as it compresses, move downward relative to the wall, with the wall exerting frictional resistance to this movement. As the wall moves outward there is a possibility that it may settle at the same time, in which case the friction may be prevented from developing, but such a settlement of the wall is unusual. Terzaghi's large scale model wall tests showed that the resultant force against the wall is at an obliquity as large or nearly as large as the friction angle. The friction angle in this case is either ϕ', the friction angle of soil against masonry, or the internal friction angle of the soil ϕ, whichever is the smaller.

The condition described above is a major variation from the conjugate stress relationship that holds in the infinite slope. Careful study of conditions existing at actual retaining walls shows that a frictional component of force may always be depended upon to act when a wall is in danger of failure. All or nearly all of the possible wall friction will develop in general and, if full friction develops the direction of the resultant force on the retaining wall will be as shown in Fig. 17·3.

For an understanding of wedge action the orientations at which failure planes occur for the active case in the infinite slope should first be noted. These orientations were shown in Fig. 16·6 by the dashed lines through point C. For the infinite slope with a level surface Fig. 17·4 illustrates the stress conditions for the active and passive cases. The failure planes for the active case are at an angle of $45 + \phi/2$ degrees to the horizontal, as shown by the dashed lines through point A. When the active case is reached in the infinite slope, slip is occurring on all planes that have a slope of $45 + \phi/2$ degrees. Similarly, if the wall in Fig. 17·5 (*a*) yields until the active case is reached, slip can occur on

Fig. 17·3 The condition of full wall friction.

planes that have a $45 + \phi/2$ slope and that are above AB, but lateral yield does not occur within the fill below point A and, therefore, slip cannot occur on planes below AB. In this case the failure or ϕ-obliquity condition is confined to the wedge-shaped zone ABC. This zone is called the *failure wedge*.

Important concepts relative to the distribution of pressure on the wall may be explained by considerations of strain conditions within the failure wedge. Let Fig. 17·5 (*a*) represent the case wherein the wall is subject to *pressure at rest*. The light grid-work on this figure is used to illustrate strains that occur in cases discussed later; it represents planes that initially are horizontal and planes on which slip may take place if an active case is reached. The pressures at rest are represented in Fig. 17·5 (*b*) by the pressure diagram CFA. The line CF is called an *intensity line*. At any elevation the distance from the intensity line to the wall surface, measured in the direction of action of the pressure, is the pressure intensity. Thus the area of the intensity diagram represents the normal component of the thrust on the wall. In the at-rest case the pressures are assumed to act in the horizontal direction, and at any depth z the pressure is approximately equal to $\frac{1}{2}\gamma z$.

Let it now be assumed that the wall yields by rotation about point A by an amount sufficient to give active pressures on the wall. During this rotation the wedge ABC distorts in essentially uniform manner throughout to the shape ABC' of Fig. 17·5 (c). The uniform distortion leads to a ϕ-obliquity condition throughout, and active pressures occur on the wall over its entire height. At any depth z the active pressure is approximately equal to $\frac{1}{4}\gamma z$ and, if wall friction is neglected, the intensity line is repre-

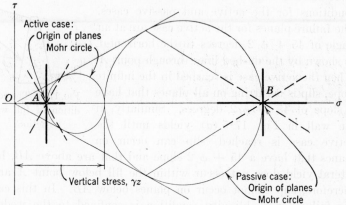

FIG. 17·4 Mohr diagram showing the active and passive states of stress in a soil mass with a level surface.

sented in Fig. 17·5 (b) by CG. The revised positions of the grid lines of (a) are shown in (c). Actually the base of the failure wedge deviates somewhat from a plane, and for the sake of simplicity the above explanation is also somewhat idealized in other respects. However, the general concept given by this explanation is essentially correct.

Another case will now be considered in which the wall starts from the at-rest condition and yields by moving outward with its surface remaining vertical. In this case the wedge collapses somewhat as shown in (d), and failure and the ϕ-obliquity condition occur only in a thin zone in the vicinity of line AB. The major portion of the wedge is not appreciably distorted, and therefore the lateral pressure on the upper portion of the wall remains about as it was in (a). In spite of this the total force on the wall in (d) is approximately the same as it was in (c), as the force triangle in (*e*) shows. In both cases the weight of wedge *ABC* is *W*, which must be in equilibrium with the intergranular force *F* and the wall thrust *P*. Force *W* has the same magnitude and direction in (*c*) and (*d*), and the other two forces have orientations that are the same in (*c*) and (*d*). Thus force *P*, representing the resultant of all pressure on the wall, must be

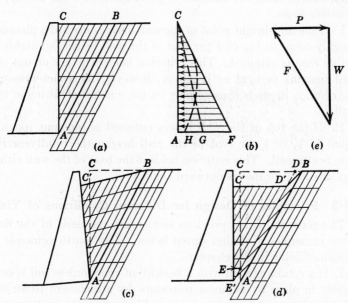

FIG. 17·5 Cross sections illustrating the action in the totally active and arching-active cases (wall friction neglected).

of essentially the same magnitude in (*c*) and (*d*). It follows that the pressure distribution on the wall in (*d*) must be roughly as represented by the curved intensity line *CH* in (*b*). The high pressures that occur near the top of the wall and correspondingly high pressures that occur on the upper portion of surface *AB* constitute an *arching action* that has been described in detail by Terzaghi (141); it is a distinguishing characteristic of the case represented by (*d*).

The above discussion shows that the stress distribution on the wall depends principally on whether or not the failure wedge distorts throughout. The case of Fig. 17·5 (*c*) with an active condition throughout and a triangular distribution of pressure on the wall is designated herein as the *totally active case*. The case of Fig. 17·5 (*d*), which shows essentially the same total thrust on the wall as occurs in (*c*) but has a roughly parabolic pressure distribution, is called herein the *arching-active case*.

For one typical dense sand Terzaghi (141) has given rough quantitative values of amounts of yield needed for the two types of active cases.

I. If the mid-height point of the wall moves outward a distance roughly equal to $\frac{1}{20}$ of 1 per cent of the wall height, an arching-active case is attained. This criterion holds whether or not the wall remains vertical as it moves; however, the exact pressure distribution depends considerably on the amount of tilting of the wall.

II. If the top of the wall moves outward an amount roughly equal to $\frac{1}{2}$ of 1 per cent of the wall height, the totally active case is attained. This criterion holds if the base of the wall either remains fixed or moves outward slightly.

17·3 Principles of Design for Different Conditions of Yield

The concepts of the previous section are the basis of the first three principles of design stated below. The fourth principle is explained later in the chapter.

I. If a retaining wall with a backfill of cohesionless soil is held rigidly in place by adjacent restraints, by attachment to an adjoining structure for example, it is likely that the wall cannot yield without breaking important members which restrain it. In such a case the wall must be designed to resist a thrust that is larger than the active value, and for the completely restrained case it should be designed to resist pressures at rest. However, this condition will not occur often, as is evidenced by the relatively small yield required to give the case discussed in the next paragraph.

II. If a retaining wall with a backfill of cohesionless soil is restrained in such a way that it is able to undergo only a limited amount of outward movement, it is likely that this movement will be sufficient to give the arching-active case but not the totally active case. Under such conditions the assumption of a triangular distribution of pressure on the wall is entirely incorrect. The actual distribution is statically indeterminate to a high degree, but is roughly of parabolic form. A common example is the distribution of stresses on the sheeting of trenches, which is discussed in Section 17·11.

III. Gravity retaining walls and sheet-pile retaining walls that have cohesionless backfills and that are not attached to any adjacent structure, and all other retaining walls that can yield a considerable amount without undesirable results, are able to attain the totally active case. Therefore, their design on the basis of active pressure and triangular distribution of pressure is rational.

IV. The above statements relative to amounts of yield do not apply to walls that retain backfills of cohesive soil and especially not to those which retain soil with a high degree of plasticity. In cohesive soils the amount of yield required to give the active thrust on a wall is not unusually large but, because of plastic flow within the clay, the pressures behind the wall continuously tend to increase unless the wall is permitted to yield continuously. The continuous yield, although it is at a slow rate, may lead to a large movement over a period of years. Nevertheless, if a wall is capable of withstanding the movement with no undesirable effects, it may be designed on the basis of the active pressures. Such a basis of design is common, but the probable life of a wall with a cohesive backfill may be relatively short. This subject is discussed in more detail in Section 17·18.

According to the above principles any wall that is capable of yielding without detrimental results may be designed on the basis of the active case. However, the pressure which will act on such a wall will in general be larger than the active pressure. Furthermore the pressure distribution diagram may not be triangular even though the wall is designed on the basis of the totally active case. These statements, which may at first appear alarming, have for their explanation the fact that any wall must have a margin of safety; that is, the wall must be capable of staying in place under a thrust somewhat larger than the active thrust. This margin of strength prevents the wall from ever reaching the amount of yield required to give active conditions. The situation need not cause concern, because the moment the wall is subjected to an increase in thrust it merely yields a small amount. This yield immediately reduces the pressure, and an amount of yield sufficient to reduce the pressures to the active values will occur if ever necessary. Measurements of pressures on retaining walls are sometimes made as a check on design theories, but such data may badly mislead the investigator unless he knows what information he seeks. Such data are more representative of the amounts of pressure the wall is capable of withstanding than of the active pressures.

17·4   The Rankine Theory

There are two well-known classical earth pressure theories, the Rankine theory and the Coulomb theory. Each furnishes expressions for active and passive pressures and thrusts caused by a cohesionless soil mass which is not subject to seepage forces. Each applies to the cross section of a long wall of constant section and gives results per unit of running length, that is, per unit

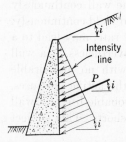

FIG. 17·6 The thrust and the pressure distribution on a vertical wall, according to the Rankine theory.

of distance normal to the section. These two theories are discussed in this and the following sections.

Rankine's theory (119) dates from 1860. It is based on the assumption that a conjugate relationship exists between the vertical pressures and the lateral pressures on vertical planes within the soil adjacent to a retaining wall. In other words, it is assumed that the presence of the wall introduces no changes in shearing stresses at the surface of contact between the wall and the backfill, since the conjugate relationship would hold, the stresses on the wall would closely resemble those on vertical planes within the infinite slope, and Rankine's theory would be correct were it not for changes in shearing stresses that are introduced by the presence of the wall.

In its simplest form the Rankine method refers to the active pressures and the active thrust on a vertical wall that retains a homogeneous cohesionless fill with surface at inclination i, as shown in Fig. 17·6. At any depth z below the surface of the fill the pressure for the totally active case acts parallel to the surface of the fill, and in accordance with equations 16·5 and 16·8 it is

$$p = \gamma z \cos i \, \frac{\cos i - \sqrt{\cos^2 i - \cos^2 \phi}}{\cos i + \sqrt{\cos^2 i - \cos^2 \phi}} \qquad (17 \cdot 1)$$

The resultant thrust on the wall for either the totally active or the arching-active case is

$$P = \tfrac{1}{2}\gamma H^2 \cos i \, \frac{\cos i - \sqrt{\cos^2 i - \cos^2 \phi}}{\cos i + \sqrt{\cos^2 i - \cos^2 \phi}} \qquad (17 \cdot 2)$$

Since the stress is of triangular distribution in the totally active case, the thrust acts at a height of ⅓H for that case. For the arching-active case the line of action of force P is at a height nearer to and possibly above mid-height. The pressures for the totally active case and the resultant thrust, as expressed by equations 17·1 and 17·2, are illustrated and their directions are shown in Fig. 17·6.

If the backfill is level, cos i becomes unity, and equations 17·1 and 17·2 reduce to the more familiar forms: *

$$p = \gamma z \, \frac{1 - \sin \phi}{1 + \sin \phi} = \gamma z \tan^2 \left(45 - \frac{1}{2}\phi \right) \qquad (17 \cdot 3)$$

$$P = \frac{1}{2}\gamma H^2 \, \frac{1 - \sin \phi}{1 + \sin \phi} = \frac{1}{2}\gamma H^2 \tan^2 \left(45 - \frac{1}{2}\phi \right) \qquad (17 \cdot 4)$$

A totally passive case exists if the backfill has been subjected to lateral compressions of sufficient magnitude to cause a ϕ-obliquity condition throughout the failure wedge. For this case

---

* The identity of the two expressions may be demonstrated as follows:

$$\tan^2 \left(45 - \frac{\phi}{2} \right) = \left[\frac{\sin \left(45 - \frac{\phi}{2} \right)}{\cos \left(45 - \frac{\phi}{2} \right)} \right]^2 = \left(\frac{0.707 \cos \frac{\phi}{2} - 0.707 \sin \frac{\phi}{2}}{0.707 \cos \frac{\phi}{2} + 0.707 \sin \frac{\phi}{2}} \right)^2$$

$$= \frac{\cos^2 \frac{\phi}{2} - 2 \cos \frac{\phi}{2} \sin \frac{\phi}{2} + \sin^2 \frac{\phi}{2}}{\cos^2 \frac{\phi}{2} + 2 \cos \frac{\phi}{2} \sin \frac{\phi}{2} + \sin^2 \frac{\phi}{2}} = \frac{1 - 2 \cos \frac{\phi}{2} \sin \frac{\phi}{2}}{1 + 2 \cos \frac{\phi}{2} \sin \frac{\phi}{2}}$$

$$= \frac{1 - \sin \phi}{1 + \sin \phi}$$

the Rankine expression for the lateral pressure at depth z is also given by equations $16 \cdot 5$ and $16 \cdot 8$; it is

$$p_P = \gamma z \cos i \, \frac{\cos i + \sqrt{\cos^2 i - \cos^2 \phi}}{\cos i - \sqrt{\cos^2 i - \cos^2 \phi}} \qquad (17 \cdot 5)$$

An expression for total thrust that is valid for either the totally passive or arching-passive case is

$$P_P = \tfrac{1}{2}\gamma H^2 \cos i \, \frac{\cos i + \sqrt{\cos^2 i - \cos^2 \phi}}{\cos i - \sqrt{\cos^2 i - \cos^2 \phi}} \qquad (17 \cdot 6)$$

Figure $17 \cdot 6$ was used to illustrate the pressures and the thrust for the totally active case, and on the basis of a much smaller stress scale it also illustrates the same items for the totally passive case.

When the face of the wall is not vertical, the lateral pressures on it can be obtained by the use of the Mohr diagram in Fig. $16 \cdot 6$. The stress for any batter of wall is given by the point of intersection of the circle and a line that passes through the origin of planes and is parallel to the wall surface. The reader who desires a complete understanding of all stresses within the failure wedge can study this diagram to advantage. However, determinations of pressures in practical problems may be obtained by the following procedure, which is more convenient and gives exactly the same results as the Mohr diagram.

In Fig. $17 \cdot 7$ a battered wall is shown in (a) and an overhanging wall in (b). In each case point A is the base of the wall,

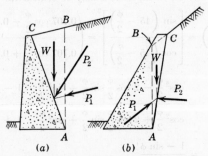

FIG. $17 \cdot 7$ Modification of the Rankine method to cases of battered walls.

and point B is the intersection of a vertical line through A and the surface of the backfill or the surface produced. Point C is the is the top of the wall. The active force across the vertical surface AB is designated by P_1. The weight of triangle ABC in both (a) and (b) is equal to the product of the area and the unit weight of the soil, and it is designated by W. There must be equilibrium between force W and the forces across surfaces AB and AC. Thus in (a), the thrust on the wall, which is designated by P_2, is the vector sum of forces P_1 and W. In (b) the thrust on the wall is the reaction to the vector sum of forces P_1 and W.

The figures show that the thrusts act at a point one third of the way up the wall. Therefore, there is a triangular distribution of pressure, but the direction of the pressure must be determined by graphical procedure as there is no simple way to express this direction.

17·5   The Coulomb Theory

The Coulomb theory (38), which was published in 1773, antedates the Rankine theory by nearly a century. It is based on the concept of a failure wedge which is bounded by the face of the wall and by a surface of failure that passes through the toe of the wall. Two assumptions are used. The main assumption is that the surface of failure is a plane, and the other assumption is that the thrust on the wall acts in some known direction. Once these assumptions have been made, the resultant thrust on the wall may easily be determined by simple considerations based on statics.

In Fig. 17·8 the three forces shown acting on the wedge must be in equilibrium. The weight of the wedge W is a known force for any arbitrarily chosen trial failure plane AB. Since an active case exists, the resultant force P_F across plane AB must be at an obliquity ϕ. The resultant force on the wall P is assumed, in the most general form of the Coulomb theory, to be at an arbitrarily chosen obliquity α. With W known in magnitude and direction and the other two forces known in direction, the magnitude of force P is easily obtained by drawing the force triangle. This lateral force P depends on the choice of failure plane, and the critical value must be found by trial or by some other procedure. The force P also depends on the obliquity angle α. Although this theory allows any choice of α, recent concepts, explained in Section 17·2, show that the friction which develops on the wall makes an angle equal to or slightly smaller than the friction angle the rational choice for this obliquity angle.

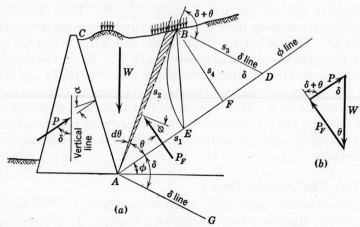

Fɪɢ. 17·8 Cross section used for considerations of the Coulomb theory.

A number of possible types of solution are based on the general procedure outlined above. The one given in the next section applies to all cases no matter how irregular the cross section is.

17·6 Rebhann's Demonstration

Rebhann (120) is credited with having presented the following demonstration of the location of the failure plane assumed in the Coulomb theory. In Fig. 17·8 (a) the active thrust P is composed of pressures that will be assumed to act at an obliquity of ϕ' at all points on the wall. The angle between P and the vertical is designated by δ. Line AE has a slope equal to the friction angle ϕ; it is called the ϕ line. Line AG is at an angle of δ, measured clockwise, from the ϕ line. Lines parallel to AG are called δ lines. The section shown in the figure is far from a simple one, thereby indicating that the demonstration applies to irregular sections; in fact it applies to any typical section through a cohesionless backfill, within which no seepage is occurring, as long as the friction angle is the same throughout the backfill. The location of an arbitrarily chosen plane, which is any one of the infinite number of planes on which failure might occur, is defined by angle θ, which is measured counterclockwise from the ϕ line. From the law of sines, in the force polygon of Fig. 17·8 (*b*)

$$P = W \frac{\sin \theta}{\sin (\delta + \theta)} \tag{17·7}$$

When θ has its critical value, which will be designated by θ_c, the lateral thrust P is a maximum. This critical value of P and conditions which exist when θ has the particular value θ_c are obtained by setting the derivative of P with respect to θ equal to zero. Thus

$$\frac{dP}{d\theta} = 0 =$$

$$\frac{\sin (\delta + \theta_c) \left[W \cos \theta_c + \sin \theta_c \left(\dfrac{dW}{d\theta} \right)_c \right] - W \sin \theta_c \cos (\delta + \theta_c)}{\sin^2 (\delta + \theta_c)}$$

wherein $(dW/d\theta)_c$ represents $dW/d\theta$ at θ equal to θ_c. This expression may be rearranged to give

$$W[\sin (\delta + \theta_c) \cos \theta_c - \cos (\delta + \theta_c) \sin \theta_c]$$

$$= \left(-\frac{dW}{d\theta} \right)_c \sin (\delta + \theta_c) \sin \theta_c$$

The expression within the bracket is equal to $\sin \delta$, giving

$$W = \left(-\frac{dW}{d\theta} \right)_c \frac{\sin (\delta + \theta_c) \sin \theta_c}{\sin \delta} \tag{17·8}$$

Originally θ was defined as the angle to an arbitrarily chosen plane. Actually the angle θ in the figure is approximately equal to the critical angle θ_c, as can be shown later.

Distances that will be used in the derivation are

$$s_1 = (AD); \quad s_2 = (AB); \quad s_3 = (BD) = (DE); \quad s_4 = (BF)$$

In addition A will be used to designate the area of the failure wedge, A_2 to designate the area ABD, and A_P to designate the area BDE.

The interpretation of equation 17·8 will be made first for the simple case of a backfill of *constant unit weight with no surcharge* above it. Later a more general case will be considered.

If a homogeneous fill with no surcharge is assumed, the change caused in W by a small change in θ may be written

$$dW = -\tfrac{1}{2}\gamma s_2{}^2\, d\theta$$

A positive $d\theta$ causes a negative dW, thus introducing the minus sign. From the above it follows that

$$\left(-\frac{dW}{d\theta}\right)_c = \frac{1}{2}\gamma s_2{}^2 \qquad (17\cdot 9)$$

From the figure it may be noted that

$$\sin \theta_c = \frac{s_4}{s_2}; \quad \frac{\sin (\delta + \theta_c)}{\sin \delta} = \frac{s_1}{s_2}; \quad \frac{\sin \theta_c}{\sin (\delta + \theta_c)} = \frac{s_3}{s_1} \quad (17\cdot 10)$$

The substitution of equation 17·9 and the first and second of equations 17·10 in equation 17·8 gives

$$W = \tfrac{1}{2}\gamma s_1 s_4 \qquad (17\cdot 11)$$

Equation 17·11 states that W must be the weight of triangle ABD, whereas W is by definition the weight of the failure wedge. Therefore this equation signifies that *for AB to be the failure plane the requirement is that the area of the failure wedge be equal to the area of triangle ABD*, or area A must equal area A_2.

The substitution of equation 17·11 and the third of equations 17·10 in equation 17·7 gives

$$P = \tfrac{1}{2}\gamma s_3 s_4$$

or

$$P = \gamma A_P \qquad (17\cdot 12)$$

This equation signifies that *the thrust on the wall is given by the weight of triangle BDE*.

In the evaluation of forces W and P by equations 17·11 and 17·12, the distances s_1 to s_4, inclusive, must of course be values that hold when $\theta = \theta_c$.

Referring again to equation 17·8, consideration will be given to the general case in which the backfill may not be of constant unit weight and there may be surcharges above the backfill. The one necessary condition is that there be a constant friction angle ϕ on the failure plane.

Let γ be the unit weight of the backfill, or if the backfill is not of constant unit weight γ will be taken as the unit weight of some given portion of the backfill. The weight W will be considered to be made up of two parts, the weight W_1, which equals $A\gamma$, and all remaining weight W_2, which includes all surcharges and all soil weight in excess of $A\gamma$. Thus

$$W = W_1 + W_2 = A\gamma\left(1 + \frac{W_2}{W_1}\right)$$

whereas

$$\left(-\frac{dW}{d\theta}\right)_c = \left(-\frac{dW_1}{d\theta}\right)_c\left(1 + \frac{dW_2}{dW_1}\right)$$

and

$$\left(-\frac{dW_1}{d\theta}\right)_c = \frac{1}{2}\gamma s_2{}^2$$

giving

$$\left(-\frac{dW}{d\theta}\right)_c = \frac{1}{2}\gamma s_2{}^2\left(1 + \frac{dW_2}{dW_1}\right)$$

The equation for this case which corresponds to equation $17\cdot11$ of the previous simpler case is

$$A\gamma\left(1 + \frac{W_2}{W_1}\right) = A_2\gamma\left(1 + \frac{dW_2}{dW_1}\right) \qquad (17\cdot13)$$

The expression $\gamma(1 + W_2/W_1)$ may be called the effective unit weight of the failure wedge and $\gamma(1 + dW_2/dW_1)$ the effective unit weight along the failure plane. Equation $17\cdot13$ signifies that, if these effective unit weights are equal, the failure plane AB must be so located as to make A equal to A_2. In any case the ratio of A to A_2 must be equal to the effective unit weight ratio of $1 + (dW_2/dW_1)$ to $1 + (W_2/W_1)$.

The equation for this case which corresponds to equation $17\cdot12$ for the previous case is

$$P = \gamma A_P\left(1 + \frac{dW_2}{dW_1}\right) \qquad (17\cdot14)$$

17·7 Coulomb Equations

The thrust P as given by the Coulomb theory may be expressed by formula if area A is of triangular shape. The formula is as follows, ϕ being the friction angle and the other angles being as shown in Fig. 17·9 (a):

$$P = \tfrac{1}{2}\gamma H^2 \left[\frac{\csc \beta \sin (\beta - \phi)}{\sqrt{\sin (\beta + \phi')} + \sqrt{\dfrac{\sin(\phi + \phi') \sin (\phi - i)}{\sin (\beta - i)}}} \right]^2$$

$$(17 \cdot 15)$$

It is interesting to note that if β equals 90 degrees and ϕ' equals i, the conditions conform to the Rankine theory, and equation 17·15 reduces to equation 17·2.

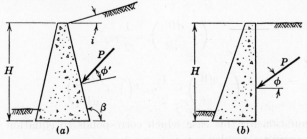

Fig. 17·9 Key to notations in Coulomb equations 17·15 and 17·16: (a) general case; (b) special case.

A special form of equation 17·15 is that in which the wall is vertical, the surface of the backfill is level, and ϕ' is equal to ϕ. Figure 17·9 (b) represents this case, and the expression for P is

$$P = \frac{1}{2} \gamma H^2 \frac{\cos \phi}{(1 + \sqrt{2} \sin \phi)^2} \qquad (17 \cdot 16)$$

The chart in Fig. 17·10 may be found convenient for determining the thrust for any case of a vertical wall retaining a fill with a level surface, in which the friction angle ϕ is between 20 and 40 degrees and the obliquity angle ϕ' has any value between zero and ϕ. This chart gives the value of K, the pressure at the base of the wall for the totally active case being

$$p_{\max} = \gamma H K$$

the thrust for either the arching-active or the totally active case being

$$P = \tfrac{1}{2}\gamma H^2 K$$

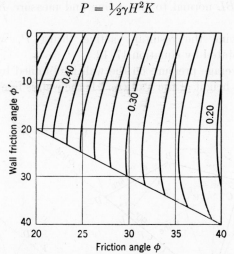

Fig. 17·10 Chart giving the active pressure coefficient K.

17·8 The Poncelet Construction

In solutions based on the Coulomb theory, line AB of Fig. 17·8 may be located in accordance with Rebhann's principle, without resort to trial-and-error methods, by a graphical procedure devised by Poncelet (113).

When the failure wedge is of triangular shape, as represented by area ACB of Fig. 17·11, the Poncelet graphical procedure and the determinations of pressures and thrust may be carried out as follows:

1. Draw the ϕ line AE and the δ line AK.
2. Through C draw the δ line CF.
3. Locate point D on the basis that $AD = \sqrt{AF \times AE}$.

Distances AF and AE may be measured and AD may then be determined by slide rule, or the graphical procedure illustrated in Fig. 17·11 (b) may be used.

4. Draw the δ line DB, thus locating point B which defines the failure plane AB.

5. Check the graphical construction as follows: Area A equals

$AB \times CJ \sin \beta$, and area A_2 equals $AB \times JD \sin \beta$; thus CJ must equal JD.

6. Draw BL normal to the ϕ line and measure $BD = s_3$ and $BL = s_4$.

7. Determine the resultant active thrust P, which equals $\frac{1}{2}\gamma s_3 s_4$, as stated by equation 17·12.

8. The average pressure on the wall is obtained by dividing P by the slope height of the wall H_S. If the wall is free to move and

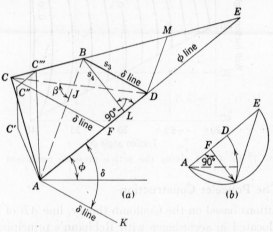

Fig. 17·11 The Poncelet construction.

if it is to be designed on the basis of totally active pressures, the maximum pressure, which occurs at the base of the wall, is twice the average pressure, and it equals $p_m = \gamma s_3 s_4 / H_S$.

If the failure wedge is not triangular in shape, the Poncelet construction may be used if the actual shape is first replaced by a triangle of equal area. If the wedge is $AC'C''C'''B$ in Fig. 17·11, the area $AC'C''C'''$ may be replaced by the equal triangular area ACC'''. Step 2 of the construction then starts at point C. Since the Poncelet construction is merely a method for making areas A and A_2 equal, the obliquity ϕ' which the lateral pressures make with the wall is not affected by the modification of the shape of the failure wedge. When the failure wedge is not a triangle, the totally active case does not give a triangular distribution of pressure, and step 8 must be omitted.

The validity of the Poncelet construction is easily demonstrated. In Fig. 17·11 DM is parallel to AB. Since areas A and A_2 must be equal, CJ equals JD, and it follows that CB equals BM. The following successive proportionalities may now be written

$$\frac{FD}{DE} = \frac{CB}{BE} = \frac{BM}{BE} = \frac{AD}{AE} = \frac{AD - FD}{AE - DE} = \frac{AF}{AD}$$

From the above expressions $AF:AD = AD:AE$. When areas A and A_2 are equal, this proportionality holds. Therefore, it is seen that step 3 of the construction fulfills the requirement that areas A and A_2 be equal.

17·9   Coulomb Theory—Passive Case

The passive case differs from the active case in that the obliquity angles at the wall and on the failure plane are of opposite sign, as shown in Fig. 17·12. The Coulomb theory uses the as-

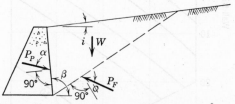

Fig. 17·12   Key to notations in the Coulomb passive equation 17·17.

sumption of plane failure for the passive case, as it did for the active case, but the critical plane is that for which the passive thrust is a minimum. The critical active thrust is a maximum value. The failure plane is at a much smaller angle to the horizontal than in the active case, as Fig. 17·4 showed for a special case. In general the passive thrust is of the order of 10 to 20 times as large as the active thrust.

The equation for the passive thrust according to the Coulomb theory is

$$P_P = \tfrac{1}{2}\gamma H^2 \left[\frac{\csc \beta \sin (\beta + \phi)}{\sqrt{\sin (\beta - \alpha)} - \sqrt{\dfrac{\sin (\phi + \alpha) \sin (\phi + i)}{\sin (\beta - i)}}} \right]^2$$

$$(17 \cdot 17)$$

The notations are shown by Fig. 17·12. The obliquity angle α is sometimes equal to the maximum wall friction angle ϕ', but under certain conditions of yield it is less than ϕ' and it may even

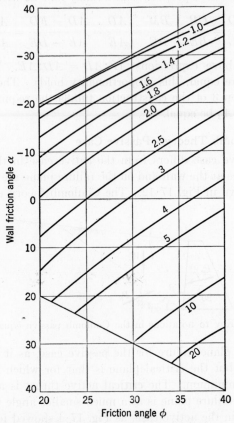

FIG. 17·13 Chart giving the passive pressure coefficient K_P. (Value of angle α is positive in Fig. 17·12.)

be negative. Therefore, it is not reasonable to assume that it is equal to ϕ' as in the active case. Equation 17·17 is valid for negative as well as for positive values of i and α.

The chart in Fig. 17·13 may be used for determining the passive thrust on any vertical wall retaining a fill that has a level surface and a friction angle between 20 and 40 degrees. This chart gives the value of K_P according to the Coulomb theory, the passive thrust being

$$P_P = \tfrac{1}{2}\gamma H^2 K_P$$

The Poncelet construction for the passive case is shown in Fig. 17·14. The ϕ line OD is laid off clockwise from the horizontal, and it intersects the backfill surface produced at C. The δ line is at angle δ measured clockwise from the ϕ line. Line AF is a

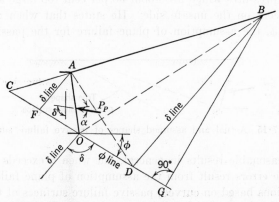

Fig. 17·14 The Poncelet construction for the passive case.

δ line. Distance OD is the mean proportional of distances OF and OC. Line DB is a δ line, and OB is the failure plane. Finally, the passive thrust is equal to $\tfrac{1}{2}\gamma(DB)(BG)$.

17·10 Validity of the Assumption of Plane Failure

The stability numbers in Table 16·1 show that the assumption of plane failure is not greatly in error for unretained slopes that have vertical or approximately vertical faces. Similarly the assumption of plane failure in the active case of the Rankine theory is in error by only a relatively small amount. It has been shown by Fellenius that the assumption of circular arcs for failure surfaces leads to active thrusts on retaining walls that in general exceed the corresponding values furnished by the Coulomb theory by less than 5 per cent.

For the passive case the assumption of a plane surface of rupture is in error by considerable amounts in some instances.

Terzaghi (Chapter VII of reference 148) has presented a more rigorous type of analysis for this case, using methods resembling those discussed in Sections 16·15 and 16·16 and assuming passive failure surfaces of the shape shown in Fig. 17·15. He quotes an example based on a vertical wall retaining a fill with a level surface and with the friction angle and the wall friction angle both equal to 30 degrees; the plane assumption in this case gives passive pressures which are about 30 per cent too large and thus 30 per cent on the unsafe side. He states that when α is less than $\frac{1}{3}\phi$, the assumption of plane failure for the passive case

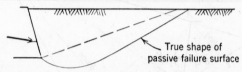

Fig. 17·15   Actual and assumed shapes of passive failure surfaces.

gives reasonable results in general, but when α exceeds $\frac{1}{3}\phi$ intolerable errors result from the assumption of plane failure.

Solutions based on curved, passive failure surfaces of the type shown in Fig. 17·15 may eventually be available in chart form, but it is now necessary to resort to graphical trial procedures when accurate determinations of the passive pressure are desired. However, these graphical procedures based on curved failure surfaces are much less complex than might at first appear, and they are valuable because they may also be used for passive pressure determinations in cohesive soils and for cases in which there are surcharges.

17·11   The Pressure Distribution on the Sheeting of Trenches

The pressure distribution which usually occurs on the sheeting of trenches is an outstanding example of the arching-active case.

In a trench such as that shown in Fig. 17·16 (a) the excavation often is first carried to the elevation of a point such as E, after which the sheeting between elevations A and E is placed and braced rigidly by wedges driven at the ends of the braces. Similarly in successive stages the same procedure is continued until the excavation and bracing are completed to the elevation of point B. While the soil is being excavated in each lift, thereby removing the pressure across a portion of surface AB, the soil at the excavation level and to a smaller degree below that level yields slightly toward the trench. Probably this yield increases somewhat with depth, $A'B'C'D'$ of Fig. 17·16 (b) representing to exaggerated scale the approximate original location of the surface which finally yields to $ABCD$. This is a case in which the yield is small at the top of the wall, but the average yield is probably of sufficient magnitude to reduce the lateral thrust to

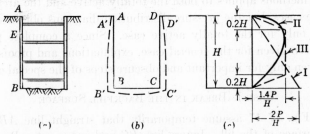

(~)   (b)   (~)

Fɪɢ. 17·16   The arching-active case in trenches.

the active value. Therefore, the pressure diagram is roughly similar to the parabolic curve of the arching-active case, shown by line CH of Fig. 17·5 (b).

Experienced contractors and foremen have long known that trench sheeting must be stronger at mid-height than at the bottom. Lack of recognition of this fact in textbooks in the past has been cited as illustrative of unsound theory, although it might more truly be called a misinterpretation of theory due to lack of understanding of concepts that have been explained in Section 17·2.

A pressure distribution recommended by Terzaghi (142, 144) for use in the design of sheeting is shown in Fig. 17·16 (c). Curve I of this figure shows the totally active distribution. Curve II is the average of a number of sets of measurements of pressures in a Berlin subway. Curve III is the recommended distribution curve. The resultant thrust represented by this recommended curve acts at the mid-height point of the wall and is equal to $1.12P$, in which P is the thrust for the totally active case. The pressures shown in Fig. 17·16 (c) are at an obliquity of zero, but this distribution pattern may be used in connection with any obliquity angle.

17·12 Determination of Thrusts and Pressure Distributions for the Totally Active Condition for Cases Involving Surcharges and Irregular Cross Sections

The Poncelet construction may be used to good advantage for the special examples which follow. In all these cases cohesionless soil with no seepage is assumed. The total thrust given by these methods applies to both the totally active and the arching-active cases, but the pressure distribution diagrams obtained are valid only for the totally active case. Since a complete proof has been given for the general case, explanations and proofs will be given only for important and obscure steps of the special cases.

Case I. Break in the Backfill Surface

In Fig. 17·17 assume temporarily that straight line ABC' is the surface of the fill. Ignore line BC and carry out a Poncelet construction, locating the failure plane OD and obtaining the

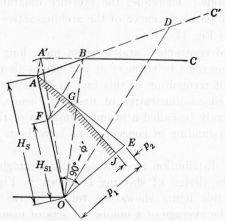

Fig. 17·17 Cross section with a break in the surface of the backfill.

pressure distribution triangle AEO. If P_1 is the total thrust on the wall according to this construction, then in the figure $p_1 = 2P_1/H_S$.

Draw BF parallel to DO. If AF is considered to be a wall, the pressure distribution triangle is AGF, and the break in the backfill surface has no effect, since the break is to the right of failure plane FB. However, below point F the break will lead to smaller pressures than those represented by line GE.

The total thrust on the wall for the actual cross section with the backfill surface ABC is obtained by a second Poncelet construction. The irregular shape introduced by the break is eliminated by replacing area OAB by the area $OA'B$ as follows: The triangles OAB and $OA'B$ have the common base OB; line AA' is constructed parallel to OB, giving equal altitudes; point A' is on line CB produced. A Poncelet construction that starts with a δ line through A', as suggested in Section 17·8, gives the thrust P.

The pressures shown by the distribution triangle AEO represent the thrust P_1, which is larger than the correct thrust P by $P_1 - P$. It may be assumed with no appreciable inaccuracy that the pressure distribution over the lower portion of the wall has a linear variation. Thus if $p_1 - p_2$ is the final value of the pressure at point O,

$$\frac{p_2}{2} \times H_{S1} = P_1 - P \quad \text{or} \quad p_2 = \frac{2(P_1 - P)}{H_{S1}}$$

The value of the moment caused by thrust P about point O may be needed in the design of the wall, and it may be expressed

$$M_O = P_1(\tfrac{1}{3}H_S \cos \phi') - (P_1 - P)(\tfrac{1}{3}H_{S1} \cos \phi')$$

CASE II. CONCENTRATED SURCHARGE ABOVE THE BACKFILL

A railroad track, the wall of a building, or any other load along a line parallel to the wall gives a loading which may be represented by a concentrated force Q which is expressed in pounds per foot of wall and which acts as shown in Fig. 17·18.

As a first step in the solution of this case the existence of force Q is disregarded and a Poncelet construction is carried through; the failure plane OD is located, the thrust P_1 is determined, and the pressure triangle AEO, wherein OE or p_1 equals $2P_1/H_S$, is obtained.

Then point A' is located on line BA produced, with the weight of triangle OAA' equal to force Q. Distance a is defined by the equation

$$Q = \tfrac{1}{2}\gamma a H_S$$

A second Poncelet construction is now used; it starts from point A' and determines the failure plane OD' and the total thrust P_2.

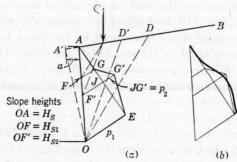

FIG. 17·18 Cross section with a concentrated surcharge on the surface of the backfill.

It may be noted that this procedure is in accordance with the requirement expressed by equation 17·13, since the area A_2 has here been made equal to $(1 + W_2/W_1)A$. The surcharge causes an additional thrust of $P_2 - P_1$, which has a distribution that is approximately as shown in (*b*). However, this distribution may be approximated with reasonable accuracy by a broken line. Lines that pass through the point of action of Q and are parallel to the failure planes OD and OD' give points F and F' on the wall, respectively. It is assumed that at point F there is no effect of surcharge and that the pressure is GF, that at point F' the pressure caused by the surcharge has its maximum value p_2, and that at point O there is no effect of surcharge and that the pressure is EO. Since $\tfrac{1}{2}p_2$ is the average added pressure over wall height OF, it is defined by the equation

$$P_2 - P_1 = \tfrac{1}{2}p_2 \times H_{S1}$$

whence

$$p_2 = \frac{2(P_2 - P_1)}{H_{S1}}$$

The use of this expression allows the locating of point G' and the completion of the distribution figure. By dividing this figure into triangles and expressing the moment about O as the sum of moments for the triangles, it may be shown that

$$M_O = \tfrac{1}{3}P_1 H_S \cos \phi' + \tfrac{1}{3}(P_2 - P_1)(H_{S1} + H_{S2}) \cos \phi'$$

CASE III. UNIFORMLY DISTRIBUTED SURCHARGE

The case in which a uniform surcharge exists or is liable to be placed above the backfill is represented by Fig. 17·19.

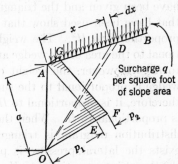

First the surcharge may be disregarded and a Poncelet construction may be used to locate the failure plane OD and to determine the thrust P_1 and the intensity triangle AEO wherein the average pressure is P_1/H_S and p_1 equals $2P_1/H_S$.

An expression for the ratio between the surcharge weight and the soil weight is now needed. If the weight notations of the last part of Section 17·6 are used, the following weight ratios may be written

FIG. 17·19 Cross section with a uniformly distributed surcharge above the backfill.

$$\frac{W_2}{W_1} = \frac{qx}{\tfrac{1}{2}\gamma ax} = \frac{2q}{\gamma a}; \quad \frac{dW_2}{dW_1} = \frac{q\,dx}{\tfrac{1}{2}\gamma a\,dx} = \frac{2q}{\gamma a}$$

The figure shows that a is the perpendicular distance from point O to line BA produced and that the surcharge q is expressed in pounds per square foot of sloping area. Since the ratios W_2/W_1 and dW_2/dW_1 are equal, the requirement expressed by equation 17·13 is simply that A_2 equal A; this requirement already has been met in the determination of the failure plane OD. Therefore, the location of the failure plane is not changed by adding the uniform surcharge. Furthermore the directions of the forces W, P_F, and P of Fig. 17·8 (b) are not changed, and when surcharge is added all forces increase in the same ratio. Let

$$\frac{2q}{\gamma a} = R \qquad\qquad (17 \cdot 18)$$

and let R be designated as the *surcharge ratio*. The total W equals $W_1(1 + R)$, and it follows that the total thrust P must equal $P_1(1 + R)$, the subscript 1 here designating the case without surcharge. The thrust caused by the surcharge is thus equal to RP_1.

The determination of the distribution of thrust RP_1 requires concepts that have not yet been presented. The formulas that have been given and the triangular pressure distribution diagrams that have been used show that the total lateral thrust is directly proportional to H^2. The weight of the failure wedge is proportional to the area of the wedge and, therefore, it also is proportional to H^2. However, the weight of the surcharge above the failure wedge is proportional to the surface dimension of the wedge and, therefore, it is proportional to H. Similarly, the lateral thrust RP is proportional to H. When the thrust is proportional to H^2, the distribution diagram is triangular, and if a totally active case exists the lateral pressure is proportional to the depth. When the thrust is proportional to H, as it is for thrust RP_1, the pressure is constant over the height of the wall. Thus p_2 in Fig. 17·19 is equal to RP_1/H_S.

The moment about the base of the wall is

$$M_O = \tfrac{1}{3}P_1 H_S \cos \phi' + \tfrac{1}{2}RP_1 H_S \cos \phi' = \tfrac{1}{3}P_1 H_S \cos \phi'(1 + \tfrac{3}{2}R)$$

The simple relationships explained above lend themselves readily to many possible comparison problems, and a thorough understanding of such problems probably is more valuable than much practice in working graphical solutions. These comparison problems are based on such relationships as the following, wherein subscripts 1 and 2 refer respectively to values due to backfill and to surcharge:

$$p_2 = R(p_1)_{\text{av}} = \tfrac{1}{2}R(p_1)_{\text{max}}; \quad P_2 = RP_1$$

$$M_{O2} = \tfrac{3}{2}RM_{O1}; \quad P_1 \frown H^2; \quad P_2 \frown H, \text{ etc.}$$

EXAMPLE. The surcharge ratio R is equal to 0.4 for a 20-ft wall. If R is decreased to 0.2 and the wall is increased in height, what height is allowable if the moment about the base must not exceed the original value?

Since $M \frown P_1 H(1 + \tfrac{3}{2}R) \frown H^3(1 + \tfrac{3}{2}R)$

$$(20)^3(1 + \tfrac{3}{2} \times 0.4) = H^3(1 + \tfrac{3}{2} \times 0.2)$$

whence
$$H = 21.3 \text{ ft} \quad Answer$$

CASE IV. BREAK IN THE SURFACE OF THE WALL

As the first step in the solution for the wall shown in Fig. 17·20 the thrust P_1, the pressure p_1, and the intensity triangle on portion AA' of the wall are determined by the usual Poncelet procedure.

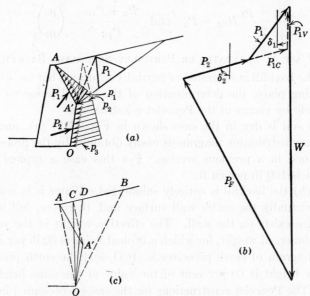

FIG. 17·20 Cross section with a break in the wall surface.

In this construction δ_1 is the angle between thrust P_1 and the vertical.

The complete force polygon for this case is shown in Fig. 17·20 (b). If force P_1 is divided into the components P_{1C} and P_{1V}, there must be equilibrium between the three forces $P_2 + P_{1C}$, $W - P_{1V}$, and P_F. Components P_{1C} and P_{1V} may be determined graphically from the force polygon.

A Poncelet construction may now be used with $W - P_{1V}$ assumed to be the weight, but two adjustments are needed. Line $A'C$ is drawn parallel to OA in (c), giving the triangular area OCB which is equal to and may be used in place of the area

$OA'AB$. Then the weight above the failure plane is reduced to $W - P_{1V}$ by removing the area OCD, which is of weight P_{1V}. The Poncelet construction starts at point D and has δ_2 for the δ angle; it locates the failure plane OB and obtains force $P_2 + P_{1C}$.

The pressure on the lower portion of the wall is assumed to vary linearly, and pressures p_2 and p_3 may be determined by the simultaneous solution of the following equations:

$$\frac{p_2 + p_3}{2} H_{S2} = P_2 \quad \text{and} \quad \frac{P_2 + P_{1C}}{P_{1C}} = \left(\frac{p_3}{p_2}\right)^2$$

Case V. Saturated or Partially Saturated Backfill

If the backfill is saturated or partially saturated but no seepage is taking place, the determination of the lateral pressures may be made by means of the Poncelet construction.

The soil is dry in the case shown in Fig. 17·21 (a), and the pressure distribution diagram is easily obtained by the procedure explained in a previous section. For this case a typical unit weight is 100 lb per cu ft.

In (b) the backfill is entirely submerged. Water is in contact with virtually the entire wall surface and, therefore, full water pressure exists on the wall. The effective weight of the soil is the submerged weight, for which a typical value is 60 lb per cu ft. The diagram of earth pressures is ACO, and the earth pressure at any height is 60 per cent of the value at the same height in (a). The Poncelet constructions for the cases represented in (b) and (a) are identical. The water pressure on the wall is represented by the distribution triangle AJO, which is shown dashed because this pressure is balanced by pressure on the other side of the wall. Water pressure diagrams need not be considered in this case, because all effects of water are cared for if the unit weights used in the design are the submerged unit weights of the backfill and the masonry. Design principles are discussed in Section 17·13.

In Fig. 17·21 (c) a partially saturated case is represented and the distribution diagrams of both (a) and (b) are shown. Above point D the soil is assumed to be dry, and the triangle AED represents the earth pressures. Between D and O the earth pressure increases the same amount per foot of depth as it does between the same points in (*b*). Therefore, line *EF* may be drawn parallel to *AC*, and the earth pressure distribution is represented by figure *AEFO*. Careful considerations of the theory show that these results are obtained with no assumptions except the characteristic assumptions of the Coulomb method. The same failure plane holds for the cases represented in (*a*), (*b*), and (*c*). The water pressure diagram *DGO* is shown dashed because it is bal-

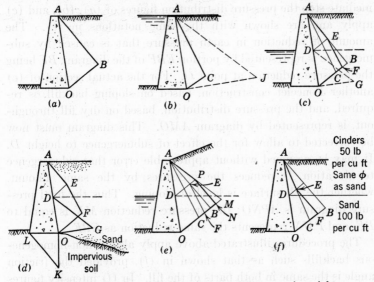

FIG. 17·21 Effects of submergence and different unit weights.

anced by water pressures on the other side of the wall. Water pressure diagrams need not be considered in (*c*), as in (*b*), if the submerged unit weight of masonry is used for the portion of the wall that is below the water surface.

In (*d*) the backfill is assumed to be a permeable soil with the water table at the same elevation as in (*c*), but the soil below the base of the wall is assumed to be impervious and there is no pool to the left of the wall. Good design would require drains through the wall to relieve the water pressure, in which case seepage forces would have to be considered, as explained later. However, if drains are omitted, or if the drains become completely plugged, the earth pressure distribution diagram is exactly as in (*c*).

However, the water pressure diagram DGO must be considered in this case. The uplift pressures on the base, as represented approximately by the water pressure diagram OKL, must also be considered in the design of the wall. In this design the true weight of the masonry must be used.

The considerations may now be extended to a sloping backfill, shown in (e). As an intermediate step in the procedure the solution based on a level backfill surface is used. For this intermediate step the pressure distribution figures of (a), (b), and (c) apply and are shown with the same notations in (e). The amount of reduction in earth pressure that is caused by submergence is represented by portion EBF of the diagram, BF being the pressure reduction at point O. For the actual section of (e) another Poncelet construction, based on sloping backfill, is required, and the pressure distribution, based on dry fill throughout, is represented by diagram AMO. This diagram must now be corrected to allow for the effect of submergence to height D. It may be assumed without appreciable error that submergence to elevation D reduces the pressures by the same amount, whether the fill surface is level or sloping. Thus the final pressure diagram is $APNO$; the pressure reduction MN is equal to BF, and PMN represents the same reduction as EBF.

The procedures illustrated above apply also to non-homogeneous backfills such as that shown in (f), provided the friction angle is the same in both parts of the fill. In (f) intensity figures for the cases of sand throughout and cinders throughout are respectively ABO and ACO. The final intensity figure for the non-homogeneous backfill is $AEFO$, wherein EF is parallel to AB.

17·13 Design Principles for Gravity Walls

Gravity walls may in general undergo displacement without damage and, therefore, need be designed to resist only the pressures of the totally active condition.

In Figs. 17·22 (a) and 17·22 (b) force P represents the active earth thrust on the wall. The obliquity of this force on the wall equals the wall friction angle ϕ'. For convenience in the design, however, force P is divided in (a) into its horizontal component P_H and vertical component P_V. The weight of the wall is represented by the vertical force W. The force between the base of the wall and the foundation is Q, which also for convenience is in (a) resolved into its horizontal component Q_H and its vertical component Q_V. A passive resistance P_P, which usually is small,

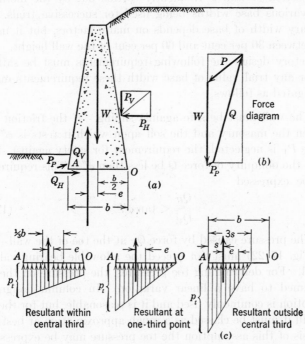

FIG. 17·22 Cross section illustrating considerations of wall stability and distributions of base pressure.

may exist on the side of the wall away from the backfill as shown. Its horizontal and vertical components are P_{PH} and P_{PV}, respectively. Often the force P_P is so small that it may be neglected.

For equilibrium of the wall under these forces it is necessary that

$$Q_V = W + P_V - P_{PV}$$

and

$$Q_H = P_H - P_{PH}$$

For any arbitrarily chosen cross section of wall, the forces P, W, and P_P and their components may be obtained and the components of Q computed by use of the above expressions. Then an expression for equilibrium of moments may be used to determine the eccentricity e of the force Q_V relative to the central point of the base of the wall. The problem of determining a satisfactory cross section of wall is frequently carried out by the method of trial, various base widths being used for successive trials. The necessary width of base depends on many factors, but it usually falls between 30 per cent and 60 per cent of the wall height. For a satisfactory design the following requirements must be satisfied, and for any trial value of base width these requirements may be investigated as follows.

1. The wall must be safe against sliding. If the friction angle between the masonry and the soil upon which it rests is ϕ'', and if force P_V is neglected, the requirement for safety against sliding is that the obliquity of force Q be less than ϕ''. This requirement may be expressed

$$\frac{Q_H}{Q_V} < \tan \phi'' \qquad (17 \cdot 19)$$

2. The pressure caused by force Q_V at the toe of the wall (point A of Fig. $17 \cdot 22$) must not exceed the allowable bearing value of the soil. For determining toe pressures, the pressure on the base is assumed to have a linear variation. In column design this assumption is commonly used and it is reasonable, but for the base of a wall it must be classed as a rough approximation at best. On the basis of this assumption the toe pressure may be expressed as follows, when the point of action of Q_V is within the central third of the base:

$$p_t = \frac{Q_V}{b}\left(1 + 6\,\frac{e}{b}\right) \qquad (17 \cdot 20)$$

in which e is the eccentricity, or the distance from the mid-point of the base to the point of action of Q_V. The first two diagrams in Fig. $17 \cdot 22$ (c) have p_t values which are given by this expression. When the point of action of Q_V is not within the central third, the above expression is valid only if tensile strength can occur at the heel. Since tension cannot generally be depended on in soils, a triangular distribution of pressure is usually assumed to exist over the portion of the base that has the dimension $3s$ in the right-hand sketch of (c), dimension s being the distance from the line of action of force Q_V to the toe. Under this condition

$$p_t = \frac{4}{3} \frac{Q}{b - 2e} \qquad (17\cdot21)$$

The subjects of allowable bearing pressures and pressure distributions below footings and walls are discussed in Chapter 19.

3. The wall must be safe against overturning. To fulfill this requirement the line of action of Q_V must cross the base of the wall. Sometimes it is specified that Q_V must act within the central third of the base, and a base width such that Q_V is at the outer edge of the central third is frequently used. This procedure assures complete safety against overturning, but restriction of Q_V to the central third is not a requirement. When this procedure is adopted it gives the advantage of relatively small toe pressures. This is a sufficient reason for its use for high walls in which toe pressures are a critical consideration.

17·14 Sheet-Pile Walls

A common type of retaining wall and one that is widely used for waterfront construction is the sheet-pile wall illustrated in Fig. 17·23.

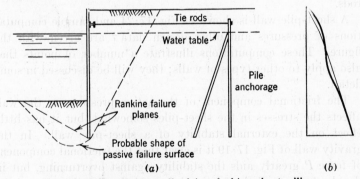

Fig. 17·23 Retaining wall of interlocking sheet piling.

The pressures which exist on the right-hand side of the wall tend to push the wall to the left, and the entire setup is so flexible that deflections of considerable magnitude can occur without damage to the wall. Thus, if failure impends, the pressures on the right of the wall reduce to totally active values. Actually the distribution probably is somewhat as shown in Fig. 17·23 (*b*), the variation from the triangular resulting from retention at the anchorage and bulging of the sheeting below the anchorage. The theoretical location of the failure plane is indicated in the figure.

A basic requirement is that there be sufficient resisting force to balance the active force. Resisting forces are provided at the toe of the wall by toe penetration and near the top of the wall by anchor rods.

The depth of toe penetration must be sufficient to hold the bottom of the wall in place, and if there is not a sufficient penetration a passive failure will occur. The passive force that holds the toe of a sheet-pile wall in place is perhaps the best example of passive resistance that can be cited. The passive failure surface according to the Rankine theory and a curved surface that is more nearly the correct one for passive failure are shown in the figure.

The anchor rods carry their load to some type of anchorage. A pile anchorage is shown in the figure. If there is a good grade of soil in the vicinity of the anchorage, use may be made of some simple type of anchorage that extends only to the depth necessary to give sufficient passive resistance to the pull of the anchor rods.

A sheet-pile wall is shown in Fig. 17·24 and sample computations of pressures and other design data † are given with the figure. These computations illustrate a number of points that also apply to other types of walls; they will be discussed in some detail.

The frictional component of the active pressure on the wall affects the stresses in the sheet-piles somewhat, but it has little effect on the external stability of a sheet-pile wall. In the gravity wall of Fig. 17·19 it is clear that the frictional component of force P greatly aids the stability against overturning, but in the sheet-pile wall the friction has no such effect because of the absence of base width. This explains the common practice of assuming ϕ' equal to zero in computations for sheet-pile walls. With ϕ' equal to zero the easiest way to determine pressures is

† A simple and rational method is used in this example. For another method see reference 22. The methods are compared on page 228 of reference 148.

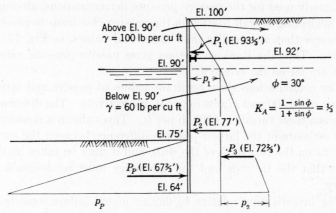

Fig. 17·24 Cross section used for the illustrative example of a stability analysis of a sheet-pile wall.

		Active	Passive
Pressures in	$\frac{1}{3} \times (100 - 90) \times 100 =$	$333 = p_1$	
pounds per	$\frac{1}{3} \times (90 - 64) \times 60 \ \ =$	$520 = p_2$	
square foot		$\overline{853} = p_1 + p_2$	
	$3 \times (75 - 64) \times 60 \ \ =$		$1,980 = P_P$
Thrusts in	$333 \times \frac{1}{2}(100 - 90) \ \ =$	$1,670 = P_1$	
pounds per	$333 \times (90 - 64) \ \ =$	$8,660 = P_2$	
foot	$520 \times \frac{1}{2}(90 - 64) \ \ =$	$6,760 = P_3$	
		$\overline{17,000} = P_A$	
	$1,980 \times \frac{1}{2}(75 - 64) \ \ =$		$10,900 = P_P$
Moments	$1,670 \times (92 - 93\frac{1}{3}) \ \ =$	$-2,200$	
about El. 92	$8,660 \times (92 - 77) \ \ =$	$130,000$	
in foot-	$6,760 \times (92 - 72\frac{2}{3}) \ \ =$	$131,000$	
pounds per			
foot		$\overline{259,000} = M_A$	
	$10,900 \times (92 - 67\frac{2}{3}) \ \ =$		$265,000 = M_P$

to use Rankine's equation (17·3). Rankine's theory is also commonly used for the passive pressure determinations, although the neglecting of wall friction in the passive case leads to passive pressures that are smaller than the actual values, as Fig. 17·13 shows. Thus the Rankine method gives passive pressure values that are far on the safe side.

The computations show resultant values of passive and active thrust of 10,900 and 17,000 lb per ft, respectively. The difference between these thrusts is 6100 lb per ft. This value is a conservative estimate of the largest possible difference between the earth thrusts on the two sides of the wall, and it may be taken as the load that the tie rods and the anchorage must be designed to carry.

The investigation relative to danger of toe failure consists of an analysis of moments about the point at which the tie rod meets the wall. The computations show passive and active moments of 265,000 and 259,000 ft-lb per ft of wall, respectively. The conservative assumption used in the passive pressure computations permit the conclusion that this wall has an adequate margin of safety relative to toe failure. If the sheeting were extended to El. 60, giving a toe penetration of 15 ft, the passive and active moments would become 546,000 and 366,000 ft-lb per ft, respectively, the ratio of these values being 1.50, and a very conservative design would be obtained.

To be in equilibrium the moments of the active and passive thrusts must, of course, be in balance. The ratio of 1.50 quoted above is, therefore, the ratio between the value the passive moment would build up to if required and the value the active moment would decrease to if ever necessary.

The water pressure will not always balance on the two sides of a wall that is subject to tidal variations. The most unfavorable situation that can occur is an absolutely tight wall with water elevations at mean tide level within the fill and at low tide level outside. A design based on a differential of one-half the maximum tidal range is too conservative in most instances. The choice of a reasonable magnitude of water differential must be based largely on judgment, and sometimes one or two feet of water pressure is added arbitrarily to the active pressures between the water level and the toe of the wall to allow for tide effect.

17·15 Seepage Forces and Drainage Facilities

If groundwater seeps through the backfill behind a retaining wall, seepage forces occur and affect the stability considerably. If the groundwater level and other conditions that affect the flow net are known, a net may be drawn and an analysis made which includes the effect of seepage forces.

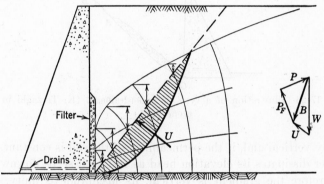

FIG. 17·25   Cross section illustrating the analysis for the lateral thrust on a wall when there is seepage within the backfill.

In the cross section shown in Fig. 17·25 it is assumed that drains through the wall and a coarse filter against the wall relieve the wall of all water pressure. The flow net for this case is shown by light lines. The seepage effect is best accounted for by an analysis based on total weights and boundary neutral forces, as explained in Section 9·18. The active thrust may be determined by a graphical procedure; plane failure is assumed and various planes are tried until the critical plane is located. On each trial plane the neutral pressure diagram and the neutral force U must be obtained from the flow net, the methods explained in Sections 16·15 and 16·16 and indicated in Fig. 17·25 being used. The vector summation of the neutral force U and the total weight W gives the body force B. Since the magnitude and direction of force B and the directions of forces P_F and P are known, the magnitude of the thrust P may be determined.

The coarse sand drain next to the wall in Fig. 17·25 prevents the occurrence of water pressure on the wall, but a more efficient location of this drain is sometimes possible. When the ground surface during the construction of the wall is similar to the slope *OAB* in Fig. 17·26, a sand filter of coarser material than the backfill often may be placed as shown. Regardless of the ground-water conditions or of the amount of surface water supplied by rain, the seepage within the failure wedge in this case is essen-

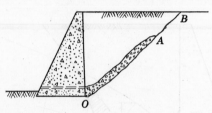

FIG. 17·26 Illustration of a type of underdrainage. (K. Terzaghi in reference 142.)

tially vertical and, if the permeability of the soil is constant, the water dissipates its elevation head as fast as it seeps downward. Therefore the gradient is vertical, its magnitude is unity, and there are no water pressures within the backfill. For the solution of this case the simple Poncelet procedure may be used. If the unit weight of the soil is taken as $[(G + e)/(1 + e)]\gamma_w$, equal approximately to 120 lb per sq ft, the effects of seepage are completely accounted for.

17·16 Non-Homogeneous Backfills

In the foregoing pages all considerations relative to the locations of critical planes were based on the assumption of homogeneous backfill. When a weaker material underlies a good grade of backfill, the critical plane may have a much different location than it would in the homogeneous case. An example is given in Fig. 17·27. Surface I is the approximate location of the critical plane for a homogeneous sand. If there is an underlying weaker material it is possible that some surface such as that labeled II is the critical one.

When there is a soil of low shearing strength beneath a retaining wall, the main problem may be one of embankment stability instead of wall stability. For example, a failure of the section shown in Fig. 17·28 might occur along the circular arc shown. The lateral pressure acting on the wall in this case is probably

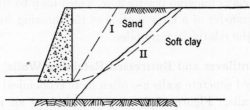

FIG. 17·27   Cross section that is susceptible to failure in the weak underlying soil.

given with reasonable accuracy by the Coulomb method, but the danger is not that the wall will be unable to retain the backfill so much as that a deepseated failure will occur in which the wall and the backfill rotate clockwise as a single mass. The piles shown may offer resistance to such a failure and, consequently,

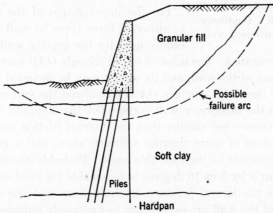

FIG. 17·28   Wall that is susceptible to a deep, circular arc failure.

deepseated failure surfaces sometimes tend to pass below the tips of piles rather than through the piles. However, it is probable that the dependable resistance to shear along an incipient rupture surface is not much larger than the resistance the piles can furnish, or the shearing resistance of the soil, whichever is the larger.

The piles and the soil are not able to act in unison to resist such a failure, because the piles are relatively rigid and they reach their limiting strain and are subject to failure when only a fraction of the shearing resistance has developed within the soil. Moreover, clays undergo plastic flow, which may be the cause of a gradual transfer of a large portion of the shearing stress within the soil to the relatively rigid piles.

17·17 Cantilever and Buttressed Retaining Walls

Reinforced concrete walls are often more economical than mass concrete walls. Figure 17·29 may be taken as an illustration of a reinforced concrete wall of constant cross section, which acts as a cantilever and is, therefore, called a *cantilever wall*. The figure may also be an illustration of a reinforced concrete wall with concrete buttresses of shape *OAB*, spaced at regular intervals along the wall; this type of structure is known as a *buttressed wall*.

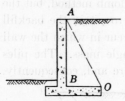

Fig. 17·29 Cantilever wall or buttressed wall.

For the investigation of the stability of either of these types of wall the procedure used for the gravity wall is sufficiently accurate.‡ The mass of soil in triangle *OAB* may be considered part of the wall, and its weight may be included with the weight of the wall. Surface *OA* is considered the surface of the wall. On the imaginary wall surface *OA* the obliquity of stress usually is somewhat smaller than the internal friction angle ϕ, as considerations of more rigorous solutions show, and a conservative value should be used for this angle. Probably an angle that is less than ϕ by 5 or 10 degrees is reasonable for most cases. In all details the lateral pressure determinations and the stability analysis of the wall are carried out as previously outlined.

17·18 Lateral Pressures in Cohesive Soils

There are two important reasons for greater complexity in problems involving lateral pressures in cohesive soil than in co-

‡ For a more rigorous solution see page 93 of reference 148.

hesionless soil. First, the shearing strength plays an important part in determining magnitudes of active pressures, and accurate determinations of shearing strengths are not easy in cohesive soils. Second, the yield required to give an active condition often is not of definite amount in plastic soils.

If a highly plastic soil is subjected to a certain magnitude of shearing stress and this stress is held constant, the soil undergoes plastic flow and shearing strain occurs continuously. Some clays exhibit plastic flow to much greater degree than others, but this phenomenon generally occurs to some degree in any cohesive soil, and it even occurs when the shearing stress is much smaller than the shearing strength. Similarly, if a plastic soil is subjected to shearing strain and then held for a time without strain, the shearing stresses slowly decrease. This is the phenomenon of *relaxation*, which is another evidence of plastic flow.

The above-mentioned phenomena make impossible a definite relationship between yield and lateral pressure in cohesive soils. If the shearing stress remains constant on the incipient failure surface within a cohesive backfill, the lateral pressure also remains constant. However, the existence of a constant shearing stress requires a slow, continuous shearing strain and, for this strain to occur, the retaining wall must slowly creep outward. On the other hand, if no shearing strain is to occur in the vicinity of the incipient failure plane, there must be no yield of the wall. Under these conditions the shearing stresses on the failure plane undergo slow relaxation, and as the shearing stresses decrease the lateral pressure must gradually increase to maintain equilibrium.

These conditions show that it is reasonable to design a wall that retains a backfill of cohesive soil on the basis of active pressure if, and only if, continuous yield can occur without undesirable consequences. If some part of the wall is connected to a rigid adjoining structure and the design is based on active pressures, a break at the point of connection is sure to occur eventually. There are many occasions in which it is entirely reasonable to design gravity walls or sheet-pile walls with cohesive backfills on the basis of their having to resist active pressure only. However, it must be expected that such walls will undergo con-

, tinuous yield, possibly at a very slow rate but sometimes at a rate that may have to be measured in inches per year. Consequently, retaining walls with cohesive backfills must in general be considered to be less permanent structures than those retaining cohesionless fills.

When conditions dictate that a wall which retains a cohesive backfill must be prevented from yielding, the wall must be designed to resist the lateral pressure at rest. In cohesive soils the lateral pressure at rest is likely to equal approximately 90 per cent of the vertical pressure, the hydrostatic pressure ratio thus being only slightly below unity. Even in a design based on these conditions the wall may be subjected to a slight outward deflection, since a jacking action may be caused by a phenomenon similar to creep. This action results from alternate expansions and contractions, which occur mainly within a limited depth at the surface of the backfill, and it is due to daily or seasonal temperature or water content fluctuations. A wall that would be able to retain a cohesive backfill without yielding would usually be prohibitively heavy.

Estimates of active pressures in cohesive soils are sometimes obtained by the procedures used for cohesionless soils; the cohesion is simply neglected or an enlarged ϕ_e value is used to allow for the cohesion. The first of these two procedures may be far from economical. The second is unsound unless due account is taken of the fact that the multiplication factor that is to be applied to ϕ_e is not a constant for a given soil but is inversely proportional to the height. The explanation of this dependence on the height is that frictional forces vary as the second power of the height, whereas cohesional forces vary only as the first power of the height. These procedures can be accepted as satisfactory for very rough estimates only. For satisfactory estimates of lateral pressures in cohesive soils some form of Coulomb's Law must be used to express the shearing strength.

17·19 Expressions for Simple Cases of Lateral Pressure in Cohesive Backfill

Lateral pressures within a cohesive backfill are easily obtained if the shearing strength of the backfill is constant, or if an average value of shearing strength can be determined. These conditions are represented by the so-called $\phi = 0$ case, which has been discussed in Section 16·33.

Let Fig. 17·30 represent a wall retaining a cohesive backfill that has an average shearing strength s_{av}. It will be assumed that failure occurs on a plane and that the obliquity of thrust on the wall is zero. The angle θ will be used to designate the slope of any trial failure plane;

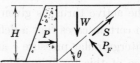

Fig. 17·30 Cross section illustrating the analysis for a simple case with a cohesive backfill.

the forces that must be considered are shown in the figure. The expression for equilibrium of components of force parallel to the failure plane may be written

$$P \cos \theta + S - W \sin \theta = 0$$

and

$$S = s_{av}H \csc \theta \quad \text{and} \quad W = \frac{\gamma H^2}{2} \cot \theta$$

whence

$$P = \frac{\gamma H^2}{2} - \frac{2s_{av}H}{\sin 2\theta}$$

It can be seen by inspection that this expression has a maximum value when $\sin 2\theta$ equals unity or θ equals 45 degrees, giving

$$P = \frac{\gamma H^2}{2} - 2s_{av}H \qquad (17\cdot22)$$

Assuming circular arcs as failure surfaces for the case covered above, Fellenius obtained for the critical arc

$$P = \frac{\gamma H^2}{2} - 1.92s_{av}H \qquad (17\cdot23)$$

which indicates that very little error is introduced by the assumption of plane failure.

The passive case is obtained for the section shown in Fig. 17·30 if the direction of action of force S is reversed. The expression for the passive thrust is

$$P_P = \frac{\gamma H^2}{2} + 2s_{av}H \qquad (17\cdot24)$$

For the cross section of Fig. 17·30 and for the assumptions used above, but for a soil for which the shearing strength is expressed by $s = c_e + \bar{\sigma} \tan \phi_e$ and in which there is no neutral pressure, the active thrust is given by equation 17·25. It is also possible in certain cases that a definite relationship may exist between the intergranular pressure $\bar{\sigma}$ and the total pressure σ_t, permitting the use of this formula when the shearing strength is expressed by $s = c_e + \sigma_t \tan \phi_e{}'$, in which $\phi_e{}'$ is a modified value of ϕ_e.

$$P = \frac{\gamma H^2}{2} \frac{1 - \sin \phi_e}{1 + \sin \phi_e} - 2c_e H \sqrt{\frac{1 - \sin \phi_e}{1 + \sin \phi_e}} \qquad (17·25)$$

17·20 Graphical Solution for the General Case in Cohesive Backfill

For the general graphical solution for the cohesive case the assumptions are the same as in the Coulomb earth pressure theory, except that the shearing strength is expressed by some form of Coulomb's Empirical Law relative to shearing strength. The obliquity angle at the wall will be designated by α, which usually may conservatively be chosen as equal to ϕ_e. Adhesion of soil to the wall is neglected. The procedure consists of successive trials of failure planes until the critical plane is found.

The method explained herein is based on the shearing strength expression

$$s = c_e + \bar{\sigma} \tan \phi_e$$

in which $\bar{\sigma}$ is an intergranular pressure. However, a simple case will be chosen for the example to be given, and it will be assumed that no pore-water pressures occur. For cases in which pore-water pressures exist on the critical plane, the flow net must be considered, and solutions for such cases may be obtained by the use of procedures outlined in Section 17·15 in conjunction with the procedure that follows.

In Fig. 17·31 a typical cross section is shown. The weight of the failure wedge is W, which equals $\frac{1}{2}\gamma ad$. The distance d is used as the length of the vector representing W. Therefore, the vectors used in this graphical method are to be multiplied by $\frac{1}{2}\gamma a$ to give the corresponding forces. In the figure JO represents vector W.

The cohesive force C is equal to $c_e m$ and, therefore, vector C must be of length $(2c_e/\gamma)(m/a)$. The expression $2c_e/\gamma$ is a length which is laid off as distance OB, along the line that is perpendicular to AG, the distance scale to which the section is plotted being used. Line BD is constructed parallel to AG. Since m/a equals OK/OB, distance OK represents vector C.

Through K a line is drawn at obliquity ϕ_e to line OK, this line being parallel to the intergranular force P_F. Through J a line

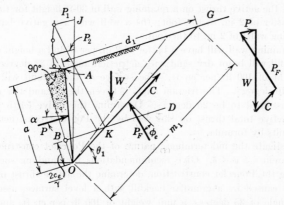

Fig. 17·31   Cross section illustrating the analysis for the general case with a cohesive backfill.

is drawn parallel to the thrust P. These two lines close the force polygon, giving vector P.

The procedure given above has the advantage of ease in the repetitions needed for several trial planes. A second trial is indicated by dashed lines in the figure. Successive trials must be made until the maximum vector P is obtained. This vector, when multiplied by $\frac{1}{2}a\gamma$, gives the thrust on the wall.

For the totally active case the point of action of the thrust may be below the point of one-third height. The explanation for this is that a cohesive slope can stand to some given height without support and, therefore, the minimum pressure on the top portion of the wall may be zero, or it may possibly be negative. In connection with the cohesive case there are many questionable factors, however, and the conservative assumption that the resultant thrust acts at the one-third point for the totally active case is commonly used.

PROBLEMS

1. The Rankine formula for a vertical wall and a level fill is much better known than the general form, and it is sometimes used when it does not apply. Determine the percentage error introduced by assuming a level fill when the slope angle i actually equals 20 degrees. Assume a friction angle of 35 degrees and a vertical wall.

2. A fill with a level surface is of granular soil with a friction angle of 35 degrees and a unit weight of 100 lb per cu ft. Using the Rankine method, determine the active thrust on a retaining wall of 30-ft height for (a) a wall with a batter of 2 in. to the foot; (b) a wall with a negative batter (an overhanging wall) of 2 in. to the foot.

3. A retaining wall will have a batter of 2 in. per ft and a height of 20 ft. The backfill will be of dry sand with a friction angle of 33 degrees and a unit weight of 100 lb per cu ft. The surface of the backfill will have a slope of 10 degrees. The friction angle between the fill and the masonry may be assumed to be 25 degrees. Determine the active earth pressure and the active total thrust on this wall by the Poncelet construction and check results by formula.

4. Investigate the indeterminate nature of the Poncelet construction for cases wherein $i = \phi - \delta$. Give recommendations for handling such cases.

5. Using the Poncelet construction, determine the active thrust on a vertical wall caused by a granular backfill with a level surface, assuming a friction angle of 35 degrees, a unit weight of 100 lb per cu ft, and a wall friction angle of zero. Demonstrate by a proof based on the graphical solution that the results are in agreement with those given by Rankine's equation 17·4.

6. Using the Poncelet construction, obtain a solution for the case of a vertical wall with $\phi = \phi' = i$, and demonstrate that the results agree with those given by the Rankine method.

7. Obtain passive pressure solutions for a vertical wall and a backfill having a friction angle of 35 degrees and a level surface. Solve for wall friction angles of both +35 degrees and −35 degrees by Poncelet construction. For comparison with these results obtain a value by the Rankine method.

8. A sheeted trench of 20-ft depth has been excavated into granular soil with a friction angle of 35 degrees and a unit weight of 105 lb per cu ft. The obliquity of stress on the sheeting may be assumed to be 25 degrees. Determine the maximum stress that would exist on the sheeting if a totally active case were to occur, and also obtain a rational pressure distribution diagram.

9. to 14. Determine the diagram of active pressure, the active thrust, and the moment about point O for the cross sections in the accompanying diagrams.

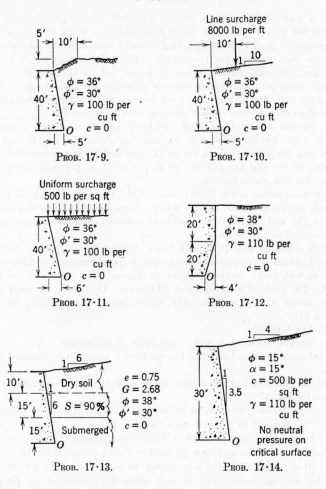

PROB. 17·9.

PROB. 17·10.

PROB. 17·11.

PROB. 17·12.

PROB. 17·13.

PROB. 17·14.

15. A vertical wall 40 ft high supports a backfill which weighs 100 lb per cu ft and has a level surface. The active pressure at the base of the wall is 1000 lb per sq ft. Later a uniform surcharge of 400 lb per sq ft is placed above the fill. Estimate the maximum active pressure and the resultant force on the wall after the surcharge is placed.

16. A cohesionless backfill with a horizontal surface has a weight of 100 lb per cu ft and carries a uniformly distributed surcharge of 500 lb per sq ft. The active pressure is 750 lb per sq ft at a point 20 ft down from the top of a retaining wall that is 40 ft high. Determine the intensity of the active pressure at the bottom of the wall.

17. A wall of 20-ft height retains a backfill of dry granular soil that weighs 100 lb per cu ft and has a level surface. When there is no surcharge above the fill, the overturning moment caused by the totally active pressure at a point at the base of the wall is 14.4 ft-tons per ft of wall. The angle of wall friction ϕ' has been assumed to be 25 degrees. The specifications permit a certain amount of uniformly distributed surcharge but state that the surcharge must not increase the overturning moment by more than 65 per cent. What surcharge can be allowed?

18. On one side of a sheet-pile bulkhead there is sand with its surface at El. $+10$. On the other side the sand surface is at El. -10 and high water and low water surfaces are at El. $+10$ and El. 0, respectively. Unit weights of the soil are 115 and 64 lb per cu ft, respectively, above and below the free water surface.

The total intergranular thrust above El. -10 on the bulkhead is 3000 pounds per running foot at high water. Assuming that the water level in the backfill and outside of the bulkhead coincide, compute the corresponding pressure at low water.

19. A retaining wall 20 ft high has a vertical face in contact with the backfill, which is composed of sand with a specific gravity of 2.70, a void ratio of 0.55, and a friction angle of 40 degrees. The surface of the fill is level. The angle of wall friction is 30 degrees. Determine the total active earth thrust on the wall and the water thrust, if any exists, for cases (a) to (d):

(a) Dry backfill.

(b) Backfill submerged, with water table at its surface.

(c) Lower 10 ft of backfill submerged, with upper 10 ft assumed to be dry.

(d) Backfill assumed to be completely saturated, with underdrainage as shown by Fig. 17·26.

(e) For the case of drainage shown in Fig. 17·25 state how the results would be expected to compare with those of (d).

20. Analyze the case in which a filter exists against the wall described in Prob. 19 and ledge underlies the sand at the elevation of the base of the wall. Heavy rainfall makes it necessary to assume that the fill occasionally has seepage throughout; at such times the surface of the fill is an equipotential line. Sketch a flow net and solve for the active thrust on the wall.

21. A certain wall 20 ft high retains a dry granular fill which weighs 100 lb per cu ft and which has a level surface. The active thrust on the wall is known to be 5000 lb per ft of wall. An increased height of wall is desired, and to keep the force on the wall within allowable limits the backfill to a depth of 10 ft is removed and replaced by cinders. The cinders may be assumed to weigh 50 lb per cu ft and to have the same friction angle as the soil. If cinders are used as a backfill to this height, what additional height may be allowed, if it is required that the active thrust on the wall be limited to its initial value?

22. Determine the base width required for the wall shown in the accompanying figure; base the computations on active pressure and the requirement that the resultant force on the base must be at the one-third point, and use (a) the Rankine theory and (b) the Coulomb theory. Also determine the base pressures and make analyses relative to danger of sliding.

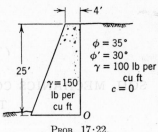

$\phi = 35°$
$\phi' = 30°$
$\gamma = 100$ lb per cu ft
$c = 0$
$\gamma = 150$ lb per cu ft

PROB. 17·22.

23. A sheet-pile bulkhead is to be constructed at a site at which the ground surface is at El. +15 on one side of the wall and at El. −15 on the other side. Water level is at El. 0 and tie rods are to be placed at El. +5. The soil is cohesionless and has a friction angle of 34 degrees. A differential head of water of 2 ft is to be assumed to account for water level fluctuations. Determine the load the tie rods must carry and the length of sheeting needed.

24. A wall with a vertical face retains a backfill with a level surface. Sketch the pressure distribution diagrams you would expect for each of the following cases, assuming reasonable values for any soil properties that are required and giving on each diagram the approximate value of the maximum pressure, expressed as a multiple of the expression γH.

(a) The fill is dry sand and the at-rest condition prevails.

(b) The fill is dry sand and a totally active condition exists.

(c) The fill is dry sand; the top of the wall has yielded a very small amount from the at-rest position whereas the bottom of the wall has yielded a relatively large amount.

(d) The fill is a saturated plastic clay; the wall is so rigidly fixed that appreciable yield is not possible; the water pressures on the wall are small and may be neglected.

(e) The fill is saturated plastic clay; the wall is free to yield but is so weak in resistance to overturning that a case of incipient failure prevails; the water table on both sides of the wall is at the level of the top of the wall.

25. For both cohesionless and cohesive soils explain the conditions which must exist to justify the design of retaining walls on the assumption that the active pressure must be resisted.

Chapter 18

SOIL MECHANICS CONSIDERATIONS RELATIVE
TO DAMS

18·1 Introductory Discussion

There are many practical applications of soil mechanics in the analysis and design of earth dams and the foundations of all types of dams. Some of these considerations of dams are beyond the scope of this text even though the dams are of earth; studies of required spillway capacities to prevent danger of overtopping are an example. Certain practical details which are related to soil cannot be covered because of lack of space; examples are the details of protection against erosion and wave action by riprap, by sodding, by berms, and so on. However, earth dams and the foundations of dams present such important problems to the soil engineer that a number of phases of this subject will be discussed.*

The fundamentals of many of these items have already been presented. Thus one value of this treatment is the general ideas it gives regarding the role of soil mechanics in practical engineering problems relative to dams. The most important of the subjects covered herein are compaction, stability, and underseepage.

18·2 Compaction

Earth dams, highway fills, and other embankments must be placed in a dense state † if they are to have maximum strength and imperviousness, if they are to be free of excessive settlement by shrinkage and, in the case of granular soils, free of danger from liquefaction. *Compaction* may be defined as the process of

---

* For detailed considerations see reference 39, especially Vol. III, or reference 106. On selection of materials see reference 96.

† See reference 18. For an example of compaction by explosives see reference 99.

bringing soils to a dense state by blows, by passages of a roller, or by some other type of loading.

In some instances, such as in certain types of dike and levee construction, it is not economically feasible to compact the soil. However, in many embankment construction projects it is specified that the density be increased by compacting, generally by the use of rollers of some type. One of the most efficient types

Fig. 18·1 Sheep's-foot rollers. (Courtesy of Caterpillar Tractor Co.)

of compacting equipment and a type that is now widely used is the *sheep's-foot roller*. In this equipment projections shaped like a sheep's-foot are attached to the drum of the roller. On a layer of soil 6 or 8 in. thick these projections cause compaction which begins at the bottom of the layer and progresses toward the top. A roller of this type is shown in Fig. 18·1.

For any given soil that is proposed to be used as a rolled-fill embankment, there is a certain water content at which a given amount of rolling with given rolling equipment gives the greatest compaction. This value is called the *optimum water content*. A laboratory test for the determination of the optimum water content was developed some years ago by R. R. Proctor (117) and the test procedure was published in 1933. This test is now known as the *Proctor compaction test*, and it plays an important part in the investigations and in the construction control of rolled-fill materials.

Proctor compaction may be viewed as a laboratory procedure designed to bring soils to approximately the same state of density as is obtained when earth dams are compacted by rolling equipment. In the test the soil is compacted in a cylinder with a diameter of 4 in. and a volume of $\frac{1}{30}$ cu ft. The compaction is accomplished by tamping the soil in three layers of about equal thickness, each layer in turn being subjected to 25 blows by a $5\frac{1}{2}$-lb hammer 2 in. in diameter at the striking surface, each blow having a free fall of 12 in.

In recent years heavier compacting equipment has come into use and, in order to reproduce the greater densities obtained with this equipment, modified compaction tests have been developed. A modified compaction procedure that has been adopted by the U. S. Corps of Engineers ‡ uses 25 blows of 18-in. drop with a 10-lb hammer on each of five layers in the Proctor cylinder.

A compaction test consists of compaction runs on a number of specimens of the soil, each specimen being at a different water content. The water content of each specimen is then plotted against some property which is a measure of the density obtained. For representing the density there are a number of possible choices, among which are the void ratio, the porosity, and the unit weight. The quantity which is commonly used is called the *unit dry weight;* it may be defined as the weight of solids per unit of volume of soil in the compacted state. Since the Proctor mold is of $\frac{1}{30}$ cu ft volume, the dry unit weight in pounds per cubic foot is 30 times the dry weight of the compacted soil specimen. Actually the entire specimen need not be dried; a small portion of it may be used to obtain the water content w, and the dry unit weight may then be obtained from the expression $30W/(1+w)$, in which W is the weight of compacted soil and water.

Curve A of Fig. 18·2 is a typical compaction curve. The abscissa of point P is the *optimum water content*, which here equals 19 per cent. The ordinate of point P is the *optimum dry*

‡ Known as the modified A.A.S.H.O. (American Association of State Highway Officials) compaction or the modified Proctor compaction; see reference 164.

unit weight, and its value for this soil is 102 lb per cu ft; this is a relatively low value for optimum dry weight. The dashed line is a curve of wet unit weight. At the right of the figure scales

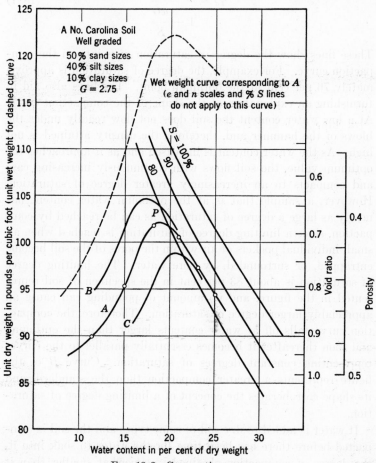

A No. Carolina Soil
Well graded
50 % sand sizes
40 % silt sizes
10 % clay sizes
G = 2.75

Wet weight curve corresponding to A
(e and n scales and % S lines
do not apply to this curve)

S = 100 %
90
80

Unit dry weight in pounds per cubic foot (unit wet weight for dashed curve)

Water content in per cent of dry weight

Void ratio

Porosity

Fig. 18·2 Compaction curves.

of void ratio and porosity are shown. The curve of wet unit weight and the alternate scales are given here to aid in the correlation of the various density characteristics; they are not usually included.

Also shown on the figure are lines that represent conditions of 100, 90, and 80 per cent saturation, respectively. Such lines may be obtained from the expression

$$\gamma_d = \frac{G\gamma_w}{1 + \dfrac{wG}{S}} \tag{18.1}$$

These lines show the degree of saturation of points on the compaction curve. For example, the degree of saturation is approximately 76 per cent at the optimum point. The lines also aid in furnishing an explanation of the shape of the compaction curve. At a low water content the soil does not flow readily under the blows of the hammer and, therefore, the density attained is not high. As the water content is increased and as it approaches the optimum value, the soil flows with continuously increasing ease and compacts to an increasingly greater degree of saturation. However, a sample that is at the optimum water content has nearly as large a degree of saturation as can be reached by compaction, since a limiting degree of saturation is reached when all small individual pockets of air within the pores of the soil become entrapped, or surrounded, by pore water. The limiting degree of saturation is about 83 per cent in the specimen of soil represented in the figure, and no amount of pounding can cause an appreciably larger degree of saturation. Therefore, the compaction curve falls off at water contents larger than the optimum, and soon thereafter it becomes essentially parallel to the curves representing constant degrees of saturation. Curve *B* of the figure represents a greater compaction than the standard, and its shape corroborates the concept of a limiting degree of saturation.

If water is added to dry soil of some types and the soil is compacted before there has been time for the water to soak into it, the degree of compaction obtained is somewhat smaller than it would be if more time were allowed. Curve *C* represents such a case. However, the difference between curves *C* and *A* usually is smaller than shown in this figure, and for many soils this time effect need not be considered.

After compaction tests have been run on representative samples of the soils proposed for an earth dam, the optimum water contents and the optimum dry weights are known. However, the various specimens tested often are soils with considerably different characteristics, and different optimum values may hold at different points in the fill. Thus there may be a difficult problem of identifying soil types but, except for this problem, the water contents that are the most favorable and the densities that should be obtained under the given compactive effort are known.

As a dam is constructed the soil usually is placed in layers of specified thickness and compacted by a specified number of passes of a specified type of roller. Specimens often are removed from the fill at intervals for testing. These specimens should not be taken at the surface of the fill, but should be obtained at a small depth, so that the benefit of the compaction of the layer above will be obtained. The samples represent a given volume of compacted soil, this volume either being the known volume of a cylindrical sampler which is forced into the ground until full, or the measured volume of the hole from which the soil is taken. If a measurement of the volume of the hole is to be obtained with reasonable accuracy, the adjacent ground surface must be level before the sample is taken. After the sample is removed a thin rubber blanket may be used to cover the surface of the hole, and the volume of dry sand or water required to fill the hole level full may be determined. From the volume and the weight of a sample and the weight of the sample after drying, the unit weight and the water content are easily obtained. Tests of this type are known as *control tests*.

The comparison of the data given by such tests with the optimum values obtained in laboratory tests furnishes a check on whether the desired compaction is obtained. If heavy rolling equipment is used and if it gives a greater degree of compaction than that represented by the laboratory test, it is possible to discover this situation in the early stages of construction, because the samples from the dam that are at lower water contents than the optimum value have dry unit weights that are larger than the optimum value. Assuming that curve *A* represents a test by the laboratory procedure in use, it may be desirable to change to a modified procedure that gives results similar to curve *B*. When the density values obtained are less than the optimum values and the water content of the soil is either above or below the optimum value, the poor results may be attributed to unfavorable water content. If the soil is at the optimum water content, but the optimum density is not obtained, it is possible that not enough passes have been made. When unexplained irregularities occur, the most likely explanation is that there has been a 'mistake in identifying the soil type, and the need of a compaction test on the specimen in question is indicated.

Penetration needles have been used to some extent as an alternate method of control. The resistance to penetration of a needle of given diameter into a given soil is a function of the density and the water content and, after calibrations are available, it sometimes is possible in quite homogeneous soils to check densities and water contents as rolling goes on by observations of penetration resistance. This is a simple method but it is not so positive as the method discussed above, and it is not always successful.

In compacting highway embankments it often is not feasible to use as heavy rolling equipment or to control the conditions as well as in earth dam construction. A common specification in highway work is that 90 or 95 per cent of the optimum unit weight be obtained.

Sometimes the soil in its natural condition in borrow pits is at a water content that is greater than the optimum. When the weather is favorable the soil dries somewhat during spreading, and on some occasions the desired water content may be obtained if the soil is spread and then is allowed to stand before rolling. However, this procedure may cause serious delays and the success of the procedure is greatly dependent on favorable weather. In many instances borrow pits that contain excess water must be classed as unsatisfactory.

A soil that is highly compacted has a tendency to swell somewhat unless a pressure that is sufficiently large to overcome this tendency is imposed on it. The amount of swelling and the force required to prevent swelling depend greatly on the soil type and the degree of compaction. Observations of the pressures required to prevent swelling are sometimes made in connection with compaction tests. If the soil near the base of a dam does not have an overburden load that is sufficiently large to prevent swelling, the dam is said to be *overcompacted*. Overcompaction often is an undesirable condition, especially in dams on relatively weak foundations, since lateral swelling of the overcompacted soil may introduce shearing strains and thus may disturb the structure in the soil of the foundation. Failures of dams have on some occasions been attributed to overcompaction.

18·3   Stability Analysis of Dams

The stability of dams may be viewed as merely a subdivision of the subject of stability of slopes. The fundamental concepts needed for stability analysis have been discussed in Chapter 16. However, analyses of dams are usually quite complex, because dams seldom have homogeneous sections and because seepage and drawdown conditions are likely to be governing factors.

In simple dams composed of soils with shearing strengths that do not vary radically over the cross section, rough analyses of stability may often be made by the use of the chart in Fig. 16·26. Failures of the downstream slope are most likely to occur when there is a full pond and the water table is at its highest elevation, causing seepage forces to have their greatest effect. Failure of the upstream slope is most likely just after the most rapid and the greatest height of drawdown takes place. For approximate solutions of these cases by the use of charts the limiting cases of seepage throughout and complete drawdown, respectively, as described in Section 16·27, may be used. Actually, however, the idealized conditions used in solutions by chart for cases of sudden drawdown involve a greater degree of approximation in dams than they do in simple embankments, because seepage always is occurring within a dam previous to drawdown.

More elaborate analyses may be made by methods of the types outlined in Sections 16·16 and 16·18. When the foundation has a much greater shearing strength than the dam, it usually is necessary to consider only rupture surfaces through the dam. A more complex case is that in which the dam has greater shearing strength than its foundation, and for this case no blanket statements can be made regarding which method is best; sometimes the methods given in Chapter 16 may be applied, and on other occasions the *sliding-block method*, which is discussed in Section 18·5 offers the best approach.

When a cross section contains a weak stratum between strata

of greater strength, as large a portion as possible of the failure surface will pass through the weak stratum. If the soil is highly stratified, with alternate layers of different strengths, a large portion of the failure surface will tend to be parallel to the strata and will pass through the weaker soil. Thus stratification tends to give variations from circular-shaped rupture surface but, if a rational averaging of shearing strength values is used, as explained in Section 16·30, the assumption of circular arcs for failure surfaces may still lead to reasonable results.

In sections of dams that are composed of saturated granular materials, the danger of liquefaction exists unless the soil is compacted to a sufficiently dense state.§ Therefore, shearing strengths of saturated, granular soils should not be assumed to be the strength for the freely drained case unless critical void ratio considerations indicate that this assumption is safe.

A special type of analysis for dams of the hydraulic-fill type is discussed in the next section.

18·4 Analysis of the Stability of Hydraulic-Fill Dams

A typical section of a hydraulic-fill dam during construction is shown in Fig. 18·3. Soil is carried by rapidly flowing water in pipes or flumes F to the extremities of the section, where the

Fig. 18·3 Cross section of a hydraulic-fill dam during construction.

water and soil are discharged; they then flow toward the center of the section.‖ The water loses velocity as it approaches the pool P. Therefore, the deposited soil is coarsest at the outer boundaries and increasingly finer at points nearer the pool. When the water reaches the pool edge E its velocity is checked, and all the remaining sand sizes and the coarser silt sizes are deposited in a narrow transition zone T. Only the fines reach

§ A slide that was believed by some engineers to have been caused by liquefaction is described in reference 100.

‖ A diagrammatic sketch that shows construction operations on a hydraulic-fill dam is given on page 422 of reference 112.

the pool, where they settle slowly and in time are consolidated to form an impervious central section which furnishes the water-tightness of the dam.

During construction the pool is practically a fluid. Danger of failure is greatest just as the end of construction is approached and, unless data to the contrary are available, conservative procedure requires the assumption of no shearing strength in the central section, even though it is known that considerable strength

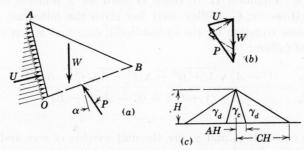

Fig. 18·4 Cross sections illustrating the stability analysis of a hydraulic-fill dam.

will develop with time. The outer section, known as the *shell*, must have sufficient strength to resist the passive force exerted on it by the central section, the *core*.

The following stability analysis for this type of section was developed by G. Gilboy (61). The forces acting on the shell are shown in Fig. 18·4 (a). The fluid thrust U acts normal to surface AO, which is the boundary between the core and the shell. In case of failure the rupture surface is assumed to be a plane,¶ this plane being represented by OB. The total weight of the shell, including its water content, is W. The resultant of forces U and W must be balanced by force P. The plane most liable to failure is the one on which force P has the greatest obliquity, and the section is stable if this maximum obliquity is less than the friction angle.

The analysis given above is an example of the use of total weights and boundary neutral forces; it is based on principles

¶ In references 61 and 63 Gilboy describes tests by the author which demonstrate that the assumption of plane failure is reasonable.

outlined in Section 9·18. The transition section at the inner portion of the shell is so much finer than the main portion of the shell that all heads are dissipated and practically all seepage forces occur within it. Therefore, no appreciable water pressures exist on the failure plane.

It may be noted that Fig. 18·4 (*a*) represents a special case of the general passive pressure condition illustrated in Fig. 17·12. This special case has a negative angle *i* and a zero value for angle *α*. Equation 17·16 could be used for a solution of this case. However, G. Gilboy (63) has given the following, more convenient equation for the hydraulic-fill dam that is just at the point of failure:

$$\sqrt{\frac{\gamma_c}{\gamma_d}} = \frac{(C - A)\sqrt{1 + B^2} + \sqrt{C - A}\sqrt{C - B}\sqrt{1 + A^2}}{(1 + C^2) - (C - A)(C - B)}$$

(18·2)

In this equation γ_c and γ_d are the unit weights of core and shell respectively, C and A are the cotangents of the outer slope angle and the core slope angle, respectively, and B equals cot ϕ. The notations are shown in Fig. 18·4 (*c*). This equation may be used to determine the value of γ_c which would just cause failure. The ratio between this value and the actual value of γ_c may then be obtained; it may be called the factor of safety with respect to core pressure.

Study of the force triangle of Fig. 18·4 (*b*) shows the beneficial effect of a steep core. If the core is flattened the force polygon becomes somewhat as shown by dotted lines, and on any trial failure plane it is seen that a greater obliquity of stress and a less stable condition result.

18·5 The Sliding-Block Analysis

A relatively simple and fairly common case, for which the use of the circular failure assumption is not reasonable, is that in which the critical surface, or a large portion of the critical surface, is approximately a horizontal plane. A good illustration is a dam with a relatively thin horizontal stratum of soil of low shearing resistance at a shallow depth below the surface of the foundation. Other examples are cases in which the foundation soils contain horizontal stratification and cases in which an overcompacted earth fill overlies a foundation consisting of a clay with structure that is susceptible to disturbance.

Embankments of these types may be investigated by the procedure sometimes designated as the *sliding-block analysis*. A simple analysis of this type is shown in Fig. 18·5. It will be assumed that the horizontal plane OD in this figure is a surface of weakness within the foundation and that it is the critical surface. The analysis consists of the consideration of the forces acting on the mass represented by triangle AOD. The horizontal

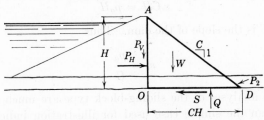

FIG. 18·5 Simple cross section used in the example of the sliding-block analysis.

forces are shown by heavy line vectors, since the analysis is based mainly on these forces. Vectors representing vertical forces are shown lightly and they will be considered in less detail. The horizontal force P_2, which is the passive, lateral resistance of the soil above point D, is also shown lightly, since it may be of inappreciable magnitude when the critical plane is at a shallow depth; it will be neglected in this example. Any failure tendency that results from weakness of the soil along line OD introduces lateral movement at all points within mass AOD, increasing the horizontal dimensions of the dam. This lateral bulging of the dam tends to reduce the lateral pressures on surface AO to active pressures, which have values that depend on the shearing characteristics of the dam and are independent of the strength of the underlying weak stratum. However, the thrust across AO may be the cause of failure of the mass AOD by sliding along the weak foundation plane OD.

Force P_H may be evaluated by active pressure considerations, and this thrust also must include any neutral force that acts across surface AO. The stability of the block AOD may be investigated by comparing thrust P_H with the available shearing resistance along surface OD. The average lateral pressure across AO is equal to P_H/H; it will be designated by p_a. The average shearing strength depends greatly on the degree to which consolidation takes place under the weight of the soil above surface OD. However, only the average, required shearing strength s_r will be considered in this simple analysis, and no attempt will be made to express the actual shearing strength in terms of the pressure. Force S must balance force P_H, whence

$$s_r CH = p_a H$$

in which C is the slope of the dam. Thus

$$s_r = \frac{p_a}{C} \qquad (18 \cdot 3)$$

Typical analyses of the sliding-block type are much more involved than the simple case used for illustration indicates. If the dam is composed of cohesive soil, the active pressure determinations may be difficult. If the weak stratum is of appreciable depth, trial failure surfaces at various depths must be considered. The consolidation conditions not only affect the shearing strengths in the weak stratum but they also may have a considerable effect on the location of the critical surface. The vertical surface through the crest of the dam is not necessarily the critical one, and other vertical surfaces nearer the toe of the dam must sometimes be considered.

An important type of sliding-block action that can occur near the toe of a dam will be cited. The overburden pressure at the base of the dam is much greater below the crest than it is nearer the toes. Therefore, overcompaction may exist near the toes when it does not occur below the crest. The swelling tendency that is inherent in overcompacted soil may lead to lateral pressures that approach passive pressure magnitudes. These pressures may cause bulging near the toe of the dam, and if the foundation soil is susceptible to remolding its shearing strength may be greatly decreased and a failure surface may develop. It is possible that the disturbance of structure may reduce the shearing strength in the foundation to such a low value that a slide will occur. However, the bulging that occurs tends to relieve the lateral pressures and, if the remolded foundation soil is of sufficient strength to resist active lateral pressures, there will be no failure, but there may be noticeable bulging near the toe of the dam.

18·6 Roofing and Piping

When a masonry dam rests on soil, local irregularities always exist in the bearing pressures on the foundation because of the inevitable local variations in soil properties. Small zones exist over which pressures are much larger or much smaller than the average values thereabout, and at some points there may actually be small gaps between the masonry and the soil. These gaps or points of low pressure would of themselves cause no concern, but when water seeps through them they may form the starting points of channels of flow, and by backward erosion such channels may in time increase to appreciable lengths. Thus the resistance to seepage along seepage paths which are in contact with masonry may be much less than it is along other paths. This phenomenon is called *roofing*.

A similar condition may exist at the abutment of a masonry dam. To prevent the formation of flow channels where soil is in contact with a vertical masonry surface the soil should be well compacted and in tight contact with the masonry at all points. Cutoffs are often used to increase the lengths of flow paths and thus decrease the danger of such channels. A batter on a wall is desirable if adjacent soil is settling relative to the wall. If the wall is settling relative to the adjacent soil, a batter is undesirable, since it causes the contact pressure to decrease. The numerous difficulties and dangers that are inherent in any case in which seepage occurs at a contact between soil and masonry are an ever-present argument in favor of earth dams at sites where the foundations are of soil.

If erosion starts at the point of exit of a flow line that has passed below or around a dam, the erosion may progress backward, aided perhaps by the presence of a flow channel that is the result of roofing. The resulting condition is called *piping*. One of the worst characteristics of piping is that it needs to occur only in one local channel to be a possible threat to the safety of a large dam.

18·7 Underseepage Considerations

The representation of seepage conditions by the flow net has been discussed in detail in Chapter 9. As stated therein, the flow net allows determinations of the following quantities which are of interest to the designer:

1. The quantity of seepage.
2. The uplift pressures.
3. The exit gradients.

Determinations of quantities of underseepage have been presented in Chapter 9. Considerations of uplift pressures and exit conditions are treated in the following sections.

These quantities can seldom be obtained accurately and, in fact, the correct order of magnitude is the best that can be hoped for in most cases. Numerous reasons can be cited. Great variations in permeability exist from point to point in any foundation. The stratification theoretically can be accounted for by the use of the stratification ratio $\sqrt{k_z/k_x}$, but this ratio seldom is accurately known. It is likely that the roofing phenomenon discussed in the previous section may occur to some degree. Variations from the two-dimensional case occur. There are also numerous other deviations from the idealized conditions assumed in any analysis. Nevertheless, the data obtained in studies of this type, if used with reason, are a valuable guide to judgment.

18·8 Uplift Pressures

The pressure head at any point at the base of a masonry dam may be determined from the flow net. In Fig. 18·6 the sketched flow net contains three paths and about 7.4 equipotential spaces. The head drop between adjacent equipotential lines is $h/7.4$ or $0.135h$; in the fractional equipotential space at the downstream end the head drop is $0.4 \times 0.135h$ or $0.055h$. The head is shown on each equipotential line in the figure. Along the equipotential line through point A all points have total heads of $0.325h$, or 5.8 ft. A standpipe which penetrates to any point on this line would show water rising to an elevation which is 32.5 per cent of the distance between tail water and head water elevations; two such standpipes are shown in the figure.

The pressure head is in all cases equal to the total head minus the elevation head. Thus at point A, where the total head equals 5.8 ft and the elevation head equals -4 ft, the pressure head equals 9.8 ft. The corresponding uplift pressure is 9.8×62.5 or

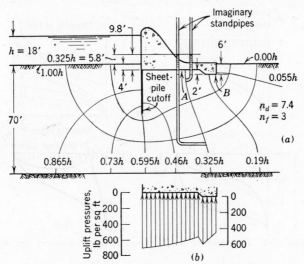

FIG. 18·6 Example of uplift pressure determinations.

610 lb per sq ft. Similarly, at point B the total head is $0.10h$, or 1.8 ft, the elevation head is -6 ft, the pressure head is 7.8 ft, and the uplift pressure is 490 lb per sq ft. By subdividing the sketched squares, pressure heads may be obtained at as many points on the base as desired, and the diagram of uplift pressures that is given in (b) may be obtained. On the base of this dam the uplift pressure does not vary a great deal; it ranges only from 700 to 490 lb per sq ft.

For the simple dam shown in Fig. 9·2, the water pressure diagram or uplift diagram is as shown in Fig. 18·7 (a). A straight line variation from full head at the heel to zero head at the toe, as shown by the dashed line, is frequently used and is usually a satisfactory approximation of this curve.

W. Weaver (166) has published results of mathematical solutions of uplift pressures below dams resting on the surface of the foundation. These solutions are based on an infinite depth of soil, but Harza (68) has shown by data obtained by use of electrical analogy apparatus that the depth does not have appreciable effect on the uplift curve. Therefore, the mathematical solutions are essentially correct for any depth of foundation soil.

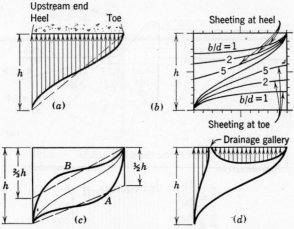

FIG. 18·7 Diagrams of uplift pressure below masonry dams.

Weaver showed that the curve of uplift pressure in (*a*) is a cosine curve relative to a vertical axis. He presented uplift pressure relationships for dams with sheeting at either the heel or the toe. Typical examples of these relationships are given in (*b*), the quantity b/d being the ratio between the base width and the sheeting depth.

The intergranular pressure distribution that exists below a dam with full reservoir resembles the pressure distribution that occurs below a retaining wall, as shown in Fig. 17·22, in that the pressures are largest near the toe. The relatively large intergranular pressure near the toe causes relatively low void ratios and permeabilities in this region. The low permeability is the cause of larger head losses below the downstream portion of the dam; an uplift diagram resembling curve A of Fig. 18·7 (*c*) results. In contrast any condition that would lead to low permeability below the upstream portion of the base would be the cause of an uplift diagram resembling curve *B*. Such a condition might be caused by grouting at the heel of the dam. The general forms of curves *A* and *B* are valid for all types of foundations, including stratified soils and ledge.

Any dam that has no cutoff at the heel and that is founded at or just below the surface of the foundation has a pressure head at the heel that is practically the full head on the dam. When a concrete dam is thoroughly bonded to ledge, it would appear reasonable to expect the head to act over only a portion of the base area and, therefore, it has often been assumed that only partial uplift pressure exists in such a case. Actually, however, the pressure head probably acts over the entire area of the first seam within the rock below the base of the dam and, if this is so, the full head should be used in estimating uplift pressures on the base. This suggestion indicates that the general trend in estimates of uplift pressures has not always been sufficiently conservative. In a case resembling *B* of Fig. 18·7 (*c*), it probably is reasonable to approximate the uplift curve by a straight line, with a pressure of $\frac{2}{3}h$ at the heel and zero at the toe, as shown by a dashed line in the figure. Such a case may exist when the upstream portion of a ledge foundation has been successfully grouted and the permeability at the upstream end has been decreased. For rough estimates for cases with uplift diagrams resembling *A*, Terzaghi (151) has recommended that it be assumed that there is a straight line variation of pressure from h at the heel to $\frac{1}{2}h$ at the toe. This distribution is also illustrated by a dashed line in (*c*), and it probably is reasonably representative of a condition that is more common than has been supposed.

Drainage galleries are sometimes used effectively to reduce uplift pressures. The case shown in Fig. 18·7 (*d*) illustrates a large reduction in uplift pressure but shows that pressures are not completely relieved downstream of the gallery. The use of a drainage gallery leads of course to a greater quantity of seepage than would otherwise occur.

The main use of the uplift pressure diagram is in the design of masonry dams on earth or on ledge. The only difference between the design procedure for this type of structure and the design procedure for the retaining wall, discussed in Section $17 \cdot 12$, is the consideration of the uplift force. A typical section

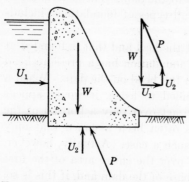

of dam and the force polygon considered in the design are shown in Fig. $18 \cdot 8$. The analysis relates to the equilibrium that must exist between the head water thrust U_1, the weight of the dam W, the uplift force U_2, and the resulting intergranular thrust P across the base. When the dam is on a soil foundation the requirements relative to

Fig. $18 \cdot 8$ The forces entering into the stability analysis of a masonry dam.

force P are the same as for the retaining wall; that is, there must be safety against

sliding, against overturning, and against excessive toe pressure. In principle the same requirements hold for masonry dams on ledge.

$18 \cdot 9$ Analysis of Safety against Piping

A simple, rational method has been proposed by L. F. Harza (68) for investigations relative to safety against piping, or toe liquefaction. The criterion of a quick condition in a homogeneous soil deposit was shown in Section $7 \cdot 5$ to be an upward gradient of $(G - 1)/(1 + e)$. This critical gradient has an approximate range of values from 0.8 to 1.2, and unity is often mentioned as a typical value. In the Harza method the maximum permissible exit gradient is the critical gradient divided by a factor of safety.

The maximum exit gradient at the toe of a dam may be determined from the flow net. For example, the head lost in the final, partial square in Fig. $18 \cdot 6$ is $0.055h$ or 1.0 ft. At the downstream end of the dam this head is lost in a distance of approximately 5 ft, which is the height of the final, partial square at the top flow line. Thus the maximum exit gradient in this case equals approximately 0.20.

The logical value for the factor of safety with respect to exit gradient depends on a number of factors for any given case, but a factor of 3 or 4 is often considered reasonable. If a critical gradient of 1.0 and a factor of safety of 4 are assumed the permissible exit gradient is 0.25. On this basis the maximum exit gradient of 0.20, mentioned in the preceding paragraph, is satisfactory.

The possibility of results being affected by roofing and other such items must always be considered, but when this method is

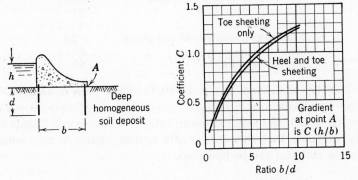

FIG. 18·9 Critical escape gradients. (L. F. Harza.)

used allowance for such items must be made largely by judgment.

Harza presented tabulations and charts of coefficients for use in determining exit gradients for simple dams on deep homogeneous deposits. Figure 18·9 is an example. The section of the dam in this figure is, of course, the transformed section.

An empirical approach to this problem has been developed by E. W. Lane (95). This approach considers that the contact path or top flow line is usually the critical path as far as danger of piping is concerned, because it is the path affected by roofing. This path is designated as the *creep path*. Lane analyzed the designs of many dams on many types of soil; in all, 278 dams were studied, 36 of which failed. From his studies he concluded that the resistance to vertical creep tends on the average to be about three times as large as the resistance to horizontal creep. Thus he defines the *weighted-creep distance* as the sum of all vertical distances along the creep path plus one third of the sum of horizontal distances along this path. He designates the quotient of the weighted-creep distance and the head as the *weighted-creep ratio*. Lane concludes that the required weighted-creep ratio depends mainly on the type of soil, and his list of the safe values for various soils is presented in Table 18·1.

TABLE 18·1 SAFE WEIGHTED-CREEP RATIOS

(According to E. W. Lane)

Material	Safe Values
Very fine sand or silt to fine sand	8.5 to 7
Medium to coarse sand	6 to 5
Fine to coarse gravel	4 to 3
Boulders with some cobbles and gravel	2.5
Soft to medium clay	3 to 2
Hard to very hard clay	1.8 to 1.6

For the dam shown in Fig. 18·10, the creep path is *ABCDEF*. The weighted-creep distance is $23 + 20 + \frac{1}{3} \times 48 + 20 + 23$, or 102 ft, and the weighted-creep ratio is $^{102}\!\!/_{16}$, or 6.4. According to Table 18·1 this dam is safe against piping on any foundation material except fine sand.

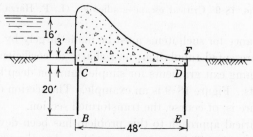

FIG. 18·10 Cross section used in the example illustrating Lane's weighted-creep ratio.

Lane recommended that portions of creep paths that are steeper than 45 degrees be weighted the same as vertical paths and that portions flatter than 45 degrees be weighted as horizontal paths. The *short path,* which is illustrated by *ABEF* of Fig. 18·10, must be considered in certain cases. Lane recommended that short path distances through the soil be given a weight of two and that the short path, weighted on this basis, be used in place of the weighted-creep path, if it is the shorter of the two weighted paths. The weighted short path in the figure has a length of $23 + 2 \times 48 + 23$, or 142 ft, which is greater than the weighted-creep distance and, therefore, is not the critical path in this case.

The most important difference between the methods proposed by Lane and Harza is that the safety according to Lane is greatly dependent on the type of soil, whereas Harza's flow net approach is based on gradients that are independent of the soil type. The rational nature of Harza's method is an important point in its favor. However, if piping is just starting at a given point, the danger of failure may depend greatly on the extent to which roofing is present and on the susceptibility of the soil to erosion, and these factors may differ greatly in different types of soil. Thus Lane's method merits special consideration in all cases in which positive protection against the starting of piping at all exit points of flow lines does not exist. A weakness of Lane's approach is its automatic limitation to average values for representing quantities which may have wide variations. Certain designs which are known to be unsafe pass Lane's requirements * and vice versa, but Lane's thorough study of all available dam designs is in itself a valuable investigation and his method of analysis should be considered whenever it appears that the creep path is likely to be the critical path.

Many details that are not mentioned herein but that are of considerable practical interest are discussed in the papers by Harza and Lane (68, 95).

18·10 Control of Seepage Forces in Dams

Any dam that retains a body of water, or any embankment that contains a sloping, free water surface, is subjected to seepage forces. One of the most important considerations in the designing of a dam for a given site is the choice of a cross section in which the seepage forces are at such locations that they tend to cause no trouble or are controlled in a positive and efficient manner. Large seepage forces are not undesirable if they occur near the center of the dam and are directed downward. If flow lines break out on the downstream slope of the dam, or rise to the ground surface downstream of the dam, it is necessary

* See discussion by A. Casagrande on page 1289 of reference 95.

either that the gradients be limited to safe magnitudes or that provisions be made to prevent erosion.

In the dam with underdrainage, which was discussed in Section 9·10, the top flow line is kept within the dam, and all seepage forces occur where they can cause no undesirable action. Such a section is shown in Fig. 18·11 (a). Two other methods of preventing the top flow line from having a breakout point on the downstream slope of the dam are shown in (b) and (c); these methods utilize a downstream coarse section and a rock toe, respectively. In all the sections shown in Fig. 18·11 protective filters of the type described in Section 7·7 must be installed wherever lines of flow pass from fine soils to coarse soils.

When the dam is of masonry or of relatively impervious earth and the foundation is of homogeneous and relatively pervious earth, the critical point is just below the toe of the dam. If the gradients at this point are too large for safety, filters may be placed above the zone of dangerous gradients as shown in Fig. 18·11 (d). An underdrain furnishing filter protection below a concrete dam is shown in (e); whether the dam is of earth or masonry this is a more positive protection than that illustrated by (d). A toe cutoff as shown in Fig. 18·9 is effective in reducing the gradient at the danger point, but this dam is subject to relatively large uplift pressures. A combination of the sections of Fig. 18·9 and Fig. 18·11 (e) is shown in (f). This arrangement gives double protection; weep holes through the dam allow the controlled escape of water from the underdrain, and the cutoff serves as protection against erosion of the underdrain. A masonry section which may be overtopped occasionally by floods usually needs the high degree of protection illustrated in (f). The upstream blanket shown in (g) leads to reduced gradients at the toe, and it may often be less expensive than a cutoff; however, with highly stratified foundation soils the blanket may not be so efficient a type of construction as it first appears to be.

When a pervious foundation is of limited depth and it is desirable to reduce the seepage, a sheet-pile cutoff such as that shown in (h) or a trench cutoff such as that shown in (i) may be used. Either of these cutoffs removes the danger of seepage forces in the foundation.

Where the foundation is of relatively impervious soil at the surface, but has coarser and more pervious strata below, the total head at any point within the coarse strata anywhere under

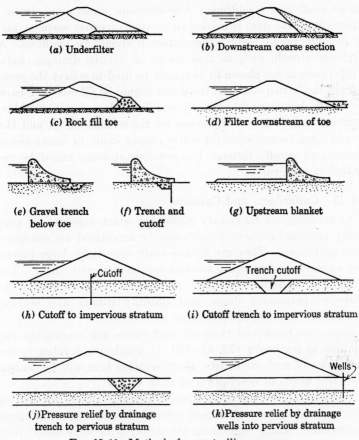

(a) Underfilter

(b) Downstream coarse section

(c) Rock fill toe

(d) Filter downstream of toe

(e) Gravel trench below toe

(f) Trench and cutoff

(g) Upstream blanket

(h) Cutoff to impervious stratum

(i) Cutoff trench to impervious stratum

(j) Pressure relief by drainage trench to pervious stratum

(k) Pressure relief by drainage wells into pervious stratum

FIG. 18·11 Methods for controlling seepage.

the dam is likely to be high. If it is assumed that the impervious strata are of uniform thickness and are intact, the head throughout the pervious strata is likely to be approximately equal to one-half the head on the dam. When the impervious strata have been pierced in some way upstream of the dam, by a few wells for example, the pressure throughout the pervious strata may approach the full head. Such cases are subject to the danger of blowouts or boils below the dam. This condition would be dangerous below an important dam, and the danger of its occurrence should be removed by relieving the pressure under controlled conditions. A continuous, impervious stratum upstream of the dam is needed to prevent excessive seepage, and if the impervious layer is not intact it should be made so. A drainage trench, such as that shown in (*j*), or drainage wells (101), such as are shown in (*k*), may be used to relieve the pressure in the buried stratum; the water should be allowed to escape where the escape can be properly handled. However, it should be noted that the amount of seepage for the sections of (*j*) and (*k*) would often be excessive for water supply dams, or water power dams, and cutoffs through the pervious stratum might be required in such cases.

18·11 Cofferdams and Caissons

Cofferdams are temporary structures which surround or partially surround an area which must be unwatered for construction operations. They are seldom truly watertight, large pumping capacities often being used in conjunction with them. The designs of cofferdams require many considerations similar to those of permanent dams, and stability studies and seepage studies are common in connection with them.

Since the numerous types of cofferdams are thoroughly explained in textbooks (73, 81, 169, 1) which are devoted to descriptions of such structures, the discussion here will be limited to a few words of description of main types.

Sandbag coffers are used where there are only a few feet of head; sandbags are also used often in connection with larger cofferdams. Earth cofferdams are simply temporary dikes; they are the oldest and simplest type of cofferdam, and they are limited to conditions of shallow water and low velocity currents. Sometimes a row of sheet piling of steel or wood is used in conjunction with an earth cofferdam. Rock-fill cofferdams are rock-fill dikes with an impervious blanket of earth or timber at the water side.

Timber cribs are used in many forms of cofferdams. The cribs are filled with rock or earth and are made watertight by a line of sheeting. Rock-filled cribs are particularly adaptable to locations on rock where there are swift currents. The cribs are cut to fit the rock contours, and wood sheeting, aided frequently by a small depth of cinder or earth fill at the toe, gives the necessary degree of watertightness. Sometimes an earth fill to the full height of the cofferdam on its inner side is used to meet the watertightness requirement and to aid in the stability requirements.

Cellular cofferdams are of wood or steel sheet piling, or a combination of the two, and they have been used a great deal for large projects. One of the most satisfactory types of cofferdams for high heads and for large projects consists of circular, self-contained cells of interlocking sheet-steel piles, with the cells joined by short connecting arcs of smaller radius; the cells should be filled with soil having as good shearing characteristics as can be obtained, and they are sometimes braced by an earth or rock fill on the inner side. Such cofferdams have been used in heights of as much as 100 ft.

A caisson is a box or shell which, after being placed in position below water, becomes an integral part of a permanent foundation. In the latter respect a caisson differs from a cofferdam, but during construction caissons commonly perform the function of excluding the water and thus they act as cofferdams.

Caissons may be of wood, metal, or concrete. Often the caisson shell is filled or partially filled with concrete. Three basic types are box caissons, open caissons, and pneumatic caissons.

Box caissons are used when no excavation is required. The box, which is watertight and is closed at the bottom, is sunk by loading until it rests on the soil, the ledge, or the pile foundation on which the finished caisson is to bear.

Open caissons are of many sizes and shapes varying from small cylindrical caissons to large rectangular caissons with many dredging wells. Through the dredging wells or openings in the caissons the excavation is carried on below water. The caisson is lowered by a combination of excavation and loading, aided sometimes by water jets to reduce the side friction on the outer surfaces of the caisson. Small open caissons are sometimes driven, pulled, or jacked down. After the caisson and the excavation within it are at final grade a tremie-concrete seal may be placed, after which the interior may be unwatered for the completion of the construction work. Theoretically, open caissons are unlimited in the depth to which they may go; one caisson of the San Francisco-Oakland bridge, completed in 1937, extended to a depth of 242 ft below water.

In pneumatic caissons the excavation is carried on in the dry in a working chamber at the bottom of the caisson; the chamber is 6 or 7 ft in height so that men can work within it. The water is excluded by maintaining the air in the working chamber at high pressure. By hand work in the dry a much better grade of work is possible in the excavation, in the final preparation of the foundation, and in the subsequent concreting. However, the expense of pneumatic caissons is large, and there are inherent difficulties in the work. Men must enter and leave the working chamber through locks, and the excavated material often is removed through locks. The maximum depth to which pneumatic caissons may be carried is about 110 ft below water, since at this depth a pressure of 50 lb per sq in. above atmospheric is required; this pressure is the limit of human endurance. Even at much smaller pressures the number of hours a man may work at one time must be limited. Precautions against caisson disease are also necessary. Caisson disease is caused when nitrogen, which is absorbed in the blood under high pressure, is released as pressure is decreased too rapidly. If the release is rapid, nitrogen bubbles are freed in the blood, they expand, they may cause blood vessels to burst, and the disease may be fatal. To prevent the disease a decompression period in the air lock is required. In addition a hospital lock is required for treatment of cases of caisson disease.

For more extensive discussions of caissons of various types, the reader is referred to the textbooks mentioned earlier in this section.

PROBLEMS

1. The following data have been obtained in a standard Proctor compaction test on a glacial till:

Water content, per cent	5.02	8.81	11.25	13.05	14.40	19.25
Weight of container and compacted soil, pounds	7.875	8.205	8.65	8.80	8.815	8.615

The specific gravity of the soil is 2.77. The container is $\frac{1}{30}$ cu ft in volume and its weight is 4.350 lb.

Plot the compaction curve and on the plot show lines of 80 and 100 per cent saturation.

2. A hydraulic-fill dam has core slopes of 1:2 (1 horizontal to 2 vertical) and outer slopes of 3:1. The unit weights of shell and core, respectively, are 120 and 130 lb per cu ft. Using a graphical analysis and assuming that the friction angle of the cohesionless shell is 40 degrees, determine whether the section is safe against failure.

3. Two designs have been proposed for a hydraulic-fill dam. The core slopes are 1:2 in the first design and 1:3 in the second, and the outer slopes are 3:1 in both designs. Demonstrate which of the designs is safer by comparing stress obliquities on horizontal planes through the shell. The core and shell may be assumed to have equal unit weights.

4. There is a stratum of very soft clay with its surface 5 ft below ground surface at the site of a proposed earth dam. The estimated shearing strength of this clay is 500 lb per sq ft. The dam is of essentially triangular shape with a height of 30 ft and slopes of 3:1. It is constructed of soil that may be assumed to be cohesionless, and that has a friction angle of 37 degrees and a unit weight of 130 lb per cu ft. It may be assumed that no neutral pressures exist in the dam. Investigate the safety of the section by use of a Poncelet construction and a sliding-block analysis.

5. A concrete dam with a base width of 40 ft will rest on a homogeneous deposit of fine sand with a porosity of 36 per cent. Horizontal and vertical permeabilities in this soil are in the ratio of 5:1. The head on the dam will be 18 ft. A line of sheet piling is to be used at the toe of the dam and the escape gradient must not exceed one fourth of the critical escape gradient. To what depth must the sheeting extend (a) according to Harza's method, and (b) according to Lane's method?

6. Determine the total uplift force on a masonry dam and the moment of this force about the heel, expressed as percentages of the values holding for the homogeneous case, for (a) a relatively compressible foundation, and (b) a foundation that has been successfully grouted below the heel. The approximate pressure distributions shown in Fig. 18·7 may be used for this problem.

Chapter 19

ACTION OF SHALLOW FOUNDATIONS
BEARING CAPACITY

19·1 Introduction

The subject of bearing capacity is perhaps the most important of all subjects in soil engineering. It may be defined as the largest intensity of pressure which may be applied by a structure or a structural member to the soil which supports it without causing excessive settlement or danger of failure of the soil in shear.

Building loads are transmitted by columns, by bearing walls, or by other bearing members to the foundation. Sometimes the foundation material is ledge or very strong soil which from experience is known to have more than ample strength; in this case there usually are no difficult foundation problems. On the other hand, the soil immediately below the structure may be of such poor quality that the loads must be carried by piles or caissons to a deep stratum of satisfactory bearing quality; cases of this type are discussed in the next chapter, the subject of which is piles and pile foundations. Such cases may fall within the scope of the present chapter, however, if there is a bearing capacity problem relative to the buried stratum. The intermediate case is that in which a building, a retaining wall, or some other type of structure bears directly on soil which will furnish a satisfactory foundation if the bearing members are properly designed; here the bearing capacity is an all-important consideration.

The two main objects of this chapter are, first, a scientific treatment of the subject of bearing capacity with the aim of developing a true understanding of the factors upon which it depends and, second, an explanation of the use of bearing capacity concepts in the design of footings.

560

19·2   The Traditional Approach

The traditional approach to the bearing capacity problem is illustrated by the building codes of many of our large cities. Practically all codes give lists of soil types, and for each type they state an allowable intensity of loading, this value frequently being called the bearing capacity. A few codes give such tables, with values subject to modifications under designated conditions. In some codes building commissioners are given the power to require smaller values than those tabulated when their judgment indicates the necessity. However, relatively few modifications of the tabulated values appear in building codes. This perhaps is in part the reason for the rather widespread but incorrect idea that the bearing capacity depends mainly on the characteristics of the soil in question and that the main difficulty in bearing capacity problems is that of identifying the soil.

Actually the bearing capacity depends on a number of variables, and sometimes it is greatly dependent on such factors as the size of the bearing area, the depth of the foundation below ground surface, the type of building, the rigidity of the building, and the amount of differential settlement it safely can withstand.

For the general run of buildings there perhaps is no better approach than the traditional approach, but with a revised meaning. Soil types can be listed, and each type can be given a *tabular value*. This tabular value is the bearing capacity of that soil under a certain definite set of conditions, preferably the simplest and most easily defined conditions. The list of tabular values should be followed by a list of allowable and required modifications to these values, which should cover, as far as possible, all conceivable variations from the definite set of conditions. No list of modifications can cover all eventualities, and therefore the building inspector or some other competent official should have the authority to make additional modifications when in his judgment they are necessary.

19·3   Bearing Capacity Determinations by Loading Tests

Loading tests are often used to obtain information on the bearing capacity and the settlement characteristics of the soil at a given site. However, loading tests are usually run on small areas whereas the information desired is the action to be expected for cases of large loaded areas and, unless the effects of the differences in size between the test and the structure are properly accounted for, the loading test may lead to a false sense of security or otherwise may be badly misleading. The proper interpretation of loading tests is far from a simple matter, and the first requirement for such interpretations is an understanding of the governing fundamentals. Concepts that are presented in sections which follow are needed, therefore, before definite statements can be made regarding the meaning of loading tests.

The usual procedure in running a loading test is to apply the load in stages, increasing the load an arbitrary amount in each stage until it is well above the design load and allowing each increment to stand for a given time or until settlement has nearly ceased. Some building codes specify a detailed loading procedure. The data observed during the test are commonly plotted to give a curve with ordinates of settlement in inches, designated by ρ, versus abscissas of intensity of loading in tons per square foot, designated by q. Such plots are called loading test curves; a number of curves of this type are shown in Fig. 19·9.

The ultimate intensity is the intensity at which shear failure is reached within the soil; at this intensity the curve becomes virtually vertical. Frequently, the failure point is not a well-defined point, because large settlements may lead to somewhat greater strength and greater resistance to settlement. A failure condition may also be said to have been reached when the settlement is excessive. However, settlements of a fraction of an inch in some instances are excessive, and settlements of several inches may be permissible in other instances.

A definite characteristic of many loading test plots is the early straight line portion extending to intensities of roughly one third or one half of the ultimate intensity. This straight line occurs in a surprisingly large percentage of loading tests. However, a continuously steepening curve may occur in a soil that has been appreciably precompressed. On the other hand a short section of opposite curvature may precede the straight line portion if the soil is loose at its surface or if the bearing plate is not thoroughly seated on the soil at the start of the test. If the early portion of the curve is a straight line, the ratio between the stress and the settlement at points on the line has a definite, constant value. This ratio is sometimes called the *coefficient of settlement*, although in tests on highway and airport subgrades it is usually called the *coefficient of subgrade reaction*. When there is deviation from the straight line, no standardized definition has been chosen for this coefficient, and reciprocals of slopes at arbitrarily chosen points or reciprocals of slopes of chords are generally used. The slope-reciprocal at the point where the plot has the least curvature is perhaps the most logical choice. Herein the stress-settlement ratio is called the coeffi-

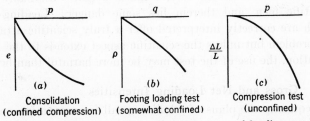

(a)
Consolidation
(confined compression)

(b)
Footing loading test
(somewhat confined)

(c)
Compression test
(unconfined)

Fɪɢ. 19·1 Comparison of shapes of various types of loading curves.

cient of settlement and is designated by C_ρ. In the metric system its units are usually kilograms per cubic centimeter. In the English system its most convenient units are tons per square foot per inch of settlement or pounds per cubic inch. In the idealized considerations herein the early portions of loading curves are considered to be straight lines.

It is instructive to compare the straight line relationship given by loading test plots with shapes of other types of loading curves. In the consolidation test there is complete lateral confinement. The typical shape of the curve has been given in Figs. 10·3 and 10·5 (a) and is shown also in Fig. 19·1 (a). If there is no precompression this curve is characterized by a continuously flattening slope. In the unconfined compression test, described in Section 15·18, the curve has the same general shape as the upper curves of Fig. 14·5 and the curve in Fig. 19·1 (c). This curve is characterized by a continuously steepening slope. The loading test curve represents a case intermediate between complete confinement and no confinement, and thus a straight line appears reasonable. As failure is approached the confinement effects are overcome, however, and the loading test in its latter stages resembles the unconfined test in that it exhibits a steepening curve. If the three curves of Fig. 19·1 were plotted to comparable coordinate scales the slope of curve (*b*) would fall between the initial slopes of the other two curves. To give comparable scales the ordinates of the loading test curve would have to be some type of strain, perhaps an average vertical strain discussed in later sections of this chapter.

Loading tests have the appearance and the reputation of being a scientific approach, and correctly so. The use of a scientific approach is one which carries much weight with many non-scientific men, and therein lies some danger. Loading tests which are correctly interpreted offer a truly scientific attack to the problem but unless the scientific aspect extends to the interpretation, the use of the test may be more harmful than helpful.

19·4 Gross and Net Loading Intensities

Frequently the plans of a building call for excavation and the placing of footings at some given depth below ground surface. In such a case the loading intensity acting on the footing is known as the *gross intensity* and the total load as the *gross load*. The gross load reduced by the weight of soil excavated from the zone directly above the footing is called the *net load;* this load divided by the area is the *net intensity*. The net intensity is usually assumed to be the effective pressure intensity, since under most conditions a load equal to the weight of excavated soil may be placed on the footing before the stresses below the footing are appreciably greater than the original values and before appreciable settlements can be observed. In all references in the following pages to bearing capacities of footings founded below the surface, the net bearing capacity is referred to unless otherwise stated.

There are cases, however, in which the gross intensity should be used as the effective intensity. One example is offered by the case in which a large area is excavated and the footings which are placed cover areas that are small as compared with the excavated area; in this case the distribution of the pressure release during excavation is so different from the distribution of pressures caused by footing loads that the gross intensity should be used as the effective value. Also in soils which undergo appreciable swelling during excavation and in cases in which the gross load is smaller than or only slightly larger than the weight of soil excavated, it may be necessary to consider the gross load as the effective load.

The bearing capacity of footings which are founded below ground surface is considerably larger than the bearing capacity at ground surface, and especially so in cohesionless soils. This increased value is one of the important factors which must be carefully considered in interpretations of loading tests.

19·5 Criteria of Satisfactory Action of Footings

Two definite requirements must be fulfilled for a footing, a mat foundation, a retaining wall, or other structure to show satisfactory action under load. First, the shearing stresses transmitted to the soil must be smaller than the shearing strength by an amount sufficient to give an ample factor of safety with respect to shearing strength. This type of requirement has been covered in previous chapters and is merely the requirement of stability. Secondly, the differential settlements which occur must not exceed amounts which are permissible as far as the requirements of the superstructure are concerned. The consolidation analysis is an example of the second requirement, there being not the slightest danger of shear failure in this case. Studies relative to shallow footings frequently involve considerations of both requirements.

It would be desirable if it could be definitely known which of the two requirements is ruling in any given case. This, however, is not always possible. It is difficult to state the amount of differential settlement which can reasonably be tolerated in many cases. The better of the arbitrary rulings appearing in building codes are largely the result of experience, and it often is not clear which of the two requirements is behind certain regulations. There may also be cases in which compromises between the two criteria enter.

Further discussion of the two criteria is given in Sections 19·26, 19·29, and 19·30.

19·6   The Pressure Bulb

The pressure bulb is a common term used to represent the zone below a footing within which appreciable stresses are caused by the footing load.   The concept of a pressure bulb is a valuable one, and the bulb should be pictured simply as a stressed zone within a homogeneous mass.

Soil characteristics and pressures below footings are not well enough known to allow an accurate plotting of contours of stress in the pressure bulb.   However, stresses below a circular loaded area on the surface of an elastic mass of infinite extent may be determined from the theory of elasticity, and from plots of stress contours for the elastic case a general picture is given which may be accepted as valid, in a roughly qualitative sense for footings on soil.

The compressive stresses on the horizontal plane are shown in Fig. 19·2 (a) * by stress contours for all points below a round uniformly loaded area of the surface of an *elastic* mass.   The maximum shearing stresses at all points are similarly represented in (b).   It may be seen that all concepts of the size of the pressure bulb depend on an arbitrary choice of the magnitude of stress at which values are considered to pass from appreciable to inappreciable.   If direct stresses are considered to be of inappreciable magnitude when they are smaller than 10 per cent of the intensity of the applied stress at the surface of loading, the contour labeled 0.1 in (a) may be said to define the outline of the pressure bulb.   On this basis the depth of the bulb is between 1.5 and 2 times the diameter.   It is, of course, an arbitrary choice, but in general the pressure bulb is considered to have a depth of roughly 1.5 times the breadth of the loaded area.

The concept explained above is proof of the logic of two principles which are of extreme importance in foundation engineering.   The first of these is the general rule regarding the depth to which preliminary borings should penetrate.   It sometimes is specified that preliminary borings at the site of a proposed building or group of buildings should be carried to a depth of 150 per cent of the smaller dimension of the building or the group.

* The diagrams in Fig. 19·2 were first presented by L. Jürgenson, reference 84.

The logic of this specification is simply that it is necessary to know the character of the soils that exist within the pressure bulb. The use of a depth in terms of the smaller dimension is reasonable because it is essentially the smaller dimension which

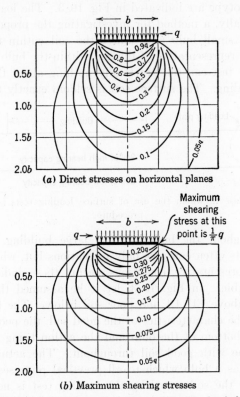

(a) Direct stresses on horizontal planes

(b) Maximum shearing stresses

FIG. 19·2 Distribution of stresses below a circular loaded area on an elastic material with a Poisson ratio of 0.45. (L. Jürgenson.)

controls in such a case. This recommended depth is sufficient for most of the borings but, unless the general geological conditions of the district are well known, one boring at least should go to a much greater depth. Often one boring should go to ledge, to check against the possible existence of a deeply buried stratum of soil with poor bearing characteristics, since such a soil, even if well below the pressure bulb, may be the cause of excessive settlements.

The second principle associated with the pressure bulb refers to loading tests which are run on small areas at a given site for the purpose of predicting the behavior of a proposed building at the site. The relative sizes of the bulbs of pressure for a test and a prototype are indicated in Fig. 19·3. The loading test is, fundamentally, a method for investigating the properties of the soil in the small bulb and, unless the soil within this bulb is reasonably representative of the soil within the bulb of the prototype, the test can tell practically nothing about the behavior of the building. The surface soil is seldom exactly the same as

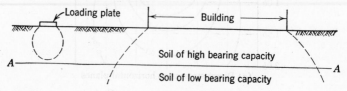

Fig. 19·3 Case in which the use of surface loading tests is an unsound procedure.

that throughout the bulb below a large building. Therefore loading tests often can give only indications but, when approximately representative conditions occur, these indications are very valuable. In Fig. 19·3, let it be assumed that there is good soil above El. *AA* and poor soil below. The loading test measures the characteristics of the good soil, the poor soil being below the bottom of the bulb and the action being about what it would be with good soil throughout. The actual building, however, has a bulb which to all practical purposes is of poor soil. Here the soil tested by the loading test is not even approximately representative of that under the building, and the test can give no information on the action of the building.

If the loading test is run on soil above the water table and the pressure bulb below the structure is largely below the water table, it may be possible to apply a rough correction for the difference between the unsubmerged and the submerged soil characteristics. In general, however, this case should be viewed as one wherein the material in the small bulb is not representative of that in the large bulb.

Pressure bulbs should be visualized as having shapes as shown by the curves of Fig. 19·2, but for approximate analyses the zone of appreciable pressures may be considered to have a simpler shape, as shown by the following considerations. In all but highly cohesive soils the shearing strength of the soil and the rigidity or resistance to shearing strain are greater in the lower portion of the bulb than they are in the upper portion, as will be demonstrated in a later section. The induced stresses in the bulb at depths greater than the breadth are relatively small when compared to those in the upper portion of the bulb, as shown by Fig. 19·2. The induced strains depend directly on the induced stresses and inversely on the rigidity and are, therefore, so small at depths greater than the breadth that they usually can be neglected without appreciable effect. Furthermore, the stressed zone is largely confined to the soil below the footing. Therefore, it appears reasonable, in approximate analyses, to assume that the pressure bulb below a square footing can be represented by a cube and the bulb below a round footing by a circular cylinder with a height of one diameter.

19·7 The Action within the Pressure Bulb

The outward picture of the action of a footing is limited to the concepts that a footing is loaded and therefore settles. The loading test curves of Fig. 19·9 are the representation of this outward picture. In addition to these data, however, an understanding of the general action within the bulb is needed before the data can be interpreted to best advantage.

The settlement of the footing is due to the vertical strains which occur within the height of the pressure bulb. These vertical strains are due in part to shearing strains or change of shape and in part to volumetric strains or decreases in void ratio. In Fig. 19·4, the full lines show a square footing before loading and the zone in which its idealized pressure bulb will form when load is applied. The original position of a small element of soil at the center of the bulb is also indicated. The displaced positions of these lines after the load is applied are shown by dashed lines, with the magnitude of the changes considerably exaggerated. If the settlement is due mainly to the squeezing out of soil from under the footing, as in a relatively dense sand which is loaded nearly to failure, the bulb and the element are distorted with little change of volume, as the figure shows. If the settlement is due mainly to compression of the soil, as in a very compressible soil subjected to a load that is small compared to the load causing failure, the changes in positions of horizontal lines would be about as shown by the figure but the changes in positions of vertical lines would be only a small fraction of those shown.

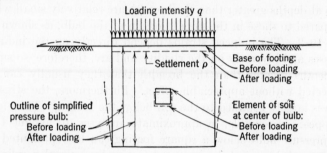

FIG. 19·4 Changes of shape caused in the pressure bulb by loading.

In Fig. 19·4 the dashed lines representing the width of the bulb after loading are not shown near ground surface because strains may be large in this zone. A rigid surface footing on sand, when carrying even a very small load, will develop a ϕ-obliquity condition under its outer edge, and a plastic zone will exist within the surrounding soil. Plastic zones of this type

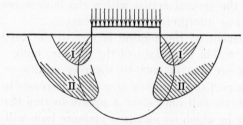

FIG. 19·5 Plastic zones below the edges of a long loaded footing on sand.
(O. K. Fröhlich.)

are shown in Fig. 19·5 for a long wall footing on the surface of a cohesionless soil; the zones shown in this figure are according to concepts developed by O. K. Fröhlich (59). Zones I are plastic under a small loading and enlarge to Zones II under greater loading. The corresponding plastic regions in Fig. 19·6 are Zones II; this figure represents the Prandtl plastic equilibrium theory which is discussed in Section 19·9. Qualitatively similar shapes of plastic zones exist below the edges of square and round footings on sand.

19·8 Outline and Descriptions of Items Discussed in Bearing Capacity Considerations

Numerous factors enter into the complex problem of determining bearing capacities for buildings which rest on many spread footings. However, some of the most important of these factors may be explained without difficulty by theoretical considerations of idealized, simple cases of isolated footings, and a number of the sections which follow are devoted to such presentations. In these analyses both the coefficient of settlement and the ultimate bearing capacity will be considered. The bearing capacities of all types of soils, ranging from cohesionless to highly cohesive, will be discussed. The most important variables on which the bearing capacity is dependent in any given soil are the dimensions of the footing, and investigations into the relationships between the bearing capacity and the breadth and shape of the footing and the depth of the footing below ground surface will be studied in considerable detail. All soils considered in these studies are assumed to be homogeneous unless otherwise stated.

In a few instances relationships will be obtained which are good for soils in general. The formulas for such cases contain two soil characteristics, sometimes the friction angle and the unit cohesion, and when two soil characteristics appear it may be concluded that the expression applies to soils in general. In other studies the considerations are limited to the extreme or limiting cases of cohesionless and very highly cohesive soils. Cohesionless soils may be defined as those in which the shearing strength depends entirely on intergranular pressures which are caused by the overburden and the footing load. Highly cohesive soils are those in which the strength is primarily caused by intrinsic pressure and in which the strength, therefore, does not vary with the depth below ground surface.

The dimension used to express the size of the footing is the breadth. This dimension is equal to the diameter of a round footing, and the smaller side of a rectangular footing. Cases covered herein will in general be limited to long footings, square footings, and round footings. The designation *long footing* applies to such cases as wall footings wherein the length is very large in comparison to the breadth.

If the footing is rigid and therefore settles the same over the entire area, the pressure intensity is not uniform, and the intensity value covered in this discussion is the average value; if the pressure is uniform the footing does not settle uniformly, and the settlement value considered is the average settlement. For either case or for any intermediate case, however, the relationships are approximately correct on the basis of such average values. Pressure distributions and differential settlements are covered in detail in Section 19·23.

Extreme care is needed to avoid confusion between the various cases considered, and in some instances designations of cases are repeated frequently in the following pages to minimize the possibility of misinterpretation.

A number of theories have been advanced which furnish expressions for the ultimate bearing capacity, whereas the coefficient of settlement is less frequently expressed by formula. For this reason ultimate bearing capacities will be considered first.

19·9 The Prandtl Solution—Ultimate Bearing Capacity of Long Footings

The Prandtl plastic equilibrium theory (115) presents an expression for the ultimate bearing capacity of long loaded areas of breadth b on ground surface. Figure 19·6 shows the three zones which, according to this theory, exist after failure is reached. Zone I is similar to the unsheared conical zone at the top of a cylindrical compression test specimen; it moves downward as a unit. Zone II is plastic; in this zone all radial planes through points A and B are failure planes, and the curved boundary is a logarithmic spiral. Zone III is forced by passive pressure upward and outward as a unit. It may be noted that all failure planes are at $45 \pm (\phi/2)$ to principal planes. The section is symmetrical up to the point of failure, with an equal chance of failure occurring as shown, or along the similar failure surface shown at the left by dashed lines.

Because of their compressibility, soils do not show close agreement with Prandtl's hypothesis, which was originally set up for metals, and in actual cases of footings loaded to failure the region corresponding to Zone III is much narrower than that

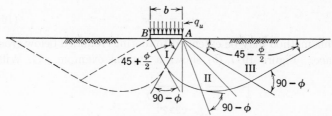

FIG. 19·6 Cross section illustrating Prandtl's plastic equilibrium theory.

shown in Fig. 19·6. However, the general concepts of the mechanics of failure given by this theory are reasonably correct.

On the basis of the assumption that the shearing strength of any soil may be expressed by

$$s = c + \sigma \tan \phi$$

and that c is a constant, Prandtl's expression for the ultimate bearing capacity of *any* soil is

$$q_u = \left(\frac{c}{\tan \phi} + \frac{1}{2}\gamma b \sqrt{K_P} \right) (K_P \epsilon^{\pi \tan \phi} - 1) \qquad (19 \cdot 1)$$

where

$$K_P = \frac{1 + \sin \phi}{1 - \sin \phi}$$

The term $\frac{1}{2}\gamma b \sqrt{K_P}$ in the above formula did not appear in Prandtl's original derivation, but was added later to account for strength caused by the overburden pressures.

19·10 The Fellenius Solution—Ultimate Bearing Capacity of Long Footings at or below the Surface of Highly Cohesive Soil

The Fellenius method of circular failure surfaces may be used to determine the ultimate bearing capacity of highly cohesive soils. The critical failure arc for a surface footing is shown in Fig. 19·7 (a) by a full line. It is seen that this surface agrees closely with the Prandtl failure surface for this case. It is not difficult to demonstrate that the circle shown is the critical one and that it furnishes for the ultimate bearing capacity of *long, surface footings on highly cohesive* soils the expression

$$q_u = 5.5c \qquad (19 \cdot 2)$$

This method may be extended to footings founded below ground surface. Figure 19·7 (*b*) shows a typical example. G. Wilson

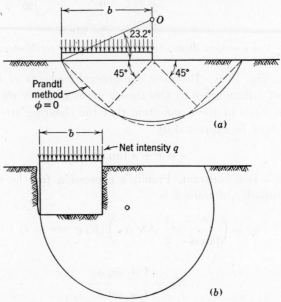

FIG. 19·7 Stability analysis of loaded footings on highly cohesive soil, based on the assumption of circular failure surfaces.

(171) found that the net value of q_u by this method has an almost exactly linear variation with the depth-breadth ratio up to depths of 1.5 times the breadth. He also gives data on locations of critical circles. The expression furnished by Wilson's results, for long footings *below the surface of highly cohesive* soils, is

$$q_{ud} = 5.5c \left(1 + 0.38 \frac{d}{b} \right) \qquad (19 \cdot 3)$$

where q_{ud} denotes the ultimate net bearing capacity at depth d.

Other methods of solution of this type have been advanced, but the circular arc method has the advantage of being simple and it gives reasonable results for both surface footings and footings at shallow depths.

19·11 The Terzaghi Solution—Ultimate Bearing Capacity of Long Footings

Terzaghi (pages 118–136 of reference 148) has presented a solution for the ultimate bearing capacity of long footings which is of more general nature than either of those given in previous sections. This method contains various assumptions which cannot be presented without going into great detail and, therefore, will not be fully explained here. Although this approach is not the most rigorous possible, all assumptions that are used are quite reasonable, and the results should be sufficiently accurate for most uses.

All soils are covered in this method by two cases which are designated by Terzaghi as general shear and local shear. *General shear* is the case wherein the loading test curve for the soil in question comes to a perfectly vertical ultimate condition at a relatively small settlement, as illustrated by curve C_1 in Fig. 19·8 (a). *Local shear* is illustrated by curve C_2 of the same figure; it is the case wherein settlements are relatively large and there is not a definite vertical ultimate limit to the curve; in explanation Terzaghi states "we specify arbitrarily, but in accordance with current conceptions, that the earth support has failed as soon as the curve passes into a steep and fairly straight tangent."

The expression for the ultimate bearing capacity of long footings *at or below the surface of any soil conforming to general shear* is

$$q_u = c(N_c) + \gamma b(\tfrac{1}{2}N_\gamma) + \gamma d(N_q) \qquad (19 \cdot 4)$$

and for any soil conforming to *local shear* the expression is

$$q_u = c(\tfrac{2}{3}N_c') + \gamma b(\tfrac{1}{2}N_\gamma') + \gamma d(N_q') \qquad (19 \cdot 5)$$

In these equations the N coefficients, which are enclosed in parentheses, depend only on the friction angle and are given for equation 19·4 by the curves of Fig. 19·8 (b) and for equation

19·5 by the curves of Fig. 19·8 (c). The final terms, expressing
the effect of depth in these equations, are valid only when *d* is
less than *b*.

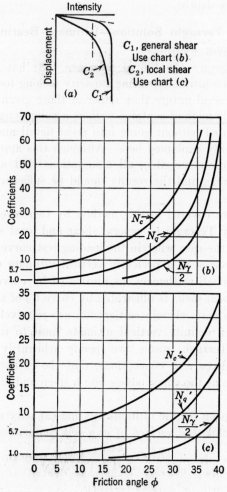

FIG. 19·8 Coefficients of the Terzaghi expressions for ultimate bearing
capacity (equations 19·4, 19·5, 19·11, and 19·12.)

Terzaghi's subdivision of the problem into two types of shear
is of course an arbitrary one, since two cases cannot cover the
wide range of conditions which necessitate the recognition of two

expressions as different as equations 19·4 and 19·5. The two equations are intended only as expressions which are approximate and conservative; they give estimates which are of much practical value but which must, in their application, be tempered with considerable judgment.

19·12 Special Cases and Comparisons—Ultimate Bearing Capacity of Long Footings

Expressions for the ultimate bearing capacity of highly cohesive soils may be obtained by setting the friction angle equal to zero in the general expressions given in the foregoing sections. Similarly, expressions for cohesionless soils may be obtained by setting c equal to zero in the general expressions. A listing of special cases follows.

At the Surface of Cohesionless Soils

Results for this special case will be presented only for friction angles of 28 and 38 degrees, but expressions for any other angle may easily be obtained from the general expressions.

According to Prandtl, from equation 19·1,

$$\text{when } \phi = 28°, \quad q_u = 12\gamma b$$
$$\text{when } \phi = 38°, \quad q_u = 50\gamma b \tag{19·6}$$

According to Terzaghi (from equations 19·4 and 19·5):
For general shear,

$$\text{when } \phi = 28°, \quad q_u = 8\gamma b$$
$$\text{when } \phi = 38°, \quad q_u = 40\gamma b$$

For local shear, $\tag{19·7}$

$$\text{when } \phi = 28°, \quad q_u = 2\gamma b$$
$$\text{when } \phi = 38°, \quad q_u = 7\gamma b$$

The above values are in general quite conservative, the ultimate bearing capacity of some dense sands being considerably larger than $50\gamma b$.

Equations 19·6 and 19·7 are the first presentation herein of a fundamental relationship which may be expressed as follows:

In a cohesionless soil the ultimate bearing capacity is proportional to the breadth of the footing.

BELOW THE SURFACE OF COHESIONLESS SOILS

Terzaghi's approach is the only one that has been discussed that furnishes an expression for this special case. For cohesionless soil, equations 19·4 and 19·5 may be written

$$q_{ud} = q_{uo}\left(1 + C\frac{d}{b}\right) \tag{19·8}$$

in which q_{ud} and q_{uo} are the ultimate bearing capacities at depths d and zero, respectively, q_{ud} being a net value and the coefficient C being equal to $2N_q/N_\gamma$ in general shear and $2N_q'/N_\gamma'$ in local shear. The term in the parentheses is called the *depth factor*.

Depth factor values may be obtained from Fig. 19·8; typical values are as follows:

For general shear

$$1 + 2.2\frac{d}{b} \quad \text{when } \phi = 28°$$

$$1 + 1.7\frac{d}{b} \quad \text{when } \phi = 38°$$

For local shear   (19·9)

$$1 + 3.4\frac{d}{b} \quad \text{when } \phi = 28°$$

$$1 + 2.4\frac{d}{b} \quad \text{when } \phi = 38°$$

Terzaghi states that the method gives satisfactory results only when d is less than b and that in all cases the allowance for depth is conservative. It therefore appears reasonable to accept $1 + 2d/b$ as a conservative expression for the depth factor for all cases of ultimate bearing capacities of cohesionless soils.

AT THE SURFACE OF HIGHLY COHESIVE SOILS

From equations 19·1, 19·2, 19·4, and 19·5, the following expressions for highly cohesive soils are obtained by setting the friction angle equal to zero.

According to Prandtl: †

$$q_u = 5.14c$$

According to Fellenius:

$$q_u = 5.5c$$

According to Terzaghi: (19·10)

For general shear,

$$q_u = 5.7c$$

For local shear,

$$q_u = 3.8c$$

The failure zones for the highly cohesive case according to Prandtl's theory are shown by dashed lines in Fig. 19·7 (a).

Reasonably good agreement is seen to exist between these expressions, and they may be accepted as applicable to any case in which the shearing strength is essentially constant. In fact, they may be used in cohesionless soils whenever a reasonably accurate value for the average shearing strength existing on the surface most liable to failure can be estimated. From this point of view the strength characteristic c is best defined as the average shearing strength.

Equations 19·10 are the first presentation herein of another fundamental relationship which may be expressed as follows: *In a highly cohesive soil the ultimate bearing capacity is a constant and is independent of the breadth of the footing.*

Below the Surface of Highly Cohesive Soils

According to equation 19·3 the effect of depth may be expressed, as for cohesionless soils, by multiplying the bearing capacity for zero depth by a *depth factor* of the form $1 + C(d/b)$. However, C is small in highly cohesive soils, and the depth factor exceeds unity by an amount which is only a small fraction of that for the cohesionless case.

According to the conservative assumptions of Terzaghi's approach, the term expressing the effect of depth becomes equal to γd when the friction angle is equal to zero. This small allowance

---

† Calculus is needed to obtain this expression, since the substitution of $\phi = 0$ gives the product of infinity and zero.

is merely the difference between the gross and the net intensities.

These considerations show that the ultimate bearing capacity is slightly greater below the surface of cohesive soils than it is at the surface, but that the amount of increase is so small that it is of minor importance.

19·13   The Terzaghi Solution for Ultimate Bearing Capacity of Square and Round Footings

For long footings, which have been discussed in foregoing sections, the displacement of soil particles as settlement occurs is perpendicular to the axis of the footing, and a two-dimensional condition of strain prevails. Below round footings the displacements occur in vertical radial planes through the center of the footing, and the analysis is more complex. For square footings the three-dimensional condition obtaining is even more complicated. This explains why theoretical analyses have been limited almost entirely to long footings.

Considerable data exist, however, to show that the only dimension having a large effect on the bearing capacity is the breadth. From a conservative analysis of experimental data, Terzaghi obtained for *round* footings at shallow depths

$$q_u = 1.3c(N_c) + 0.6\gamma b(\tfrac{1}{2}N_\gamma) + \gamma d(N_q) \qquad (19\cdot11)$$

and for *square* footings

$$q_u = 1.3c(N_c) + 0.8\gamma b(\tfrac{1}{2}N_\gamma) + \gamma d(N_q) \qquad (19\cdot12)$$

In these equations the N coefficients are those used in equation 19·4 and given by the curves of Fig. 19·8 (*b*). For cases of local shear the N' coefficients from curves of Fig. 19·8 (*c*) should be used instead, as explained in the comparison of equations 19·5 and 19·4.

19·14   Use of Shear Test Data in Determining Ultimate Bearing Capacities

In cohesionless materials the friction angle is easily obtained by laboratory tests. When the density of the soil is known, tests are not always necessary, since the friction angle may often be estimated with sufficient accuracy after visual examination by an experienced engineer. In cohesive soils shearing tests may be used to determine the effective soil properties c_e and ϕ_e as explained in Section 15·22. After these soil properties are known they may be used for c and ϕ for figuring bearing capacities by the formulas and charts presented in the preceding sections.

A simple and direct determination of the ultimate bearing capacity of a cohesive soil may be obtained if the unconfined compressive strength of the soil is known.‡ According to equations 19·10, the ultimate bearing capacity is equal to the average shearing strength multiplied by a constant; this constant is indicated by the various methods represented in equations 19·10 to be between 5.1 and 5.7, the average value being 5.4. According to Section 15·18 the shearing strength is approximately equal to one half of the compressive strength. The combination of these two relationships gives the approximate expression

$$q_u = 2.7 p_c \qquad (19·13)$$

where p_c is the compressive strength. Bearing capacities in many cases are limited by allowable settlement but in all instances the allowable bearing capacity must be less than the ultimate bearing capacity by an amount sufficient to give a reasonable factor of safety. In this connection it is interesting to note that bearing capacity values based on experience and given for Boston clays in the Building Code of the City of Boston § are in quite close agreement with $1.5 p_c$.

19·15 Size Effects

The size of footing is a variable that might, from intuition alone, be expected to have an important effect on the bearing capacity. Formulas expressing relationships between the breadth of long footings and the ultimate bearing capacity have already been given in preceding sections. However, a satisfactory explanation of the reasons for these relationships has not yet been presented. Furthermore, the rational approach requires a true understanding of the effects of size on both the ultimate bearing capacity and the coefficient of settlement.

For the investigations of the effect of breadth in this section and the four sections which follow, all other variables are elimi-

‡ This method is suggested on page 1503 of reference 32.
§ See values quoted in Section 19·32.

nated. The plane of bearing of the footings is assumed to be the
ground surface, and an ideal soil mass is considered which is of
absolutely homogeneous nature to a great depth and is either
entirely above or entirely below the water table. The considerations are limited to individual footings and to average bearing
intensities and average settlements. For greatest ease in grasping
the reasoning of the cases presented the footings may be considered square, but all general relationships that are developed
apply also for various sizes of round and rectangular footings.

For the investigations of the effect of size of footing a comparison will be made between the data which would be obtained from
two loading tests, one for a small area and the other for a larger
area. The extreme cases of highly cohesive soil and cohesionless
soil will be considered first and intermediate cases later.

The desired concepts for the highly cohesive case may be obtained most simply by an analogy based on steel, which is a
material resembling a highly cohesive soil in that it has a constant strength. Consider two steel beams, one short and the
other long. The lengths of these two beams may be accepted in
many ways as analogous to the vertical dimensions of the pressure bulbs below two sizes of footings. Actually the analogy is
not perfect, since when under load the pressures are constant
over the lengths of the beams and they vary over the heights
of the bulbs. If the analogy is accepted, however, the desired
relationships are easily obtained; if a more rigorous demonstration is desired reference may be made to Section 19·17. Since
buckling need not be considered in this analysis the two beams
would fail in direct compression under the same intensity of compressive stress. Similarly the ultimate bearing capacity of the
two sizes of footings on highly cohesive soil is the same; this has
already been stated by equations 19·10, and it is shown graphically in the loading test plots of Fig. 19·9 (a).‖ If the two
beams are subjected to the same compressive stress, the strains
in them are alike, and the compressions are proportional to the
lengths. Similarly, if the two footings are loaded to the same
bearing intensity, the average strains within the two pressure
bulbs are the same. It follows that the settlements resulting

‖ For the first presentation in English of the four relationships shown by
Figs. 19·9 (a) and 19·9 (b) see page 276 of reference 149.

from the compressions of the bulbs are proportional to the heights of the bulbs and therefore are proportional to the breadth of the footings. This relationship is also shown by Fig. 19·9 (*a*). This relationship may be expressed by the statement that the *coefficient of settlement is inversely proportional to the breadth of footings on a highly cohesive soil.*

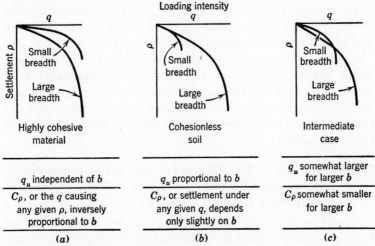

q_u independent of b	q_u proportional to b	q_u somewhat larger for larger b
C_ρ, or the q causing any given ρ, inversely proportional to b	C_ρ, or settlement under any given q, depends only slightly on b	C_ρ somewhat smaller for larger b
(*a*)	(*b*)	(*c*)

Fig. 19·9 Illustrations of idealized loading test curves with statements of approximate size relationships.

In cohesionless soils the relationships which exist are entirely different from those in highly cohesive soils, because the strength of cohesionless soils is not constant. Both shearing strengths and resistances to distortion in a cohesionless soil are directly proportional at all points to the pressure, and thus they are approximately proportional to the depth below ground surface. The average shearing strength and the average resistance to distortion within a pressure bulb are, therefore, proportional to the vertical dimension of the bulb, which in turn is proportional to the breadth of the footing. As explained in the previous paragraph, relationships for the *highly cohesive* case are:

$$\text{strength} = \text{constant}; \quad q_u = \text{constant}; \quad C_\rho = \frac{\text{constant}}{b} \quad (19·14)$$

whereas in *cohesionless* soils

$$\text{strength} = \text{constant} \times b$$

and since both q_u and C_ρ are in both cases directly proportional to the strength characteristics, it follows that for cohensionless soils

$$q_u = \text{constant} \times b; \quad C_\rho = \text{constant}$$

$$\text{(approx.)} \; \P$$

$$(19 \cdot 15)$$

These relationships are also shown and stated in Fig. 19·9 (b).

For the great majority of soils the size relationships fall between those for the two limiting cases shown in Figs. 19·9 (a) and 19·9 (b), and the general case is shown in (c).

A clear understanding of the reasons for the relationships stated below the curves of Fig. 19·9 is very important; some readers may find that the explanations given above are sufficient for this understanding, whereas others may feel that more detailed demonstrations, such as those given in the following sections, are needed.

19·16 Analysis of Size Effects for the Case of Cohesionless Soil—Surface Footings Loaded to a Given Fraction of the Ultimate Loading Intensity

Equations 19·6 and 19·7 indicate that the ultimate bearing capacity is proportional to the breadth for footings on cohesionless soil. From this statement, the proof of which still remains to be given, it follows that the loading intensity is proportional to the breadth, when footings of various breadths are loaded to some given percentage of the ultimate bearing capacity. Under such a loading on a number of footings that are of similar shape but are of various sizes, it is possible to make detailed comparisons of stresses, stress systems, and strains throughout the various pressure bulbs.

This detailed study and those given in following sections can be justified by the importance of a complete understanding of size effects. In addition, a more fundamental justification can be suggested: There are no better examples of true soil mechanics than those offered by these studies, and there is nothing more

---

¶ A more correct statement, which is demonstrated in the next section, is that C_ρ in cohesionless soil is of the same order of magnitude for all sizes of footings, but its magnitude is slightly smaller for large than for small footings.

important to the soil mechanics specialist than the intuition for soil action which studies of this type help to furnish. These detailed analyses are summarized in Table 19·1.

Let it be assumed that the two surface footings shown in Fig. 19·10 are rigid and that the soil is homogeneous and absolutely cohesionless. Let the breadth of footing 2, the larger footing, be n times that of footing 1; for the constant n, which may be of any magnitude, the value chosen for purposes of illustration in the figure is 4. Footing 1 carries an average intensity of loading q, and since intensities in this analysis are proportional to breadths the average intensity on footing 2 is nq. Point A_1 is any point within the stressed zone below footing 1; point A_2 is the homologously located point below footing 2.

The comparison defined in the above paragraph may be considered to be based on square areas, but the discussion which follows actually is valid as long as the two areas compared are geometrically similar. For example, the areas could be round, or they could be geometrically similar L-shaped areas. The only restriction relative to the distributions of pressures on the footings is that the resultant loads must act at homologously located points. The underground may be considered homogeneous, but it can be non-homogeneous as long as homologous distance ratios are maintained for all strata; for example, the upper half of each bulb can be of one material with the lower half of another material.

The analysis which follows covers, in succession, comparisons of stresses, stress ratios, strains, settlements, and safety factors for the two footings.

Before the footing loads are applied the vertical stress on the horizontal plane through A_2 is n times as large as the corresponding stress at A_1, since point A_2 is n times as deep as A_1. Presumably the pressure on vertical planes through A_2 and A_1 are lateral pressures at rest [*] and are equal to about one-half the vertical pressures; at any rate, if the underground conditions are truly homologous, lateral pressures at A_2 and A_1 are in the ratio of n to 1. Thus all corresponding preloading stresses, and all corresponding dimensions of the Mohr diagrams of preloading stresses at A_2 and A_1, are in the ratio of n to 1.

[*] See Section 17·2.

If the material below the footings were elastic and if there were like surface intensities on the two areas, then, according to the general form of equation 11·5 there would be like stresses induced at points A_2 and A_1. For surface stresses in the ratio n to 1, as is the case here, the induced stresses at A_2 and A_1 would be in the ratio of n to 1. Actually the above-mentioned equation is for vertical stresses only, but reference to elastic theory shows

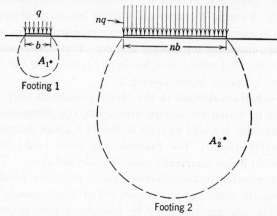

FIG. 19·10 Footings considered in the homologous analysis.

that all other stresses obey the same relationship. In a non-elastic material the magnitudes of induced stresses may differ greatly from those given by elastic equations but, as long as the same law of transmission of stress holds below both the large and the small footings, and as long as surface intensities are in the ratio of n to 1, the induced stresses at A_2 and A_1 must also be in the ratio n to 1. For the sake of completeness it should be mentioned that, even if both footings are on the same homogeneous soil, the law of stress transmission may differ somewhat at homologous points because of the different pressures at these points; this is a fine point, however, and the assumption used for this analysis is that the same law of stress transmission holds at homologous points. Thus all corresponding dimensions of the Mohr diagrams of induced stresses at A_2 and A_1 are in the ratio of n to 1. This conclusion is identical with the statement that a set of stress contours of the types shown in Fig. 19·2 must be equally applicable to the two footings of Fig. 19·10.

The final stress on any plane at any point must equal the sum of the preloading stress and the induced stress. Since both the preloading stresses and the induced stresses for the two footings are in the ratio of n to 1, it naturally follows that the ratio of final stresses at homologous points must be in the ratio of n to 1. A Mohr circle that represents the preloading stresses, the induced stresses, or the final stresses at any point below the larger footing is also applicable, on the basis of a scale n times as large, to the corresponding stress system at the homologous point below the smaller footing.

The next step in the analysis is the consideration of data on stress-strain relationships to obtain information on the strains caused by the above-mentioned stresses.

Figure 19·11 presents stress-strain plots from cylindrical compression tests, on a loose sand in (a) and on a dense sand in (b). These plots are like the conventional type of plot, as illustrated in Fig. 14·5, except that a different abscissa scale is used. The percentage change in length-diameter ratio, which is used here, is a true measure of the shearing strain within the sample, whereas the conventional abscissa of $\Delta L/L_0$ is an indirect and incomplete measure. In each plot three tests are shown, these three tests differing in that the minor principal stresses used in testing are 15, 30, and 60 lb per sq in., respectively. The test data shown here are for tests conducted under a constant value of the minor principal stress, σ_3.

Two types of strain contribute to the settlement, the shearing strain and the volumetric strain. Each must be investigated separately. The shearing strain will be considered first.

A point immediately noticeable is that all curves in the upper plots in Fig. 19·11 are essentially the same. This similarity in shapes of curves of σ_1/σ_3 versus shearing strain under different magnitudes of stresses is not peculiar to constant σ_3 tests, but has been shown by laboratory research to hold for any group of tests all of which are run on a given soil under a given pattern of loading. Thus, although Fig. 19·11 is based on shear tests with σ_3 constant, and although it is unlikely that σ_3 remains constant during loading at many points in a pressure bulb, it may be concluded that the relationships between σ_1/σ_3 and shearing strain during loading would be nearly alike at points A_2 and A_1 of Fig.

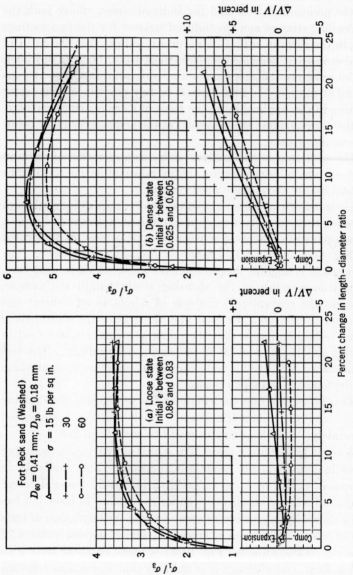

FIG. 19·11 Stress-strain curves for a sand, showing shape changes and volumetric strains at various pressures.

19·10 just as they are nearly alike at high and low pressures in Fig. 19·11. At points A_2 and A_1 corresponding stresses before and after loading are in the ratio of n to 1, or, in this case 4 to 1. A ratio of 4 to 1 also exists between corresponding stresses in the high and low pressure tests presented in Fig. 19·11. The Mohr diagrams for the points A_2 and A_1, both before and after loading, are geometrically similar; thus the changes in σ_1/σ_3 ratios at the two points during loading are approximately the same. For an example of strains over a given σ_1/σ_3 range on the curves of Fig. 19·11, the range in (a) between initial and final σ_1/σ_3 values of 2.0 and 3.0 on the 60 and 15 lb per sq in. curves will be used; the abscissa differences over this range are 3.5 and 2.3 per cent, respectively. It is seen, therefore, that for a given σ_1/σ_3 change, the shearing strain is of the same order of magnitude for both pressures, being slightly greater for the case of greater pressure. The curves of (b) show the same situation.

The volume changes shown in (a) for the range considered above are volume decreases, and the volumetric strains are 0.7 and 0.3 per cent for the 60 and 15 lb per sq in. tests, respectively. In the curves of (b) the volume changes are largely volume increases. It is seen that the volumetric strains for a given σ_1/σ_3 range are not alike for high pressure and low pressure tests, being considerably larger in general for larger pressures, but such differences are usually of minor significance because volumetric strains usually are too small in cohesionless soils to have much effect on settlements.

The vertical compressions, expressed as percentages of the heights of the samples, may be computed from the strains quoted in the above paragraphs. For the 60 lb per sq in. test the compressions resulting from the shearing strain and the volumetric strain are 2.3 and 0.2 per cent, respectively,† the total being 2.5

† The compression attributable to shearing strength alone is here taken as that which would occur during the given shearing strain if the volume were to remain constant, that is, $LD^2 = $ constant; under this condition a 3.5 per cent change in L/D gives a change in L of $\frac{2}{3} \times 3.5$ per cent, or 2.3 per cent. The compression due to volumetric strain alone is taken as that which would occur under the given volumetric strain if there were no shearing strain; a volumetric strain of 0.7 per cent under this condition gives linear strains in all directions of $\frac{1}{3} \times 0.7$ per cent, or 0.2 per cent.

TABLE 19·1 RATIOS OF HOMOLOGOUS [1] STRESSES, STRAINS, SETTLEMENTS, AND SAFETY FACTORS FROM AN IDEALIZED COMPARISON OF THE ACTION OF TWO SIZES OF GEOMETRICALLY SIMILAR SURFACE FOOTINGS—RATIO OF n:1 BETWEEN CORRESPONDING LINEAR DIMENSIONS

Ratio of	I Cohesionless	II Cohesionless	III Highly Cohesive	IV Highly Cohesive
1. *Surface loading intensity*	n:1	1^-:1	1:1	1:n
2. Total loads	n^3:1	$(n^2)^-$:1	n^2:1	n:1
3. Preloading stresses	n:1	n:1	(Note 5)	(Note 5)
4. Induced stresses	n:1	1^-:1	1:1	1:n
5. Final stresses	n:1	(Note 4)		
6. σ_1/σ_3, preloading stresses	1:1	1:1		
7. σ_1/σ_3, induced stresses	1:1	1:1	(Note 6)	
8. σ_1/σ_3, final stresses	1:1	1:1		
9. Shearing strains caused by induced stresses	1^+:1		1:1	
10. Volumetric strains caused by induced stresses	(Note 2)		1:1	
11. Average vertical direct strains	1^+:1		1:1	
12. *Settlement*	n^+:1	1:1 (Note 3)	n:1 (Note 7)	1.1
13. *Safety factor relative to shear failure*	1:1	n^+:1	1:1	n:1

[1] *Homologous values* are values at points, planes, or zones, at or below the two footings, which in every respect are in geomtrically similar locations relative to the two footings.

[2] The volumetric strains are larger for the larger footing (see Fig. 19·11). However, volumetric strains in general cause much less settlement than that caused by shearing strains.

[3] The ratio of settlements (item 12) is $1/n^+$ times as large for II as for I. If it is assumed that the early portions of loading test curves are straight lines, it follows that ratios of loading (items 1, 2, and 4) must also be $1/n^+$ times as large and the ratio of safety factors n^+ times as large for II as for I.

[4] When ratios of preloading stresses and induced stresses are not alike, the total stress relationship is different at different relative depths within the bulbs. The induced stresses predominate in the upper portion of the bulb and the preloading stresses predominate in the lower portion of the bulb; thus the detailed analysis of I cannot be carried through.

[5] The preloading stresses are in this case the high internal pressures. Total stresses need not be considered since the distortions and the compressions are the result of induced stresses only.

[6] The Mohr diagrams of induced stresses are identical at homologous points for the case of III.

[7] Settlements due to compressions require times in the ratio n^2:1.

per cent; for the 15 lb per sq in. test the corresponding compressions are 1.5 and 0.1 per cent with a total of 1.6 per cent.

The significance of the above example is made clearer by a consideration of Fig. 19·4. In this figure the small element shown at the center of the pressure bulb undergoes stresses and strains which are roughly equal to the average values of stress and strain throughout the bulb. The stress-strain actions of elements of this type are represented, except for σ_3 variation, by the curves of Fig. 19·11. Therefore the various curves of Fig. 19·11 may be accepted as representative of the comparative stress-strain action of bulbs below various sizes of footings.

Settlements depend on a summation based on the vertical direct strains over the height of the pressure bulb. The height of the bulb below footing 2 is n times that below footing 1, whereas the average vertical direct strain is slightly greater below 2 than below 1. Therefore the *settlement of footing 2 is somewhat greater than n times that of footing 1.*

The steps of this analysis are summarized in column I of Table 19·1. The first and main conclusion is that stated just above. The σ_1/σ_3 values for both footings have been considered in detail and have in all instances been alike at homologous points. Thus a second conclusion is that the factors of safety relative to shear failure are alike for the two sizes. It follows that the ultimate bearing capacity is proportional to the breadth of the footing, as stated without proof at the beginning of the section. It also follows that, when loaded to any given percentage of the ultimate bearing capacity, the settlement is somewhat greater than proportional to the breadth of the footing, and that the coefficient of settlement depends only to a minor degree on breadth, its value being somewhat smaller for larger breadths. These statements are illustrated by Fig. 19·12.

In this figure curve I represents the loading test curve for footing 1. Arbitrarily chosen points on this curve are A_1, B_1, and so on. If the pressure values of each of these points is multiplied by n, which here is assumed to equal 4, and the settlement values are also multiplied by n, points A_2, B_2, and so on, and curve II are obtained. Curves I and II are in the relationship stated in the previous section and shown in Fig. 19·9 (b). If the settlement values of the various points of curve I are, instead, multiplied by a constant somewhat larger than n (this constant in this instance being taken as 6) curve III is obtained. It may be noted that this value of 6 is 50 per cent greater than n; this conforms roughly to the numerical example given above because the aver-

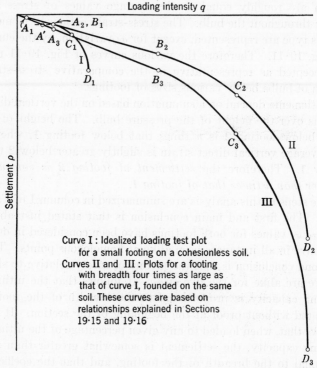

FIG. 19·12 Curves showing size effects in cohesionless soil.

age vertical strain of 2.5 per cent for the test at larger pressures is about 50 per cent greater than the 1.6 per cent value for the test at smaller pressures. Curves I and III illustrate the relationship shown by column I of Table 19·1.

The difference between curves II and III of Fig. 19·12 may frequently be considerable. However, the real value of this analysis is the general trend it demonstrates, and a high degree of accuracy can seldom be depended on in practical applications of the relationships under discussion. For these reasons the difference between curves II and III is not of major importance, and the simple relationship, presented in Fig. 19·9 (*b*), is satisfactory for the great majority of applications.

19·17 Analysis of Size Effects for the Case of Cohesionless Soil—Surface Footings Loaded to the Intensities which Cause a Given Settlement

For a second analysis let it be assumed that the two geometrically similar footings which were considered in the previous section are to be loaded by amounts which cause the same settlement. The necessity of a reasonable factor of safety against ultimate failure will in general restrict allowable loading intensities to the straight line portion of the loading test curve. Thus, in this analysis it will be assumed that the loading intensities considered are on the straight line portion of the curve.

The final results of this analysis may be taken directly from Fig. 19·12. More detailed results may be obtained, however, by the procedure shown in Table 19·1, column II. In the previous analysis, item 12 of the table shows a settlement ratio of n^+ to 1. The conditions representing the present analysis would be obtained if the larger footing had $1/n^+$ times as much settlement, as it would if the loading intensity on this footing were made $1/n^+$ times as large. Such a loading gives the settlement ratio of 1 to 1 shown for item 12 in column II. Ratios of applied loads and stresses are also $1/n^+$ times as large as in column I, and thus the ratios in column II for items 1, 2, and 4 are as given. The ratio of factors of safety in this case is n^+ times as large as that of the previous case; therefore it is n^+ to 1, as shown in item 13.

This analysis cannot be carried through in as much detail as the previous one because preloading and induced stresses are in different ratios. The preloading stresses are in the ratio of n to 1, as in the previous analysis, but in the present analysis the induced stresses at homologous points are independent of n. The total stresses are therefore in no such simple ratio as the n to 1 ratio given as item 5 in column I of Table 19·1. In the upper part of the bulb the preloading stresses are practically zero, and thus the total stresses are predominantly induced stresses which are about alike at homologous points below the two footings. In the lower portion of the bulb the induced stresses are small, and therefore the total stresses are predominantly the preloading stresses and thus are in the ratio of n to 1 at homologous points. For this case there is no way of carrying through the steps represented by items 5 and 8 of the table.

The main conclusions for the case wherein settlements are alike are that surface loading intensities are approximately alike, with the larger footing having a somewhat smaller intensity, whereas the larger footing has a safety factor against shear failure which is somewhat more than n times as large as that of the smaller footing. These relationships are clearly shown by Fig. 19·12.

19·18　Analysis of Size Effects for the Case of Highly Cohesive Soils—Footings under a Given Loading Intensity

Two geometrically similar surface footings on a highly cohesive soil, loaded to the same loading intensity at homologous points, may easily be compared by a procedure similar to that used in Section 19·16 for cohesionless soils.

For highly cohesive materials the preloading stress is the intrinsic pressure, which is the source of virtually all the strength of the soil. Since this strength is constant the strains which occur depend only on induced stresses; preloading and total stresses need not be considered here.

Since applied surface intensities are alike at homologous points of the two areas, all induced homologous stresses are equal, and the Mohr diagrams for homologous points below the footings are the same in all dimensions.

Since the strength is constant it follows that both the shearing strains and the volumetric strains are alike at homologous points.

Since the strains are alike in all respects at homologous points, the two final conclusions are easily reached. The settlement for the large footings is n times that for the smaller footing, and the factors of safety with respect to shearing strengths are alike at all homologous points. These relationships, however, are subject to time effects which have not yet been considered.

The time required for shearing strains to take place depends on viscous or plastic characteristics of the type discussed in Section 10·15. Therefore it depends only on soil characteristics and induced stresses, and shearing strains will take place just as quickly for the large as for the small footing. The major portion of such strains should occur in a relatively short time. The volumetric strains require drainage, and the rate at which these strains occur depends greatly on the lengths of drainage paths. The lengths of corresponding drainage paths for the two geometrically similar cases under consideration are in the ratio n to 1. Concepts from one-dimensional cases should not be assumed to hold in the three-dimensional case until their validity is demonstrated. However, it is not difficult to demonstrate, for this case of geometrically similar systems, that the time required for the occurrence of any given percentage of the ultimate volume change is about proportional to the square of the length of the drainage path, as in the consolidation theory outlined in Chapter 10. Thus, for the two footings, any given percentage of the ultimate settlement due to drainage occurs in times which are in the ratio of n^2 to 1.

Both the settlement due to shearing strain and that due to compression are, in general, appreciable parts of the total settlement in highly cohesive soils, and since the two components of settlement obey different time laws, the superimposed effect leads to a complicated situation. In a small loading test, say on a 2 by 2 ft area, most of the settlement may occur in a typical case within a few days, whereas in a large bulb such as that below a 100 by 100 ft mat foundation the time required would be about $(50)^2$ times as long; this means that the settlement may go on for decades. The amount of settlement occurring under a given loading intensity is, as shown above, proportional to the size of the footing, and the larger settlement of larger footings is sometimes all the more dangerous in that the time lag may delay the settlement, making it appear smaller than its true amount until attention to it has been relaxed.

This case is summarized, except for time effects, in column III of Table 19·1.

19·19 Analysis of Size Effects for the Case of Highly Cohesive Soils—Footings Loaded to the Intensities which Cause a Given Settlement

If the two sizes of footings are to be so loaded as to meet the condition that their settlements be alike, it is easily seen after study of the preceding section that the large footing can be loaded only to $1/n$th as great an intensity as that on the smaller. The larger footing in this case has, however, a factor of safety n times as large as that of the smaller.

This case is needed to complete the series; it is summarized in column IV of Table 19·1. Time effects enter as in the previous case, but no new concepts need be considered.

19·20 Approximate General Expression for the Coefficient of Settlement for Any Soil

This analysis covers the effects of both size and depth in any homogeneous soil and furnishes a general expression for the coefficient of settlement in terms of two soil properties. Its scope is limited to the straight line portion of the loading test curve, however, and it does not include ultimate bearing capacity considerations.

The ratio between the direct stress σ_z on the horizontal plane, and the vertical compressive strain ϵ_z, at a point at any depth below the surface of a homogeneous soil deposit, is a stress-strain modulus which will be designated by M_z. This ratio must not be called an elastic modulus, since soils are elastic only to a limited degree, but its units are the same as those of the modulus of elasticity.

The modulus M_z has values which vary with pressure. Only in highly cohesive material, in which there is a constant intrinsic pressure p_i, is there a constant modulus. In cohesionless soils the pressure depends on the weight of overlying soil and to a smaller degree on pressures caused by the footing load; therefore the modulus in such a soil is proportional to the unit weight γ, and at any given depth it is approximately proportional to the depth. In a soil which falls between the classifications of cohesionless and highly cohesive, the modulus depends on both types of pressure; it may be expressed approximately by

$$M_z = C_a \gamma z + C_b p_i \qquad (19·16)$$

where C_a and C_b are constants for the given soil.

An approximate general relationship between loading intensity, settlement, and depth and breadth of footing may be obtained by using average values for stress, strain, and modulus within the pressure bulb. On this basis

$$\frac{(\sigma_z)_{\mathrm{av}}}{(\epsilon_z)_{\mathrm{av}}} = (M_z)_{\mathrm{av}} \qquad (19\cdot17)$$

Figure $19\cdot13$ represents the general case under consideration. A fairly good idea of average stress within the bulb may be ob-

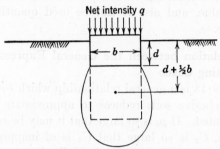

Net intensity q

FIG. $19\cdot13$ The footing considered in the general derivation of the relationship between breadth, depth, loading intensity, and settlement.

tained from Fig. $19\cdot2$; if the average stress is designated by $C_c q$, this figure indicates that the value of C_c is approximately $\frac{1}{2}$. The average vertical strain within the bulb may be expressed as the settlement ρ divided by the bulb depth. If the bulb shape is assumed to be a cube, the depth is equal to the breadth b and the average strain is ρ/b. The average modulus is the value holding at the mid-point of the bulb, where z equals $d + (b/2)$. Inserting these average values in the above equation gives

$$\frac{C_c q}{\dfrac{\rho}{b}} = C_a \gamma \left(d + \frac{b}{2} \right) + C_b p_i$$

whence

$$\frac{q}{\rho} = \left(\frac{C_a \gamma}{2 C_c} \right) \left(1 + \frac{2d}{b} \right) + \left(\frac{C_b p_i}{C_c} \right) \frac{1}{b}$$

If γ, p_i, C_a, C_b, and C_c are assumed to be constant, the relationship, which is valid for any soil, may be written

$$\frac{q}{\rho} = C_1 \left(1 + \frac{2d}{b} \right) + \frac{C_2}{b} \qquad (19\cdot18)$$

wherein C_1 and C_2 are soil constants and q/ρ is the coefficient of settlement. If the loading is applied over the entire excavated area, the intensity q is the net intensity.

The expression derived above is of highly approximate nature, as will later be shown by numerical examples. However, it presents lines of reasoning that are needed for the understanding of bearing capacities of soils of all degrees of cohesion. It therefore has much qualitative value, and also it can be used quantitatively to a limited degree.

19·21 Correlation between the General Expression and the Limiting Cases

Equation 19·18 is a general relationship which for cohesionless and highly cohesive soils reduces to approximate relationships already presented. If p_i is so large that it may be considered the only pressure, C_2 is so large that C_1 is of inappreciably small magnitude in comparison, and the following equation, which holds for *highly cohesive soils*, is obtained

$$\frac{q}{\rho} = \frac{C_2}{b} \quad \text{or} \quad \frac{q_1}{q_2} = \frac{\rho_1}{\rho_2} \times \frac{b_2}{b_1} \qquad (19 \cdot 19)$$

In the second expression above, the subscripts 1 and 2 refer to values for any two sizes of footing on the given soil. This is the same relationship that appears in Fig. 19·9 (a); it states that the coefficient of settlement is inversely proportional to the breadth. It may be noted that this expression is independent of depth d, the amount the footing is buried below ground surface; this indicates that depth has no appreciable effect on settlements in highly cohesive soil.

For a cohesionless soil, C_2 equals zero. For a footing at ground surface, d equals zero. Thus for *surface footings on cohesionless soil*

$$\frac{q}{\rho} = C_1 \qquad (19 \cdot 20)$$

This expression, which states that the coefficient of settlement has the same value for all breadths, appears in Fig. 19·9 (b). The minor amount of variation with breadth, shown in Fig. 19·12, does not appear in this approximate solution.

19·22   The Effect of Depth on the Coefficient of Settlement in Cohesionless Soils

When footings are founded below ground level in cohesionless soil, C_2 is zero in equation 19·18, and the equation becomes

$$\frac{q}{\rho} = C_1\left(1 + \frac{2d}{b}\right) \quad \text{or} \quad \frac{q_1}{q_2} = \frac{\rho_1}{\rho_2} \times \frac{\left(1 + \dfrac{2d}{b}\right)_1}{\left(1 + \dfrac{2d}{b}\right)_2} \quad (19\cdot21)$$

This equation shows that it is not the depth which directly affects the results; the important factor is the ratio of depth to breadth. The term $(1 + 2d/b)$ is the depth factor, as stated in Section 19·12. Its large effect is shown in that for a depth equal to one-half the breadth its value is 2 and therefore the coefficient of settlement is twice the value holding for a surface footing. The load, moreover, may be more than doubled in such an instance, because the q value which applies in the equation is the net value. This large increase in resistance to compression appears reasonable when it is noted that the zones of the type shown in Fig. 19·5 below the edges of buried footings do not reach the ϕ-obliquity condition or grow nearly so rapidly for buried footings as they do for surface footings.

The ultimate bearing capacity of footings on granular soil also increases at a rate which is at least proportional to the depth factor, as has been shown in Section 19·12. However, both the ultimate and the coefficient of settlement relationships are based on the assumption of undisturbed, homogeneous soil, and it is possible that disturbance to the soil during construction may sometimes affect these relationships, and especially that relative to settlements. Terzaghi ‡ has called attention to the fact that the loosening of soil during the excavation for buried footings in deep shafts in sands may lead to settlements that are as large as those which would occur under the same loading at ground surface.

‡ For a stimulating discussion presenting various controversial points of view relative to depth effects see reference 32.

19·23 Numerical Example—Determination of Expression for Coefficient of Settlement for a Given Soil

For a material which conforms approximately to one of the limiting cases of cohesionless or highly cohesive soil the coefficient of settlement for any size of footing may be estimated from the results of a single loading test on any size of footing. For such estimates either equation 19·19 or 19·20 would be used. For soils in general, however, loading tests on at least two breadths of footings must be available before such estimates are possible. The concept that the data of two tests permit such predictions is an important one and is illustrated by the following example. A factor that must be recognized and will be considered after the example is the very low probable precision of predictions of this type.

Let it be assumed that two surface loading tests have been run on a certain soil which has been classified as dirty sand. A loading test on a 2 by 2 ft area gives a coefficient of settlement of 2 tons per sq ft per in.; a larger and more expensive test on a 6 by 6 ft area gives a coefficient of settlement of 1 ton per sq ft per in.

The two tests, written as two equations in the form of equation 19·18 with C_1 and C_2 as two unknowns, permit a solution for C_1 and C_2:

$$\text{2-ft footing: } 2 = C_1 + \frac{C_2}{2}$$

$$\text{6-ft footing: } 1 = C_1 + \frac{C_2}{6}$$

whence

$$C_2 = 3 \quad \text{and} \quad C_1 = \tfrac{1}{2}$$

and for any footing, at any depth, on this soil

$$\frac{q}{\rho} = \frac{1}{2}\left(1 + \frac{2d}{b}\right) + \frac{3}{b} . \tag{19·22}$$

It may be noted that any units may be used in this solution as long as they are used consistently throughout. In equation 19·22, q/ρ is in tons per square foot per inch of settlement and b and d are in feet.

An instructive study of the relationship between breadth and settlement of surface footings is furnished by equation 19·22, values being as follows under an intensity of loading of 2 tons per sq ft:

b in feet	1	2	4	6	8	10	20	40	80	∞
ρ in inches	(0.6)	1	1.6	2	2.3	2.5	3.1	3.5	3.7	4

The settlement of a 1-ft breadth is given in parentheses because the straight line portion of the curve may not extend as high as 2 tons per sq ft for this breadth.

This study shows that in footings of small size the settlement is roughly proportional to the breadth, a relationship which would be expected only in highly cohesive soils, whereas in large sizes the settlement is nearly independent of the breadth. The explanation is that the small amount of cohesion resulting from the small percentage of fine particles, with perhaps some capillary pressure due to small amounts of capillary moisture, gives sufficient cohesion to predominate over the pressure due to depth in considerations of small footings. For larger sizes, however, the cohesion is hardly appreciable. In the above example the internal pressure is equivalent to the pressure of a 3-ft depth of soil.

A very pertinent study of the degree of precision of the analysis may now be made. If the two loading tests were repeated with every effort made to reproduce results as closely as possible, it would be fortunate if the new data should check within 10 or 20 per cent. Assuming 15 per cent differences, leading to coefficients of 2.3 and 0.85 tons per sq ft per in., respectively, for the 2-ft and 6-ft sizes, the extrapolated prediction for settlement under 2 tons per sq ft for the area of 40-ft breadth becomes 8.5 in., or nearly three times as large as that previously obtained. This indicates the desirability of using such analyses with discretion and, if possible, using the average data of two or more tests for each breadth tested in an investigation of this type.

The above considerations do not disprove the fundamental soundness of any of the concepts which have been developed, but they do show that the dependability of numerical results is often limited to order of magnitude. Variations of the type mentioned above are, moreover, only one of the possible sources of low precision. Another feature which may cause even greater effect is the approximate validity of expressions assumed in the derivation.

For soils possessing a small amount of cohesion the above analysis indicates that one test on a large area might be sufficient for the information desired but a single small loading test is likely to be quite misleading. It may also be concluded that for soils with any appreciable amount of cohesion, knowledge of footing action requires at least two tests on different breadths, one of the areas being as large as can be economically justified.

19·24 Numerical Example—Settlement Prediction

Let it be assumed that the building of Fig. 19·14 is 50 ft by 80 ft in plan, that the basement was excavated to groundwater table, that the two loading tests of the previous section were run at that grade, and that well points or some other method of lowering the

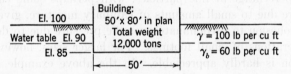

FIG. 19·14   The cross section assumed in the illustrative example.

water table were used to complete the excavation. A rough estimate is wanted relative to the settlement to be expected. The weight of the building and the unit weight of the soil are given in the figure.

Equation 19·22 may be used for this crude prediction, but several points must be noted. Since these points do not necessarily have a large effect on the answer, they are mentioned mainly because of their fundamental importance.

In the loading tests the q values were the applied intensities since no overburden existed around the loaded areas at the time of loading. For the building the value that should be used for q is the net intensity:

$$q = \frac{12,000}{50 \times 80} - \frac{10 \times 100 + 5 \times 122.5}{2000} = 2.19 \text{ tons per sq ft}$$

Since the water is removed from the area which becomes the

basement the total unit weight of the soil below the water table is used above in figuring the release due to the last five feet of excavation; the same results are obtained, however, if the submerged unit weight is used and a 5-ft uplift pressure on the base is also included.

The breadth is taken as 50 ft because the narrower of the two dimensions of a rectangular area is the one that comes the nearer to being the controlling dimension.§

The value of d in the depth factor must be that depth of soil which, when multiplied by the unit weight of the soil in the bulb, gives the pressure existing at the elevation of the foundation. The 10-ft depth of soil between El. 100 and El. 90 gives the same pressure as $10 \times (100/60)$ ft of submerged soil, and therefore the effective depth is

Thus
$$d = 5 + 10 \times \tfrac{100}{60} = 21.7 \text{ ft}$$

and
$$\frac{2.19}{\rho} = \frac{1}{2}\left(1 + \frac{2 \times 21.7}{50}\right) + \frac{3}{50}$$

$$\rho = 2.2 \text{ in.}$$

The many bold assumptions and the extreme degree of extrapolation, which may greatly affect the accuracy of this figure for settlement, have already been discussed. After such factors as the possibility of disturbance to the soil during excavation and the effect of loading and unloading caused by the lowering and raising of the water table during construction have been recognized, it is obvious that there is much question regarding the amount of dependability that can be attached to the numerical value. It might be reasonable to conclude that the settlement is not likely to be less than 1 in. whereas, if it could be known that the loading test data are accurate and that the effects of soil disturbance and other unconsidered factors are small, it might be concluded that the settlement is not likely to exceed 3 in.

§ The effect of the larger dimension of a rectangular footing on the ultimate bearing capacity is discussed in reference 65. Few data are available on this effect at pressures that are small compared to the ultimate, but it is generally accepted that the larger dimension has much less effect than the smaller dimension.

The answer at least represents consideration of the trends introduced by the major variables known to affect settlements, and as such it has value as an indication.

19·25 The Perimeter Shear Concept

According to an approach developed by W. S. Housel (75) the total load that may be placed on a footing when a given allowable settlement has been specified may be expressed by

$$Q = nA + mP \qquad (19·23)$$

wherein A is the area and P the perimeter of the footing; n designates the unit compressive strength of the pressure bulb, and m the unit perimeter shear. The unit perimeter shear may be defined as the load-carrying ability per foot of perimeter, furnished on the vertical cylindrical surface which passes through the perimeter of the footing by the shearing resistance developed when the footing and the soil below it settle relative to the soil outside.

This approach leads to the same expression as that obtained in a previous section. If both sides of equation 19·18 are multiplied by the area, the expression obtained for the total load, for the case of surface footings, is

$$Q = C_1 \rho A + C_2 \rho \frac{A}{b}$$

This expression agrees with that above since ρ represents a given allowable settlement and A/b is, for any given shape, proportional to the perimeter.

The unit perimeter shear is of small magnitude in sands. This is in agreement with previously developed concepts, since the perimeter shear is proportional to constant C_2 of equation 19·18 and this constant, as shown in Section 19·21, is proportional to the intrinsic pressure p_i. An explanation of this case is given by Fig. 19·5, in which the shaded zones reach the ϕ-obliquity condition quickly because the soil therein has little resistance to distortion; thus the shearing resistance that can be developed on a vertical surface through these zones is small.

In highly cohesive soils the second term of equation 19·23 predominates, indicating that most of the load is in this case carried by perimeter shear. This condition is in agreement with concepts already developed, and it also agrees with the discussion in Section 19·29 in connection with which the distribution curve of Fig. 19·19 (*c*) is given.

It may be claimed that concepts relative to the pressure bulb and concepts concerning the two bearing capacity criteria, with the detailed considerations of stress and strain which have been given, offer a more complete understanding of the problem than can be obtained from the perimeter shear concept. However, the two approaches are similar in principle, their differences being mainly in terminology.

19·26 Relationships between Bearing Capacity and Breadth

A final representation of the effect of breadth on bearing capacity may now be given in which consideration is given to both of the bearing capacity criteria explained in Section 19·4. In this representation all soil types are considered, but the approach is limited to surface footings and either to cases of isolated footings and mat foundations or to groups of footings in which individual footings are spaced so widely that they have no effect on each other.

For each soil type the criterion of safety against ultimate failure will be considered first. This criterion may be expressed

$$q_a \lessgtr \frac{q_u}{F} \qquad (19\cdot24)$$

in which q_a is the allowable bearing intensity and F is the factor of safety against ultimate failure. For this demonstration it is assumed that the value chosen for F is constant for any given soil.

The forms of the equations discussed in Section 19·12 show that the above expression is proportional to breadth in cohesionless soils and constant in highly cohesive soils. Equations of the form of 19·1 and 19·4 indicate that for soils in general this expression is equal to a constant plus the product of the breadth and a second constant. In accordance with these relationships the curves labeled q_u/F in each of the plots of Fig. 19·15 are obtained.

The second criterion is that of safety against excessive settlement. This requirement is indefinite and not easily expressed.

Actually, it is mainly differential settlements which concern the foundation engineer, and large settlements can usually be tolerated if they can be kept alike in magnitude at all parts of a foundation. In general, however, the differential settlements are largest when the average settlements are largest and, on the assumption that the magnitude of settlement may be accepted as a measure of the amount of probable differential settlement, the settlement requirement is frequently expressed in the form

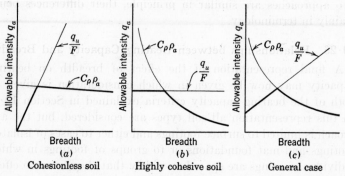

Fig. 19·15　Relationships between allowable bearing intensity and breadth.

of a maximum allowable settlement. Similarly, loading tests are accepted as demonstrating satisfactory bearing soils if the settlements under loads somewhat larger than the design loads do not cause settlements exceeding some specified amount, often approximately ½ in. This does not necessarily mean that ½ in. is the allowable settlement of the proposed structure; it is more likely to mean that soils showing the largest settlements in loading tests will tend to show the largest settlements when loaded by buildings and that the specified allowable settlement in loading tests is presumably the measure, based on experience, of a soil which will give about the largest permissible differential settlements under the load of a typical building. On this basis the expression for the coefficient of settlement C_ρ may be rearranged to give

$$q_a = C_\rho \rho_a \qquad (19 \cdot 25)$$

wherein ρ_a is the allowable settlement.

Equations 19·20, 19·19, and 19·18 express the coefficient of settlement as constant in cohesionless soil, inversely proportional to the breadth in highly cohesive soil, and equal to a constant plus a second constant divided by the breadth for soils in general. Figure 19·12 indicates, however, that in cohesionless soil the coefficient of settlement decreases slightly with increasing breadth. In accordance with these relationships the curves labeled $C_{\rho}\rho_a$ in each of the plots of Fig. 19·15 are obtained.

Heavy lines are used to represent the criterion which governs in the various breadth ranges of the curves of Fig. 19·15. For soils in general and for the conditions assumed, this figure indicates that the bearing intensity has a maximum value at some intermediate breadth and is considerably smaller at very small or very large breadths.

It may be claimed that expressions 19·24 and 19·25, and especially the latter, are not adequate representations of allowable intensities, and it is possible that consideration should be given to other expressions. For example, the ratio between the maximum differential settlement and the average settlement tends to be greater for large than for small buildings of any given type of construction. Possibly the limiting settlement criterion covers this condition, since larger differential settlements can usually be tolerated in larger buildings, but it can be claimed that a criterion which directly expresses a limitation of differential settlement is needed. It is probable, however, that other expressions which might be considered would in general give curves which would fall between those shown for the two criteria represented in Fig. 19·15.

19·27 Effects of Water

A number of effects which result from the presence of water must be recognized in connection with bearing capacity and related foundation problems.

If the pressure bulb in a cohesionless soil is entirely below the water table, the unit weight of the soil is the submerged value, expressed by $[(G-1)/(1+e)]\gamma_w$. Since the ultimate bearing capacity is proportional to the unit weight, as equations such as 19·6 show, the theoretical value for the submerged case is of the order of 50 to 60 per cent as large as it is for soil above the water table. When the water table fluctuates, the smaller or submerged value must of course be used in the zone of fluctuation. To a limited degree the same reasoning holds for coefficients of settlement as for ultimate bearing capacities, because the rigidity of sands depends on intergranular pressure, which in turn depends on the effective unit weight. If bearing capacity values are corrected in proportion to effective unit weights, loading tests in which the bulb is above the water table may sometimes be used for rough predictions of the action of large footings which are on the same soil but have their bulbs below the water table. Such predictions may be inaccurate, however, because of the effect of increased strength due to capillary pressures in bulbs which are above the water table. Moreover, many soils show a somewhat larger settlement when submerged and loaded to a given percentage of the ultimate bearing capacity than they do when dry. A very rough relationship is that settlements in a given soil are about twice as large under a given loading when the soil is submerged as they are when it is essentially dry.

Upward flow of water in an excavation during construction may loosen the soil; it is another effect of water that must be considered with care. This important practical matter is widely recognized, and some building codes require the use of the tabular value for the loose state in such a situation.

Still another effect is the swelling which some fine-grained soils undergo when in the presence of water. This swelling decreases the shearing strength, and thus the ultimate bearing capacities are greatly decreased. Such soils may present numerous unusual foundation problems.

So many important practical problems exist relative to the proper handling of water during construction that a book could be written on this subject alone. Well points, sumps, and the like may be used to lower the water table and to lessen the danger of loosening of the soil by upward flow, and, since they also lead to much better working conditions, their cost may often be an excellent investment. Flow net studies may often be made to give information on the gradients and pressures to be expected. Problems of this type are interesting, and important applications of methods outlined in Chapter 9 and the difference between a good and a bad choice of procedure may often make much difference in the difficulties encountered, the expense, and the quality of final results on a project. These problems are closely related to the subject matter but are beyond the scope of this text.

19·28   Buried Strata of Low Bearing Capacity

A subsoil condition which requires careful consideration is that of a buried stratum with a bearing capacity which is much less than that of the deposit above it. This is a case in which loading tests on small surface footings must not be used, for reasons explained in Section 19·6 and illustrated in Fig. 19·3.

A good example of this case is a condition which is common in Boston. A layer of soft blue clay, which in many localities is more than 100 ft thick, exists below large portions of the district, with the surface of the clay roughly 10 or 20 ft below mean low water. Between the clay and the present ground surface the materials are largely fill and are generally of poor character. However, immediately above the soft blue clay, a deposit of fairly coarse and fairly dense sand of varying thickness occurs over a part of the district. In some localities the blue clay is found to have a crust of limited depth which is of medium to stiff consistency. These relatively thin strata which just overlie the soft blue clay are in some localities the only satisfactory bearing strata within 100 ft of ground surface and, therefore, it is very important that they be used if at all possible.

When footings are founded at or near the surface of a good stratum which overlies a poorer stratum, the pressures applied at the footing level spread out with increasing depth, and thus the induced pressures reaching the poorer stratum are of considerably smaller magnitude. Often, if the depth of the good stratum is large, the stresses reaching the poorer stratum may be well within permissible values. Thus the need for some simple method for rough analyses of such cases is evident.

In case of the type under consideration the poorer material is usually a fine-grained, highly compressible soil, and the settlements which it undergoes are due mainly to compression rather than to shearing strain. Such cases have been considered in Chapters 10 and 12 under the subjects of consolidation and settlement analysis. However, it is not the detailed settlement analysis which is desired here, but a simple method of deciding whether or not the poorer stratum controls in the determination of the permissible magnitude of loading. The most unfavorable stresses in the buried stratum are at its surface, and whether the danger is from excessive compression or possibly from lateral flow of the clay, the problem is conservatively handled if the stress at the surface of the buried stratum is limited to the bearing capacity which would be reasonable on this soil at ground surface.

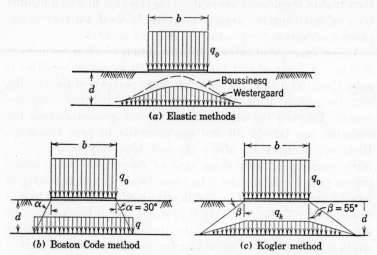

FIG. 19·16 Pressures induced on the surface of a buried stratum.

A number of approximate methods are available for obtaining stresses at the surface of buried deposits. Formulas from the theory of elasticity might be used, although question regarding their validity in soils makes them no more dependable than simpler approaches. The distribution curves obtained from the Westergaard and the Boussinesq elastic solutions, as expressed by equations 11·9 and 11·5, respectively, are illustrated in Fig. 19·16 (a).

A simpler method is to assume that the stress spreads with depth to a larger area, defined by lines through the edges of the surface area at angle α to the vertical, and that on this larger area the stress is uniformly distributed, as shown in (b). The uniform stress is, of course, not the true picture but, as a measure of the degree to which the surface of the buried stratum is stressed, this simple approach is often satisfactory. The expression for the case shown in (b), for square or round footings, is

$$\frac{q}{q_0} = \left[\frac{\dfrac{b}{d}}{\dfrac{b}{d} + 2\tan\alpha}\right]^2 \qquad (19\cdot 26)$$

and for a long footing the relationship is

$$\frac{q}{q_0} = \frac{\dfrac{b}{d}}{\dfrac{b}{d} + 2\tan\alpha} \qquad (19\cdot 27)$$

where q and q_0 are, respectively, the stresses at the surface of the buried stratum and at ground surface, b/d is the ratio of breadth to depth, and α is the spread angle. The spread angle is commonly assumed to be equal to 30 degrees or more. In the Boston Code, which is discussed in later sections, the spread angle is taken as 30 degrees, which is a fairly conservative choice. In Fig. 19·17 the curves labeled A represent the above equations for a 30-degree angle of spread and give q/q_0 values directly for any value of b/d.

Another simple approach, advanced by Kögler,‖ is shown in Fig. 19·16 (c). The stress on the surface of the buried stratum is assumed to be uniform below the loaded surface area, and outside it is assumed to vary linearly to zero at a distance defined by the spread angle β. The equation for Kögler's method for square or round footings is

$$\frac{q_k}{q_0} = \frac{\left(\dfrac{b}{d}\right)^2}{\left(\dfrac{b}{d}\right)^2 + 2\left(\dfrac{b}{d}\right)\tan\beta + \dfrac{4}{3}\tan^2\beta} \qquad (19\cdot 28)$$

‖ Representations of similar types are discussed in reference 89.

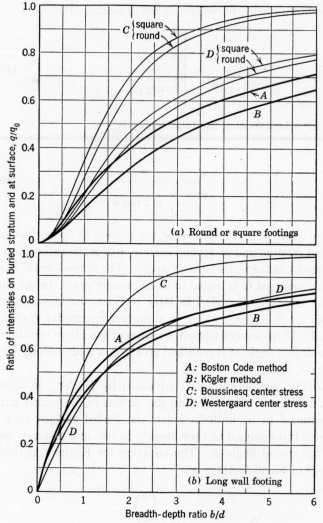

A: Boston Code method
B: Kögler method
C: Boussinesq center stress
D: Westergaard center stress

Fig. 19·17   Curves for use in determining pressures on buried strata.

and for a long footing the expression is

$$\frac{q_k}{q_0} = \frac{\dfrac{b}{d}}{\dfrac{b}{d} + \tan \beta} \qquad (19 \cdot 29)$$

wherein q_k is the stress on the central portion of the buried stratum and the spread angle β recommended by Kögler is 55 degrees. In Fig. 19·17 curves representing the above equations with the 55-degree spread angle are labeled B.

The light curves of Fig. 19·17 are for the elastic cases represented in Fig. 19·16 (*a*), the intensity of *q* being the maximum intensity at depth *d*. It is seen from Fig. 19·17 that the Boussinesq formula gives relatively large values of q/q_0 but that the other three approaches are in reasonable agreement with each other. Use of any one of these three approaches is probably conservative and sufficiently accurate for the rough indications usually desired from such a method.

For square or round footings Fig. 19·17 shows that the stress on the buried stratum is about one-fifth that at the surface when the breadth-depth ratio is 1; this figure is worth remembering.

19·29 Pressure Distributions and Differential Settlements

The distribution of pressure is very different below footings on cohesionless soil from that below footings on cohesive soil. The distribution also depends greatly on the rigidity of the footing, being entirely different below rigid and below flexible footings. The pattern of the differential settlement of flexible footings is also dependent on the type of soil below the footing. Little has been said in the preceding pages about these important variations, the intensities of loading and the settlements considered up to this point being the average values.

The policy of first developing concepts for limiting cases will be continued in this section, and perfectly flexible and perfectly rigid footings will be studied relative to pressure distributions and differential settlements. Separate studies of these items will be carried out for cohesionless and for highly cohesive soils.

The general concepts arrived at are valid for square, round, or long footings.

Consider first a *flexible footing on the surface of a cohesionless soil,* carrying a *uniformly distributed load.* Since the footing is completely flexible the uniform distribution of pressure also acts on the surface of the soil. The soil just outside of the edge of the footing is not under pressure and has no strength. Therefore, when the given intensity of load is applied, the outer edge of the

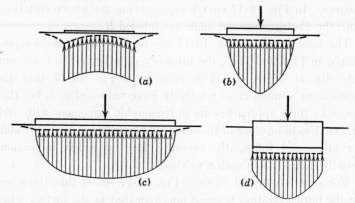

Fig. 19·18 Pressure distributions and differential settlements in cohesionless soils.

footing undergoes a relatively large settlement. Below the center of the footing the soil develops strength and rigidity as fast as it is loaded from above and from surrounding points, and because of this the settlement is relatively small. Figure 19·18 (*a*) shows the uniform loading diagram for this case, with the curve of settlement shown by heavy dashed lines.

For a *rigid footing resting on cohesionless soil* the settlement must be uniform. Under uniform settlement the high resistance to compression in the soil below the center of the footing, as compared to the lack of resistance to compression below the edge, must result in a relatively large pressure under the center and no pressure at the edge. This case with constant settlement and an approximately parabolic pressure distribution is shown in Fig. 19·18 (*b*). If the average pressure is relatively small, or if the width of the footing is large, this pressure distribution is somewhat flatter over the central portion of the footing, as shown in Fig. 19·18 (c), being nearer ellipsoidal than parabolic in shape but still having zero pressure at the edges.

For *rigid footings founded below the surface of a cohesionless deposit* there is some strength below the edge of the footing and, therefore, the pressure is not zero at the edge but is more like that shown in the distribution curve in Fig. 19·18 (d). For very

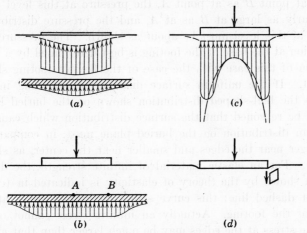

(a)   (c)

(b)   (d)

Fig. 19·19 Pressure distributions and differential settlements in highly cohesive soils.

deep rigid footings on sand the distribution may be more like that discussed below for cohesive soils.

A *uniformly loaded flexible footing on highly cohesive soil* gives conditions that can best be visualized by considering the stresses and strains caused in a typical thin horizontal layer of soil within the height of the pressure bulb. The uniform surface distribution transmits a bell-shaped distribution of pressure to this subsurface layer, as explained in Chapter 11 and as illustrated in Fig. 19·19 (a). The greater stress below the center of the footing at this subsurface layer must cause a greater compressive strain at this location. All horizontal layers below ground surface similarly show maximum compression below the center of the footing, and thus the surface settlement must have the dished pattern shown, with a much greater settlement under the center than under the edge of the footing.

A *rigid footing on highly cohesive soil* must undergo uniform settlement. Thus the underground horizontal layers discussed in the preceding paragraph must, on the average, be compressed nearly as much under the edges as under the center of the footing. The layer shown in (b) is at a depth of slightly less than $\frac{1}{2}b$ and may be accepted as representative of the average of all such layers. If the compression of this layer is nearly as large at point *B* as at point *A*, the pressure at this level must be nearly as large at *B* as at *A*, and the pressure distribution curve at this level must be about as shown. The pressure distribution at the base of the footing is best determined by a comparison of this case with the case of the flexible footing shown in (a). If the uniform surface distribution occurring in (a) causes the bell-shaped distribution shown on the buried layer, it can be reasoned that the surface distribution which causes a uniform distribution on the buried plane must, in comparison, be larger near the edges and smaller near the center, as shown in (c). For an elastic material of infinite strength, the distribution shown by the theory of elasticity is indicated in (c) by a light dashed line; this curve shows an infinite stress at the edge of the footing. Actually an infinite stress cannot occur, but the stress at the edges may be much larger than that at the center.

Another explanation of the large stresses under the edges of rigid footings on clay may be obtained by simple reasoning. The settlement of the footing forces the soil below the corner of the footing to subside, but the soil a short distance out from under the footing subsides much less. A little element of soil which was originally square must therefore be strained in shear to the shape shown in (d). A large vertical force is required to furnish the shearing stress that must exist on the left-hand face to cause the shearing strain of this highly cohesive element. This force must be provided by load from the footing, and it is this load that is resisted by perimeter shear and is the explanation of the larger edge pressure. Below the edges of rigid surface footings on sand this same shearing strain occurs, but it requires no force to cause it, owing to the lack of rigidity in the sand. However, in deeply buried, heavily loaded footings on sand a distribution similar to that in (c) may hold; this is not in disagreement with the concepts which have been developed because the sand in the bulb below a deeply buried footing may be essentially of constant strength and may thus resemble the character of a highly cohesive soil.

Numerical values of pressures for the variable distributions in Figs. 19·18 and 19·19 cannot be given because the actual magnitudes depend on numerous factors. However, a knowledge of the general forms of these distributions is very important to the structural designer. An assumption commonly used in the design of rigid footings is that the pressure is uniform, and no definite recommendation for a better procedure can be given. After a design has been prepared on this basis, however, it should be reviewed and should be strengthened at locations where the true distribution gives greater stresses than are given by the assumed distribution. For example, in Fig. 19·19 (c), the bending moment in the spread footing is much larger for the distribution shown than it is for a case of uniform soil reaction; additional reinforcing steel is needed to carry this greater moment, but the percentage to be added must be determined mainly by judgment since the actual distribution is known only qualitatively.

19·30 Pressure Distributions for Cases of Eccentric Loading

The common procedure for figuring pressures below eccentrically loaded areas involves the assumption of linear variation

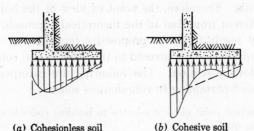

(a) Cohesionless soil   (b) Cohesive soil

Fig. 19·20 Pressure distributions below retaining walls.

of pressure. A good example of such determinations, based on retaining walls, has already been given in Section 17·12. The dashed lines in Fig. 19·20 represent a typical eccentric case under this assumption. Pressure distribution diagrams on the basis

of concepts explained in the previous section are shown for cohesionless soil in (*a*) and for cohesive soil in (*b*).

In (*b*) two items of danger may be noted. The bending moments are larger in the cantilever toe than shown by conventional analyses based on linear variation, and the toe pressure
which often is a limiting consideration, as explained in Section
17·13, is also much larger actually than when estimated on the
basis of linear variation.

19·31 Comparison of Theoretical Concepts and Building Code Specifications—Cohesionless Soils

Theoretical considerations of footings founded at or below the
surface of cohesionless or highly cohesive soil have been discussed in the preceding sections of this chapter. A comparison
will now be made between concepts which have been obtained
and procedures commonly specified in modern engineering practice.

In this discussion, the specifications of the Building Code of
the City of Boston will be referred to. This code may be accepted as more reasonable and more thorough than most other
codes; it is used here, however, not to illustrate what a code
should contain, but simply as an example of a code.

Building code specifications must be as simple and as practical
as possible.¶ The allowable bearing values quoted in codes are
usually the reflection of many years of construction experience
on local soils. Therefore, the point of view of the building code
is very different from that of the theoretical approach, and much
profit may result from the proposed comparisons.

Cohesionless soils are covered in this section and cohesive soils
in the following section. The following are excerpts from the
Boston code * pertaining to cohesionless soils:

¶ An important point of view relative to building codes is expressed by
the following quotation:

"Their prescriptions are usually narrow, partly with a view to enabling
men unskilled in building science to apply them, and partly with a view
to facilitate control by a highly superficial system of inspection on the part
of the public building authority." (From an editorial, *Engineering News-
Record*, Nov. 13, 1930.)

* The code excerpts given in this chapter and in Chapter 20 are from
reference 37, the Building Code of the City of Boston, 1944 edition. They

[1] The terms used . . .† shall be interpreted in accordance with generally accepted geological and engineering nomenclature. Certain terms shall . . . have more specific interpretations, as follows: . . . *Gravel*—An uncemented mixture of mineral grains one-quarter inch or more in diameter. *Sand*—A type of soil possessing practically no cohesion when dry, and consisting of mineral grains smaller than one-quarter inch in diameter. *Coarse Sand*—A sand consisting chiefly of grains which will be retained on a 65-mesh sieve. *Fine Sand*—A sand consisting chiefly of grains which will pass a 65-mesh sieve. *Compact Gravel, Compact Sand*—Deposits requiring picking for removal and offering high resistance to penetration by excavating tools. *Loose Gravel, Loose Sand*—Deposits readily removable by shoveling only. . . .

[2] The maximum pressure on [cohesionless] soils under foundations shall not exceed the [following] allowable bearing values . . . except when determined [from loading tests] . . ., and in any case subject to the modifications of subsequent paragraphs . . .

	[Tabular Values, tons per square foot]
Gravel, sand-gravel mixtures, compact	5
Gravel, sand-gravel mixtures, loose; sand, coarse, compact	4
Sand, coarse, loose; sand, fine, compact	3
Sand, fine, loose	1

[3] For areas of foundations smaller than three feet in least lateral dimension, the allowable bearing values shall be one-third of the [tabular] bearing values multiplied by the least lateral dimension in feet.

[4] The allowable bearing values . . . may exceed the tabulated values by two and one-half per cent for each foot of depth of the loaded area below the lowest ground surface immediately adjacent, but shall not exceed twice the tabulated values.

[5] Whenever, in an excavation, an inward or upward flow of water develops, . . . if such flow of water seriously impairs the structure of the bearing material, the allowable bearing value shall be reduced to that of the material in loose condition.

[6] Whenever the allowable load on a bearing material . . . is in doubt, the commissioner may require [loading] tests to be made to

---

are quoted herein with the permission of John J. Mahoney, Building Commissioner of the City of Boston. The excerpts given in this section are from code sections 2904 (*a*), (*b*), (*d*), and (*h*), 1915 (*a*), and 1916 (*a*), (*c*), and (*e*).

† A series of dots indicates an omission of words; the insertions in brackets have been made by the author.

enable him to determine such load, as, in his opinion, will not cause dangerous or objectionable settlements. . . . The loaded area shall be , . . at least four square feet. . . . The loaded area shall be the full size of the pit and at such depth that the ratio of the width of the loaded area to its depth below the immediately adjacent ground surface is the same as the larger of the following two values: [A] Ratio of the width of any footing to its depth below the immediately adjacent ground surface. [B] Ratio of the width of the entire foundation or group of footings to its depth below the average surrounding ground surface. A test load shall be applied which will produce a unit pressure equal to that for which the proposed foundations are designed. This load shall be allowed to remain undisturbed until no measurable settlement occurs during a period of twenty-four hours. . . . At least four hours shall elapse between the application of successive increments. The total load shall be allowed to remain undisturbed until no measurable settlement occurs during a period of twenty-four hours. [On cohesionless soils] when the design load . . . causes settlement of less than three-eighths inch and twice the design load causes settlement of less than one inch, the design load shall be allowed. . . .

The two subjects which are of greatest interest in this comparison are the effects of breadth of footing and depth of footing on the bearing capacity.

With respect to the breadth of footing the only modification to the tabular values for surface footing on cohesionless soils in this code is given in item [3]; this item expresses a restriction of intensities, on small areas, to values proportional to the breadth. Thus the code is in agreement with the theoretical concepts, shown in Fig. 19·15 (a), on the general nature of the effects of breadth.

Numerical checks on the tabular values are also of much interest and may easily be made. According to expressions 19·6 and 19·7 the ultimate bearing capacity has a maximum value which is of the order of $50\gamma b$. The unit weight would not exceed about 130 lb per cu ft. Thus, a rough upper limit for the ultimate bearing capacity for footings of 3-ft breadth on granular soil is

$$\frac{50 \times 130 \times 3}{2000} \text{ or } 9.8 \text{ tons per sq ft}$$

This value indicates that the tabular value of 5 tons per sq ft is none too conservative for the 3-ft breadth of footing. In the consideration of a lower limit it would appear from expressions 19·6 and 19·7 that the possibility of ultimate bearing capacities which are as small as $10\gamma b$ should surely be recognized. In submerged soils unit weights of 50 lb per sq ft and less are common. Thus, a small value of ultimate bearing capacity for a 3-ft breadth, but not necessarily the lower limit, is

$$\frac{10 \times 50 \times 3}{2000} = 0.75 \text{ ton per sq ft}$$

It would appear that there are many loose granular soils on which 1 ton per sq ft, which is the smallest tabular value given in the code, is unsafe. In general it may be concluded that the tabular values given above for granular soils are not sufficiently conservative for narrow surface footings.

With respect to depth of footings, item [4] of the code states a small modification which may be recognized, at least, as a modification in the correct direction. As a numerical example, a footing of 8-ft breadth, founded at a depth of 6 ft below ground surface, will be considered. According to the code the tabular value may be increased 6×2.5 or 15 per cent because of the depth. According to equations 19·9 and 19·21 the depth factor, which is conservatively expressed as $1 + (2d/b)$, is equal to 2.5, indicating an allowable increase of 150 per cent because of the depth. The obvious conclusion is that the code allowance for the effect of depth is far too small for small breadths of footings. The code allowance agrees with the depth factor expression much more closely for larger areas, and the two actually are in agreement for a bearing area of 80-ft breadth.

Since the bearing capacity values given in building codes represent extensive experience, it would appear logical to accept them as reasonable for typical footings. An explanation of the apparent inconsistencies pointed out above is that the great majority of footings are founded below ground surface. Thus experience has led to reasonable values for the commonest case, in which there is some depth, but it has not correctly interpreted the degree to which the strength in such a case is caused by the depth. It therefore gives questionable values for small footings under the less common condition of zero depth.‡

The depth factor expression shows that additional bearing capacity is easily obtained in cohesionless soils merely by excavation to a greater depth. This fact should surely be used to full advantage for all footings at which it is important to restrict settlements to small values, even though building codes do not give sufficient recognition to the advantage of depth.

Item [5] is a type of requirement which calls for no detailed comment in this comparison. It is important, of course, that there be no unfavorable changes in the character of the soil during construction, and a reduction in the allowable bearing value must be specified for cases in which such changes occur. No comment is needed relative to the general information given in items [1], [2], and [6].

19·32 Comparison of Theoretical Concepts and Building Code Specifications—Highly Cohesive Soils

The following are excerpts from the Boston code § relative to *cohesive soils:*

[1] . . . *Clay*—A fine-grained, inorganic soil possessing sufficient cohesion when dry to form hard lumps which cannot readily be pulverized by the fingers. *Hard Clay*—A clay requiring picking for removal, a fresh sample of which cannot be molded in the fingers. *Medium Clay*—A clay which can be removed by spading, a fresh sample of which can be molded by a substantial pressure of the fingers. *Soft Clay*—A clay which, when freshly sampled, can be molded under relatively slight pressure of the fingers. *Rock Flour* (*Inorganic Silt*)—A fine-grained, inorganic soil consisting chiefly of grains which will pass a 200-mesh

‡ For a stimulating discussion of factors discussed herein see reference 32. The following statement by A. Casagrande from page 387 of this reference is of particular interest:

"Specifications for the allowable load for sands, as generally given in building codes . . . for narrow, interior wall footings that are founded at the surface or at a shallow depth beneath immediately adjacent ground surface . . . are not sufficiently conservative. . . . [on the other hand the values usually given] are far too conservative for the case of footings founded at considerable depth."

§ See footnote in previous section. The excerpts in this section are from code sections 2904 (*a*), (*b*), (*e*), (*f*), and (*g*) and 1916 (*b*) and (*f*).

sieve, and possessing sufficient cohesion when dry to form lumps which can readily be pulverized with the fingers.

[2]

	[Tabular Values, tons per square foot]
Hard clay	6
Medium clay	4
Soft clay	1
Rock flour, shattered shale, or any deposit of unusual character not provided for herein	Value to be fixed by the commissioner

[3] The tabulated bearing values [for cohesive soils] . . . apply only to pressures directly under individual footings, walls, and piers. When structures are founded on or are underlain by deposits of these classes, the total load over the area of any one bay or other major portion of the structure, minus the weight of excavated material, divided by the area, shall not exceed one-half the tabulated bearing values.

[4] Where the bearing materials directly under a foundation overlie a stratum having smaller allowable bearing values, these smaller values shall not be exceeded at the level of such stratum. Computation of the vertical pressure in the bearing materials at any depth below a foundation shall be made on the assumption that the load is spread uniformly at an angle of 60° with the horizontal; but the area considered as supporting the load shall not extend beyond the intersection of 60° planes of adjacent foundations.

[5] When loading tests are made on [cohesive soils], . . . suitable methods shall be used to prevent evaporation from the materials being tested. [The loading test procedure on clays is the same as specified in the previous section under sands.]

[6] Whenever the proposed foundation rests on or is underlain by [medium or soft clay or rock flour] . . ., the results of loading tests must be interpreted in conjunction with accurate soil profiles showing magnitude and variation of the thickness of these strata. If this information, in the opinion of the commissioner, is not sufficient to determine whether the design load will cause excessive settlement, as might occur due to a thick stratum of clay, or dangerous differential settlement, as might occur when the underlying clay stratum varies considerably in thickness, the commissioner may require an analysis to be made of the probable magnitude, rate and distribution of settlement of the proposed structure. Such analysis may be based upon [A] A study of settlement records of nearby structures having essentially the same foundation conditions. [B] Consolidation tests and other investigations of undisturbed

samples of the compressible materials. . . . if necessary, the allowable loads shall be reduced or special provisions be made in the design of the structure to prevent dangerous differential settlements.

The effect of size of footing is the subject of main interest in this comparison. Item [3] prescribes the limitation of the average net intensity over an entire building or main portion of a building to one-half the tabular value. It is seen that this limitation corresponds to a limited degree to the trend of the lower curve in the range of larger breadths in Fig. 19·15 (*b*), this curve being based on a specified maximum settlement. However, if the condition wanted is the limitation of the settlement of the building to the settlement which an isolated footing would undergo when under the tabular value of bearing intensity, the average net intensity below the building must be limited to the tabular value multiplied by the ratio of the breadths of the individual footing and the building, which usually is much smaller than one-half. Thus item [3] may be criticized for not calling for a sufficient modification to correct adequately for breadth effect. However, it may be noted that the commissioner may require special investigations, as stated in item [6], in cases in which, in his opinion, there is danger of excessive settlement.

No modification for depth of footings is given in the code for clays. This is in reasonable agreement with the conclusion stated for highly cohesive soil in the final paragraph of Section 19·12. However, many soils which possess an appreciable amount of cohesion can support considerably larger net loading intensities when the foundations are at an appreciable distance below ground surface than they can when the foundations are at or near ground surface. For such soils an allowance of greater bearing intensities for deep footings should be included. Its omission is understandable, however, since the proper amount of allowance depends on the relative amount of cohesion, and no methods generally acceptable to building codes have been developed for expressing this item. A method based on equation 19·18 could be considered, but it can be argued that this expression is in too theoretical a form for use in code specifications and also that elaborate experimental justification is needed under field conditions before procedures based on it can be specified in codes.

The case of buried critical strata is covered by item [4], which may be recognized as one of the methods given in Section 19·29 and represented in Figs. 19·16 and 19·17.

No theory is represented by item [5]. It is obvious that clays should be as close to the natural condition as possible in all tests, and disturbance of the clay or drying out due to evaporation must not be permitted previous to testing.

Item [6] presents an important specification which does not appear in many building codes. Since all cases cannot be properly covered by the simplified form in which most building code requirements are stated, it is necessary that there be some provision for requiring adequate studies of all cases in which there is danger of excessive settlement. Chapter 12 of this book covers both the comparisons with settlement conditions of nearby structures and the consolidation analysis, which are specified in item [6] as investigations which may be called for by the commissioner.

19·33 Settlement Behavior of Foundations Consisting of Many Spread Footings

The factors influencing the settlements of a foundation made up of many spread footings are more numerous and are much more complex than those of isolated footings. However, the basic factors entering such cases may be explained in quite simple manner by the simplified building shown in Fig. 19·21. Let it be assumed that the footings are 10 ft square, that they carry 300 tons each, that they rest on the ground surface, and that they are spaced at 20-ft centers, giving a building 190 ft by 190 ft in plan.

Three cases will be discussed, a cohesionless soil being assumed first; later a highly cohesive clay will be assumed and the same three cases will be considered. Case A is shown by the left-hand half of Fig. 19·21. There is no floor slab between the footings, and ledge exists at depth d_a which is a short distance below the bottoms of the pressure bulbs of the individual footings. Case B is shown in the right-hand portion of the figure. A heavy floor slab forms a rigid connection between all footings, and the foundation is assumed to be homogeneous to a depth greater than the height of the pressure bulb of the entire building. Case C is the same as case A down to depth d_a, but it has the deep soil stratum that occurs in case B.

For considerations of these cases, when founded on *cohesionless soil*, it will be assumed that estimates, based on data from loading tests, show that an isolated 10 by 10 footing would settle ½ in. under a loading intensity of 3 tons per sq ft.

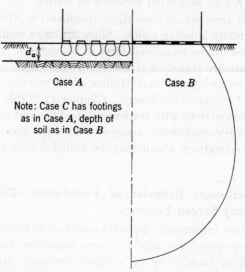

Note: Case *C* has footings
as in Case *A*, depth of
soil as in Case *B*

Fig. 19·21 Cases considered in analyses of multiple footings.

In case A it is possible that the footings are close enough together to cause each footing to interfere slightly with the settlement of all adjacent footings. Thus the lateral movement shown in Fig. 19·4 may be somewhat smaller for each footing of the group than it would be for an isolated footing. However, the footings are far enough apart to allow the deductions that this group action probably is of minor importance in this instance, and that the settlement of each footing of the group should be nearly as large as the ½-in. value occurring for the isolated footing. The ground surface between each footing would not settle this amount; it would settle much less or it might even heave a small amount.

The degree to which the settlement of a footing is affected by the presence of adjacent loaded footings is hard to express exactly, but it is not hard to state in general terms. The closer the spacing of the footings, the greater the effect. If the footings are connected by a floor slab, the effect is much greater, and especially if the floor has appreciable rigidity and is bonded to the footings. One extreme case is that of no interference, where no connection exists to cause stress on the soil between the footings, and where the footings are so widely spaced that the zones subject to stress or strain do not overlap appreciably; this condition may require a somewhat greater spacing than that of this example. At the other extreme is the case in which footings do not act individually but are virtually united by very close spacing or, as in case B, by a rigid slab which causes the ground surface at and between footings to settle the same amount.

In case B, on cohesionless soil, the entire foundation acts as a unit 190 ft square with an average intensity of loading of $(100 \times 300)/(190)^2$ or 0.83 tons per sq ft. On the basis of a coefficient of settlement which is independent of size, as shown in Fig. 19·9 (b), the average settlement is $\frac{1}{2} \times 0.83/3$ or 0.14 in. In accordance with Fig. 19·18 (a) the settlement will be larger at the edges than at the center unless the building as a whole is of very rigid construction. However, the average settlement for case B is much less than the settlement in case A, and it may be concluded that for cohesionless soils case B is by far the more favorable of the two cases.

The behavior in case C may be determined by a comparison of the stress conditions in case C with the stress conditions of the other two cases. In Section 11·4 and Table 11·1, it has been shown that the stresses, which are caused at relatively large depths below a given surface load, are essentially the same whether the given load is a point load or is distributed over a small area. Similar considerations may be used to show that the stresses in the lower half of the large pressure bulbs of cases B and C are essentially alike and that the stresses at any point below depth d_a will not be greatly different for these two cases. Therefore, it may be considered that below depth d_a the action within the pressure bulbs is approximately the same for cases B and C. Within the zone above depth d_a the stresses in case A are somewhat affected by the presence of the rigid ledge surface,‖ but the action in this zone is approximately the same in cases A and C. Thus the settlement for case C will be approximately equal to the sum of the settlement for case A, and the settlement due to strains at depths greater than depth d_a in case B. Settlements are small in case B; therefore considerations of the large pressure bulb are of minor importance as compared to considerations of the small pressure bulbs in cohesionless soils. Consequently, it may be concluded that the settlement for case C is virtually the same as for case A. The greater settlement occurring near the edges in case B does not occur in case C because this settlement was caused mainly by strains near ground surface.

These same three cases will next be considered for *highly cohesive* soils which obey the idealized law that the coefficient of settlement is inversely proportional to the breadth of the loaded area, as shown in Fig. 19·9 (a). It will be assumed that estimates based on data from loading tests indicate that an isolated 10 by 10 footing on the highly cohesive soil settles ½ in. under a pressure of 3 tons per sq ft.

For case A on highly cohesive soil, as on cohesionless soil, the footings act virtually as isolated footings, and a settlement of nearly ½ in. is to be expected at each footing.

For case B on highly cohesive soil the average loading intensity is 0.83 ton per sq ft, as on cohesionless soil, but the settlement varies directly as the breadth and, therefore, it is approximately equal to

$$\frac{1}{2} \times \frac{0.83}{3} \times \frac{190}{10} = 2.5 \text{ in.}$$

As indicated by Fig. 19·19 (a), the settlement will be larger below the center of the building than at the outside, unless the building is of very rigid construction, in which case the pressure distribution will resemble that shown in Fig. 19·19 (c). How-

‖ The effect of rigid boundary surfaces of this type and of flexible boundary surfaces have been investigated for elastic masses. For information on the stresses occurring in such cases see, for example, references 13, 84, and 111.

ever, the point of major interest is that a much greater settlement occurs in case B than in case A in highly cohesive soils.

For case C on highly cohesive soil, as on cohesionless soil, the settlement is slightly less than the sum of the settlements for cases A and B. Case A has settlements of minor importance on highly cohesive soil; thus considerations of the large bulb in case C are of much more importance than considerations of the small bulbs, and the difference between the settlements of cases B and C is small.

Detailed considerations of intermediate cases and more complex cases cannot be attempted herein because of space limitations. However, soils in general fall between the extremes of cohesionless soil and highly cohesive soil. Moreover, the range of the conditions possible in the general run of buildings may be considered to be represented roughly by the extreme examples given by cases B and C.

In connection with such studies it should be noted that the settlement patterns and the stress distribution patterns below rigid footings, which have been presented in Section 19·29 and shown in Figs. 19·18 and 19·19 and which apply to case B, are also indicative to a smaller degree of trends that occur in any intermediate case having a limited degree of rigidity of framework or continuity of footings.

19·34 Balanced Design

Footing loads are not so definite and not so constant as might be inferred from discussions based on the simplified conditions of previous sections. One reason for this situation is that a large portion of the live load acts only a small percentage of the time. Therefore, the average footing loads with respect to time are often much smaller than the maximum, or design values, of footing loads, and settlements in some soils may depend much more on average than on maximum loads. Moreover, the ratio between the time-average values and the maximum values tends to be considerably different for exterior footings and interior footings.

Balanced design is a procedure which recognizes these conditions and attempts to correct for the differential settlements that they tend to cause. Its basic principle is the proportioning

of footing areas according to the time-average loads, called
balanced loads, rather than according to the maximum loads.
The balanced load on each of the various columns of a building
is taken as the dead load plus some given percentage of the
maximum live load; the percentage chosen depends considerably
on the type of occupancy of the building and, presumably, it
represents a conservatively chosen value of the ratio between
the time-average live load and the maximum live load.

The balanced loading principle is logical for cases in which a
large portion of the settlements is the result of consolidation
which takes place slowly. However, in the form commonly used,
balanced design is based on the assumption that a constant *balanced intensity* will lead to equal settlement at all footings, regardless of the breadth of the footings, the type of soil, and other
factors. Therefore, the balanced design procedure which is
usually followed is not rational in certain cases because it does
not recognize fundamental relationships which have been explained in foregoing sections. A discussion of such cases will
be given after a brief explanation of the procedure.

Each footing must of course be safe when subjected to the
maximum live load. The balanced design procedure which is
usually followed consists in first designing the column having
the largest ratio of live to dead load, usually an interior column,
by making its bearing area equal to the quotient of the maximum total load and the allowable bearing capacity. The balanced intensity q_b, which is to be used for any given case, may
next be determined; it is the intensity this footing carries when
under the balanced load, assumed in this example to equal the
dead load plus 40 per cent of the live load. The bearing areas
of all other footings may now be chosen, since they are to be
taken as equal to the balanced load divided by the balanced
intensity. A check will show that all footings except that first
designed automatically carry somewhat less than their allowable
bearing capacity when under maximum load. Figure 19·22 presents a simple example of this procedure. The example shows
that balanced design tends to give larger footing areas below
exterior columns than would otherwise be used. The main result of balanced design is, therefore, that it introduces smaller
settlements than would otherwise occur at exterior footings.

Allowable bearing capacity, $q_a = $ 2.5 tons per sq ft. Loads given in columns 2 and 3 of table below.

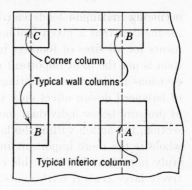

Col-umn	Loads, tons				Area, A sq ft	Balanced Loading, q_b tons per sq ft	A sq ft	Max q, tons per sq ft
	Dead Q_D	Live Q_L	$Q_D + Q_L$	$Q_D + 0.4Q_L$	$\dfrac{Q_D + Q_L}{q_a}$	$\dfrac{Q_D + 0.4Q_L}{A}$	$\dfrac{Q_D + 0.4Q_L}{q_b}$	$\dfrac{Q_D + Q_L}{A}$
A	120	128	248	171	99 [1]	1.73 [1]	99	2.50
B	90	65	155	116			67	2.32
C	80	32	112	93			54	2.08

[1] Determination based on column having largest Q_L/Q_D value.

FIG. 19·22 Portion of the plan of the simple building used in the example of the conventional, balanced design procedure.

For buildings on cohesionless soil with any degree of continuity between footings any procedure that gives a trend toward smaller exterior settlements is desirable, because such a trend counteracts the tendency toward larger settlement at exterior columns, which occurs somewhat as in Fig. 19·18 (a) for the idealized case. However, the logic of classifying the procedure giving this trend as balanced design is open to question in this case, because practically all the settlement which the maximum load can cause will occur in a cohesionless soil on the first occasion of maximum loading and, therefore, the use of balanced loadings has no justification.

For buildings on highly cohesive soils the usual form of balanced design can be severely questioned. Designs based on time-average values of loads rather than on the infrequently occurring maximum loads can be accepted as reasonable. The assumption that a given loading intensity leads to equal settlements for all sizes of footings is far from sound. However, this item is not the most important one in this situation, because the revisions in the sizes of footings that are introduced by the use of balanced design affect only the action within the small bulbs of pressure below individual footings. As shown in the previous section, the action within the large bulb below the building as a whole is the more important in highly cohesive soil. Thus the truly important factor in this case is the tendency toward relatively large central settlements, as illustrated in Fig. 19·19 (a). The trend toward smaller exterior settlements, which is given by the use of balanced design, has only a minor effect in cohesive soil, but what effect it does have is in the wrong direction, since it tends to increase the differential settlements. Thus balanced design works against its purpose in this case. Methods that may be considered if differential settlements must be avoided are discussed in the next section.

When there is ledge or other highly incompressible material at a relatively shallow depth, as illustrated by case A of Fig. 19·21, an entirely different case exists. There is no large bulb in such a case and, therefore, the settlement that occurs depends on the action of the small bulbs. According to equation 19·19 isolated footings of various sizes on highly cohesive soil settle the same amount if

$$q \sim \frac{1}{b}$$

If all footings are square or if all footings are round the expression for q in terms of the total load Q is

$$q \sim \frac{Q}{b^2}$$

When equal values of q are to be used for all footings, the latter of the above expressions becomes the familiar relationship

$$b^2 \sim Q$$

but when the relationship expressed by the first of the above expressions is to be used, the right-hand sides of the first two expressions are proportional, whence

$$b \sim Q \qquad (19 \cdot 30)$$

Expression $19 \cdot 30$ indicates that the settlements will be constant if the breadths of footings are made proportional to the loads on the footings. Time-average loads are perhaps the most reasonable loads to use in this connection.

A rational, balanced design procedure for this special case, based on the relationship given above, may be carried out as follows. The footing which is to be designed first is the one with the smallest value for the expression Q_b^2/Q_t, wherein Q_b and Q_t are the balanced and the maximum loads, respectively. The area of this footing is the quotient of the maximum load and the allowable bearing capacity. After the breadth of this footing is known, the constant of proportionality between the balanced load and the breadth may be determined. The breadths of the other footings may then be easily obtained.

This special case applies only to highly cohesive soils, and to instances in which the individual bulbs act independently and there is no large bulb below the entire structure. Two situations in which such conditions prevail may be mentioned. They are the case of shallow depth, mentioned in the previous paragraph, and the case of zero net load ¶ wherein the weight of excavation equals the weight of the structure. In this latter case there is no pressure bulb below the building as a whole because of the zero net loading, but there are appreciable net loadings on the individual footings since the building load is concentrated on the footing areas.

19·35 Types of Foundations for Difficult Sites

This chapter has dealt largely with considerations of common types of foundations. As a final subject a number of special types of foundations will be touched on briefly. It often happens that in large, expensive, and important structures it is essential that differential settlements be prohibited or, at least, that they be limited to relatively small values. In such cases the cost of

¶ An example of this case is given in reference **135**.

the structure usually is so great that large sums are available, if needed, for satisfactory foundations. When the underground conditions at the site are difficult, as in the relatively common case in which deep compressible strata are present, large sums may be necessary. The following is a list of foundation types which can be considered in such cases, with comments on the applicability and the limitations of each type.

1. *Long piles or caissons* may be used to transmit the load to a good bearing stratum. This procedure avoids completely the difficulties introduced by the compressible layer and, if the cost is not excessive, it is likely to be the best solution. However, when compressible strata of great thickness occur, the cost may be prohibitive.

2. *Rigid construction in the basement* and the lower stories may be used to prevent differential settlements. This is another solution that often is satisfactory if the high cost can be justified. An example is the Albany Telephone Building in which the basement and lower two stories were built as a rigid truss of the Vierendel type. When there is horizontal variation in the thickness or in the compressibility of the buried stratum, a rigid building may tip, but the plane of the foundations remains free of dishing. It should be noted that the structural units which are in contact with the soil in this type of construction must be designed for a stress distribution resembling either Fig. 19·18 (*c*) or Fig. 19·19 (*c*).

3. *Jacking units* or facilities for jacking may be built into each individual footing in order that differential settlements may be eliminated as they occur. This method may also be expensive and, moreover, it requires checkups on the settlements at frequent intervals when the structure is new. In the past it has been used mainly for rambling structures which cover large areas, the Yankee Stadium in New York City being an example, but it also may be considered for other types of structures. Attempts to remedy large differential settlements in either old or new buildings by improvised jacking methods are frequently the cause of numerous cracks in the walls and other damage, and for this reason such procedures are not always desirable. However, jacking usually may be expected to furnish a successful solution of the settlement problem, if adequate facilities are incorporated

in the design and if the adjustments are carefully controlled and are made in sufficiently small amounts.

4. *Preloading the site* is a procedure that may be considered for cases in which the settlements occur quite rapidly. By piling construction materials or any other available load on the site and allowing it to stand until the compressible stratum is consolidated to pressures that approach the magnitude of those which the final structure will impose, most of the inherent settlement is caused before construction. It is reported that this method has been used in Holland. In the United States it has had little use, largely because any construction procedures which involve long delays do not tend to be popular in this country.

When a period of half a year or more is available for preloading a foundation that will compress rapidly, this method may be considered, and it may be the cheapest method for accomplishing the desired results. Conceivably, drainage wells * could be considered as a means of speeding up the settlement in impervious soils, but if such a procedure is used the method is no longer an inexpensive one.

5. *The net load may be reduced by increasing the depth of excavation.* As an example, it may be noted that when the depth of excavation is increased 10 ft the net loading intensity is reduced by roughly ½ ton per sq ft, and a sub-basement is obtained. Considerably smaller settlements may occur with this amount of load reduction, and sometimes the sub-basement may have value which balances the cost of the extra excavation. When the excavation extends to below the water table, the handling of the water may lead to a considerable added expense, but this may partially be balanced by the greater reduction in net load which is furnished by buoyancy. It should be noted that the advantage of this procedure may be lost if the soil is disturbed by the excavation. Moreover, when there is a critical layer some distance below the foundation, the lowering of the plane of loading brings the load closer to the critical layer, and a part of the advantage disappears. In general this procedure is only a partial solution, because even with zero net loads some settlements must be expected.† The advantages it gives will

---

* The use of drainage wells is explained in references 101 and 158.

† Explained in more detail in references 32 and 135.

vary in large degree with the conditions of each case, but in many instances it will greatly relieve differential settlements at relatively small expense.

6. *The types of construction that are best adapted to with-standing differential settlements may be used.* Brick bearing walls can undergo relatively large differential settlements without showing distress. Even concrete construction can stand quite large differential settlements if they occur slowly so that there can be some degree of adjustment to them by slow plastic flow in the concrete. In some cases differential settlements of many inches are allowable if they occur slowly. However, in such cases high maintenance costs must be expected in the repairing of wall cracks, in repairs where service pipes enter the buildings, and so on.

7. *Revisions in design to give more favorable stress distributions* may be considered. The form of stress distribution on compressible soil which gives uniform settlement is shown by Fig. 19·19 (c). There may be occasions on which the building framing systems can be revised to cause a relatively large portion of the load to be carried by outer columns or by exterior bearing walls and thus to give pressures more closely resembling the distribution in this figure. For example, there are occasions on which heavy central towers can be avoided, and on which storage rooms with large loads can be placed near the end walls rather than near the center of the building. Although they offer only a partial solution, such revisions may sometimes cause a considerable relief of differential settlements.

PROBLEMS

1. Obtain simple equations for the ultimate bearing capacity of long footings resting on the surface of cohesionless soil with a friction angle of 33 degrees, using general expressions given by (a) Prandtl and (b) Terzaghi.

2. Unconfined compression tests on test pit samples of blue clay and yellow clay from a certain project near Boston show average values of compressive strengths as follows: "stiff yellow clay" (of consistency requiring 12 blows to drive typical dry-sample spoon 1 ft), 3.7 tons per sq ft; "soft blue clay" (3 blows), 0.8 ton per sq ft; remolded, soft blue clay, 0.1 ton per sq ft. Determine tabular values for these clays. Compare results with values from the Boston code.

3. Compare the action of loaded areas on highly cohesive and cohesionless soil, with particular reference to:

(*a*) Effect of size of area on ultimate load intensity.

(*b*) Effect of size of area on settlement under a given unit load well below the ultimate.

(*c*) Effect of depth of loaded area below surface on settlement.

4. In each of the following cases let q_1 designate the intensity of pressure that causes a 5 by 5 ft footing to undergo a settlement ρ_1 and assume that $4q_1$ is the ultimate bearing capacity. For each case give an estimate of the load causing a settlement of ρ_1 and the load causing failure. All estimates are to be expressed as multiples of q_1.

(*a*) Assume the soil is cohesionless, and assume

    (1) A 20 by 10 ft surface footing.

    (2) A 1 by 1 ft surface footing.

    (3) A 10 by 8 ft footing 3 ft below ground surface.

(*b*) Assume the soil to be highly cohesive and give estimated values for the same dimensions of footings as listed in (*a*).

5. Several loading tests on 3-ft square areas and 6-ft square areas on the surface of a given soil deposit furnish average determinations of coefficient of settlement of 1.8 and 1.3 tons per sq ft per in., respectively, for the two sizes. On the basis of these results obtain an expression for coefficient of settlement in terms of breadth and depth factor for this soil.

6. Additional loading tests on square areas of other sizes have been obtained on the soil represented in Prob. 5. For breadths of 2, 4, and 8 ft, average values of coefficient of settlement are 2.4, 1.7, and 1.0 ton per sq ft per in., respectively. Present all data on a plot in which the coordinates are the coefficient of settlement and the reciprocal of the breadth. Sketch the straight line best fitting the data, and by rational interpretation of the plot obtain an expression in the form called for in Prob. 5.

7. A building is 80 ft by 60 ft in plan, and it will be located at a site where an 8-ft depth of dry soil overlies the soil represented by Prob. 5. The water table is at an 8-ft depth. The dry soil has a weight of 100 lb per cu ft, and the soil below has a buoyant weight of 65 lb per cu ft. The building will have a gross weight of 10,000 tons, and it will be founded at a depth of 15 ft. Estimate the settlement of the building.

8. Two loading tests have been run on the surface of a deep stratum of relatively homogeneous soil predominantly granular but containing a small proportion of clay sizes. The first test on a 2-ft by 2-ft area shows a settlement of ¼ in. under a loading intensity of 2 tons per sq ft; the second test on a 4-ft by 4-ft area shows a settlement of ⅜ in. at 2 tons per sq ft. Make a rough estimate of the settlement of an 80-ft by 60-ft building with a rigid floor slab and with a total net load of 7200 tons, founded 10 ft below the surface of this stratum.

9. It is proposed to support a building on Gow caissons carried through a 16-ft layer of organic silt to the top of a deep deposit of sand. The silt and sand weigh respectively 90 and 110 lb per cu ft, and the water table is well below the surface of the sand. Loading tests on plates 2 ft in diameter on the sand surface at the bottom of test pits 10 ft square carried through the silt show an average settlement of ½ in. under a pressure of 2 tons per sq ft. Estimate the base diameter needed for a caisson carrying a column load of 220 tons if the allowable settlement is ¼ in.

10. A building, 60 by 40 ft, gives a net loading at the ground surface of 1 ton per sq ft. Show the distribution of pressure on the top of a clay layer 20 ft below the surface, under the long center line of the building, according to

(a) The Westergaard equations.
(b) The Kögler method.
(c) The Boston code method.

11. At a certain site a buried sand layer of variable thickness overlies soft blue clay. An intensity of 5 tons per sq ft is reasonable on the sand, and generally 1 ton per sq ft may be allowed on the soft clay. According to the criterion of spread at 30 degrees to the vertical, what thickness of sand is necessary before the permissible loading on a 12-ft diameter area at the surface of the sand is not limited by the presence of the underlying clay?

12. Sketch and explain the distributions of pressure occurring below rigid, square surface footings on (a) cohesionless soils and (b) highly cohesive soils. Comment on any differences between these distributions and those commonly assumed for design purposes, and state an opinion on how such differences should be given consideration.

13. The lower stories of a building underlain by a deep deposit of clay are to be designed as a rigid truss to insure uniform settlement. It is proposed to compute the stresses in the truss members on the basis of a uniformly distributed soil reaction. Criticize this procedure.

14. Compare the foundation requirements of some other building code with those of the Boston Building Code and with the theoretical concepts that have been presented. For this comparison the best choice is a code that is of particular interest to the individual making the comparison, but any code that is available may be used.

15. A 35-ft by 35-ft building on a homogeneous sand deposit has 4 rows of columns in each direction at 10-ft spacing, and 5 by 5 footings may be assumed throughout. The basement excavation is to 10 ft below ground, and footings bear at an elevation 12 ft below ground. The net load of the structure is 1200 tons. Loading tests on a 2-ft by 2-ft area at ground surface show a ½-in. settlement at 1 ton per sq ft, and a large loading test on an 8-ft by 8-ft area shows a ¾-in. settlement at 1 ton per sq ft. Make rough estimates of the building settlements for two extreme cases, (a) assuming a rigid mat foundation, and (b) assuming individual footings that act independently with every footing carrying the same load.

16. A building is founded on many spread footings, and the live loads and dead loads may be assumed to be respectively as follows: on interior columns, 105 and 115 tons; on side wall columns, 80 and 55 tons; on corner columns, 70 and 25 tons. The allowable bearing capacity of the soil is given as 2 tons per sq ft. Determine the required sizes of footings (*a*) based on bearing capacity considerations only, and (*b*) by balanced design based on dead load plus 50 per cent of live load.

17. Discuss the logic of the use of balanced design for a case such as that covered by Prob. 16 for all significant combinations of the following conditions: cohesionless soils as compared to highly cohesive soils; complete continuity and rigidity of the floor slab between the columns as compared to practically no continuity; cases in which the large bulb must be considered as compared to cases in which the large bulb may be ignored.

18. A large and relatively heavy building is to be erected on a site underlain by a thick stratum of compressible clay. It is essential that differential settlements be kept to a minimum. Describe briefly six possible types of construction that might be considered, giving comments on conditions for which each type is most advantageous.

Chapter 20

ACTION OF PILES

PILE FOUNDATIONS

20·1 Introduction

Piles and pile foundations have been in common use since prehistoric times. Until some time in the nineteenth century, wood piles were the only common type; since then steel, concrete, and composite piles of many kinds have come into wide use.

The commonest function of piles is to carry load which cannot be adequately supported at a certain level to a depth at which adequate support is available. When a pile passes through poor material and its tip penetrates a small distance into a stratum of good bearing capacity, it is called a *bearing pile*. The poor grade of material which is penetrated may vary all the way from water, as in wharf piles, to materials that would ordinarily serve to support surface footings but cannot be used when there are severe settlement restrictions. When piles extend a portion of the way through deep strata of limited supporting ability and develop their carrying capacity by friction on the sides of the pile, they are called *friction piles*. There also are many cases in which the load-carrying capacity of piles results from a combination of point resistance and skin friction.

Another important use of piles is to furnish lateral support to earth embankments. Sheet piles are commonly used for this purpose, as explained in Section 17·14 and illustrated in Fig. 17·23. This figure also shows a pile anchorage which is designed to carry a horizontal load; in addition the vertical pile in this anchorage is an illustration of an uplift pile, that is, a pile which resists uplift by skin friction. Batter piles are used in many structures to aid in resisting horizontal loads, typical types of installation being indicated by Figs. 17·23 and 17·28. Short piles are sometimes driven into loose sand deposits for the purpose of compacting the soil. When there is danger that the soil below or near a given structure may be carried away by erosion, it may be necessary, regardless of the bearing characteristics of the soil, to support the structure on piles which extend below all possible erosion. There are other uses of piles which do not fall under the heading of foundations; for example, piles are much used as fenders in wharf structures.

20·2 Requirements of Piles

For the satisfactory action of a pile foundation a number of distinct requirements exist. The pile must be able, as a column, to carry the load imposed on it. There must be sufficient area of contact between the pile and the soil so that the pile load can be transferred to the surrounding soil by bearing at the point or by skin friction at the sides or by a combination of bearing and skin friction. The soil characteristics must be such that the soil below and at the sides of the pile is able to carry the load transferred to it by all piles of the foundation without failure and without excessive settlements.

Many foundation engineers look upon piles mainly as structural members which must be chosen for best economy and which must be strong enough as columns to carry their load. According to this viewpoint, piles are similar to spread footings and may be viewed more as a part of the structure than as a part of the foundation.

The soil engineer is more interested in the requirements which refer to the soil and its characteristics. The requirement of sufficient contact area with the soil is an important one and is the one which is investigated when a loading test is run on a single pile. The final requirement—that the soil must be capable of resisting all stresses reaching it—is perhaps the most important and is one which has sometimes been overlooked. This chapter deals mainly with these two requirements.

A pile must of course have sufficient column strength, but investigation of this item requires no complicated considerations. An important requirement in this respect is safety against buckling. If a pile extends above ground for a considerable distance, in air or in water, a careful investigation relative to danger of buckling is necessary but does not differ from similar investigations for columns in general.

If a considerable length of pile is imbedded in a poor grade of soil which is very weak in resistance to shear and compression, the question whether or not there is danger of buckling often arises. In a study of this subject A. E. Cummings (43) compared lateral pressures required to prevent buckling with the passive lateral pressures available in low grade soils, and his findings indicate that even very soft soils are able to provide lateral pressures which are sufficient to prevent buckling under the axial loads ordinarily used on foundation piles.

20·3 Types of Piles and Pile Hammers

Numerous textbooks * on foundation types devote a large portion of their space to descriptions of piles and pile hammers. There is also a wealth of valuable information in the pamphlets and catalogues of manufacturers of piles and pile equipment. Any engineer specializing in pile foundations should have a detailed familiarity with this literature. Since a textbook of fundamentals obviously cannot cover such subjects, this section gives, therefore, only a brief outline of this material.

Wood piles are the commonest type, the easiest to handle, and the type that stands hard handling best. In a large percentage of cases they are the cheapest type. To be permanent they must be cut off below permanent groundwater. This is not difficult but it becomes a considerable expense when it entails much extra excavation, sheeting, and pumping. When the piles must extend above groundwater their life can be greatly lengthened by creosoting or other treatment, but this increased cost, together with the lack of permanence, may make other types of piles cheaper in the long run. Treatment is also necessary in wharves where the piles are subject to the ravages of marine borers. The lengths most commonly used are market lengths ranging generally from 20 to 40 or 50 ft, the upper limit being the length of a freight car. However, there are numerous individual cases of uses of piles

---

* For example, references 3, 8, 73, 81, 36, and 47; there are also a number of German textbooks on foundation engineering that contain considerable amounts of descriptive material of this type; for example, references 1, 17, 57, and 128.

over 100 ft long. Many types of wood are used for piles, the commonest types differing considerably in different parts of the country. Wood piles are stronger if cut in winter when the sap is down. The range of loads commonly used on wood piles is from about 10 to 25 tons per pile.

Concrete piles are of two main types, *precast* and *cast-in-place*. Precast piles are of various shapes of cross section, either with or without taper. They are formed, poured, and cured before being driven or jetted into place. Reinforcing steel is required, the amount usually being determined by stresses occurring during handling and varying from 1 to 3 per cent. The reinforcement is often fabricated as a unit. Precast piles excel in marine installations where the pile is placed in open water. They also are especially adaptable to cases in which the pile extends above ground with its upper portion serving as a column, such as in trestles. Generally precast piles are specially designed for each job, often with unfavorable requirements of space for casting and time for curing, but with the advantage of getting exactly the dimensions desired. There are no general requirements for cutoff, but when a pile has to be cut the cutting is difficult. Dense concrete and often surface protection against the action of sea water on the reinforcing are necessary. Precast concrete piles have been used with diameters as large as 30 in. and lengths of over 100 ft, with loads per pile of over 100 tons. The common range of allowable load is from 20 to 75 tons per pile. Jetting is commonly used in connection with the driving of precast piles, a hole through the center of the pile often being left for this purpose. Such piles generally can be driven without difficulty through materials in which there would be danger of overdriving if wood piles were used.

Cast-in-place piles are used more commonly than precast piles in building foundations. Not being subjected to stresses before and during placing, they frequently are not reinforced. These piles are of two types. If a steel shell is left in the ground a *cased pile* results; and if the steel shell which is driven to receive the concrete is removed an *uncased* or *shell-less pile* results. The main advantage of the uncased pile is that it is less costly than any other type of concrete pile. An important disadvantage is the danger of decreased strength due to mixing of mud and water with the concrete or to effects of forces on the pile due to driving adjacent piles. This danger is greatest in soils in which there are alternate hard and soft strata. To reduce the danger from disturbance during the driving of adjacent piles, specifications commonly state that all shells within 5 ft of any shell-less pile must be driven before the concrete of that pile is placed and that there is to be no driving within a much larger distance for several days after the concrete is placed. A far from insignificant disadvantage is that shell-less piles may be sufficiently strong in the great majority of cases, but in the infrequent case in which they are damaged the presence of the resultant danger may be entirely unknown. Since cast-in-place piles are commonly known by trade names these names are mentioned in connection with the brief descriptions below. *Raymond piles,* a widely used type of cased pile, have a light tapering steel shell which is driven by the aid of a collapsible mandrel or core which fits within the shell. Since the shell is in contact with the soil during driving and thereafter, the skin friction developed acts as load-carrying capacity. In the *MacArthur encased pile* a heavier casing is driven with the aid of a core and with a pan at the bottom to prevent the entrance of soil; after the core is removed a light permanent corrugated casing is lowered; after concreting the driving casing is pulled. This type of pile is low in skin friction and therefore is more adaptable to bearing piles than to friction piles. The *monotube pile* has a fluted shell available both with and without taper and heavy enough to stand direct driving. It is concreted and left in the ground, forming a strong but relatively expensive pile. *Pipe piles* ranging roughly from 10 to 22 in. in diameter may be either closed-ended or open-ended; if the latter, soil may be jetted or blown out from within the pipe after driving. After concreting, the strength of the pipe is a major portion of the total strength. The cost of pipe piles is high, but when used for bearing piles and carried to sound ledge they can carry large loads. Opportunity for inspection before concreting is an advantage of all cased piles.

In shell-less piles a casing which in most cases is of constant diameter and is relatively heavy is driven with the aid of a core and pulled during or after concreting. An example of this type is the *Simplex pile,* which uses a shoe that prevents soil from entering the casing, this shoe being left in the ground. In the *MacArthur pedestal pile* the core prevents the entrance of soil. After the core is withdrawn, a 6-ft depth of concrete is placed, the shell is withdrawn about 3 ft, the core is again inserted, and the concrete is forced out to form a pedestal. The concrete in the rest of the height of the pile is tamped, after the casing is pulled, to give a pile fully as large as the outside diameter of the casing. The *Franki pile* is driven by placing a charge of concrete in the shell just before the start of driving, and by tamping on the concrete the shell is forced into the ground. A pedestal is formed on this type of pile as explained above. The concrete then is placed in small amounts and each lift is tamped to give a horizontal bulge or corrugation in the pile.

Composite piles of numerous types are used. The *Raymond composite pile* consists of a wood pile cut at the top for 18 in. to about an 8-in. diameter to produce a *tenon*. The wood pile is driven and then a tapered corrugated shell is placed over the tenon and driven. The wooden section does not extend above the groundwater table and the upper section is cased concrete. This type of pile has the advantage of wood piles without the cutoff requirement.

Steel piles, of 8 to 14 in. rolled H-sections, have proved successful in certain types of pile installations. Examples are cases in which the piles are to extend above ground as a column, or where the piles must be subjected to hard driving. A small volume of soil is displaced, and bearing piles of this type may be driven at relatively close spacing. The steel is subject to corrosion and protection is sometimes used; however, experience has shown that corrosion is not usually a serious problem in such piles. Where the compressive strength of the pile is the limiting factor, stresses of 8000 to 10,000 lb per sq in. are generally allowed. These piles require heavy hammers for driving, and steam hammers delivering 7 to 15 foot-kips of energy per blow are commonly used.

Sheet piles may be of wood, steel, or precast concrete. *Wakefield triple-lap timber sheet piling* was once extensively used and still is used. *Interlocking steel sheet piling* walls are now widely used in a number of types of sections and weights. Steam hammers are usually used for driving, and steel sheet piles may be pulled by inverted steam hammers or by special extractors.

This type of sheet piling is not especially watertight, but there are methods of increasing the watertightness. Cellular dams of steel sheet piles are used as cofferdams, as described in Section 18·11, and they also are used as permanent structures. Other common, permanent installations which use sheet piles are docks, cutoff walls, and retaining walls of the type explained in Section 17·13.

A number of types of small caissons are used for fields of work overlapping those served by the heavier and more expensive types of piles. The distinction between caissons and piles is that the soil is removed from caissons and displaced laterally for piles; strictly speaking, the open-ended pipe pile is, therefore, a caisson. The *Gow caisson*, often called the *Gow pile*, is widely used in Boston where the conditions, as explained in Section 19·24, are especially favorable to its use. Casings large enough for men to work within them are used in convenient lengths, each successive length being slightly smaller in diameter so that it can be dropped through the one above. Excavation proceeds within the casings until good bearing is approached. The last few feet of excavation is carried down without casing, and a bell is formed to give a bearing area that is much larger than the shaft area. The casing is pulled as concrete is placed. The *Chicago caisson* or *Chicago well* is excavated in about 6-ft lifts without sheeting; then vertical sheeting is placed and held by hoops or frames.

Pile drivers are of numerous types, and *pile hammers* are classified as *drop hammers, single-acting steam hammers,* and *double-acting steam hammers*. Drop hammers are satisfactory for light work and are often preferable for water work where a light weight of equipment is important, but otherwise steam hammers are more commonly used nowadays. Drop hammers of 500 lb are sometimes used, but common weights range from 2000 to 4000 lb. Specifications of the A.R.E.A. require a 3000-lb hammer for wood piles and a height of drop of not over 20 ft. Heights of drop are commonly between 10 and 15 ft, the range of desirable magnitudes of energy being from 30,000 to 50,000 ft-lb per blow.

Steam hammers are called single-acting when steam pressure is used to raise the hammer, whereas the drop is caused by gravity. In double-acting hammers steam acts to aid gravity during the drop. Most steam hammers can be run by compressed air also. Single-acting hammers give 50 to 60 blows per minute. Double-acting hammers are lighter and more compact, and they operate at greater rapidity with about twice as many blows per minute. Driving with steam hammers involves a greater first cost than driving with drop hammers but the total cost may be much less. Included in the many advantages claimed for steam hammers over drop hammers are: better alignment control; less punishment to piles, less wear on the driver, and less damage nearby; equally effective driving at all heights and better adaptability to driving at low elevations, below water, and in other inaccessible locations; keeping of the pile in motion with roughly three times as fast progress.

For driving precast concrete piles, steam hammers are usually used. If drop hammers are used, the hammer should be at least as heavy as the pile, and the drop should not be more than 8 ft. The A.R.E.A. specifications call for a steam hammer with striking parts weighing at least 2500 lb. Another desirable specification requires the use of a hammer which gives in each blow about 3750 ft-lb per cu yd of concrete in the pile.

A large part of the weight of steam hammers is in the frame, with the driving parts representing usually one half or less of the weight. The heaviest hammers weigh as much as 20 tons, with 10 tons of striking parts and energies per blow of over 25 ft-tons.

Jetting often aids greatly in getting piles to the desired final grade, and for bearing piles there can be little objection to its use as long as driving is continued until satisfactory resistance is obtained after the jet is turned off. In connection with the driving of friction piles jetting may cause sufficient disturbance to some types of soil to make its use objectionable in some cases.

The choice of the best type of pile and the best type of hammer to be used for a given project depends on many factors, a thorough discussion of which is beyond the scope of this book. For such a choice full information is required regarding the subsoil conditions, the characteristics of the soil involved, the observed action of adjacent structures, the type of structure to be built, and the allowable settlement. Also of much importance in the making of such a choice is an understanding of soil action in relation to pile driving, which is the main subject of the following sections.

20·4 Dynamic and Static Resistances

When a pile is being driven the resistance to penetration is a dynamic resistance. When a pile, as a unit in a pile foundation, is loaded by a building, the resistance to penetration is a static resistance.

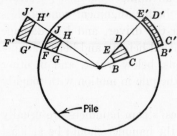

FIG. 20·1 The displacement and distortion of soil caused by a pile during driving.

Both the dynamic resistance and the static resistance are composed in general of point resistance and skin friction. However, in some soils the magnitudes of the dynamic and static resistances may be very different. In spite of this difference frequent use is made of estimates of dynamic resistance, given by dynamic pile formulas, for indications of the static load the pile is capable of carrying. Before the logic of this precedure can be justified or disproved an understanding is needed of soil action during both dynamic and static loading and of the basis of dynamic pile formulas.

20·5 Action in Clays under Various Types of Pile Loadings

The essential difference between the actions of piles under dynamic and static loadings rests in the inherent time effects of the soil penetrated. Clays show pronounced time effects. Therefore they show the greatest difference between dynamic and static action.

Consider piles driven into a deep deposit of a soft impervious clay that is completely saturated and that has considerable strength of the type which is lost when the structure is disturbed.

Since any pile has a volume of many cubic feet, an equal volume of clay must be displaced when the pile is driven. This is evident at a site where many piles are driven into a saturated impervious soil, since the ground surface may be observed to heave considerably because of the displaced volume of clay.

If it is assumed that the soil undergoes horizontal displacements which are equal in all directions, the shaded element of soil *BCDE* on the horizontal cross section in Fig. 20·1 is suddenly forced to the shape and position represented approximately by *B'C'D'E'*. Under the large shearing strain which this figure indicates, there must be a considerable amount of disturbance to the soil structure. Thus the clay loses much strength at points adjacent to a pile, and only a relatively small amount of skin friction exists during driving. In some clays nearly all the strength is lost and there is very little skin friction. There may be some question about the distance that this remolding effect extends outward from the pile,† but undoubtedly the structure is considerably disturbed for an appreciable distance and somewhat disturbed for a considerably larger distance.

In Fig. 20·2 a pile of radius *AO* is shown imbedded in a clay stratum. The various curves show relationships between shearing strengths of the clay and distances from the pile, the origin being at point *O*. The shearing strength represents the largest value that the skin friction per unit of surface area of the pile can attain.

Curve I represents the shearing strength *before* the pile is driven and, therefore, before there has been disturbance to the structure. The strength at point *B* is *BC*, and if the soil is homogeneous the strength has the same value at all other distances from the line which later will be the center line of the pile.

Immediately after the driving of the pile the shearing strength is represented by curve II. The clay which before driving was at point *A* has moved about to point *O*; that originally at point *O* has moved to point *F*. The skin friction now cannot exceed *OE*, which is the reduced shearing strength and is but a small fraction of the original strength *BC*.

The clay at point *O* has been remolded, and therefore the greater part of its intergranular pressure has disappeared. Pre-

† One estimate is that "the clay immediately surrounding the pile to a distance of ½ diameter of the pile is completely remolded, and to a distance of 1½ diameters it is sufficiently affected to result in a large increase in compressibility of the clay." Quoted by A. Casagrande in reference 29.

sumably, however, the total overburden pressure, consisting of intergranular pressure plus pore-water pressure, is essentially unchanged; at least it has not decreased in magnitude. The lost intergranular pressure must, therefore, have been transferred to the pore water in the form of hydrostatic excess pressure. Thus there is a large hydrostatic excess pressure in the clay adjacent to the pile which decreases with distance from the pile because of

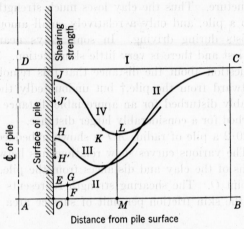

FIG. 20·2 Shearing strengths in saturated clay before and after pile-driving operations.

decreased disturbance. In addition, the lateral pressures adjacent to the pile may have been considerably increased by the outward displacement of soil during driving. The gradients resulting from these excess pressures immediately set up seepage and start a process of consolidation. Flow must always be from points of high excess pressure to points of lower pressure; therefore the direction of flow is radially away from the pile. However, there also may be some upward flow, and if the pile is porous it may soak up water from the clay immediately adjacent to it. During consolidation, while water flows outward, clay particles must move radially toward the pile; the clay thus decreases in void ratio adjacent to the pile surface and expands a small amount at distances farther from the pile. After the driving of the pile is completed, the consolidation proceeds rapidly at the pile surface and builds up skin friction at a fairly fast rate. Ample evidence of this increasing skin friction may be obtained by a *redriving test,* which consists simply in allowing the pile to stand for a while and then driving it again. The fact that the heavy removable shells of shell-less cast-in-place concrete piles, of types such as the Simplex pile, are pulled as soon as possible after driving, because otherwise ordinary pulling equipment might not be successful in removing these expensive shells, is additional evidence of the increasing skin friction. In Fig. 20·2, distance *OH* represents the skin friction in redriving, and curve III represents the strength as a function of distance from the pile. If curve III represents strengths occurring a day or so after driving, curve IV gives a rough idea of strengths some time later, say a few weeks after driving. Since the soil at a distance from the pile expands slightly during consolidation, strength curves III and IV may be a small distance below curve II in this region, as shown in the figure. The strengths for the redriving case are those for the first few blows, because continued redriving causes further remolding and a certain amount of recurrence of loss of skin friction.

It is possible that the pile may be so smooth that the resistance to shear at the surface is less than the shearing strength in the clay a small distance from the pile surface. In this case skin frictions are represented by points *H'* and *J'* instead of *H* and *J*.

If a loading test is run on this pile a few weeks after driving, the skin friction is represented roughly by distance *OJ*. If a pile is pulled a few weeks after driving, it is known from experience that large masses of soil may stick to the pile and come up with it. The relative strength values at points *J*, *K*, and *L* explain this; for a uniform condition the failure surface would not pass through *J* where the circumference is a minimum, nor through *L* where the minimum strength occurs, but would take place where the product of strength and circumference is a minimum, perhaps at point *K*.

The point resistance of the pile during driving is the next item for consideration. The point resistance is large during driving because it equals the force required to cause all the remolding mentioned above. Soil which has a high undistorted strength must be pushed out of the way. It cannot be compressed, because saturated soils are not compressible when acted on by dynamic loads, and water can escape only if sufficient time is allowed. Moreover, there is no convenient place for the soil to go; a column of soil, extending all the way to ground surface, must be heaved up to allow the pile to penetrate the soil below its tip. Practically all the resistance to driving in many clays of the type under consideration is point resistance.

If a static load is placed on a pile, and if it is assumed for the moment that this load is carried mainly by point resistance, the loading of the soil below the tip sets up large hydrostatic excess pressures, and drainage immediately commences. In a relatively short time, one of two things must happen; either this load causes the pile tip to penetrate into the consolidating clay below, or skin friction grips the side of the pile to prevent this penetration, and thus relaxes the load at the point. The latter of these is the one that actually happens in ordinary loading tests on piles in deep homogeneous clay deposits. There is ample evidence that the point resistance is small in such cases and, therefore, that in loading tests the resistance is mainly due to skin friction.

A graphical representation of the relative amounts of skin friction and point resistance for the operations of driving, redriving, loading, and pulling is given in Fig. 20·3. The most important relative magnitudes represented in this figure have already been explained. The point resistance to redriving may be somewhat greater than to driving, but this is a minor point. The skin friction during the pulling of the pile may be nearly the same as during loading if the pile is not tapered; for tapered piles the skin friction is considerably smaller in pulling. Resistance to pulling also depends greatly on the speed of pulling. The point resistance to pulling is that due to one atmosphere of suction. The one comparison which is of outstanding importance is the total resistance to driving as compared to the total resistance to loading. This figure shows that these resistances are of entirely different nature, and although they may be alike occasionally, such an equality is merely a coincidence.

Dry sands may have essentially the same values for point resistance and skin friction during driving, redriving, and loading. However, piles are seldom used in sands unless the sand is underlain by a poorer material which also must be penetrated by the piles, or unless the sand is in loose state and the piles are used for the single purpose of increasing the density. In saturated sands pile driving will tend to make loose sands denser and dense sands looser as explained in Chapter 14. Driving in loose, saturated sand may cause a temporary *quick* condition; when this is the case redriving will show increased strength, as in clays. How-

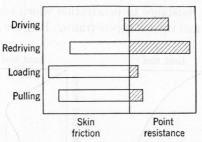

Driving

Redriving

Loading

Pulling

Skin friction   Point resistance

Fɪɢ. 20·3 Relative resistances to various operations on a pile in a saturated clay of high structural strength.

ever, differences between driving and redriving in sands usually are not large, perhaps because the volumetric changes which occur are caused progressively as the pile penetrates, and at any one time they are occurring only in the vicinity of the tip of the pile.

Clays which are partially saturated are harder to analyze than saturated clays. In general partially saturated clays are not likely to lose so much strength because of structural disturbance. They do not offer as large point resistance during driving, because they are relatively compressible. Whereas the surface of a saturated clay undergoes heaving during pile-driving operations, the surface of a partially saturated clay may subside, since such soils frequently undergo considerable amounts of compaction and increase greatly in density when piles are driven into them. Dynamic and static resistances are usually different in partially saturated clays, and sometimes these differences may even be larger than they are for saturated clays. For example, the difference in point resistance during driving would be much less in partially saturated soil than that shown for saturated soil in Fig. 20·3, and this difference would tend to give a much larger

difference in total resistance between driving and loading than
the figure shows.

Conclusions relative to the importance of the differences existing between static and dynamic resistances will follow the discussions of loading tests and dynamic formulas.

20·6 Loading Tests on Piles

Loading tests offer the only dependable method of determining
the amount of resistance to penetration which can be developed
between a pile and the soil it penetrates. Because of group action

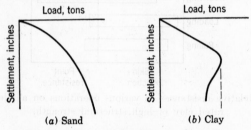

FIG. 20·4 Plots of loading tests on piles.

it usually is not possible to develop all this resistance for all piles
of a pile foundation, but the information given by the loading test
has much value nevertheless.

Loading tests are sometimes quite expensive. Many tons of
dead weight must be placed on a platform above the pile, or a
strong reaction must be available to jack against. Occasionally,
in building renovations, a structure which exists above the foundation may be used for a jacking reaction. Sometimes a heavy
beam can be used to jack against with the ends of the beam
held in place by two heavy trucks or by anchor piles or some
other type of anchorage to the ground. However, the use of
many tons of dead loading is sometimes the most feasible procedure. It is because of the expense, the inconvenience, and the
time required for such tests that frequent use is made of the
much cruder and less dependable indications of loading capacity
that are given by dynamic formulas.

A typical example of loading test specifications is given in
Section 20·11. Loading test data are presented in the form of

curves with the load, usually in tons, plotted against settlement, usually in inches, as shown in Fig. 20·4. In a pile-loading test on sand, such as that shown in (*a*), there is a continuously increasing slope. In a test on clay, as shown in (*b*), the plot may be practically a straight line nearly to failure. Therefore, the test must be carried to failure in clay, or the magnitude of the failure load cannot be determined. On clays or fine silts, in tests which are loaded by dead weights, the failure occurs suddenly and the pile may without warning subside many feet into the ground, if free to do so. When the pile is loaded by some type of jack it is found that the actual loading curve passes a maximum load and then decreases as shown by the full line in (*b*).

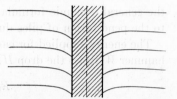

Fig. 20·5 Distortions occurring in the soil adjacent to a loaded friction pile.

Let it be assumed that a pile has been driven into a clay deposit, that sufficient time has elapsed for essentially complete consolidation, and that the pile has then been loaded. Let the light horizontal lines of Fig. 20·5 represent the position of surfaces, within the soil, which before loading were horizontal; these lines probably do not conform to the original strata because of disturbance during driving. Actual strengths within the clay are perhaps about as shown by curve IV of Fig. 20·2; however, for this discussion let it be assumed that the soil has constant strength. After a loading test has been carried nearly to failure the surfaces have been bent from the horizontal to the positions shown in Fig. 20·5. The main portion of the load is transferred by skin friction in the form of downward vertical shearing stresses on the soil against the pile. The resulting shearing strains are represented by the deviations of the light lines from the horizontal. At a distance of one radius from the pile surface the circumference is twice the pile circumference; the shearing stress there is thus only half as large as the skin friction, and the shearing strains are, perhaps, slightly less than half of the values at the pile surface. Thus it is seen that the stresses and strains caused by the loading of one pile die out quite quickly with distance from the pile. This is at least a partial explanation of the fact that settlements which are obtained in loading tests are small and may be only a small fraction of the settlement the proposed structure, as a whole, will undergo. Thus the loading test furnishes the limiting value of the resisting force a soil can exert on a pile, and it also gives indications relative to the strains required adjacent to the pile to develop this resistance.

20·7 Derivation of the General Dynamic Pile Formula

The derivation of the equation which has sometimes been called the general dynamic formula, and which expresses the resistance to the penetration of piles during driving, follows.

The energy supplied for each blow is equal to the weight of the hammer W times the drop H, or

$$E_0 = WH \qquad (20·1)$$

Part of this energy is lost in friction in the leads and in wind resistance. If e_1 is the efficiency of the drop and v is the velocity of the hammer as it hits the pile the energy reaching the pile is

$$E_1 = We_1H = \frac{Wv^2}{2g} \qquad (20·2)$$

Values sometimes used for e_1 are 0.75 for drop hammers and 0.90 for single-acting steam hammers. ‡

A considerable amount of energy is lost in the impact. If e_2 designates the efficiency of the impact, the energy available after impact may be written.

$$E_2 = e_2E_1 = We_2e_1H \qquad (20·3)$$

The expression that is used for e_2 is obtained from impact relationships developed by Sir Isaac Newton. Its applicability to pile driving has recently been questioned § and will be given further mention at the conclusion of this derivation.

Newton's impact relationship applies to two free, massive bodies. The two bodies in the pile problem are the hammer and

‡ See Hiley tabulations, for example, in reference 47.

§ The questionable applicability of this impact relationship and other questionable relationships used in this derivation have been considered in detail in reference 42.

the pile, with masses, respectively, of W/g and W_p/g. Since energy may be expressed as one-half the product of mass and velocity squared, the efficiency of the impact may be written

$$e_2 = \frac{\dfrac{W}{g}u^2 + \dfrac{W_p}{g}u_p{}^2}{\dfrac{W}{g}v^2 + \dfrac{W_p}{g}v_p{}^2} \qquad (20 \cdot 4)$$

The masses, weights, and velocities which appear in this equation are those shown in Fig. 20·6.

If the hammer is too light it rebounds from the pile, the velocity u is negative, and the energy $\frac{1}{2}(W/g)u^2$ of the hammer after impact is lost and therefore should be omitted from the numerator of the above equation. However, if specifications call for a hammer of reasonable weight, as they usually do, this detail need not be considered.

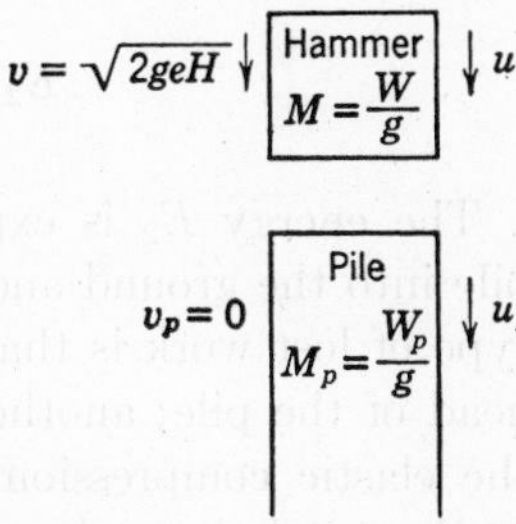

The impulse is defined as the product of force and time. The impulses of the two free bodies, for the period of contact during impact, are equal. The momentum change is the product of mass and velocity change and is equal to the impulse. The statement of this equality of impulse, or equality of momentum change, for these two bodies, which here are assumed to be free, massive bodies, is

$$v = \sqrt{2geH} \downarrow \boxed{\begin{array}{c}\text{Hammer}\\ M = \dfrac{W}{g}\end{array}} \downarrow u$$

$$v_p = 0 \quad \boxed{\begin{array}{c}\text{Pile}\\ M_p = \dfrac{W_p}{g}\end{array}} \downarrow u_p$$

FIG. 20·6 The velocities before (at the left) and after (at the right) the impact of a hammer on a pile.

$$\frac{W}{g}(v - u) = \frac{W_p}{g}(v_p - u_p) \qquad (20 \cdot 5)$$

According to Newton the ratio of relative velocities after and before impact is a constant which depends only on the characteristics of the materials of the two bodies. This constant will be called the *coefficient of elastic restitution* and will be designated by n:

$$n = \frac{u_p - u}{v - v_p} \qquad (20 \cdot 6)$$

In the majority of pile-driving operations the impact will be between wood and steel, for which the value of n is approximately $\frac{1}{4}$.

The velocity of the pile before impact is usually zero, and even when the use of a steam hammer keeps the pile in motion this velocity is of inappreciable magnitude. Thus v_p in equation 20·4 may be assumed to be equal to zero. The solution of simultaneous equations 20·5 and 20·6 then furnishes expressions for u and u_p which, when substituted in equation 20·4, give

$$e_2 = \frac{W + n^2 W_p}{W + W_p} \qquad (20 \cdot 7)$$

and equation 20·3 may be written

$$E_2 = e_1 W H \frac{W + n^2 W_p}{W + W_p} \qquad (20 \cdot 8)$$

The energy E_2 is expended in the useful work of forcing the pile into the ground and in a number of kinds of lost work. One type of lost work is that used in the crushing of the fibers at the head of the pile; another type of lost work includes that used in the elastic compression of the pile and of the surrounding soil. If the total dynamic resistance to compression is Q and if this resistance acts throughout the distance of penetration ρ caused by any blow, the useful work is $Q\rho$. If the fibers of the pile head are crushed an overall amount ρ_f, the work thus expended is approximately equal to $Q\rho_f$. If the combined elastic compressions result in a subsidence of the top of the pile of ρ_e, followed by a rebound of the same amount, the elastic energy represented is the product of ρ_e and the average compressive force. Since this compressive force varies from zero to the maximum value Q, its average value is approximately $\frac{1}{2}Q$, and the lost elastic energy may be written $\frac{1}{2}Q\rho_e$. Other losses which occur are usually neglected. The energy E_2 is therefore expressed

$$E_2 = Q(\rho + \tfrac{1}{2}\rho_e + \rho_f) \qquad (20 \cdot 9)$$

The elastic shortening of a bearing pile of constant cross section A, composed of a material of modulus of elasticity E, is easily expressed. In comparison to vertical pressures the lateral pressures are so small they may be neglected and

$$E = \frac{\text{stress}}{\text{strain}} = \frac{\dfrac{Q}{A}}{\dfrac{\rho_e}{L}}$$

whence

$$\rho_e = \frac{QL}{AE} \qquad (20 \cdot 10)$$

The elastic shortening of a friction pile is considerably smaller than the value given by equation $20 \cdot 10$, and for a pile with constant area, with no point resistance and with uniform friction over its length, it can easily be shown that the elastic shortening is $QL/3AE$. However, ρ_e in equation $20 \cdot 9$ includes the effect of elastic compression in the soil. These two deviations from the conditions represented by equation $20 \cdot 10$ are difficult of evaluation but they counteract each other somewhat. If C is defined as the ratio between the actual elastic displacement of the top of the pile and the displacement occurring for a bearing pile as expressed by equation $20 \cdot 10$, the following expression holds for the actual displacement.

$$\rho_e = \frac{CQL}{AE} \qquad (20 \cdot 11)$$

Methods have been developed for the actual measurement of ρ_e during driving, but in the absence of such data a value for C may be estimated and the above expression may be used.

Combining equations $20 \cdot 8$, $20 \cdot 9$, and $20 \cdot 11$ gives

$$Q = \frac{e_1 WH}{\rho + \dfrac{CQL}{2AE} + \rho_f} \cdot \frac{W + n^2 W_p}{W + W_p} \qquad (20 \cdot 12)$$

This is sometimes considered to be the most convenient form of the general dynamic pile formula although it must be solved by trial since the resistance Q appears on the right-hand side. The following form is cumbersome but it is frequently used:

$$Q = \frac{(\rho + \rho_f)AE}{CL} \left[\sqrt{1 + \frac{2CLe_1 WH}{(\rho + \rho_f)^2 AE} \cdot \frac{W + n^2 W_p}{W + W_p}} - 1 \right] \qquad (20 \cdot 13)$$

A number of pile formulas that are quite well known are obtained by slight simplifications of the general formula. For example, the assumption that C is equal to unity in equation 20·13 gives the *Hiley formula*:‖

$$Q = \frac{(\rho + \rho_f)AE}{L}\left[\sqrt{1 + \frac{2Le_1WH}{(\rho + \rho_f)^2AE}\frac{W + n^2W_p}{W + W_p}} - 1\right] \quad (20·14)$$

and the assumptions of C equal to unity, e_1 equal to unity, ρ_f equal to zero, and n^2 equal to zero give the *Redtenbacker formula*:

$$Q = \frac{\rho AE}{L}\left[\sqrt{1 + \frac{2LW^2H}{\rho^2AE(W + W_p)}} - 1\right] \quad (20·15)$$

It has already been mentioned that the general dynamic pile formula, as given by equations 20·12 and 20·13, may be severely criticized because of the use of questionable assumptions. The assumptions used in their derivation have been stated above, and a critical review of them is now possible.

The impact relationship used is valid for two free massive bodies. The pile can in no sense of the word be called a free body, since important frictional forces act on its sides and bearing forces on its end. Furthermore the pile cannot be called massive. According to Cummings (42) Newton himself stated that his impact expression did not apply for ". . . bodies . . . which suffer some such extension as occurs under the strokes of a hammer." For these reasons the use of the Newtonian impact expression and the equation of conservation of momentum are questionable. Moreover, the expression for loss in impact includes elastic strain energy which also is included in the term $\frac{1}{2}Q\rho_e$ of equation 20·9. This duplication is another unreasonable item in the derivation of the general formula.

From these considerations it must be concluded that the values of resistance which are given by dynamic formulas are, at best, of low accuracy. There is no proof, however, that they differ from the correct values by anywhere near the large amount of difference known to exist between dynamic and static resistances.

‖ For further comment on the Hiley formula see Section 20·10.

20·8 The *Engineering News* Formula

A pile formula which has been extensively used in the United States for many decades is the *Engineering News* formula. For the allowable static load on a pile that is driven by a *drop hammer* the formula is

$$Q_a = \frac{2WH'}{\rho'' + 1''} \tag{20·16}$$

whereas the resistance when driven by a *single-acting steam hammer* is

$$Q_a = \frac{2WH'}{\rho'' + 0.1''} \tag{20·17}$$

In these formulas Q_a is the allowable static load per pile, this load being in the same units as W; H' is the drop in feet and ρ'' is the settlement per blow in inches.

Equations 20·16 and 20·17 may be derived from general equation 20·12 by the use of additional, highly simplifying assumptions. Originally, however, the *Engineering News* formula was probably obtained by a much more empirical approach. The assumptions which reduce equation 20·12 to the *Engineering News* formula may be stated as follows. Let Q_a be equal to $Q/6e_1$; thus an allowable load is adopted which is equal to the dynamic resistance divided by a factor of safety that is somewhat smaller than 6; assume e_2 to be equal to unity; assume that the expression $\frac{1}{2}\rho_e + \rho_f$ is equal to 1 in. for a drop hammer and is equal to 0.1 in. for a single-acting steam hammer. The latter two assumptions may well be called oversimplifications because constants are used for terms which vary over wide ranges of values.

Some engineers like the *Engineering News* formula because of its simplicity. It has also been found that, when compared with loading test data, the *Engineering News* formula sometimes shows better agreement than is obtained by use of more complex dynamic formulas. Examples of this agreement are commonest for the commonest weights of hammers and piles, and they may be due in part to the empirical nature of the *Engineering News* formula which might lead to better agreement than is obtained from more theoretical expressions for a limited range of conditions. However, when too light a hammer is used, the *Engineering News* formula tends to give much too large values of resistance. Of course, specifications should call for the use of satisfactory weights of hammers but, since specifications often fail to cover all important requirements, it can be claimed that there is some advantage in a formula with broader applicability. The numerical examples in Section 20·12 give further demonstration of these points.

20·9   The Kreuter Method

It is known that the dynamic resistance does not differ appreciably for different heights of drop of the hammer. If two or more heights of drop can be used during the final few inches of driving, the resistance may be computed from data easily observed during driving by a method attributed to Kreuter (92). The use of this method avoids the need of oversimplifying assumptions and the need of evaluating ρ_e, which is the most difficult term to determine. However, the method is applicable only to drop hammers because different drops usually are not possible with steam hammers, which have fixed strokes.

A convenient form of the general formula, which is given by equations 20·3 and 20·9, is

$$Q = \frac{e_2 e_1 W H}{\rho + \frac{1}{2}\rho_e + \rho_f} \qquad (20 \cdot 18)$$

For investigation of the relationship between height of drop and penetration, this may be rearranged to give

$$H = \rho \frac{Q}{e_2 e_1 W} + \left(\frac{1}{2}\rho_e + \rho_f\right)\frac{Q}{e_2 e_1 W} \qquad (20 \cdot 19)$$

The term $e_2 e_1 W$ is a constant which may be evaluated for any given case, since W is always known, e_1 can be estimated with reasonable accuracy, and e_2 as expressed by equation 20·7 contains only known quantities. In addition, ρ_e and ρ_f are essentially constant. Thus for varying heights of drop the only variables in this equation are H and ρ, and the equation may be written

$$H = \rho \frac{Q}{e_2 e_1 W} + H_0 \qquad (20 \cdot 20)$$

Here H_0 is a constant; if ρ equals zero, H equals H_0, and thus H_0 is the height of drop—actually the maximum height of drop—giving zero penetration. If drops of H_1 and H_2 are used in turn and they give penetrations of ρ_1 and ρ_2 respectively, two expressions in the form of equation $20\cdot20$ may be written and the second subtracted from the first:

$$(H_2 - H_1) = (\rho_2 - \rho_1) \frac{Q}{e_2 e_1 W}$$

whence)

$$Q = e_2 e_1 W \frac{H_2 - H_1}{\rho_2 - \rho_1} \qquad (20\cdot21)$$

If more than two drops are used the data may best be interpreted by use of a plot of the form of Fig. $20\cdot7$. The slope of the straight line best fitting the points may then be used in place of the term $(H_2 - H_1)/(\rho_2 - \rho_1)$ of equation $20\cdot21$.

This method is valuable also because data from each project at which it is used may be collected and tabulated for use in cases wherein different drops are not possible. From observations of the amount of crushing of fibers in the pile head and from the data given by the use of two or more heights of drop it

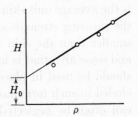

Fig. $20\cdot7$ The Kreuter plot.

also is possible to evaluate ρ_e and ρ_f of equation $20\cdot19$. From the determinations of ρ_e at various projects data on coefficient C of equation $20\cdot11$ may be obtained.

$20\cdot10$ Other Formulas for Resistance to Penetration

Dean (47) lists at least two dozen dynamic pile formulas and, in addition, many amended and modified forms; for example, he gives seventeen modified forms of the *Engineering News* or the Wellington formula. All these formulas are empirical, they are based on questionable assumptions, or they are the general formula modified by various simplifying assumptions. Thus there is little value in further detailed discussion of most of these formulas in a text on fundamentals.

However, one example which is deserving of mention is the

Hiley (71) formula which has been given as equation 20·14. For many types and sizes of piles Hiley presented tabulations of many factors entering the formula; these factors include the elastic compression of the pile, of followers, and of the ground, the efficiency of the drop, the efficiency of impact, and so on. Entire books (for example, reference 2) have since been devoted mainly to extensions of Hiley's approach, sometimes with extensive tabulations.

An entirely different type of pile formula, sometimes called the static type, should also be mentioned. Such expressions are of the form

$$Q_s = A_f\tau + A_t q \tag{20·22}$$

where Q_s is the ultimate static resistance, A_f and A_t are the pile areas providing skin friction and point resistance respectively, τ is the average unit skin friction, and q is the bearing capacity. If the shearing strength at a distance from the pile is considerably smaller than the skin friction, the product of shearing strength and some area that is larger than A_s may be smaller than $A_s\tau$ and should be used in place of it. Safety factors are frequently included in such formulas. For friction piles in clay the final term can often be neglected. If a reasonable value for τ could be obtained this form would be very valuable; numerous attempts have been made to collect values for this quantity.¶

The skin friction and the shearing strength sometimes are and sometimes are not alike, but both depend on the magnitude of the lateral pressure and, in clays, on the degree of structural disturbance and the degree to which consolidation has occurred. The difficulties of evaluating such strength characteristics have been discussed in Chapter 15. As soon as attempts are made to give typical skin friction values for the various soil types, questions of terminology enter and, for example, the many soils which are designated as soft clay have skin frictions and shearing strengths which might range all the way from roughly 500 to 2000 lb per sq ft. However, it is not unlikely that in the future this type of expression will come into more use and dynamic formulas will be used less than they are at present.

¶ For example, see page 860 of May 1941, reference 3.

20·11   Building Code Specifications on Piles

The following excerpts from the Building Code of the City of Boston (37) * are given as examples of code requirements relative to piles and pile foundations.

[1] The allowable pile loading shall be limited by the provision that the vertical pressures in the bearing materials at or below the points of the piles produced by the loads on all piles in a foundation shall not exceed the allowable bearing values of such materials, as specified in . . . [Sections 19·25 and 19·26]. Piles or pile groups shall be assumed to transfer their loads to the bearing materials by spreading the load uniformly at an angle of sixty degrees with the horizontal, starting at a polygon circumscribing the piles at the top of the satisfactory bearing stratum in which they are embedded, but the area considered as supporting the load shall not extend beyond the intersection of the sixty degree planes of adjacent piles or pile groups.

[2] The allowable load on each pile shall be further limited by the requirement that such load shall not cause excessive movement of the pile relative to the soil. Satisfactory proof of this load for all soil conditions and all types of piles can be obtained from load tests conducted [as follows: The pile] . . . shall be loaded to at least twice the proposed working load, the load being applied in increments of not over 10,000 pounds. At least four hours shall elapse between the addition of successive increments. Measurements of the settlement, accurate to one thirty-second inch, shall be taken and recorded immediately before and after each increment of load is added. In determining the settlement, proper deduction shall be made for elastic compression of the pile under the test load. The allowable pile load shall not exceed one-half of that causing a total settlement of one-half inch which remains constant for forty-eight hours . . .

[3] In the absence of . . . [loading tests as] proof of the supporting capacity, the load on any pile shall not exceed the allowable value determined in accordance with [the following formulas and provisions †] . . .

$$Q_a = \frac{2WH'}{\rho'' + 1''} \text{ for drop hammers}$$

$$Q_a = \frac{2WH'}{\rho'' + 0.1''} \text{ for steam hammers}$$

* See footnotes in Section 19·31. The excerpts given in the present section are from code sections 2908, 2909, 2910, and 2917.

† Notations in the formulas have been revised to agree with those used in this text.

. . . [The quantities and units in the formulas are as explainéd in Section 20·8.] For double-acting steam hammers the value of ρ'' must be determined only when the hammer is operating at the maximum number of blows per minute as scheduled in the Manufacturers' Specifications. . . . The data used in determining driving resistance shall be obtained during the driving and not upon redriving when a pile has been allowed to stand more than one hour after having been driven. When driving wooden piles, broomed heads shall be cut to sound wood before making penetration measurements. For cast-in-place concrete piles in which the driven casing is withdrawn leaving a shell pile of smaller diameter than the outer casing, the pile driving formula may be used for piles in [medium clays and soft clays] . . . and it may also be used for piles driven into soils of other classes when the supporting capacity obtained from the formula is at least doubled in the last three feet of driving.

[4] The commissioner shall require a competent inspector, qualified by experience and training and satisfactory to him, to be on the work at all times while piles are being driven. The inspector shall make an accurate record of the material and the principal dimensions of each pile, of the weight and fall of the hammer, if a single-acting steam hammer or drop hammer, and the size and make, number of blows per minute, and energy per blow, if a double-acting steam hammer, together with the average penetration of each pile for at least the last five blows and the grades at tip and cut-off. A copy of these records shall be filed and kept in the office of the commissioner . . .

[5] The method of driving shall be such as not to impair the strength of the pile and shall meet with the approval of the commissioner. A steel or iron follower may be used subject to his approval. It shall be equipped with a suitable socket encasing the pile head sufficiently to prevent damage while driving. Shattered, broomed or otherwise damaged pile heads shall be cut back to sound material before driving with the follower. If a wooden driving block is used, it shall, at the time it is used for measuring the penetration, be of sound hard wood equal to oak, not more than twelve inches in height, with the grain parallel to the axis of the pile, and shall be enclosed in a steel casing of adequate strength to resist lateral distension. . . . Where piles are driven through soft soil to hard bearing material, providing high point resistance, the grades of all piles or pile shells previously driven shall be measured to detect uplift; and if uplift occurs in any pile or pile shell while other piles are being driven, such pile or pile shells shall be rejected and additional piles driven to obtain the required resistance. . . . Piles shall not be jetted except with specific approval of the commissioner. After jetting, piles shall be driven to the required resistance. . . . Additional

piles shall be driven to replace piles injured during driving, and to supplement piles having capacity less than required by the design. . . . Types of pile construction not specifically provided for in this part shall meet such additional requirements as may be prescribed by the commissioner.

[6] Every wooden pile shall be in one piece, cut from a sound live tree, and free from defects which may materially impair its strength or durability. It shall be butt-cut above the ground swell, and shall have substantially uniform taper from butt to tip. Wooden piles shall measure at least six inches in smallest diameter at the tip, at least eleven inches in smallest diameter two feet from the butt and at least ten inches in smallest diameter at the cut-off, these measurements being taken under the bark. The axis of a wooden pile shall not deviate from a straight line more than one inch for each ten feet of length nor more than six inches. . . . The load . . . for piles of the minimum dimensions . . . shall not exceed twelve tons for spruce, Norway pine, and woods of similar strength, nor sixteen tons for oak, southern yellow pine, and woods of similar strength. These limits may be increased one ton for each inch by which the diameters at both cut-off and tip exceed the minima specified. . . . Piles shall be cut to sound wood before capping is placed. The cut-off grade shall be determined by the commissioner so as to be below the probable permanent ground water level. . . . The center-to-center spacing of wooden piles shall be not less than twenty-four inches nor less than twice the butt diameter. . . . [Not included herein are Boston code specifications that refer to other types of piles and that are in the same general form as those given for wooden piles in this item.]

The requirements of piles, as stated in Section 20·2, were that each pile must be strong enough to carry its load, each pile must be able to transfer its load to the soil in satisfactory manner, and the soil must be able to carry the stresses caused by all piles in combination. In the above excerpts it is seen that these three requirements are covered in items [6], [2], and [1], respectively. Item [3] refers to dynamic resistance determination as an alternate to the loading tests of item [2]. Item [4] refers to proper control and records of allowable loading, and item [5] contains specifications for driving procedure.

The formulas in item [3] are the *Engineering News* formulas that have been discussed in Section 20·8.

20·12   Numerical Examples of Dynamic Resistance Determinations

EXAMPLE 1. A wood pile is 100 ft long, 140 sq in. in average area, 4400 lb in weight, and has a modulus of elasticity of 1.5×10^6 lb per sq in. This pile is driven by a 3000-lb drop hammer with a 10-ft drop to a final penetration of ½ in. per blow. Rough estimates of the probable bearing capacity are desired by the use of (a) the *Engineering News* formula and (b) the Hiley formula. Also desired is (c) the load allowable on the pile as a column, according to the Boston Code.

According to the *Engineering News* formula, which is equation 20·16,

$$Q_a = \frac{2 \times 3000 \times 10}{0.50 + 1} = 40{,}000 \text{ lb or 20 tons}$$

The factor of safety associated with this value is $6e_1$, as stated in Section 20·8.

The Hiley formula is equation 20·14. Using in this equation the commonly accepted values of $e_1 = 0.75$, $n^2 = 0.06$, and $\rho_f = 0.05$ in. gives

$$Q = \frac{(0.5 + 0.05)(140)(1.5 \times 10^6)}{(100 \times 12)} \times$$

$$\left\{ \sqrt{1 + \frac{2(100 \times 12)(0.75)(3000)(10 \times 12)}{(0.5 + 0.05)^2(140)(1.5 \times 10^6)} \left[\frac{3000 + (0.06)(4400)}{3000 + 4400} \right]} - 1 \right\}$$

$$= 126{,}000 \text{ lb or 63 tons}$$

Before this determination is compared with other values a factor of safety must be applied to it.

The allowable load on this pile according to item [6] of Section 20·11 is 12 tons plus 1 ton for each additional inch of diameter above the specified minimum value. Since the specified average minimum diameter is about 8 in. and the diameter of this pile is somewhat greater than 13 in., the allowable load based on the strength of the wood is 17 tons.

The results of all determinations given above are assembled in Table 20·1. To give results that are on a comparable basis, all the resistances obtained from dynamic formulas have been refigured on the basis of a factor of safety of 3, and the results are given in parentheses in the table. It is seen that for the 100-ft pile the three formulas give values which are of the same order of magnitude.

TABLE 20·1 RESISTANCE DATA
(Examples of Section 20·12)

		Resistances in Tons	
Example 1	Engineering News formula	20	(30) [1]
100-ft wood	Hiley formula	63	(21)
pile	Maximum load specified by code	17	
Example 2	Engineering News formula	20	(30)
20-ft wood	Hiley formula	134	(45)
pile	Maximum load specified by code	13	
Example 3	Engineering News formula	95	(190)
Heavy precast	Hiley formula	87	(29)
concrete pile	Maximum load specified by code	45	

[1] Figures in parentheses are values obtained by dynamic formulas adjusted to a factor of safety of 3.

EXAMPLE 2. A 20-ft wood pile with 60 sq in. average area and 375 lb weight is to be driven, and it is proposed to use the same hammer and the same height of drop and to drive to the same penetration per blow as in Example 1. The same data are desired as in Example 1.

By the *Engineering News* formula the result is the same as in Example 1, namely, 20 tons. The Hiley formula, used as shown in Example 1, gives 134 tons for the dynamic resistance. The pile has an average diameter of about 9 in., and thus item [6] of the Boston Code limits the load to about 13 tons.

The results of this example are summarized in Table 20·1. Conclusions relative to the resistance values for this case must be made with care. It should first be noted that the soil in Example 2 must have much greater resistance to penetration than that which exists in Example 1. This may be deduced from equation 20·22, which shows that, if the piles of the two examples were in the same soil, the larger of the two piles would have much greater resistance to penetration and therefore would undergo a smaller penetration under a given blow of the hammer. Next it may be noted that on the basis of strength in compression the Boston Code allows only about 13 tons on the short pile considered in this example. Since resistances which are much larger than this value are given by the Hiley formula, it is indicated that much too severe a blow has been used on the small pile. Dynamic formulas cannot be expected to cover such limitations as the allowable compressive strength of the pile, and the fact that the *Engineering News* formula apparently does roughly reflect this limitation, by giving a resistance of 20 tons when the strength in compression is 13 tons, is perhaps an indication that the formula is more empirical than it usually is considered to be. If so, it might be expected that in the relatively common case of a small wood pile this formula would give a reasonable value for allowable load, even when the pile is overdriven, as it is here, whereas for less common types of piles, which were not considered in the empirical development of the formula, it might give poor results.

EXAMPLE 3. A precast concrete pile is 80 ft long, 256 sq in. in area, and 21,300 lb in weight, and has a modulus of elasticity of 3×10^6 lb per sq in. This pile is driven by a heavy duty double-acting steam hammer, delivering an energy per blow of 19,000 ft lb, to a final penetration of 0.1 in. per blow. The total weight of the hammer is 13,000 lb and the weight of striking parts is 3600 lb. Rough estimates are desired of the bearing capacity, as given by the methods called for in Example 1.

According to the *Engineering News* formula, which in this case is considered to be based on a factor of safety of 6,

$$Q_a = \frac{2 \times 19,000}{0.1 + 0.1} = 190,000 \text{ lb or 95 tons}$$

Assuming that ρ_f equals 0.05 in. and n^2 equals 0.06, and omitting the weight of the yoke of the hammer since a large part of this weight is supported by steam pressure, the total dynamic resistance according to the Hiley formula is

$$Q = \frac{(1 + 0.05)(256)(3 \times 10^6)}{960} \times$$

$$\left[\sqrt{1 + \frac{2(960)(19,000 \times 12)}{(0.1 + 0.05)^2(256)(3 \times 10^6)} \frac{3600 + (0.06)21,300}{3600 + 21,300}} - 1 \right]$$

$$= 174,000 \text{ lb or 87 tons}$$

A section of the Boston Code that is not included in Section 20·11 herein states that the allowable load on a precast concrete pile of 169 sq in. area must not exceed 30 tons, whereas larger piles may be loaded to the same intensity as represented by these figures. On this basis a load of 45 tons may be allowed on this pile.

The values given above are collected in Table 20·1. This comparison of results demonstrates an important limitation of the *Engineering News* formula. When a very light hammer hits a heavy pile most of the energy is dissipated as loss in impact. Of course, specifications should prohibit the use of excessively light hammers, but in this extreme case the heavy duty hammer which is used is of light weight when compared with the heavy concrete pile; in fact no hammer is made that is heavy enough to avoid a large impact loss in the driving of such a pile. Since the *Engineering News* formula contains no impact term, it does not give reasonable results when the impact loss is large. In this example it indicates an allowable resistance which is several times as large as that given by the Hiley formula. Moreover, the *Engineering News* value here is more than twice as large as the allowable load on the basis of the strength of the pile in compression.

20·13   Final Discussion of the Applicability of Dynamic Formulas

The comparisons of dynamic and static action in Section 20·5 show that dynamic and static resistances in clays are of entirely different nature. Therefore, for predicting static resistances in clays dynamic formulas can furnish crude results at best and sometimes may give results which are entirely in error. Nevertheless, dynamic formulas have been and still are widely used, and many engineers believe that such formulas have much value. Furthermore, some engineers who oppose the use of dynamic formulas for determining allowable resistances are in favor of their use, indirectly, inasmuch as they recommend driving the various piles of a given foundation to the same penetration per blow, and thus, presumably, to the same dynamic resistance.

The existence of differences between dynamic and static resistances are shown, most simply and inexpensively, by redriving tests. An appreciably greater resistance encountered during redriving is a strong indication that dynamic and static resistances are not alike. Loading tests give more positive data, and it may well be claimed that not enough tests of this type are run. However, lack of funds and time often prevents their use. If loading tests are not feasible, no substitute has been offered for the indications which are given by dynamic formulas, even though they are of questionable accuracy.

Arguments for and against the use of dynamic formulas have been stated by numerous engineers in the discussion of a recent report (3); the reader is referred to these discussions if he is interested in their many points of view.

It has not been sufficiently recognized that two factors contribute to the limited value of dynamic formulas: (1) the questionable dependability of the dynamic values obtained; (2) the question whether dynamic resistances are representative of static resistances.

Recent discussions (42) of item 1 have proved without doubt that the accuracies which can be obtained in determinations of dynamic resistances are crude at best. However, there is good basis for the claim that this point has been overemphasized in recent years and that item 2, as discussed in Section 20·5, is much more important than item 1.

20·14   Action of Pile Groups

After the action of single piles is known from loading tests, a prediction of the action of groups of bearing piles may require practically no additional considerations. However, in certain cases of friction pile foundations, the action of pile groups may be extremely complex and only distantly related to loading test results.

A typical bearing pile usually penetrates a short distance into a soil stratum of good bearing characteristics, and the pile transfers its load to the soil in a small pressure bulb which surrounds the imbedded pile tip. The individual pressure bulbs at the tips of adjacent piles of the group may overlap somewhat, but the actions of adjacent bearing piles ordinarily are essentially independent. If the stratum in which the piles are imbedded and all strata below have ample bearing capacity, each pile of the pile group is capable of carrying essentially the same load as that carried by single piles in the loading tests. If compressible soils exist below the pile tips, the settlement of the pile group may be much greater than the settlements observed in the loading tests, even though the bearing intensity may be smaller than the allowable value. However, if the bearing stratum is essentially

incompressible and there are no softer strata below, the settlement of a group of bearing piles may be essentially equal to the
settlements observed in loading tests on isolated piles. In this
case the piles may, if desired, be spaced about as closely as it is
practicable to drive them.

In a large group of closely spaced friction piles the actions of
the piles overlap and the distribution of load to the various piles
is far from uniform, even though equal load on each pile may
frequently be assumed in designing such foundations. The most
important concepts which are needed for an understanding of the
group action occurring in such a case are illustrated by Fig. 20·8.
Assume that piles A and B are two adjacent piles of a friction
pile foundation and that pile A is loaded first and pile B later.
Before either pile is loaded the conditions are as shown in (a);
CD is a horizontal reference line within the soil and squares E
and F represent reference elements within the clay. After pile A
is loaded the conditions are as shown in (b). The original position of the reference line is shown lightly and the displaced position is shown by the heavy line $C'D'$; this line conforms to those
previously shown in Fig. 20·4. The reference elements have been
distorted to the shapes E' and F'. The pile exerts a shearing
stress τ_1 on element E'. The soil on the outer side of element F'
offers vertical support to the element by the shearing stress τ_3.
The distortions shown in the figure indicate that even at fairly
large radial distances from the pile the major portion of the skin
friction is transferred to the soil by shearing stresses on vertical
cylindrical surfaces. Unless the pile has a relatively short length
it may be concluded that τ_3 multiplied by the circumference over
which it acts is nearly as large as τ_1 multiplied by its circumfer-
ential distance.

Now let it be assumed that pile B is loaded. If this pile were
loaded separately, the displacements and distortions that would
be caused would copy those considered for pile A; they are shown
in (c). When the two piles are loaded simultaneously an overlapping of stresses occurs between them and gives the much more
complex situation shown in (d). Element F_i is symmetrically
loaded by the two piles; therefore the distortions shown in F' and
F'' of (b) and (c), respectively, are not possible. Furthermore,

it is not possible for shears on vertical planes to be transferred outward indefinitely, as for the single pile. Since square F_i must be symmetrical after distortion, the shearing stresses it takes on its sides are much smaller than those on F' and F''. It follows that τ_{1i} must be much smaller than τ_1. To carry the pile load the pile must settle further, causing larger distortions on the

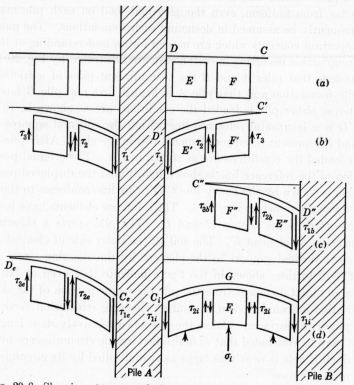

FIG. 20·8 Shearing stresses and shearing strains in the soil adjacent to loaded, single, friction piles and pile groups.

outer side of the piles and increasing the skin friction there to τ_{1e}. Since the frictional force represented by τ_{1i} cannot be transmitted by shear beyond point G, equilibrium requires that this force be no larger than the force which represents the resistance to compression and is made up of vertical direct stresses of the type of σ_i. To the left of pile A, in contrast, much of the skin friction is transferred, by shearing stresses on vertical planes, to a large distance from the pile.

The concept that two piles greatly interrupt each other's development of skin friction applies in much greater degree to large groups of closely spaced friction piles than it does to the two piles considered above. Thus it must be concluded that in foundations of friction piles the distribution of load to the various piles is far from uniform. If the centrally located piles settle more on loading than the exterior piles it is possible that they may develop a slightly greater skin friction than if all piles settle like amounts. In any case, however, each exterior pile carries a much greater load than an interior pile.

20·15 Considerations of Spacing of Friction Piles

Consider next that pile B of Fig. 20·8 is one pile of a large pile foundation with conditions as follows. This pile is surrounded on all sides by other piles. The pile foundation is capped by a large concrete mat that carries a heavy building load. The piles are wood piles with the smallest diameter allowed by the Boston code and, in accordance with item [6] of Section 20·22 herein, they have an allowable load of 12 tons each. The soft clay between and below the tips of the piles has an allowable bearing capacity of 1 ton per sq ft. The spacing of the piles is the same in both directions, and it is designated by b.

The considerations of the previous section indicated that no dependence should be placed on the existence of any shearing stress on vertical planes midway between this pile and adjacent piles. Therefore, on a horizontal area of magnitude b^2, at the elevation of the tip of the pile, the total load may equal the allowable pile loading of 12 tons, whereas the allowable load on this area of soft clay is qb^2. Since q equals 1 ton per sq ft, the minimum allowable value for dimension b, assuming that the piles are to carry 12 tons each, is 3.5 ft. Furthermore, it may be noted that, if a heavier and stronger pile were used, the minimum spacing would be even larger.

A loading test on such a pile might show a loading capacity which, even after being divided by a generous safety factor, is much larger than 12 tons. However, this value represents the total skin friction or, possibly, the column strength of the pile, whereas only a part of the skin friction can be developed on the pile in the actual foundation. Therefore, the only requirement of the friction pile in this case and, moreover, the only function it can perform, is the distribution of the load of the pile, in this case 12 tons, over an area at the tip that in this example is 12 sq ft.

Item [1] of the code excerpts appearing in Section 20·11 herein is not in agreement with the concept that there is no spreading of interior pile loads in friction pile foundations, but otherwise this item expresses the requirements illustrated by the example which has been given. This example is particularly interesting because it shows that the bearing capacity of the soil at the tips of friction piles is often the factor which determines the spacing of the piles and that spacings of the order of 4 ft are sometimes the minimum that should be used. For bearing piles, in contrast, it would be reasonable to use spacings of 2 ft, a distance more often mentioned in building codes for wood piles.

For the case considered above the exterior piles would settle approximately the same amounts as the interior piles and would, therefore, be subjected to loads of much more than 12 tons, if they were to be at 3.5-ft spacing. Therefore, it is indicated that the use of exterior piles of considerably greater strength or at considerably closer spacing would be desirable.

20·16 Settlement of Foundations of Friction Piles

The settlement of friction pile foundations may be considered to result from three causes:

1. Settlement results from compression of the pile and from the movement of the piles relative to the immediately adjacent soil. This item is illustrated by Figs. 20·8 (a) and 20·8 (b) and, when full skin friction is developed, this settlement corresponds to that observed in a loading test on a single pile.

2. Settlement is caused by compression occurring in the soil between the piles.

3. Settlement is introduced by compression which occurs in compressible strata below the tips of the piles.

The settlements of items 2 and 3 generally are of much larger magnitude than of item 1. However, these settlements may occur very slowly in saturated soils because of slow consolidation.

Accurate estimates of the amount of settlement occurring under item 2 are not possible because of the partial disturbance to the structure of the soil between the piles. Estimates of item 3 may be made by the methods outlined in Chapter 12.

The above considerations show that little attention should be paid to the settlements observed in loading tests on friction piles, since the major factors contributing to the settlement of a completed pile foundation are not represented in loading tests.

20·17 Loads Caused on Bearing Piles by Negative Skin Friction

If subsidence or consolidation occurs in the soil which surrounds a group of bearing piles, the piles may have to support a considerable weight of soil. Such a condition can occur when bearing piles have been driven into a fill which has recently been placed. It can result if fill is placed around piles after the driving of the piles. This condition is also possible when bearing piles that are driven through a soft soil cause a sufficient amount of structural disturbance to introduce consolidation and lead to a subsidence of the soil which is larger than the settlement which the piles undergo when they are loaded. More specifically, this condition occurs in any case in which the soil subsides relative to the piles. In all such cases reference lines of the type shown in Fig. 20·5 bend up rather than down as they approach the pile, and the pile must support the soil instead of the soil supporting the pile and its load, as in friction pile foundations.

When this condition occurs it is obvious that the pile must be capable of supporting the soil weight as well as all other loads that the pile is designed to carry. Also, when fill is to be placed around an existing pile foundation, the ability of the piles to carry the added load should be thoroughly investigated. Failure to consider loads of this type is understandable in certain cases, because their existence is not always obvious and they may be overlooked unless careful analyses are made. However, such loads may often be large, since negative values of unit skin friction can be as large as positive values, and pile failures that are caused by such loads are not uncommon.

20·18   Settlements Resulting from Disturbance to Soil Structure during Pile Driving

The disturbance of soil structure during pile driving and possible effects of this disturbance in the form of increased settlements after the final loading of a pile foundation are subjects which have raised much controversy. It is well known that a remolded clay, when subjected to a given load, consolidates to a considerably smaller void ratio than that reached under the same load by the same clay in undisturbed state. Therefore, structural disturbance results in increased settlements, but there has been much difference in opinion regarding the amount of the increase. The magnitude of this settlement increase depends largely on such factors as the distance the disturbance extends from the pile, the type of soil, and the degree to which it is disturbed, and the details of the action in the complicated consolidation process subsequent to driving. Definite magnitudes cannot be quoted for such settlements, but it is possible that in some soils they are much larger than many engineers suspect.

20·19   Emergency Uses and Questionable Uses of Piles

There is a tendency for engineers sometimes to think of piles as a cure-all—that is, to assume that an unsatisfactory foundation condition is always improved by putting in piles.

It is true that there are occasions on which a superintendent of construction can avoid much difficulty by placing a few piles which the specifications do not call for. When working against time in an excavation in which unexpectedly bad conditions are developing this may be especially true. It must be recognized, however, that there are cases in which the use of piles may be undesirable. Usually it is bearing piles that are used to advantage in emergencies, whereas it is friction piles which are more likely to be undesirable.

An example is given by the fairly common occurrence of a stratum at or near ground surface which is composed of soil having a high bearing capacity but a limited thickness, this stratum being underlain by a deep bed of soft plastic clay. A light building that is to be constructed on this site would in many cases be founded at or just below the surface of the good stratum. If it is discovered, after construction has started, that this stratum is thinner or is of poorer character under one wing of the building than was originally expected, there may be need for a revision in the design. If friction piles extending well into the clay are added below the questionable wing, greater settlements must be expected in that region. On some occasions such a procedure may be the best one available. However, careful consideration should first be given to all possible alternate procedures which would avoid disturbance to the clay and, if piles are finally used below a portion of the structure, provisions should be made in the design so that differential settlements will not endanger the building.

Actually no single procedure is, or can be, a cure-all in foundation engineering. In any major foundation problem there are many factors that must be considered, and no two cases are exactly alike. Any approaches which propose to reduce pile-driving operations or any other type of foundation engineering operations to a list of rules which are to be followed automatically are sure to be the cause of unsatisfactory results frequently.

20·20 Conclusion

In the choice of types of foundations, and in the design of a pile foundation or any other type of foundation, judgment and experience are the most important requirements.

Aids to judgment of several types are furnished by a familiarity with soil mechanics and they are a help to the designing engineer which he cannot afford to overlook.

Loading tests on piles are an example of quantitative soil mechanics data. Such data are of well-recognized value but may be misinterpreted unless the engineer is familiar with the fundamentals involved. For example, data on magnitudes of settlements in loading tests may easily be misinterpreted by an engineer unless he is familiar with group action of piles.

Data which may be of some quantitative value, but which have definite limits in their numerical accuracy and must therefore be used with much discretion, may be classed as a second type of aid to judgment. Information which is based on observations during pile driving, and which is obtained by the use of dynamic formulas, is an example. The amount of dependence which can

be placed on information of this type, whether it is on pile resistance or some other subject, is often by its very nature the
subject of much controversy.

A third type of aid to judgment offered by soil mechanics is
that given by qualitative concepts. Examples that are of interest
in connection with pile foundations are remolding effects, general
concepts of consolidation, and group action of piles, with stress
and strain considerations as an important subheading under
each. Moreover, an understanding of such concepts is valuable
in the development of improved foundation practices. The explanation of such concepts and the development of an appreciation of their value has been the main aim of this book.

PROBLEMS

1. Compare and explain the magnitudes of skin friction and point resistance of piles (a) during driving into deep deposits of saturated clay and (b)
during loading by the construction of a building.

2. Determine and plot curves of dynamic resistance versus penetration
per blow, obtaining curves by both the Hiley formula with a factor of safety
of 3 included and the *Engineering News* formula, and determining points on
all curves at penetrations of ⅛, ¼ and ½ in. per blow. Curves are to be
obtained for the eight cases given by four types of piles, each driven by two
types of hammers. The piles to be considered are (a) a 38-ft wood pile,
18-in. butt, and 10-in. tip, weighing 45 lb per cu ft; (b) a 38-ft precast concrete pile with 15-in. diameter; (c) a 38-ft. Simplex pile with 16-in. inside
diameter and ¾-in. shell; and (d) a 38-ft Raymond pile, with 22-in. butt
and 8-in. tip, an average area of 56 sq in., and driven parts weighing 6 tons.
The hammers are a 1000-lb drop hammer with a 10-ft drop and a single-
acting steam hammer with striking parts weighing 2500 lb and a stroke of
3½ ft. The efficiency of the drop may be taken as 0.75 for the drop hammer and 0.9 for the steam hammer. For the plastic compression ρ_f and the
coefficient n, values of 0.05 in. and 0.25, respectively, may be used in all
cases. For other quantities not given, reasonable values are to be assumed.

3. In a driving test on a wood pile weighing 2400 lb, in which a 2200-lb
drop hammer and different heights of drop were used, the following data
were recorded:

Fall of hammer in feet	8	12	16
Penetration of pile in inches per blow	5⁄16	11⁄16	1 1⁄16

Using only the data above and the general dynamic pile formula, which is
equation 20·12, and assuming $n = 0.25$ and $e = 0.75$, estimate the dynamic
resistance to penetration of the pile.

4. From a number of loading tests on piles at a given site a fairly accurate idea has been obtained of the amount of load a single pile can carry and the amount of settlement it undergoes when loaded. Discuss the degree to which these values of load and settlement may be expected to hold if the site is to be used for (*a*) a wharf structure on widely spaced piles penetrating through water and soft soil to practical refusal at a shallow depth into highly resistant soil, and (*b*) a building supported by closely spaced friction piles imbedded in a plastic soil.

REFERENCES

The following list is intended primarily to give the sources of material referred to in the text. For more extensive lists of references and bibliographies reference may be made to a number of the publications listed herein, for example, references 7, 147, and 117.

1. AGATZ, A., and E. SCHULTZE, *Der Kampf des Ingenieurs gegen Erde und Wasser in Grundbau.* Berlin: Springer, 1936.
2. ALLIN, R. V., *The Resistance of Piles to Penetration.* London: Spon, 1935.
3. American Society of Civil Engineers, "Pile Driving Formulas," Committee on Bearing Value of Pile Foundations, *Proceedings,* May 1941. Discussion in *Proceedings* of September 1941 to March 1942, inclusive, and May 1942.
4. American Society of Civil Engineers, "Pile Foundations and Pile Structures," *Manual of Engineering Practice* No. 27, 1946.
5. American Society of Civil Engineers, "Progress Report," Earths and Foundations Committee, *Proceedings,* May 1933.
6. American Society of Civil Engineers, "Soil Mechanics Nomenclature," *Manual of Engineering Practice* No. 22, 1941.
7. American Society of Civil Engineers, "Selected Bibliography on Soil Mechanics," *Manual of Engineering Practice* No. 18, 1940.
8. American Society of Civil Engineers, "Timber Piles and Construction Timbers," *Manual of Engineering Practice* No. 17, 1939.
9. American Society for Testing Materials, *A.S.T.M. Standards* 1944, pp. 614–650, 1390–1412.
10. ATTERBERG, A., "Die Plastizitaet und Bindigkeit liefernde Bestandteile der Tone," *Int. Mitteil. Bodenkunde,* Vol. 3, 1913.
11. BERTRAM, G. E., "An Experimental Investigation of Protective Filters," Harvard Graduate School of Engineering *Pub.* No. 267, 1940.
12. BESKOW, G., *Tjälbildningen och tjällyftningen.* Stockholm: Sveriges Geologiska Undersokning, Series C, No. 375, 1935.
13. BIOT, M. A., "Effect of Certain Discontinuities on the Pressure Distribution in a Loaded Soil," Harvard University *Bull.* No. 172 (Physics), Vol. 6, 1935.
14. BIOT, M. A., "General Theory of Three-Dimensional Consolidation," *J. App. Phys.,* 1941.
15. Boston Society of Civil Engineers, *Contributions to Soil Mechanics, 1925 to 1940.* Publication containing 14 articles originally appearing in the *Journal,* 1940.
16. BOUSSINESQ, J., *Application des potentiels à l'etude de l'equilibre et du mouvement des solids elastiques.* Paris: Gauthier-Villars, 1885.

17. BRENECKE, L., and E. LOHMEYER, *Der Grundbau* (3 Vols.). Berlin: Ernst, 1934.

18. BUCHANAN, S. J., "Levees in the Lower Mississippi Valley," *Trans. Am. Soc. C. E.*, 1938.

19. BURMISTER, D. M., "A Study of the Physical Characteristics of Soils— with special reference to Earth Structures," Department of Civil Engineering, Columbia University, *Bull. No. 6*, 1938.

20. BURMISTER, D. M., "The Theory of Stresses and Displacements in Layered Systems and Application to the Design of Airports Runways," *Proc. Highway Res. Bd.*, 1943.

21. CAMPBELL, F. B., "Graphical Representation of the Mechanical Analyses of Soils," *Trans. Am. Soc. C. E.*, 1939.

22. Carnegie-Illinois Steel Corp., *Sheet Steel Piling*. 1936.

23. CASAGRANDE, A., "Classification and Identification of Soils," *Proc. Am. Soc. C. E.*, June 1947.

24. CASAGRANDE, A., "Reports on Cooperative Research on Stress-Deformation and Strength Characteristics of Soils," submitted to U. S. Waterways Experiment Station, Harvard University, 1940 to 1944. Unpublished, reviewed in reference 126.

25. CASAGRANDE, A., "Research on the Atterberg Limits of Soils," *Public Roads*, Oct. 1932.

26. CASAGRANDE, A., "Seepage through Dams," *J. New England Water Works Assoc.*, June 1937. Reprinted in reference 15.

27. CASAGRANDE, A., "The Determination of the Pre-Consolidation Load and its Practical Significance," *Proc. Int. Conf. Soil Mechanics*, Vol. III, Harvard University, 1936.

28. CASAGRANDE, A., "The Hydrometer Method for Mechanical Analysis of Soils and Other Granular Materials," report from Department of Civil and Sanitary Engineering, Massachusetts Institute of Technology, 1931. Unpublished.

29. CASAGRANDE, A., "The Structure of Clay and its Importance in Foundation Engineering," *J. Boston Soc. C. E.*, April 1932. Reprinted in reference 15.

30. CASAGRANDE, A., and S. G. ALBERT, "Research on the Shearing Resistance of Soils," Massachusetts Institute of Technology, 1930. Unpublished.

31. CASAGRANDE, A., and N. CARRILLO, "Shear Failure of Anisotropic Materials," *J. Boston Soc. C. E.*, April 1944.

32. CASAGRANDE, A., and R. E. FADUM, "Applications of Soil Mechanics in Designing Building Foundations," *Trans. Am. Soc. C. E.*, 1944.

33. CASAGRANDE, A., and R. E. FADUM, "Notes on Soil Testing for Engineering Purposes," Harvard Graduate School of Engineering *Soil Mechanics Series* No. 8, 1940.

34. CASAGRANDE, L., "Näherungsverfahren zur Ermittlung der Sickerung in geschütteten Dämmen auf undurchlässiger Sohle," *Die Bautechnik*, Heft 15, 1934.

35. CASAGRANDE, L., "Setzungsbeobachtungen an Brückenbauten der Reichs-autobahnen," *Proc. Int. Assoc. Bridge and Structural Eng.;* Berlin: 1936.

36. CHELLIS, R. D., *Pile-Driving Handbook.* New York: Pitman, 1944.

37. City of Boston, *Building Code of the City of Boston.* 1944.

38. COULOMB, C. A., "Essai sur une application des règles des maximis et minimis à quelques problèmes de statique relatifs à l'architecture," *Mém. acad. roy. pres. divers savants,* Vol. 7, Paris: 1776.

39. CREAGER, W. P., J. D. JUSTIN, and J. HINDS, *Engineering for Dams.* 3 Vols., New York: Wiley, 1945.

40. CULMANN, K., *Die graphische Statik.* Zurich: 1866.

41. CUMMINGS, A. E., "Distribution of Stresses under a Foundation," *Trans. Am. Soc. C. E.,* 1936.

42. CUMMINGS, A. E., "Dynamic Pile Driving Formulas," *J. Boston Soc. C. E.,* Jan. 1940. Reprinted in reference 15.

43. CUMMINGS, A. E., "The Stability of Foundation Piles against Buckling under Axial Load," *Proc. Highway Res. Bd.,* Part II, 1938.

44. DACHLER, R., *Grundwasserstroemung.* Vienna: Springer, 1936.

45. DARCY, H., *Les fontaines publiques de la ville de Dijon.* Paris: Dijon, 1856.

46. DAWSON, R. F., "Settlement Studies on San Jacinto Monument," *Civil Engineering,* Sept. 1938.

47. DEAN, A. C., *Piles and Pile Driving.* London: Crosby-Lockwood, 1935.

48. ENKEBOLL, W., "Investigation of Consolidation and Structural Plasticity in Clay," Massachusetts Institute of Technology. Doctorate thesis, 1947. Unpublished.

49. FADUM, R. E., "Influence Values for Vertical Stresses in a Semi-Infinite Elastic Solid due to Surface Loads," Harvard Graduate School of Engineering. Unpublished.

50. FAHLQUIST, F. E., "New Methods and Technique in Subsurface Explorations," *J. Boston Soc. C. E.,* April 1941.

51. FANCHER, G. H., J. A. LEWIS, and K. B. BARNES, Mineral Industries Experiment Station, *Bull.* 12, Penn. State College, 1933.

52. FELLENIUS, W., "Calculation of the Stability of Earth Dams," *Trans. 2nd Cong. on Large Dams,* Vol. 4, Washington: 1936.

53. FELLENIUS, W., *Erdstatische Berechnungen mit Reibung und Kohäsion, Adhäsion, und unter Annahme kreiszylindrischer Gleitflächen.* Rev. ed., Berlin: Ernst, 1939.

54. FIDLER, H. A., "A Machine for Determining the Shearing Strength of Soils," Record of the *Proc. Conf. on Soils and Foundations,* Corps of Engineers, U. S. Army, Boston: 1938.

55. FIDLER, H. A., "Investigation of Stress-Strain Relationships of Granular Soils by a New Cylindrical Compression Apparatus," Massachusetts Institute of Technology. Doctorate thesis, 1940. Unpublished.

56. FIELDS, K. E., and W. L. WELLS, "Pendleton Levee Failure," *Trans. Am. Soc. C. E.,* 1944.

57. FOERSTER, M., *Taschenbuch fur Bauingenieure.* 2 Vols., Berlin: Springer, 1928.

58. FORCHHEIMER, P., *Hydraulik.* 3d ed., Leipzig: Teubner, 1930.

59. FRÖHLICH, O. K., *Druckverteilung im Baugrunde.* Vienna: Springer, 1934.

60. FRONTARD, M., "Cycloides de glissement des terres," *Comptes rendues,* Paris: 1922.

61. GILBOY, G., "Hydraulic-Fill Dams," *Proc. Int. Comm. on Large Dams,* World Power Conf., Stockholm: 1933.

62. GILBOY, G., "Improved Soil Testing Methods," *Eng. News-Record,* May 21, 1936.

63. GILBOY, G., "Mechanics of Hydraulic-Fill Dams," *J. Boston Soc. C. E.,* July 1934. Reprinted in reference 15.

64. GILBOY, G., "Soil Mechanics Research," *Trans., Am. Soc. C. E.,* 1933.

65. GOLDER, H. Q., "The Ultimate Bearing Pressure of Rectangular Footings," *J. Inst. Civil Eng.,* London: Dec. 1941.

66. GOULD, J. P., "The Effect of Radial Flow in Settlement Analysis," Massachusetts Institute of Technology. S.M. thesis, 1946. Unpublished.

67. GRIM, R. E., "The Clay Minerals in Soils and Their Significance," *Proc. Purdue Conf. on Soil Mechanics,* 1940.

68. HARZA, L. F., "Uplift and Seepage under Dams on Sand," *Trans. Am. Soc. C. E.,* 1935.

69. HAZEN, A., "Discussion of 'Dams on Sand Foundations,' by A. C. Koenig," *Trans. Am. Soc. C. E.,* Vol. 73, p. 199, 1911.

70. HEILAND, C. A., *Geophysical Exploration.* New York: Prentice-Hall, 1940.

71. HILEY, A., "Pile Driving Calculations with Notes on Driving Forces and Ground Resistance," London: *The Structural Engineer,* July, Aug. 1930.

72. HOGENTOGLER, C. A., *Engineering Properties of Soil.* New York: McGraw-Hill, 1937.

73. HOOL, G. A., and W. S. KINNE, revised by R. R. ZIPPRODT, and E. J. KILCAWLEY, *Foundations, Abutments and Footings.* 2d ed., New York: McGraw-Hill, 1943.

74. HOUGH, B. K., JR., "Technique of Determining Shearing Strength of Soils," Progress Report of Special Committee of Soil Mechanics and Foundations Division, *Proc. Am. Soc. C. E.,* Feb. 1942.

75. HOUSEL, W. S., "A Practical Method for the Selection of Foundations Based on Fundamental Research in Soil Mechanics," University of Michigan *Eng. Res. Bull.* No. 13, Oct. 1929.

76. HVORSLEV, M. J., "A Ring Shearing Apparatus for the Determination of the Shearing Resistance and Plastic Flow of Soils," *Proc. Int. Conf. Soil Mechanics,* Harvard University, 1936.

77. HVORSLEV, M. J., "Piston Samplers and Their Use in Various Types of Soil," Presented at Annual Meeting, Am. Soc. C. E., New York: 1943. Unpublished.

78. HVORSLEV, M. J., "The Present Status of the Art of Obtaining Undisturbed Samples of Soil," Preliminary Report of the Committee on Sampling and Testing, Soil Mechanics and Foundations Division, Am. Soc. C. E., 1940. (*Note:* A final, comprehensive report of this research entitled "Subsurface Exploration and Sampling of Soils for Civil Engineering Purposes" has been prepared and is scheduled for publication early in 1948.)

79. HVORSLEV, M. J., "Torsion Tests and Their Place in the Determination of the Shearing Resistance of Soils," *Proc. A.S.T.M.*, 1939.

80. HVORSLEV, M. J., *Über die Festigkeitseigenschaften gestörter bindiger Böden.* Danmarks Naturvidenskabelige Samfund, Kopenhagen: 1937.

81. JACOBY, H. S., and R. P. DAVIS, *Foundations of Bridges and Buildings.* New York: McGraw-Hill, 1941.

82. JÁKY, J., "The Stability of Earth Slopes," *Proc. Int. Conf. Soil Mechanics,* Vol. II, Harvard University, 1936.

83. JOHNSON, H. L., "Improved Sampler and Sampling Technique for Cohesionless Soils," *Civil Engineering,* June 1940.

84. JÜRGENSON, L., "The Application of Theories of Elasticity and Plasticity to Foundation Problems," *J. Boston Soc. C. E.,* July 1934. Reprinted in reference 15.

85. JÜRGENSON, L., "The Shearing Resistance of Soils," *J. Boston Soc. C. E.,* July 1934. Reprinted in reference 15.

86. KEEN, B. A., *The Physical Properties of Soils.* New York: Longmans, 1931.

87. KJELLMAN, W., "Report on an Apparatus for Consummate Investigation of the Mechanical Properties of Soils," *Proc. Int. Conf. Soil Mechanics,* Vol. II, Harvard University, 1936.

88. KNAPPEN, T. T., and R. R. PHILIPPE, "Practical Soil Mechanics at Muskingum," *Eng. News-Record,* Mar. 26, Apr. 9, 23, May 7, 1936.

89. KÖGLER, F., and A. SCHEIDIG, "Druckverleilung im Baugrunde," a series of articles in *Die Bautechnik,* 1927–1929.

90. KOZENY, J. S., "Grundwasserbewegung bei freiem Spiegel, Fluss und Kanalversicherung," *Wasserkraft und Wasserwirtschaft,* No. 3, 1931.

91. KOZENY, J. S., *Sitzungsber.,* Akad. Wissenschaften, Vienna: 1927.

92. KREUTER, F., "A New Method for Determining the Supporting Power of Piles," minutes of *Proc. Inst. Civil Eng.,* Vol. 124, Part 2, 1895–1896.

93. KREY, H., *Erddruck, Erdwiderstand und Tragfähigkeit des Baugrundes.* Berlin: Ernst, 1936.

94. KRYNINE, D. P., *Soil Mechanics.* New York: McGraw-Hill, 1941.

95. LANE, E. W., "Security from Under-Seepage: Masonry Dams on Earth Foundations," *Trans. Am. Soc. C. E.,* 1935.

96. LEE, C. H., "Selection of Materials for Rolled-Fill Earth Dams," *Trans. Am. Soc. C. E.,* 1938.

97. LEGGET, R. F., *Geology and Engineering*. New York: McGraw-Hill, 1939.

98. LOVE, A. E. H., *A Treatise on the Mathematical Theory of Elasticity*. Cambridge (England) University Press: 1934.

99. LYMAN, A. K. B., "Compaction of Cohesionless Foundation Soils by Explosives," *Trans. Am. Soc. C. E.*, 1942.

100. MIDDLEBROOKS, T. A., "Fort Peck Slide," *Trans. Am. Soc. C. E.*, 1942.

101. MIDDLEBROOKS, T. A., and W. H. JERVIS, "Relief Wells for Dams and Levees," *Proc. Am. Soc. C. E.*, June 1946.

102. MOHR, H. A., "Exploration of Soil Conditions and Sampling Operations," 3d ed., Harvard Graduate School of Engineering *Pub.* No. 21, 1943.

103. MOHR, O., "Über die Darstellung des Spannungszustandes und des Deformation-zustandes eines Körper-elements," *Zivilingenieur*, p. 113, 1882.

104. MUSKAT, M., *The Flow of Homogeneous Fluids through Porous Media*. New York: McGraw-Hill, 1937.

105. NADAI, A., *Plasticity*. New York: McGraw-Hill, 1931.

106. National Resources Committee, *Low Dams, A Manual of Design for Small Water Storage Projects*. Washington: 1938.

107. NEWMARK, N. M., "Influence Charts for Computation of Stresses in Elastic Foundations," Engineering Experiment Station Bulletin, Series No. 338, University of Illinois, Nov. 10, 1942.

108. NEWMARK, N. M., "Simplified Computation of Vertical Pressures in Elastic Foundations," Circular No. 24, Experiment Station *Circ.* 24, University of Illinois, 1935.

109. NORTON, F. H., and S. SPEIL, "The Measurement of Particle Sizes in Clays," *J. Am. Ceramic Soc.*, March 1938.

110. PECK, R. B., "Earth Pressure Measurements in Open Cuts, Chicago Subway," from a symposium, "Earth Pressure and Shearing Resistance of Plastic Clay," *Proc. Am. Soc. C. E.*, June 1942.

111. PICKETT, G., "Stress Distribution in a Loaded Soil with Some Rigid Boundaries," *Proc. Highway Res. Bd.*, Part II, 1938.

112. PLUMMER, F. L., and S. M. DORE, *Soil Mechanics and Foundations*. New York: Pitman, 1940.

113. PONCELET, V., "Mém. sur la stabilité des revêtements et de leurs Foundations," Mém. de l'officier du génie, Vol. 13, 1840.

114. PORTER, O. J., "The Preparation of Subgrades," *Proc. Highway Res. Bd.*, Part II, 1938.

115. PRANDTL, L., "Härte plashecher Körper," *Nach. Ges. Wiss. Göttingen*, 1920.

116. PRENTIS, E. A., and L. WHITE, *Underpinning; Its Practice and Applications*. New York: Columbia University Press, 1931.

117. PROCTOR, R. R., "Fundamental Principles of Soil Compaction," *Eng. News-Record*, Aug. 31, Sept. 7, 21, 28, 1933.

118. Purdue Conference on Soil Mechanics and its Applications, *Proceedings*. Purdue University, Lafayette, Ind., 1940.

119. RANKINE, W. J. M., "On the Stability of Loose Earth," *Phil. Trans. Royal Soc., London,* 1857.

120. REBHANN, G., *Theorie des Erddruckes und der Futtermauern.* Vienna: 1871.

121. RENDULIC, L., "Ein Beitrag zur Bestimmung der Gleitsicherheit," *Der Bauingenieur,* No. 19/20, 1935.

122. RÉSAL, J., *La poussée des terres.* Paris: 1910.

123. RUTLEDGE, P. C., "Description and Identification of Soil Types," Purdue Conference on Soil Mechanics, *Proceedings,* 1940.

124. RUTLEDGE, P. C., "Neutral and Effective Stresses in Soils," Purdue Conference on Soil Mechanics, *Proceedings,* 1940.

125. RUTLEDGE, P. C., "Relation of Undisturbed Sampling to Laboratory Testing," *Trans. Am. Soc. C. E.,* 1944.

126. RUTLEDGE, P. C., "Review of the Cooperative Triaxial Research Program of the War Department, Corps of Engineers," The Technological Institute, Northwestern University, 1944. Published in "Soil Mechanics Fact Finding Survey, Progress Report: Triaxial Shear Research and Pressure Distribution Studies on Soils," prepared under the auspices of, and published by, U. S. Waterways Experiment Station, April 1947.

127. RUTLEDGE, P. C., "Theories of Failure of Materials Applied to the Shearing Resistance of Soils," Purdue Conference on Soil Mechanics, *Proceedings,* 1940.

128. SCHOKLITSCH, A., *Der Grundbau.* Vienna: Springer, 1932.

129. SHARPE, C. F. S., *Landslides and Related Phenomena.* Columbia University Press, 1938.

130. SHEPHERD, E. R., and R. M. HAINES, "Seismic Subsurface Exploration on the St. Lawrence River Project," *Trans. Am. Soc. C. E.,* 1944.

131. STRATTON, J. H., and G. A. HATHAWAY, "Military Airfields, A Symposium," *Trans. Am. Soc. C. E.,* 1945.

132. Swedish Geotechnical Commission, "Statens Järnvägars geotekniska Kommission, Slutbetänkande," 1922.

133. TABER, S., "Discussion on Frost Heaving," *Proc. Highway Res. Bd.,* 1932.

134. TAYLOR, D. W., "Abstracts of Selected Theses on Soil Mechanics," Department of Civil and Sanitary Engineering, Massachusetts Institute of Technology, 1941.

135. TAYLOR, D. W., "An Unusual Foundation Problem: The Alumni Pool Building," *J. Boston Soc. C. E.,* Oct. 1944.

136. TAYLOR, D. W., "Limit Design of Foundations and Embankments," *Proc. Highway Res. Bd.,* 1939.

137. TAYLOR, D. W., "Reports on Cooperative Research on Stress, Deformation and Strength Characteristics of Soils," submitted to U. S. Waterways Experiment Station, Massachusetts Institute of Technology, 1940 to 1944. Unpublished. Reviewed in reference 126.

138. TAYLOR, D. W., "Research on Consolidation of Clays," Department of Civil and Sanitary Engineering, Massachusetts Institute of Technology, 1942.

139. TAYLOR, D. W., "Stability of Earth Slopes," *J. Boston Soc. C. E.*, July 1937. Reprinted in reference 15.

140. TAYLOR, D. W., and T. M. LEPS, "A Comparison of Results of Direct Shear and Cylindrical Compression Tests," *Proc. A.S.T.M.*, 1939.

141. TERZAGHI, K., "A Fundamental Fallacy in Earth Pressure Computations," *J. Boston Soc. C. E.*, April 1936. Reprinted in reference 15.

142. TERZAGHI, K., "Distribution of the Lateral Pressure of Sand on the Timbering of Cuts," *Proc. Int. Conf. Soil Mechanics*, Vol. I, Harvard University, 1936.

143. TERZAGHI, K., *Erdbaumechanik auf bodenphysikalischer Grundlage.* Leipzig: Deuticke, 1925.

144. TERZAGHI, K., "General Wedge Theory of Earth Pressure," *Trans. Am. Soc. C. E.*, 1941.

145. TERZAGHI, K., "Large Retaining-Wall Tests," *Eng. News-Record*, Feb. 1, 22, Mar. 8, 29, Apr. 19, 1934.

146. TERZAGHI, K., "Settlement of Structures in Europe," *Trans. Am. Soc. C. E.*, 1938.

147. TERZAGHI, K., "Stability of Slopes of Natural Clay," *Proc. Int. Conf. Soil Mechanics*, Vol. I, Harvard University, 1936.

148. TERZAGHI, K., *Theoretical Soil Mechanics.* New York: Wiley, 1943.

149. TERZAGHI, K., "The Science of Foundations," *Trans. Am. Soc. C. E.*, 1929.

150. TERZAGHI, K., "Undisturbed Clay Samples and Undisturbed Clays," *J. Boston Soc. C. E.*, July 1941.

151. TERZAGHI, K., "Zur statischen Berechnung der Gewichtsstaumauern," *Die Bautechnik*, Oct. 19, 1934.

152. TERZAGHI, K., and O. K. FRÖHLICH, *Theorie der Setzung von Tonschichten.* Vienna: Deuticke, 1936.

153. TIMOSHENKO, S., *Theory of Elasticity.* New York: McGraw-Hill, 1934.

154. TSCHEBOTARIOFF, G. P., "Settlement Studies of Structures in Egypt," *Trans. Am. Soc. C. E.*, 1940.

155. U. S. Engineer Corps, "Compaction Tests and Critical Density Investigations of Cohesionless Materials for Franklin Falls Dam," Boston District, 1938.

156. U. S. Engineer Corps, *Engineering Manual*, Chapter XX, "Design of Runways, Aprons and Taxiways at Army Air Force Stations." Prepared by the Office, Chief of Engineers, Department of the Army, for use by Division and District Offices of the Corps of Engineers. Frequently revised.

157. U. S. Engineer Corps, "Report on Barksdale Field Service Behavior Tests," Little Rock, Ark., District, 1944.

158. U. S. Engineer Corps, "The Influence of Drain Wells on the Consolidation of Fine-Grained Soils," Providence District, 1944.

159. U. S. Waterways Experiment Station, "Field and Laboratory Investigation of Design Criteria for Drainage Wells," *Tech. Memo.* No. 195–1, 1942.

160. U. S. Waterways Experiment Station, "Investigation of Filter Requirements for Underdrains" (revised), *Tech. Memo.* No. 183–1, 1941.

161. U. S. Waterways Experiment Station, "Investigation of Foundation and Design; Little Grassy Dam, Carbondale, Ill.," *Tech. Memo.* No. 179–1, 1941.

162. U. S. Waterways Experiment Station, "Soil Mechanics Fact Finding Survey: Seepage Studies," *Tech. Memo.* No. 175–1, 1941.

163. U. S. Waterways Experiment Station, "Soil Pressure Cell Investigation, Interim Report," *Tech. Memo.* No. 210–1, 1944.

164. U. S. Waterways Experiment Station, "The California Bearing Ratio Test as Applied to the Design of Flexible Pavements for Airports," *Tech. Memo.* No. 213–1, 1945.

165. VAN DEN BROEK, J. A., "Theory of Limit Design," *Trans. Am. Soc. C. E.,* 1940.

166. WEAVER, W., "Uplift Pressure on Dams," *Math. and Physics,* June 1932.

167. WENZEL, L. K., "Methods for Determining Permeability of Water-Bearing Materials," U. S. Geological Survey *Water-Supply Paper* 887, 1942.

168. WESTERGAARD, H. M., "A Problem of Elasticity Suggested by a Problem in Soil Mechanics: Soft Material Reinforced by Numerous Strong Horizontal Sheets" in *Contributions to the Mechanics of Solids, Stephen Timoshenko 60th Anniversary Volume.* New York: Macmillan, 1938.

169. WHITE, L., and E. A. PRENTIS, *Cofferdams.* New York: Columbia University Press, 1940.

170. WIEGNER, G., "Über eine neue Methode der Schlammanalyse," Landw. Vers.-Stat., 1918.

171. WILSON, G., "The Calculation of the Bearing Capacity of Footings on Clay," London: *J. Inst. of Civil Eng.,* Nov. 1941.

172. WINGATE, R. H., "A Settlement Study Interrelating Building Frame Stresses and Soil Stresses," Massachusetts Institute of Technology S.M. thesis, 1938. Unpublished. Abstracted in reference 134.

173. WINTERKORN, H. F., and R. B. B. MOORMAN, "A Study of Changes in Physical Properties of Putnam Soil Induced by Ionic Substitution," *Proc. Highway Res. Bd.,* 1941.

174. ZUNKER, F., "Das Verhalten des Bodens zum Wasser" in Vol. 6 of E. Blanck, *Handbuch der Bodenlehre.* Berlin: Springer, 1930.

INDEX